M000249884

LAW IN LITERATURE

LAW IN LITERATURE:
Legal Themes in Short Stories

edited by
Elizabeth Villiers Gemmette

Copyright 1995
Elizabeth Villiers Gemmette

ISBN 0-87875-472-5

Printed in the United States of America

Copyright Acknowledgments

Cover photograph shows detail of the wood engraving on "A few lines on occasion of the Untimely end of Mark & Phillis. Who were executed at Cambridge Sept. 18th for Poysoning their Master" (1755). Courtesy of the New-York Historical Society, N.Y.C.

Excerpts from "Antigone" by Sophocles, from *The Complete Greek Drama* by Whitney J. Oates and Eugene O'Neill, Jr., eds. Copyright 1938 and renewed 1966 by Random House, Inc. Reprinted by permission of Random House, Inc.

"Some of Us Had Been Threatening Our Friend Colby" from *Amateurs* by Donald Barthelme, published by Farrar, Straus and Giroux, 1976. Used by permission of Wylie, Aitken & Stone, Inc.

"The Bicentennial Man," copyright © 1976 by Random House, Inc., from *The Bicentennial Man and Other Short Stories* by Isaac Asimov. Used by permission of Doubleday, a division of Bantam Doubleday Dell Publishing Group, Inc.; UK and British Commonwealth, Victor Gollancz Ltd.

"Harrison Bergeron" by Kurt Vonnegut, from *Welcome to the Monkey House* by Kurt Vonnegut, Jr. Copyright © 1961 by Kurt Vonnegut, Jr. Used by permission of Dell Books, a division of Bantam Doubleday Dell Publishing Group, Inc.; British Commonwealth, Donald C. Farber.

"The Lynching of Jube Benson" from *The Heart of Happy Hollow* by Paul Laurence Dunbar, published by Dodd, Mead & Co., 1904.

"The Corpus Delicti" from *The Strange Schemes of Randolph Mason* by Melville Davisson Post, published by G.P. Putnam's Sons, 1896.

"The Benefit of the Doubt" by Jack London first appeared in *The Saturday Evening Post*, November 12, 1910 and the *Birmingham Weekly Post*, January 17, 1914. Reprinted from *The Night-Born and Other Stories by Jack London* printed by D. Appleton-Century Company, Inc., New York, 1939.

"In A Grove" is reprinted from *Rashomon and Other Stories* by Ryunosuke Akutagawa, translated by Takashi Kojima, with the permission of Liveright Publishing Corporation. Copyright © 1952, 1970 by Liveright Publishing Corporation.

"Story of the Chief of Old Cairo" from *The Arabian Nights*. Reprinted from *The 101 World's Great Mystery Stories*, published by Blue Ribbon Books, 1928.

"Beyond Any Doubt" by Robert O'Neil Bristow is reprinted from *Alfred Hitchcock's Mystery Magazine*, January 1962, Volume 7, Number 1. Used by permission of the author.

"A Jury of Her Peers" by Susan Glaspell from *Ellery Queen Anthology*. Copyright © 1946 Susan Glaspell. Reprinted by permission of Curtis Brown, Ltd.

"Colonel Starbottle for the Plaintiff" by Bret Harte from *A Niece of Snapshot Harry's and Other Tales* by Bret Harte, published by Houghton, Mifflin and Company, 1903.

"Triumph of Justice," from *Mixed Company* by Irwin Shaw, published by Random House, Inc., 1950. © Irwin Shaw. Reprinted with Permission of the Estate of Irwin Shaw; UK and Foreign Languages, Tessa Sayle Agency.

"How the Pretty Maid of Portillon Convinced Her Judge" by Honoré de Balzac from *Droll Stories*, published by John Camden Hotten, 1874.

"A Wasted Day" from *Once Upon a Time* by Richard Harding Davis, published by Charles Scribner's Sons, 1910.

"In the Penal Colony" from *The Metamorphosis, The Penal Colony, and Other Stories* by Franz Kafka, translated by Willa and Edwin Muir. Copyright 1948 and renewed 1975 by Schocken Books Inc. Reprinted by permission of Schocken Books, published by Pantheon Books, a division of Random House, Inc.; UK and Commonwealth, Martin Secker and Warburg Limited.

"The Pit and the Pendulum" by Edgar Allan Poe. Reprinted from *American Prose* (1607-1865) by Walter C. Bronson, published by The University of Chicago Press, 1916.

"The Tell-Tale Heart" from *The Works of Edgar Allan Poe*, published by Stone & Kimball, 1894.

"The Minister's Black Veil" from *Twice-Told Tales* by Nathaniel Hawthorne, published by Houghton, Mifflin and Company, 1883.

"Mateo Falcone" by Prosper Mérimée. Reprinted from *Prosper Mérimée*, published by G.P. Putnam's Sons, 1903.

"Barn Burning" from *Collected Stories of William Faulkner* by William Faulkner. Copyright 1950 by Random House, Inc. Copyright renewed 1977 by Jill Faulkner Summers. Reprinted by permission of Random House, Inc.; in the British Commonwealth by Curtis Brown Ltd., London.

"Hard to Be Good" from *Hard to be Good* by Bill Barich. Copyright © 1982, 1983, 1984, 1986, 1987 by Bill Barich. Reprinted by permission of Farrar, Straus and Giroux, Inc.; UK and the Commonwealth, ICM.

"Paul's Case" by Willa Cather from *The Troll Garden*, published by McClure, Phillips & Co., 1905.

"Sicilian Honor" by Luigi Pirandello. Reprinted by permission of the Pirandello Estate and Toby Cole, Agent. © E.P. Dutton, N.Y. 1939; in the rest of the world, excluding the United States and Canada, The International Copyright Bureau Ltd.

"Han's Crime" by Shiga Naoya from *Modern Japanese Literature*, an anthology compiled and edited by Donald Keene, translated by Ivan Morris, published by Grove Press, Inc., 1956. Used by permission of the publishers.

"The Catbird Seat" by James Thurber. Copyright © 1945 James Thurber. Copyright © 1973 Helen Thurber & Rosemary A. Thurber. From *The Thurber Carnival*, published by Harper & Row. Permission granted by Rosemary A. Thurber; UK and Commonwealth, excluding Canada, Hamish Hamilton Ltd.

"The Animus Furandi" from *The Strange Schemes of Randolph Mason* by Melville Davisson Post, published by G.P. Putnam's Sons, 1896.

"Rosalie Prudent," "The Assassin," and "Hippolyte's Claim" from *The Complete Short Stories of Guy de Maupassant*, published by Walter J. Black Co., 1903.

"Under the Lion's Paw" from *Main-Travelled Roads* by Hamlin Garland, published by Harper & Bros., 1893.

"The Negotiable Cow" and "Fardell & Potts: The Reasonable Man" taken from *Uncommon Law* by A.P. Herbert, published by Methuen & Co., Ltd., London, 1935. Permission of A P Watt Limited on behalf of Crystal Hale and Jocelyn Herbert.

"The Most Outrageous Consequences" from *Attorneys at Law, Forbes, Hathaway, Bryan & Devore* by James Reid Parker. Copyright 1941 by James Reid Parker. Used by permission of Doubleday, a division of Bantam Doubleday Dell Publishing Group, Inc.

"Counsel for Oedipus" from *Collected Stories* by Frank O'Connor. Copyright 1954 by Frank O'Connor. Reprinted by permission of Alfred A. Knopf, Inc.; in the British Commonwealth and Canada, Peters, Frasier & Dunlop.

"Madame Filippa is Accused of Wronging Her Husband" by Giovanni Boccaccio from *The Decameron*, translated by J.M. Rigg, Volume II, printed privately from the Navarre Society Limited, 1900.

Bibliography from *A List of One Hundred Legal Novels* by Wigmore, 17 Illinois Law Review 26 (1922), reprinted with corrections, from Wigmore, *A List of Legal Novels*, 2 Illinois Law Review 574 (1908). Used by permission of Northwestern University Law School.

Bibliography from *Wigmore's 'Legal Novels' Expanded: A Collaborative Effort* by Richard H. Weisberg and Karen L. Kretschman. Reprinted from the New York State Bar Journal, February, 1978, pp. 127-132. Used by permission of the New York State Bar Journal.

"God Sees the Truth, But Waits," "How Much Land Does a Man Need?" and "Too Dear!" from *Twenty-Three Tales by Leo Tolstóy*, translated by Louise and Aylmer Maude, published by Oxford University Press, 1906.

"The Two Drovers" from *The Works of Sir Walter Scott*, Volume II, published by Houghton Mifflin Company, 1913.

Every reasonable effort has been made to trace the owners of copyright materials in this book, but in some instances this has proven impossible. The author and publisher will be glad to receive information leading to more complete acknowledgments in subsequent printings of the book and in the meantime extend their apologies for any omissions.

Contents

Preface

I feel more contented when I remember that I have two pro-
fessions, and not one. Medicine [Law] is my lawful wife
and literature my mistress. When I am bored with one I
spend the night with the other. Though this is irregular, it is
not monotonous, and besides neither loses anything through
my infidelity.

Letter from Anton Pavlovich
Chekhov to A. S. Suvorin
August 29, 1888

Law in Literature: Legal Themes in Short Stories came about as the direct
result of two events: prior to attending law school I had taught literature at
the State University of New York at Albany; and during my second
semester of law school I chose a jurisprudence course to fulfill my first-year
elective. As that jurisprudence course progressed, I found myself constantly reminded of literary works which I had read, some of which I had
also taught—Robert Browning's dramatic monologue *The Ring and the
Book*; Kurt Vonnegut, Jr.'s short story "Harrison Bergeron"; Jean
Anouilh's play *Antigone*; Fyodor Dostoyevsky's novel *Crime and Punishment*. It occurred to me that the legal philosophy being taught in jurisprudence could be taught equally well through fiction. In order to determine
how such a course might best be structured, I undertook a survey of 175
accredited law schools to determine whether or not such a course was already being offered in the law school curriculum. That survey resulted in
an article entitled "Law and Literature: An Unnecessarily Suspect Class in
the Liberal Arts Component of the Law School Curriculum," which was
published by *Valparaiso University Law Review* in the winter of 1989.

In 1987, 38 of the 135 law schools that responded to my survey reported offering a course that utilized literature as the text. The law schools
and/or the professors of the various courses reported the following reasons
for the inclusion of their courses in the law school curriculum: (1) to bring
about the configuration of law and letters by exposing the student to grand
literary style; (2) to teach the student to read a text critically; (3) to bring together in the student a balance between Rationalism and Romanticism—a
balance between the head and the heart, a balance between the Dionysian
and the Apollonian forces. With such equally high ideals, I set about the

task of preparing my own outline for such a course.

One major task in preparing to teach a new course is that of selecting a suitable textbook, but in reviewing the course materials used by the various professors who responded to my survey, I soon saw that no such text existed. Although there was some overlap in the works assigned, with Melville's *Billy Budd*, Camus' *The Stranger*, and Kafka's *The Trial* being the most favored selections, the courses tended to be extremely diverse either emphasizing law in literature by utilizing some or all of the literary genres of the short story, the novel, poetry, and drama; or tending to place the emphasis on literature in law by using statutes, appellate decisions, and jurisprudential writings as the text. For my own purpose, none of these approaches was satisfactory. I needed a single primary textbook comprised of literary works that lent itself to supplementary material. Hence, I ventured on this book, which is an anthology of forty law-related short stories and which concludes with lists of law-related fiction and films.

By using short stories, I intended this work to be adaptable as a text in either undergraduate or graduate courses while also being of interest to practicing lawyers and the lay public. Who is not interested in the short stories of Kurt Vonnegut, Jr., and Isaac Asimov? This volume contains not only the anticipated "law" stories, but stories by Melville and Hawthorne dealing with the human condition of guilt, and a social satirist and a science fiction writer struggling with the themes of equality and obedience to the law—stories that might not strike the reader as "law" stories unless read in the context of this anthology.

In considering this work an anthology of short stories, it should be noted here that several pieces are not usually thought of as short stories; rather, they comprise selections from lengthier works—notably the excerpts from Sophocles' *Antigone* and Boccaccio's *Decameron*. This raises the question of what defines the short story form. In reviewing Melville's *Twice-Told Tales*, Poe tells us:

> A skillful artist has constructed a tale. He has fashioned his thoughts to accommodate his incidents, but having deliberately conceived a certain *single effect* to be wrought, he then invents such incidents, he then combines such events, and discusses them in such tone as may best serve him in establishing this preconceived effect. If his very first sentence tend not to the outbringing of this effect, then in his very first step he has committed a blunder. In the whole composition there should be no word written of which the tendency, direct or indirect, is not to the one pre-established design.

With Poe's statement in mind, I have included the above-mentioned excerpts on the premise that they fit Poe's definition of the short story. (*Antigone* is a serious attempt to deal with the conflicts between Divine law and positive law, and "Madame Filippa is Accused of Wronging Her Husband" from *The Decameron* is a satirical piece dealing with domestic relations.

Even though I was handicapped by not having an adequate text-book, I undertook the challenge of teaching an undergraduate course in law and literature, not really knowing how well one field might complement the other. One exercise that suggested itself to me became particularly useful to the students as they read law-related short stories. The exercise became known as "Briefing Short Stories/Plotting Legal Cases." The analogy be-tween the two processes will be readily apparent to anyone versed in the two fields of law and literature. Consider the following classic diagram for a short story's plot. It illustrates the elements of the short story form:

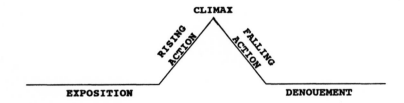

In the exposition we are introduced to the characters, the setting, and the general conflict. The rising action moves the reader through one or more crises to the climax, which is the pivotal moment of the story. This moment is followed by the falling action, which is a result of action at the climax and in which the reader is led inevitably toward the denouement—the French word for "untying the knot"—or the resolution.

Law students are often bewildered when they are asked to brief a case and wonder about this strange activity, but they would not be bewil-dered if only they realized that this activity is already familiar to them. Consider the following diagram:

The law student is asked to "brief," that is, "to make terse," a lengthy case in order to grasp the facts, to discuss the legal ramifications of those facts, to state the issue or issues, to dissect the court's rationale for its holding, and to state that holding. Generally, it is simple. If we tell the student to "plot the case," then the activity is familiar after all. If the freshman is told to brief a short story, then he or she understands the nature of plotting.

As the title of this book suggests, this is a book about law *and* litera-ture. Although the stories were chosen primarily for the legal issues that they raise, they were also chosen for their inherent literary value. At times, literary terms will be mentioned in the brief introductions to each section—point of view, satire, carpe diem, tone; these references are included to enrich the reading of the stories and to emphasize the usefulness of inter-relating literature and law. Isn't the whole of human experience told by way of stories whether in the courtroom or on the pages of a book? In brief, this work attempts to expose the reader to some of the world's greatest writers, to help the reader to read a text critically, to focus on our ultimate condition, to bring about a balance between Rationalism and Romanticism, and to introduce legal themes—to connect the areas of life's experience into a less fragmented whole.

Part One
Establishing Laws

1

Natural, Divine, and Positive Law

Now therefore hearken, O Israel, unto the statutes and unto the judgments, which I teach you. . . . Ye shall not add unto the word which I command, neither shall you diminish aught from it, that ye may keep the commandments of the Lord your God which I command you.

Deuteronomy, 4, 1-2

But in natural justice is nothing but the prisoner's overt act to be considered? How can we adjudge to shameful death a fellow-creature innocent before God and whom we feel to be so?—Does that state it aright? You sign sad assent. Well, I too feel that, the full force of that. It is Nature. But do these buttons that we wear attest our allegiance to Nature? No, to the King.

Billy Budd
Herman Melville

In any discussion of "laws," those of us who are not legal philosophers or theologians usually refer to "positive laws"—those laws laid down and dictated by a group of people, for the governance of other people; but two other kinds of laws preoccupy the thinking of jurisprudential scholars and theologians—Divine laws and natural laws. Divine laws are commanded by God. Natural laws, on the other hand, are to some the immutable rules of nature that are learned through the rational process of reason; to others they are laws that emanate from God; still others postulate that they are an ethical response to both positive and Divine laws, having both a moral and a legal basis.

Positive laws result from the social contract that comes into being as people seek each other out and form groups—initially for the purpose of sharing the responsibility of securing food, shelter, clothing, and safety; then, when the groups become more advanced, for the more sophisticated goals of developing and maintaining complicated structures of political and sociological ideals. To safeguard each group's cohesiveness, laws are developed not only for dealing with other groups—primitive laws created by tribes in the past, complicated international laws today—but for regulating the actions of the group's own citizens. These positive laws in highly developed groups take the form of constitutions, statutes, and common law. It has been said that to partake of the benefits that membership in the group provides, each citizen owes loyalty to the state and has an implied contract to obey its laws without question. Conflicts develop, however, when Divine, natural, and positive laws are not in harmony. Consider the following situations which, although not new, offer examples of such conflicts:

- A husband and wife refuse a blood transfusion for their dying newborn in accordance with their religious beliefs and in violation of a court order even though they know that the baby will die without such medical intervention.

- A conscientious objector who belongs to no organized religious group claims to follow a natural and higher law than the positive law that requires him to serve his country in combat.

If positive laws are established by men for the utilitarian purpose of providing the greatest good for the greatest number, how are those laws to be applied in the above situations? Should we respect the couple's religious beliefs and allow the baby to die but force the conscientious objector to serve his country? Would such acts favor Divine law over natural law? The U. S. Constitution provides for religious freedom, but what is a religion? To what extent are those religious freedoms protected? Suppose the couple above refused the blood transfusion but belonged to no organized religious group? Suppose the conscientious objector formed his own group of two thousand followers but followed no orthodox religious mandates? The separation of the Church and the State naturally resulted in two codes that coexist and which do not necessarily have the same aims or goals.

In the following two short stories, Tolstóy addresses the supposed inferiority of positive law and the perceived superiority of Divine law, and Sophocles deals with the conflicts between obedience to Divine law and obedience to positive law.

In Tolstóy's "God Sees the Truth, but Waits," the protagonist finds himself wrongly accused of murder, and he is subjected to positive laws that are not adequate to discover the truth. Divine law offers the only escape for him, and he imagines that God will forgive the one who wronged him even if he himself cannot. Is God's act of waiting vengeful or forgiving? Why does God wait?

In the Sophocles excerpts, Antigone defies the positive laws of the State to afford a proper burial to her dead brother, in accordance with the laws of the god Zeus, even though such a burial is in opposition to the edict of the State and will cost her her life. Antigone makes a choice that she feels is dictated by the laws of the gods, but Ismene claims that she does not dishonor the gods by not helping Antigone bury their brother in accordance with such laws. Might we assume that Zeus sees the truth, but waits?

God Sees the Truth, but Waits
Leo Tolstóy

In the town of Vladímir lived a young merchant named Iván Dmítrich Aksënov. He had two shops and a house of his own.

Aksënov was a handsome, fair-haired, curly-headed fellow, full of fun and very fond of singing. When quite a young man he had been given to drink and was riotous when he had had too much; but after he married he gave up drinking except now and then.

One summer Aksënov was going to the Nízhny Fair, and as he bade good-bye to his family his wife said to him, 'Iván Dmítrich, do not start to-day; I have had a bad dream about you.'

Aksënov laughed, and said, 'You are afraid that when I get to the fair I shall go on the spree.'

His wife replied: 'I do not know what I am afraid of; all I know is that I had a bad dream. I dreamt you returned from the town, and when you took off your cap I saw that your hair was quite grey.'

Aksënov laughed. 'That's a lucky sign,' said he. 'See if I don't sell out all my goods and bring you some presents from the fair.'

So he said good-bye to his family and drove away.

When he had travelled half-way, he met a merchant whom he knew, and they put up at the same inn for the night. They had some tea together, and then went to bed in adjoining rooms.

It was not Aksënov's habit to sleep late, and, wishing to travel while it was still cool, he aroused his driver before dawn and told him to put in the horses.

Then he made his way across to the landlord of the inn (who lived in a cottage at the back), paid his bill, and continued his journey.

When he had gone about twenty-five miles he stopped for the horses to be fed. Aksënov rested awhile in the passage of the inn, then he stepped out into the porch and, ordering a *samovár* to be heated, got out his guitar and began to play.

Suddenly a *tróyka* drove up with tinkling bells, and an official alighted, followed by two soldiers. He came to Aksënov and began to question him, asking him who he was and whence he came. Aksënov answered him fully, and said, 'Won't you have some tea with me?' But the official went on cross-questioning him and asking him, 'Where did you spend last night? Were you alone, or with a fellow-merchant? Did you see the other merchant this morning? Why did you leave the inn before dawn?'

Aksënov wondered why he was asked all these questions, but he described all that had happened, and then added, 'Why do you cross-question me as if I were a thief or a robber? I am travelling on business of my own, and there is no need to question me.'

Then the official, calling the soldiers, said, 'I am the police-officer of this district, and I question you because the merchant with whom you spent last night has been found with his throat cut. We must search your things.'

They entered the house. The soldiers and the police-officer un-strapped Aksënov's luggage and searched it. Suddenly the officer drew a knife out of a bag, crying, 'Whose knife is this?'

Aksënov looked, and seeing a blood-stained knife taken from his bag, he was frightened.

'How is it there is blood on this knife?'

Aksënov tried to answer, but could hardly utter a word, and only stammered: 'I—don't know—not mine.'

Then the police-officer said, 'This morning the merchant was found in bed with his throat cut. You are the only person who could have done it. The house was locked from inside, and no one else was there. Here is this blood-stained knife in your bag, and your face and manner betray you! Tell me how you killed him and how much money you stole?'

Aksënov swore he had not done it; that he had not seen the merchant after they had had tea together; that he had no money except eight thousand rúbles of his own, and that the knife was not his. But his voice was bro-ken, his face pale, and he trembled with fear as though he were guilty.

The police-officer ordered the soldiers to bind Aksënov and to put him in the cart. As they tied his feet together and flung him into the cart, Aksënov crossed himself and wept. His money and goods were taken from him, and he was sent to the nearest town and imprisoned there. Enquiries as to his character were made in Vladímir. The merchants and other inhabi-tants of that town said that in former days he used to drink and waste his time, but that he was a good man. Then the trial came on: he was charged with murdering a merchant from Ryazán and robbing him of twenty thou-sand rúbles.

His wife was in despair, and did not know what to believe. Her children were all quite small; one was a baby at the breast. Taking them all with her, she went to the town where her husband was in gaol. At first she was not allowed to see him; but, after much begging, she obtained permis-sion from the officials and was taken to him. When she saw her husband in prison-dress and in chains, shut up with thieves and criminals, she fell down and did not come to her senses for a long time. Then she drew her children to her, and sat down near him. She told him of things at home, and asked about what had happened to him. He told her all, and she asked, 'What can we do now?'

'We must petition the Tsar not to let an innocent man perish.'

His wife told him that she had sent a petition to the Tsar, but that it had not been accepted.

Aksënov did not reply, but only looked downcast.

Then his wife said, 'It was not for nothing I dreamt your hair had turned grey. You remember? You should not have started that day.' And passing her fingers through his hair she said: 'Ványa dearest, tell your wife the truth; was it not you who did it?'

'So you, too, suspect me!' said Aksënov, and, hiding his face in his hands, he began to weep. Then a soldier came to say that the wife and children must go away, and Aksënov said good-bye to his family for the last time.

When they were gone, Aksënov recalled what had been said, and when he remembered that his wife also had suspected him, he said to himself, 'It seems that only God can know the truth; it is to Him alone we must appeal and from Him alone expect mercy.'

And Aksënov wrote no more petitions, gave up all hope, and only prayed to God.

Aksënov was condemned to be flogged and sent to the mines. So he was flogged with a knout, and when the wounds caused by the knout were healed, he was driven to Siberia with other convicts.

For twenty-six years Aksënov lived as a convict in Siberia. His hair turned white as snow, and his beard grew long, thin, and grey. All his mirth went; he stooped; he walked slowly, spoke little, and never laughed, but he often prayed.

In prison Aksënov learnt to make boots, and earned a little money, with which he bought *The Lives of the Saints*. He read this book when it was light enough in the prison; and on Sundays in the prison-church he read the epistle and sang in the choir for his voice was still good.

The prison authorities liked Aksënov for his meekness, and his fellow-prisoners respected him: they called him 'Grandfather,' and 'The Saint.' When they wanted to petition the prison authorities about anything, they always made Aksënov their spokesman, and when there were quarrels among the prisoners they came to him to put things right, and to judge the matter.

No news reached Aksënov from his home, and he did not even know if his wife and children were still alive.

One day a fresh gang of convicts came to the prison. In the evening the old prisoners collected round the new ones and asked them what towns or villages they came from, and what they were sentenced for. Among the rest Aksënov sat down near the newcomers, and listened with downcast air to what was said.

One of the new convicts, a tall, strong man of sixty, with a closely-cropped grey beard, was telling the others what he had been arrested for.

'Well, friends,' he said, 'I only took a horse that was tied to a sledge, and I was arrested and accused of stealing. I said I had only taken it to get home quicker, and had then let it go; besides, the driver was a personal friend of mine. So I said, "it's all right." "No," said they, "you stole it." But how or where I stole it they could not say. I once really did something wrong, and ought by rights to have come here long ago, but that time I was not found out. Now I have been sent here for nothing at all . . . Eh, but it's lies I'm telling you; I've been to Siberia before, but I did not stay long.'

'Where are you from?' asked some one.

'From Vladímir. My family are of that town. My name is Makár, and they also call me Semënich.'

Aksënov raised his head and said: 'Tell me, Semënich, do you know anything of the merchants Aksënov, of Vladímir? Are they still alive?'

'Know them? Of course I do. The Aksënov are rich, though their father is in Siberia: a sinner like ourselves, it seems! As for you, Gran'dad, how did you come here?'

Aksënov did not like to speak of his misfortune. He only sighed, and said, 'For my sins I have been in prison these twenty-six years.'

'What sins?' asked Makár Semënich.

But Aksënov only said, 'Well, well—I must have deserved it!' He would have said no more, but his companions told the new-comer how Aksënov came to be in Siberia: how some one had killed a merchant and had put a knife among Aksënov's things, and he had been unjustly condemned.

When Makár Semënich heard this he looked at Aksënov, slapped his own knee, and exclaimed, 'Well, this is wonderful! Really wonderful! But how old you've grown, Gran'dad!'

The others asked him why he was so surprised, and where he had seen Aksënov before; but Makár Semënich did not reply. He only said: 'It's wonderful that we should meet here, lads!'

These words made Aksënov wonder whether this man knew who had killed the merchant; so he said, 'Perhaps, Semënich, you have heard of that affair, or maybe you've seen me before?'

'How could I help hearing? The world's full of rumours. But it's long ago, and I've forgotten what I heard.'

'Perhaps you heard who killed the merchant?' asked Aksënov.

Makár Semënich laughed, and replied, 'It must have been him in whose bag the knife was found! If someone else hid the knife there—"he's not a thief till he's caught," as the saying is. How could anyone put a knife into your bag while it was under your head? It would surely have woke you up?'

When Aksënov heard these words he felt sure this was the man who had killed the merchant. He felt terribly unhappy, and all sorts of images rose in his mind. There was the image of his wife as she was when he parted from her to go to the fair. He saw her as if she were present; her face and her eyes rose before him, he heard her speak and laugh. Then he saw his children, quite little, as they were at that time: one with a little cloak on, another at his mother's breast. And then he remembered himself as he used to be—young and merry. He remembered how he sat playing the guitar in the porch of the inn where he was arrested, and how free from care he had been. He saw in his mind the place where he was flogged, the executioner, and the people standing around; the chains, the convicts, all the twenty-six years of his prison life, and his premature old age. The thought of it all made him so wretched that he was ready to kill himself.

'And it's all that villain's doing!' thought Aksënov. And his anger was so great against Makár Semënich that he longed for vengeance, even if he himself should perish for it. He kept saying prayers all night, but could get no peace. During the day he did not go near Makár Seménich, nor even look at him.

A fortnight passed in this way. Aksënov could not sleep at nights and was so miserable that he did not know what to do.

One night as he was walking about the prison he noticed some earth that came rolling out from under one of the shelves on which the prisoners slept. He stopped to see what it was. Suddenly Makár Seménich crept out from under the shelf, and looked up at Aksënov with frightened face. Aksënov tried to pass without looking at him, but Makár seized his hand and told him that he had dug a hole under the wall, getting rid of the earth by putting it into his high boots and emptying it out every day on the road when the prisoners were driven to their work.

'Just you keep quiet, old man, and you shall get out too. If you blab they'll flog the life out of me, but I will kill you first.'

Aksënov trembled with anger as he looked at his enemy. He drew his hand away, saying, 'I have no wish to escape, and you have no need to kill me; you killed me long ago! As to telling of you—I may do so or not, as God shall direct.'

Next day, when the convicts were led out to work, the convoy soldiers noticed that one or other of the prisoners emptied some earth out of his boots. The prison was searched and the tunnel found. The Governor came and questioned all the prisoners to find out who had dug the hole. They all denied any knowledge of it. Those who knew would not betray Makár Seménich, knowing he would be flogged almost to death. As last the Governor turned to Aksënov, whom he knew to be a just man, and said:

'You are a truthful old man; tell me, before God, who dug the hole?'

Makár Seménich stood as if he were quite unconcerned, looking at the Governor and not so much as glancing at Aksënov. Aksënov's lips and hands trembled, and for a long time he could not utter a word. He thought, 'Why should I screen him who ruined my life? Let him pay for what I have suffered. But if I tell, they will probably flog the life out of him, and maybe I suspect him wrongly. And, after all, what good would it be to me?'

'Well, old man,' repeated the Governor, 'tell us the truth: who has been digging under the wall?'

Aksënov glanced at Makár Seménich and said, 'I cannot say, your honour. It is not God's will that I should tell! Do what you like with me; I am in your hands.'

However much the Governor tried, Aksënov would say no more, and so the matter had to be left.

That night, when Aksënov was lying on his bed and just beginning to doze, some one came quietly and sat down on his bed. He peered through the darkness and recognized Makár.

'What more do you want of me?' asked Aksënov. 'Why have you come here?'

Makár Seménich was silent. So Aksënov sat up and said, 'What do you want? Go away or I will call the guard!'

Makár Seménich bent close over Aksënov, and whispered 'Iván Dmítrich, forgive me!'

'What for?' asked Aksënov.

'It was I who killed the merchant and hid the knife among your things. I meant to kill you too, but I heard a noise outside; so I hid the knife in your bag and escaped through the window.'

Aksënov was silent and did not know what to say. Makár Semënich slid off the bed-shelf and knelt upon the ground. 'Iván Dmítrich,' said he, 'forgive me! For the love of God, forgive me! I will confess that it was I who killed the merchant, and you will be released and can go to your home.'

'It is easy for you to talk,' said Aksënov, 'but I have suffered for you these twenty-six years. Where could I go to now? My wife is dead, and my children have forgotten me. I have nowhere to go. . .'

Makár Semënich did not rise, but beat his head on the floor. 'Iván Dmítrich, forgive me!' he cried. 'When they flogged me with the knout it was not so hard to bear as it is to see you now . . . yet you had pity on me and did not tell. For Christ's sake forgive me, wretch that I am!' And he began to sob.

When Aksënov heard him sobbing he, too, began to weep.

'God will forgive you!' said he. 'Maybe I am a hundred times worse than you.' And at these words his heart grew light and the longing for home left him. He no longer had any desire to leave the prison, but only hoped for his last hour to come.

In spite of what Aksënov had said, Makár Semënich confessed his guilt. But when the order for his release came, Aksënov was already dead.

Excerpts from *Antigone*
Sophocles

ANTIGONE

Ismene, sister, mine own dear sister, knowest thou what ill there is, of all bequeathed by Oedipus, that Zeus fulfils not for us twain while we live? Nothing painful is there, nothing fraught with ruin, no shame, no dishonour, that I have not seen in thy woes and mine.

And now what new edict is this of which they tell, that our Captain hath just published to all Thebes? Knowest thou aught? Hast thou heard? Or is it hidden from thee that our friends are threatened with the doom of our foes?

ISMENE

No words of friends, Antigone, gladsome or painful, hath come to me, since we two sisters were bereft of brothers twain, killed in one day by a twofold blow; and since in this last night the Argive host hath fled, I know no more, whether my fortune be brighter, or more grievous.

ANTIGONE

I knew it well, and therefore sought to bring thee beyond the gates of the court, that thou mightest hear alone.

ISMENE

What is it? 'Tis plain that thou art brooding on some dark tidings.

ANTIGONE

What, hath not Creon destined our brothers, the one to honoured burial, the other to unburied shame? Eteocles, they say, with due observance of right and custom, he hath laid in the earth, for his honour among the dead below. But the hapless corpse of Polyneices—as rumour saith, it hath been published to the town that none shall entomb him or mourn, but leave unwept, unsepulchred, a welcome store for the birds, as they espy him, to feast on at will.

Such, 'tis said, is the edict that the good Creon hath set forth for thee and for me,—yes, for *me*,—and is coming hither to proclaim it clearly to those who know it not; nor counts the matter light, but, whoso disobeys in aught, his doom is death by stoning before all the folk. Thou knowest it now; and thou wilt soon show whether thou art nobly bred, or the base daughter of a noble line.

ISMENE

Poor sister,—and if things stand thus, what could I help to do or undo?

ANTIGONE

Consider if thou wilt share the toil and the deed.

ISMENE

In what venture? What can be thy meaning?

ANTIGONE

Wilt thou aid this hand to lift the dead?

ISMENE

Thou wouldst bury him,—when 'tis forbidden to Thebes?

ANTIGONE

I will do my part,—and thine, if thou wilt not,—to a brother. False to him will I never be found.

ISMENE

Ah, over-bold! when Creon hath forbidden?

ANTIGONE

Nay, he hath no right to keep me from mine own.

ISMENE

Ah me! think, sister, how our father perished, amid hate and scorn, when sins bared by his own search had moved him to strike both eyes with self-blinding hand; then the mother wife, two names in one, with twisted noose did despite unto her life; and last, our two brothers in one day,—each shedding, hapless one, a kinsman's blood,—wrought out with mutual hands their common doom. And now we in turn—we two left all alone—think how we shall perish, more miserably than all the rest, if, in defiance of the law, we brave a king's decree or his powers. Nay, we must remember, first, that we were born women, as who should not strive with men; next, that we are ruled of the stronger, so that we must obey in these things, and in things yet sorer. I, therefore, asking the Spirits Infernal to pardon, seeing that force is put on me herein, will hearken to our rulers; for 'tis witless to be over busy.

ANTIGONE

I will not urge thee,—no, nor, if thou yet shouldst have the mind, wouldst thou be welcome as a worker with *me*. Nay, be what thou wilt; but I will bury him: well for me to die in doing that. I shall rest, a loved one with him whom I have loved, sinless in my crime; for I owe a longer allegiance to the dead than to the living: in that world I shall abide for ever. But if *thou* wilt, be guilty of dishonouring laws which the gods have stablished in honour.

ISMENE

I do them no dishonour; but to defy the State,—I have no strength for that.

ANTIGONE

Such be thy plea;—I, then, will go to heap the earth above the brother whom I love.

. . . .

CREON

Sirs, the vessel of our state, after being tossed on wild waves, hath once more been safely steadied by the gods: and ye, out of all the folk, have been called apart by my summons, because I knew, first of all, how true and constant was your reverence for the royal power of Laïus; how, again, when Oedipus was ruler of our land, and when he had perished, your steadfast loyalty still upheld their children. Since, then, his sons have fallen in one day by a twofold doom,—each smitten by the other, each stained with a brother's blood,—I now possess the throne and all its powers, by nearness of kinship to the dead.

No man can be fully known, in soul and spirit and mind, until he hath been seen versed in rule and law-giving. For if any, being supreme guide of the State, cleaves not to the best counsels, but, through some fear, keeps his lips locked, I hold, and have ever held, him most base; and if any makes a friend of more account than his fatherland, that man hath no place in my regard. For I—be Zeus my witness, who sees all things always—would not be silent if I saw ruin, instead of safety, coming to the citizens; nor would I ever deem the country's foe a friend to myself; remembering this, that our country is the ship that bears us safe, and that only while she prospers in our voyage can we make true friends.

Such are the rules by which I guard this city's greatness. And in accord with them is the edict, which I have now published to the folk touching the sons of Oedipus;—that Eteocles, who hath fallen fighting for our city, in all renown of arms, shall be entombed, and crowned with every rite that follows the noblest dead to their rest. But for his brother, Polyneices,—who came back from exile, and sought to consume utterly with fire the city of his fathers and the shrines of his fathers' gods,—sought to taste of kindred blood, and to lead the remnant into slavery;—touching this man, it hath been proclaimed to our people that none shall grace him with sepulture or lament, but leave him unburied, a corpse for birds and dogs to eat, a ghastly sight of shame.

Such the spirit of my dealing; and never, by deed of mine, shall the wicked stand in honour before the just; but whoso hath good will to Thebes, he shall be honoured of me, in his life and in his death.

. . . .

CREON
And what is it that disquiets thee thus?

. . . .

CREON
What sayest thou? What living man hath dared this deed?

. . . .

GUARD
O king, against nothing should men pledge their word; for the afterthought belies the first intent. I could have vowed that I should not soon be here again,—scared by thy threats, with which I had just been lashed: but,—since the joy that surprises and transcends our hopes is like in fulness to no other pleasure,—I have come, though 'tis in breach of my sworn oath, bringing this maid; who was taken showing grace to the dead. This time there was no casting of lots; no, this luck hath fallen to me, and to none else. And now, sire, take her thyself, question here, examine her, as thou wilt; but I have a right to free and final quittance of this trouble.

CREON
And thy prisoner here—how and whence hast thou taken her?
GUARD
She was burying the man; thou knowest all.
CREON
Dost thou mean what thou sayest? Dost thou speak aright?
GUARD
I saw her burying the corpse that thou hadst forbidden to bury. Is that plain and clear?

. . . .

CREON
Thou—thou whose face is bent to earth—dost thou avow, or disavow this deed?
ANTIGONE
I avow it; I make no denial.
CREON (*TO* GUARD)
Thou canst betake thee wither thou wilt, free and clear of a grave charge.

(*Exit* Guard)

(*To* Antigone)   Now, tell me thou—not in many words, but briefly—knewest thou that an edict had forbidden this?
ANTIGONE
I knew it: could I help it? It was public.
CREON
And thou didst indeed dare to transgress that law?
ANTIGONE
Yes, for it was not Zeus that had published me that edict; not such are the laws set among men by the Justice who dwells with the gods below; nor deemed I that thy decrees were of such force, that a mortal could override the unwritten and unfailing statutes of heaven. For their life is not of to-day or yesterday, but from all time, and no man knows when they were first put forth.

Not through dread of any human pride could I answer to the gods for breaking *these*. Die I must,—I knew that well (how should I not?)—even without thy edicts. But if I am to die before my time, I count that a gain: for when any one lives, as I do, compassed about with evils, can such an one find aught but gain in death?

So for me to meet this doom is trifling grief; but if I had suffered my mother's son to lie in death an unburied corpse, that would have grieved me; for this, I am not grieved. And if my present deeds are foolish in thy sight, it may be that a foolish judge arraigns my folly.

2

Obedience
to Positive Law

A common and natural result of an undue respect for law is,
that you may see a file of soldiers, colonel, captain, corporal, privates, powder-monkeys and all, marching in admirable order over hill and dale to the wars, against their
wills, aye, against their common sense and consciences,
which makes it very steep marching indeed, and produces a
palpitation of the heart.

Civil Disobedience
Henry David Thoreau

If the people say, "Go wipe out South America," the Army
will do it. Majority rules, and if a majority tells me, "Go to
South Vietnam," I will go. If it tells me, "Lieutenant Calley," or "Rusty Calley" or "Whatever, go massacre one
thousand communists." But—I won't advocate it. I'm
against massacre, and I won't preach it: I won't be a hypocrite for it. Or maybe *that* is a hypocrite, but I'll do as I'm
told to. I won't revolt. I'll put the American people above
my own conscience, always. I'm an American citizen.

Lieutenant Calley,
told to John Sack

In the previous section Antigone disobeyed positive laws in favor of the
laws of the Gods and the protagonist in "God Sees the Truth, but Waits"
relied on God to right man's wrongs. We considered whether the conscientious objector who is without a religious affiliation and who relies only on
a moral sense of justice has less or more rights than people who claim religious freedom as their excuse or justification to disobey the law. This section deals with disobedience of the law by people who claim no religious
justification for their acts.

To begin, any discussion of disobedience raises several questions.
First, should obedience to the laws of the State be total and absolute as
claimed by Lieutenant Calley as his defense to his massacre of women and
children in South Vietnam? Next, should people disobey the laws laid
down for their rule if they feel that the rules are unjust or in conflict with

their consciences? Finally, if citizens feel the rules set forth by rulers are unjust, *how* should they proceed to disobey or change those laws? In *Civil Disobedience* Thoreau asks:

> Unjust laws exist: shall we be content to obey them, or shall we endeavor to amend them, and obey them until we have succeeded, or shall we transgress them at once? Men generally, under such a government as this, think that they ought to wait until they have persuaded the majority to alter them.

"Some of Us Had Been Threatening Our Friend Colby," by Donald Barthelme, is an intriguing story of a group of men who have developed a code of ethics that contradicts the one established by its society. The group's intention and plan is to hang Colby because he has "gone too far." We are never told how Colby has transgressed the rules laid down by the group. The narrator only informs us that the group is aware that hanging Colby is against the law, but it feels that it has a "*moral* right to do so because he was *our* friend, *belonged* to us. . . ." The traditional concept of moral rights is unhinged in this story, and we question whether, rather than assume that, the group should be charged and tried for murder. Colby accepts his fate with just a little squirming and quibbling. The blind obedience that he exhibits to the group's code is analogous to the obedience exhibited by many followers of the Reverend Jim Jones in the murder-suicide of November 18, 1978, in Guyana, South America. Hundreds willingly drank or subjected themselves to injections of Kool-Aid spiked with cyanide rather than submit to the rules of the society from which they had withdrawn. Normally, consent is no defense to murder, but if an individual agrees to be killed, in the name of religion or as a moral right, are the perpetrators really guilty of murder? Should the charge be one of aiding and abetting a suicide? Notice that Colby's group does not attempt to change the laws, it just disobeys them without much forethought or consideration.

Unlike the group in "Some of Us Had Been Threatening Our Friend Colby," who create their own laws and summarily disregard the laws of the state, the protagonist in Isaac Asimov's "The Bicentennial Man" agonizes over the conflicts caused by the three laws of robotics that were laid down by man for robots. In the short story:

• The more human Andrew Martin becomes, the less he gives blind obedience to the law.

• The robot manages to bring about changes to the laws through a change in public opinion and, in turn, a change in the attitude of the key courts and the legislature in order to establish conditions under which "robot-harming orders are forbidden." Ultimately, however, he cannot persuade the lawmakers to accede to his final request for humanity.

• Although Andrew works through the so-called proper channels

for legal reform, he is informed that the "robot-harming" laws are really unenforceable.

- Unable to reach "humanity" or "equality" through the methods
provided for changing the law, the robot manipulates the Three Laws of
Robotics. He finds a "loophole in the law" to persuade the robot surgeon
that the law requiring the surgeon not to inflict damage on a human being
does not apply to an operation on a robot.

- Andrew Martin asks the judge if he wishes to be a slave. In
seeking a release from involuntary servitude, Andrew states, ironically, that
freedom "is without price."

Some of Us
Had Been Threatening
Our Friend Colby
Donald Barthelme

Some of us had been threatening our friend Colby for a long time, because of the way he had been behaving. And now he'd gone too far, so we decided to hang him. Colby argued that just because he had gone too far (he did not deny that he had gone too far) did not mean that he should be subjected to hanging. Going too far, he said, was something everybody did sometimes. We didn't pay much attention to this argument. We asked him what sort of music he would like played at the hanging. He said he'd think about it but it would take him a while to decide. I pointed out that we'd have to know soon, because Howard, who is a conductor would have to hire and rehearse the musicians and he couldn't begin until he knew what the music was going to be. Colby said he'd always been fond of Ives's Fourth Symphony. Howard said that this was a "delaying tactic" and that everybody knew that the Ives was almost impossible to perform and would involve weeks of rehearsal, and that the size of the orchestra and chorus would put us way over the music budget. "Be reasonable," he said to Colby. Colby said he'd try to think of something a little less exacting.

Hugh was worried about the wording of the invitations. What if one of them fell into the hands of the authorities? Hanging Colby was doubtless against the law, and if the authorities learned in advance what the plan was they would very likely come in and try to mess everything up. I said that although hanging Colby was almost certainly against the law, we had a perfect *moral* right to do so because he was *our* friend, *belonged* to us in various important senses, and he had after all gone too far. We agreed that the invitations would be worded in such a way that the person invited could not know for sure what he was being invited to. We decided to refer to the event as "An Event Involving Mr. Colby Williams." A handsome script was selected from a catalogue and we picked a cream-colored paper. Magnus said he'd see to having the invitations printed, and wondered whether we should serve drinks. Colby said he thought drinks would be nice but was worried about the expense. We told him kindly that the expense didn't matter, that we were after all his dear friends and if a group of his dear friends couldn't get together and do the thing with a little bit of *éclat*, why, what was the world coming to? Colby asked if he would be able to have drinks, too, before the event. We said, "Certainly."

The next item of business was the gibbet. None of us knew too much about gibbet design, but Tomás, who is an architect, said he'd look it up in old books and draw the plans. The important thing, as far as he recollected, was that the trapdoor function perfectly. He said that just roughly, counting labor and materials, it shouldn't run us more than four hundred dollars. "Good God!" Howard said. He said what was Tomás figuring on, rosewood? No, just a good grade of pine, Tomás said. Victor asked if unpainted pine wouldn't look kind of "raw," and Tomás replied that he thought it could be stained a dark walnut without too much trouble.

I said that although I thought the whole thing ought to be done really well and all, I also thought four hundred dollars for a gibbet, on top of the expense for the drinks, invitations, musicians, and everything, was a bit steep, and why didn't we just use a tree—a nice-looking oak, or something? I pointed out that since it was going to be a June hanging the trees would be in glorious leaf and that not only would a tree add a kind of "natural" feeling but it was also strictly traditional, especially in the West. Tomás, who had been sketching gibbets on the backs of envelopes, reminded us that an outdoor hanging always had to contend with the threat of rain. Victor said he liked the idea of doing it outdoors, possibly on the bank of a river, but noted that we would have to hold it some distance from the city, which presented the problem of getting the guests, musicians, etc., to the site and then back to town.

At this point, everybody looked at Harry, who runs a car-and-truck-rental business. Harry said he thought he could round up enough limousines to take care of that end but that the drivers would have to be paid. The drivers, he pointed out, wouldn't be friends of Colby's and couldn't be expected to donate their services, any more than the bartender or the musicians. He said that he had about ten limousines, which he used mostly for funerals, and that he could probably obtain another dozen by calling around to friends of his in the trade. He said also that if we did it outside, in the open air, we'd better figure on a tent or awning of some kind to cover at least the principals and the orchestra, because if the hanging was being rained on he thought it would look kind of dismal. As between gibbet and tree, he said, he had no particular preferences and he really thought that the choice ought to be left up to Colby, since it was his hanging. Colby said that everybody went too far, sometimes, and weren't we being a little Draconian? Howard said rather sharply that all that had already been discussed, and which did he want, gibbet or tree? Colby asked if he could have a firing squad. No, Howard said, he could not. Howard said a firing squad would just be an ego trip for Colby, the blindfold and last-cigarette bit, and that Colby was in enough hot water already without trying to "upstage" everyone with unnecessary theatrics. Colby said he was sorry, he hadn't meant it that way, he'd take the tree. Tomás crumpled up the gibbet sketches he'd been making, in disgust.

Then the question of the hangman came up. Pete said did we really need a hangman? Because if we used a tree, the noose could be adjusted to the appropriate level and Colby could just jump off something—a chair or stool or something. Besides, Pete said, he very much doubted if there were any free-lance hangmen wandering around the country, now that capital punishment has been done away with absolutely, temporarily, and that we'd probably have to fly one in from England or one of the South American countries, and even if we did that how could we know in advance that the man was a professional, a real hangman, and not just some money-hungry amateur who might bungle the job and shame us all, in front of everybody? We all agreed then that Colby should just jump off something and that a chair was not what he should jump off of, because that would look, we felt, extremely tacky—some old kitchen chair sitting out there under our beautiful tree. Tomás, who is quite modern in outlook and not afraid of innovation, proposed that Colby be standing on a large round rubber ball ten feet in diameter. This, he said, would afford a sufficient "drop" and would also roll out of the way if Colby suddenly changed his mind after jumping off. He reminded us that by not using a regular hangman we were placing an awful lot of the responsibility for the success of the affair on Colby himself, and that although he was sure Colby would perform creditably and not disgrace his friends at the last minute, still, men have been known to get a little irresolute at times like that, and the ten-foot-round rubber ball, which could probably be fabricated rather cheaply, would insure a "bang-up" production right down to the wire.

At the mention of "wire," Hank, who had been silent all this time, suddenly spoke up and said he wondered if it wouldn't be better if we used wire instead of rope—more efficient and in the end kinder to Colby, he suggested. Colby began looking a little green, and I didn't blame him, because there is something extremely distasteful in thinking about being hanged with wire instead of rope—it gives you sort of a revulsion, when you think about it. I thought it was really quite unpleasant of Hank to be sitting there talking about wire, just when we had solved the problem of what Colby was going to jump off of so neatly, with Tomás's idea about the rubber ball, so I hastily said that wire was out of the question, because it would injure the tree—cut into the branch it was tied to when Colby's full weight hit it—and that in these days of increased respect for the environment, we didn't want that, did we? Colby gave me a grateful look, and the meeting broke up.

Everything went off very smoothly on the day of the event (the music Colby finally picked was standard stuff, Elgar, and it was played very well by Howard and his boys). It didn't rain, the event was well attended, and we didn't run out of Scotch, or anything. The ten-foot rubber ball had been painted a deep green and blended in well with the bucolic setting. The two things I remember best about the whole episode are the grateful look Colby gave me when I said what I said about the wire, and the fact that nobody has ever gone too far again.

The Bicentennial Man
Isaac Asimov

The Three Laws of Robotics:

1. A robot may not injure a human being or, through inaction, allow a human being to come to harm.
2. A robot must obey the orders given it by human beings except where such orders would conflict with the First Law.
3. A robot must protect its own existence as long as such protection does not conflict with the First or Second Law.

1.

Andrew Martin said, "Thank you," and took the seat offered him. He didn't look driven to the last resort, but he had been.

He didn't, actually, look anything, for there was a smooth blankness to his face, except for the sadness one imagined one saw in his eyes. His hair was smooth, light brown, rather fine, and there was no facial hair. He looked freshly and cleanly shaved. His clothes were distinctly old-fashioned, but neat and predominantly a velvety red-purple in color.

Facing him from behind the desk was the surgeon, and the nameplate on the desk included a fully identifying series of letters and numbers, which Andrew didn't bother with. To call him Doctor would be quite enough.

"When can the operation be carried through, Doctor?" he asked.

The surgeon said softly, with that certain inalienable note of respect that a robot always used to a human being, "I am not certain, sir, that I understand how or upon whom such an operation could be performed."

There might have been a look of respectful intransigence on the surgeon's face, if a robot of his sort, in lightly bronzed stainless steel, could have such an expression, or any expression.

Andrew Martin studied the robot's right hand, his cutting hand, as it lay on the desk in utter tranquillity. The fingers were long and shaped into artistically metallic looping curves so graceful and appropriate that one could imagine a scalpel fitting them and becoming, temporarily, one piece with them.

There would be no hesitation in his work, no stumbling, no quivering, no mistakes. That came with specialization, of course, a specialization so fiercely desired by humanity that few robots were, any longer, independently brained. A surgeon, of course, would have to be. And this one, though brained, was so limited in his capacity that he did not recognize Andrew—had probably never heard of him.

Andrew said, "Have you ever thought you would like to be a man?"

The surgeon hesitated a moment as though the question fitted nowhere in his allotted positronic pathways. "But I am a robot, sir."

"Would it be better to be a man?"

"It would be better, sir, to be a better surgeon. I could not be so if I were a man, but only if I were a more advanced robot. I would be pleased to be a more advanced robot."

"It does not offend you that I can order you about? That I can make you stand up, sit down, move right or left, by merely telling you to do so?"

"It is my pleasure to please you, sir. If your orders were to interfere with my functioning with respect to you or to any other human being, I would not obey you. The First Law, concerning my duty to human safety, would take precedence over the Second Law relating to obedience. Otherwise, obedience is my pleasure. . . . But upon whom am I to perform this operation?"

"That does not matter," said Andrew calmly.

"I must not inflict damage," said the surgeon.

"On a human being, you must not," said Andrew, "but I, too, am a robot."

2.

Andrew had appeared much more a robot when he had first been—manufactured. He had then been as much a robot in appearance as any that had ever existed, smoothly designed and functional.

He had done well in the home to which he had been brought in those days when robots in households, or on the planet altogether, had been a rarity.

There had been four in the home: Sir and Ma'am and Miss and Little Miss. He knew their names, of course, but he never used them. Sir was Gerald Martin.

His own serial number was NDR—He forgot the numbers. It had been a long time, of course, but if he had wanted to remember, he could not forget. He had not wanted to remember.

Little Miss had been the first to call him Andrew because she could not use the letters, and all the rest followed her in this.

Little Miss—She had lived ninety years and was long since dead. He had tried to call her Ma'am once, but she would not allow it. Little Miss she had been to her last day.

Andrew had been intended to perform the duties of a valet, a butler, a lady's maid. Those were the experimental days for him and, indeed, for all robots anywhere but in the industrial and exploratory factories and stations off Earth.

The Martins enjoyed him, and half the time he was prevented from doing his work because Miss and Little Miss would rather play with him.

It was Miss who understood first how this might be arranged. She said, "We order you to play with us and you must follow orders."

Andrew said, "I am sorry, Miss, but a prior order from Sir must surely take precedence."

But she said, "Daddy just said he hoped you would take care of the cleaning. That's not much of an order. I *order* you."

Sir did not mind. Sir was fond of Miss and of Little Miss, even more than Ma'am was, and Andrew was fond of them, too. At least, the effect they had upon his actions were those which in a human being would have been called the result of fondness. Andrew thought of it as fondness, for he did not know any other word for it.

It was for Little Miss that Andrew had carved a pendant out of wood. She had ordered him to. Miss, it seemed, had received an ivorite pendant with scrollwork for her birthday, and Little Miss was unhappy over it. She had only a piece of wood, which she gave Andrew together with a small kitchen knife.

He had done it quickly and Little Miss said, "That's *nice*, Andrew. I'll show it to Daddy."

Sir would not believe it. "Where did you really get this, Mandy?" Mandy was what he called Little Miss. When Little Miss assured him she was really telling the truth, he turned to Andrew. "Did you do this, Andrew?"

"Yes, Sir."

"The design, too?"

"Yes, Sir."

"From what did you copy the design?"

"It is a geometric representation, Sir, that fit the grain of the wood."

The next day, Sir brought him another piece of wood, a larger one, and an electric vibro-knife. He said, "Make something out of this, Andrew. Anything you want to."

Andrew did so and Sir watched, then looked at the product a long time. After that, Andrew no longer waited on tables. He was ordered to read books on furniture design instead, and he learned to make cabinets and desks.

Sir said, "These are amazing productions, Andrew."

Andrew said, "I enjoy doing them, Sir."

"Enjoy?"

"It makes the circuits of my brain somehow flow more easily. I have heard you use the word 'enjoy' and the way you use it fits the way I feel. I enjoy doing them, Sir."

3.

Gerald Martin took Andrew to the regional offices of United States Robots and Mechanical Men, Inc. As a member of the Regional Legislature he had no trouble at all in gaining an interview with the Chief Robopsychologist. In fact, it was only as a member of the Regional Legislature that he qualified as a robot owner in the first place—in those early days when robots were rare.

Andrew did not understand any of this at the time, but in later years, with greater learning, he could review that early scene and understand it in its proper light.

The robopsychologist, Merton Mansky, listened with a gathering frown and more than once managed to stop his fingers at the point beyond which they would have irrevocably drummed on the table. He had drawn features and a lined forehead and looked as though he might be younger than he looked.

He said, "Robotics is not an exact art, Mr. Martin. I cannot explain it to you in detail, but the mathematics governing the plotting of the positronic pathways is far too complicated to permit of any but approximate solutions. Naturally, since we build everything about the Three Laws, those are incontrovertible. We will, of course, replace your robot—"

"Not at all," said Sir. "There is no question of failure on his part. He performs his assigned duties perfectly. The point is, he also carves wood in exquisite fashion and never the same twice. He produces works of art."

Mansky looked confused. "Strange. Of course, we're attempting generalized pathways these days. . . . Really creative, you think?"

"See for yourself." Sir handed over a little sphere of wood on which there was a playground scene in which the boys and girls were almost too small to make out, yet they were in perfect proportion and blended so naturally with the grain that that, too, seemed to have been carved.

Mansky said, "*He* did that?" He handed it back with a shake of his head. "The luck of the draw. Something in the pathways."

"Can you do it again?"

"Probably not. Nothing like this has ever been reported."

"Good! I don't in the least mind Andrew's being the only one."

Mansky said, "I suspect that the company would like to have your robot back for study."

Sir said with sudden grimness, "Not a chance. Forget it." He turned to Andrew, "Let's go home now."

"As you wish, Sir," said Andrew.

4.

Miss was dating boys and wasn't about the house much. It was Little Miss, not as little as she was, who filled Andrew's horizon now. She never forgot that the very first piece of wood carving he had done had been for her. She kept it on a silver chain about her neck.

It was she who first objected to Sir's habit of giving away the productions. She said, "Come on, Dad, if anyone wants one of them, let him pay for it. It's worth it."

Sir said, "It isn't like you to be greedy, Mandy."

"Not for us, Dad. For the artist."

Andrew had never heard the word before and when he had a moment to himself he looked it up in the dictionary. Then there was another trip, this time to Sir's lawyer.

Sir said to him, "What do you think of this, John?"

The lawyer was John Feingold. He had white hair and a pudgy belly, and the rims of his contact lenses were tinted a bright green. He looked at the small plaque Sir had given him. "This is beautiful. . . . But I've heard the news. This is a carving made by your robot. The one you've brought with you."

"Yes, Andrew does them. Don't you, Andrew?"

"Yes, Sir," said Andrew.

"How much would you pay for that, John?" asked Sir.

"I can't say. I'm not a collector of such things."

"Would you believe I have been offered two hundred and fifty dollars for that small thing? Andrew has made chairs that have sold for five hundred dollars. There's two hundred thousand dollars in the bank out of Andrew's products."

"Good heavens, he's making you rich, Gerald."

"Half rich," said Sir. "Half of it is in an account in the name of Andrew Martin."

"The robot?"

"That's right, and I want to know if it's legal."

"Legal?" Feingold's chair creaked as he leaned back in it. "There are no precedents, Gerald. How did your robot sign the necessary papers?"

"He can sign his name and I brought in the signature. I didn't bring him in to the bank himself. Is there anything further that ought to be done?"

"Um." Feingold's eyes seemed to turn inward for a moment. Then he said, "Well, we can set up a trust to handle all finances in his name and that will place a layer of insulation between him and the hostile world. Further than that, my advice is you do nothing. No one is stopping you so far. If anyone objects, let *him* bring suit."

"And will you take the case if suit is brought?"

"For a retainer, certainly."

"How much?"

"Something like that," and Feingold pointed to the wooden plaque.

"Fair enough," said Sir.

Feingold chuckled as he turned to the robot. "Andrew, are you pleased that you have money?"

"Yes, Sir."

"What do you plan to do with it?"

"Pay for things, sir, which otherwise Sir would have to pay for. It would save him expense, sir."

5.

The occasions came. Repairs were expensive, and revisions were even more so. With the years, new models of robots were produced and Sir saw to it that Andrew had the advantage to every new device until he was a paragon of metallic excellence. It was all at Andrew's expense.

Andrew insisted on that.

Only his positronic pathways were untouched. Sir insisted on that.

"The new ones aren't as good as you are, Andrew," he said. "The new robots are worthless. The company has learned to make the pathways more precise, more closely on the nose, more deeply on the track. The new robots don't shift. They do what they're designed for and never stray. I like you better."

"Thank you, Sir."

"And it's your doing, Andrew, don't you forget that. I am certain Mansky put an end to generalized pathways as soon as he had a good look at you. He didn't like the unpredictability. . . . Do you know how many times he asked for you so he could place you under study? Nine times! I never let him have you, though, and now that he's retired, we may have some peace."

So Sir's hair thinned and grayed and his face grew pouchy, while Andrew looked rather better than he had when he first joined the family.

Ma'am had joined an art colony somewhere in Europe and Miss was a poet in New York. They wrote sometimes, but not often. Little Miss was married and lived not far away. She said she did not want to leave Andrew and when her child, Little Sir, was born, she let Andrew hold the bottle and feed him.

With the birth of a grandson, Andrew felt that Sir had someone now to replace those who had gone. It would not be so unfair to come to him with the request.

Andrew said, "Sir, it is kind of you to have allowed me to spend my money as I wished."

"It was your money, Andrew."

"Only by your voluntary act, Sir. I do not believe the law would have stopped you from keeping it all."

"The law won't persuade me to do wrong, Andrew."

"Despite all expenses, and despite taxes, too, Sir, I have nearly six hundred thousand dollars."

"I know that, Andrew."

"I want to give it to you, Sir."

"I won't take it, Andrew."

"In exchange for something you can give me, Sir."

"Oh? What is that, Andrew?"

"My freedom, Sir."

"Your—"

"I wish to buy my freedom, Sir."

6.

It wasn't that easy. Sir had flushed, had said "For God's sake!" had turned on his heel, and stalked away.

It was Little Miss who brought him around, defiantly and harshly—and in front of Andrew. For thirty years, no one had hesitated to talk in front of Andrew, whether the matter involved Andrew or not. He was only a robot.

She said, "Dad, why are you taking it as a personal affront? He'll still be here. He'll still be loyal. He can't help that. It's built in. All he wants is a form of words. He wants to be called free. Is that so terrible?

Hasn't he earned it? Heavens, he and I have been talking about it for years.
"Talking about it for years, have you?"
"Yes, and over and over again, he postponed it for fear he would hurt you. I *made* him put it up to you."
"He doesn't know what freedom is. He's a robot."
"Dad, you don't know him. He's read everything in the library. I don't know what he feels inside but I don't know what *you* feel inside. When you talk to him you'll find he reacts to the various abstractions as you and I do, and what else counts? If someone else's reactions are like your own, what more can you ask for?"
"The law won't take that attitude," Sir said angrily. "See here, you!" He turned to Andrew with a deliberate grate in his voice. "I can't free you except by doing it legally, and if it gets into the courts, you not only won't get your freedom but the law will take official cognizance of your money. They'll tell you that a robot has no right to earn money. Is this rigmarole worth losing your money?"
"Freedom is without price, Sir," said Andrew. "Even the chance of freedom is worth the money."

7.

The court might also take the attitude that freedom was without price, and might decide that for no price, however great, could a robot buy its freedom.
The simple statement of the regional attorney who represented those who had brought a class action to oppose the freedom was this: The word "freedom" had no meaning when applied to a robot. Only a human being could be free.
He said it several times, when it seemed appropriate; slowly, with his hand coming down rhythmically on the desk before him to mark the words.
Little Miss asked permission to speak on behalf of Andrew. She was recognized by her full name, something Andrew had never heard pronounced before:
"Amanda Laura Martin Charney may approach the bench."
She said, "Thank you, your honor. I am not a lawyer and I don't know the proper way of phrasing things, but I hope you will listen to my meaning and ignore the words.
"Let's understand what it means to be free in Andrew's case. In some ways, he *is* free. I think it's at least twenty years since anyone in the Martin family gave him an order to do something that we felt he might not do of his own accord.
"But we can, if we wish, give him an order to do anything, couch it as harshly as we wish, because he is a machine that belongs to us. Why should we be in a position to do so, when he has served us so long, so faithfully, and earned so much money for us? He owes us nothing more. The debt is entirely on the other side.
"Even if we were legally forbidden to place Andrew in involuntary servitude, he would still serve us voluntarily. Making him free would be a

trick of words only, but it would mean much to him. It would give him everything and cost us nothing."

For a moment the Judge seemed to be suppressing a smile. "I see your point, Mrs. Charney. The fact is that there is no binding law in this respect and no precedent. There is, however, the unspoken assumption that only a man can enjoy freedom. I can make new law here, subject to reversal in a higher court, but I cannot lightly run counter to that assumption. Let me address the robot, Andrew!"

"Yes, your honor."

It was the first time Andrew had spoken in court and the Judge seemed astonished for a moment at the human timbre of the voice. He said, "Why do you want to be free, Andrew? In what way will this matter to you?"

Andrew said, "Would you wish to be a slave, your honor?"

"But you are not a slave. You are a perfectly good robot, a genius of a robot I am given to understand, capable of an artistic expression that can be matched nowhere. What more could you do if you were free?"

"Perhaps no more than I do now, your honor, but with greater joy. It has been said in this courtroom that only a human being can be free. It seems to me that only someone who wishes for freedom can be free. I wish for freedom."

And it was that that cued the Judge. The crucial sentence in his decision was: "There is no right to deny freedom to any object with a mind advanced enough to grasp the concept and desire the state."

It was eventually upheld by the World Court.

8.

Sir remained displeased and his harsh voice made Andrew feel almost as though he were being short-circuited.

Sir said, "I don't want your damned money, Andrew. I'll take it only because you won't feel free otherwise. From now on, you can select your own jobs and do them as you please. I will give you no orders, except this one—that you do as you please. But I am still responsible for you; that's part of the court order. I hope you understand that."

Little Miss interrupted. "Don't be irascible, Dad. The responsibility is no great chore. You know you won't have to do a thing. The Three Laws still hold."

"Then how is he free?"

Andrew said, "Are not human beings bound by their laws, Sir?"

Sir said, "I'm not going to argue." He left, and Andrew saw him only infrequently after that.

Little Miss came to see him frequently in the small house that had been built and made over for him. It had no kitchen, of course, nor bathroom facilities. It had just two rooms; one was a library and one was a combination storeroom and workroom. Andrew accepted many commissions and worked harder as a free robot than he ever had before, till the cost of the house was paid for and the structure legally transferred to him.

One day Little Sir came. . . . No, George! Little Sir had insisted on that after the court decision. "A free robot doesn't call anyone Little Sir," George had said. "I call you Andrew. You must call me George."

It was phrased as an order, so Andrew called him George—but Little Miss remained Little Miss.

The day George came alone, it was to say that Sir was dying. Little Miss was at the bedside but Sir wanted Andrew as well.

Sir's voice was quite strong, though he seemed unable to move much. He struggled to get his hand up. "Andrew," he said, "Andrew— Don't help me, George. I'm only dying; I'm not crippled. . . . Andrew, I'm glad you're free. I just wanted to tell you that."

Andrew did not know what to say. He had never been at the side of someone dying before, but he knew it was the human way of ceasing to function. It was an involuntary and irreversible dismantling, and Andrew did not know what to say that might be appropriate. He could only remain standing, absolutely silent, absolutely motionless.

When it was over, Little Miss said to him, "He may not have seemed friendly to you toward the end, Andrew, but he was old, you know, and it hurt him that you should want to be free."

And then Andrew found the words to say. He said, "I would never have been free without him, Little Miss."

9.

It was only after Sir's death that Andrew began to wear clothes. He began with an old pair of trousers at first, a pair that George had given him. George was married now, and a lawyer. He had joined Feingold's firm. Old Feingold was long since dead but his daughter had carried on and eventually the firm's name became Feingold and Martin. It remained so even when the daughter retired and no Feingold took her place. At the time Andrew put on clothes for the first time, the Martin name had just been added to the firm.

George had tried not to smile, the first time Andrew put on the trousers, but to Andrew's eyes the smile was clearly there.

George showed Andrew how to manipulate the static charge so as to allow the trousers to open, wrap about his lower body, and move shut. George demonstrated on his own trousers, but Andrew was quite aware that it would take him awhile to duplicate that one flowing motion.

George said, "But why do you want trousers, Andrew? Your body is so beautifully functional it's a shame to cover it—especially when you needn't worry about either temperature control or modesty. And it doesn't cling properly, not on metal."

Andrew said, "Are not human bodies beautifully functional, George? Yet you cover yourselves."

"For warmth, for cleanliness, for protection, for decorativeness. None of that applies to you."

Andrew said, "I feel bare without clothes. I feel different, George."

"Different! Andrew, there are millions of robots on Earth now. In this region, according to the last census, there are almost as many robots as there are men."

"I know, George. There are robots doing every conceivable type of work."

"And none of them wear clothes."

"But none of them are free, George."

Little by little, Andrew added to the wardrobe. He was inhibited by George's smile and by the stares of the people who commissioned work.

He might be free, but there was built into him a carefully detailed program concerning his behavior toward people, and it was only by the tiniest steps that he dared advance. Open disapproval would set him back months.

Not everyone accepted Andrew as free. He was incapable of resenting that and yet there was a difficulty about his thinking process when he thought of it.

Most of all, he tended to avoid putting on clothes—or too many of them—when he thought Little Miss might come to visit him. She was old now and was often away in some warmer climate, but when she returned the first thing she did was visit him.

On one of her returns, George said ruefully, "She's got me, Andrew. I'll be running for the Legislature next year. Like grandfather, she says, like grandson."

"Like grandfather—" Andrew stopped, uncertain.

"I mean that I, George, the grandson, will be like Sir, the grandfather, who was in the Legislature once."

Andrew said, "It would be pleasant, George, if Sir were still—" He paused, for he did not want to say, "in working order." That seemed inappropriate.

"Alive," said George. "Yes, I think of the old monster now and then, too."

It was a conversation Andrew thought about. He had noticed his own incapacity in speech when talking with George. Somehow the language had changed since Andrew had come into being with an innate vocabulary. Then, too, George used a colloquial speech, as Sir and Little Miss had not. Why should he have called Sir a monster when surely that word was not appropriate?

Nor could Andrew turn to his own books for guidance. They were old and most dealt with woodworking, with art, with furniture design. There were none on language, none on the way of human beings.

It was at that moment it seemed to him that he must seek the proper books; and as a free robot, he felt he must not ask George. He would go to town and use the library. It was a triumphant decision and he felt his electropotential grow distinctly higher until he had to throw in an impedance coil.

He put on a full costume, even including a shoulder chain of wood. He would have preferred the glitter plastic but George had said that wood was much more appropriate and that polished cedar was considerably more valuable as well.

He had placed a hundred feet between himself and the house before gathering resistance brought him to a halt. He shifted the impedance coil out of circuit, and when that did not seem to help enough, he returned to his home and on a piece of notepaper wrote neatly, "I have gone to the library," and placed it in clear view on his worktable.

10.

Andrew never quite got to the library. He had studied the map. He knew the route, but not the appearance of it. The actual landmarks did not resemble the symbols on the map and he would hesitate. Eventually he thought he must have somehow gone wrong, for everything looked strange.

He passed an occasional field robot, but at the time he decided he should ask his way, there were none in sight. A vehicle passed and did not stop. He stood irresolute, which meant calmly motionless, and then coming across the field toward him were two human beings.

He turned to face them, and they altered their course to meet him. A moment before, they had been talking loudly; he had heard their voices; but now they were silent. They had the look that Andrew associated with human uncertainty, and they were young, but not very young. Twenty perhaps? Andrew could never judge human age.

He said, "Would you describe to me the route to the town library, sirs?"

One of them, the taller of the two, whose tall hat lengthened him still farther, almost grotesquely, said, not to Andrew, but to the other, "It's a robot."

The other had a bulbous nose and heavy eyelids. He said, not to Andrew, but to the first, "It's wearing clothes."

The tall one snapped his fingers. "It's the free robot. They have a robot at the Martins who isn't owned by anybody. Why else would it be wearing clothes?"

"Ask it," said the one with the nose.

"Are you the Martin robot?" asked the tall one.

"I am Andrew Martin, sir," said Andrew.

"Good. Take off your clothes. Robots don't wear clothes." He said to the other, "That's disgusting. Look at him."

Andrew hesitated. He hadn't heard an order in that tone of voice in so long that his Second Law circuits had momentarily jammed.

The tall one said, "Take off your clothes. I order you."

Slowly, Andrew began to remove them.

"Just drop them," said the tall one.

The nose said, "If it doesn't belong to anyone, he could be ours as much as someone else's."

"Anyway," said the tall one, "who's to object to anything we do? We're not damaging property. . . . Stand on your head." That was to Andrew.

"The head is not meant—" began Andrew.

"That's an order. If you don't know how, try anyway."

Andrew hesitated again, then bent to put his head on the ground. He tried to lift his legs and fell, heavily.

The tall one said, "Just lie there." He said to the other, "We can take him apart. Ever take a robot apart?"

"Will he let us?"

"How can he stop us?"

There was no way Andrew could stop them if they ordered him not to resist in a forceful enough manner. The Second Law of obedience took precedence over the Third Law of self-preservation. In any case, he could not defend himself without possibly hurting them and that would mean breaking the First Law. At that thought, every motile unit contracted slightly and he quivered as he lay there.

The tall one walked over and pushed at him with his foot. "He's heavy. I think we'll need tools to do the job."

The nose said, "We could order him to take himself apart. It would be fun to watch him try."

"Yes," said the tall one thoughtfully, "but let's get him off the road. If someone comes along—"

It was too late. Someone had indeed come along and it was George. From where he lay, Andrew had seen him topping a small rise in the middle distance. He would have liked to signal him in some way, but the last order had been "Just lie there!"

George was running now and he arrived somewhat winded. The two young men stepped back a little and then waited thoughtfully.

George said anxiously, "Andrew, has something gone wrong?"

Andrew said, "I am well, George."

"Then stand up. . . . What happened to your clothes?"

The tall young man said, "That your robot, mac?"

George turned sharply. "He's no one's robot. What's been going on here?"

"We politely asked him to take his clothes off. What's that to you if you don't own him?"

George said, "What were they doing, Andrew?"

Andrew said, "It was their intention in some way to dismember me. They were about to move me to a quiet spot and order me to dismember myself."

George looked at the two and his chin trembled. The two young men retreated no further. They were smiling. The tall one said lightly, "What are you going to do, pudgy? Attack us?"

George said, "No. I don't have to. This robot has been with my family for over seventy years. He knows us and he values us more than he values anyone else. I am going to tell him that you two are threatening my life and that you plan to kill me. I will ask him to defend me. In choosing between me and you two, he will choose me. Do you know what will happen to you when he attacks you?"

The two were backing away slightly, looking uneasy.

George said sharply, "Andrew, I am in danger and about to come to harm from these young men. Move toward them!"

Andrew did so, and the two young men did not wait. They ran fleetly.

"All right, Andrew, relax," said George. He looked unstrung. He was far past the age where he could face the possibility of a dustup with one young man, let alone two.

Andrew said, "I couldn't have hurt them, George. I could see they were not attacking you."

"I didn't order you to attack them; I only told you to move toward them. Their own fears did the rest."

"How can they fear robots?"

"It's a disease of mankind, one of which it is not yet cured. But never mind that. What the devil are you doing here, Andrew? I was on the point of turning back and hiring a helicopter when I found you. How did you get it into your head to go to the library? I would have brought you any books you needed."

"I am a—" began Andrew.

"Free robot. Yes, yes. All right, what did you want in the library?"

"I want to know more about human beings, about the world, about everything. And about robots, George. I want to write a history about robots."

George said, "Well, let's walk home. . . . And pick up your clothes first. Andrew, there are a million books on robotics and all of them include histories of the science. The world is growing saturated not only with robots but with information about robots."

Andrew shook his head, a human gesture he had lately begun to make. "Not a history of robotics, George. A history of *robots*, by a robot. I want to explain how robots feel about what has happened since the first ones were allowed to work and live on Earth."

George's eyebrows lifted, but he said nothing in direct response.

11.

Little Miss was just past her eighty-third birthday, but there was nothing about her that was lacking in either energy or determination. She gestured with her cane oftener than she propped herself up with it.

She listened to the story in a fury of indignation. She said, "George, that's horrible. Who were those young ruffians?"

"I don't know. What difference does it make? In the end they did no damage."

"They might have. You're a lawyer, George, and if you're well off, it's entirely due to the talent of Andrew. It was the money *he* earned that is the foundation of everything we have. He provides the continuity for this family and I will *not* have him treated as a wind-up toy."

"What would you have me do, Mother?" asked George.

"I said you're a lawyer. Don't you listen? You set up a test case somehow, and you force the regional courts to declare for robot rights and get the Legislature to pass the necessary bills, and carry the whole thing to the World Court, if you have to. I'll be watching, George, and I'll tolerate no shirking."

She was serious, and what began as a way of soothing the fearsome old lady became an involved matter with enough legal entanglement to make it interesting. As senior partner of Feingold and Martin, George plotted strategy but left the actual work to his junior partners, with much of it a matter for his son, Paul, who was also a member of the firm and who re-

ported dutifully nearly every day to his grandmother. She, in turn, discussed it every day with Andrew.

Andrew was deeply involved. His work on his book on robots was
delayed again, as he pored over the legal arguments and even, at times,
made very diffident suggestions.

He said, "George told me that day that human beings have always
been afraid of robots. As long as they are, the courts and the legislatures
are not likely to work hard on behalf of robots. Should there not be something done about public opinion?"

So while Paul stayed in court, George took to the public platform.
It gave him the advantage of being informal and he even went so far some-
times as to wear the new, loose style of clothing which he called drapery.
Paul said, "Just don't trip over it on stage, Dad."

George said despondently, "Ill try not to."

He addressed the annual convention of holo-news editors on one
occasion and said, in part:

"If, by virtue of the Second Law, we can demand of any robot unlimited obedience in all respects not involving harm to a human being, then
any human being, *any* human being, has a fearsome power over any robot,
any robot. In particular, since Second Law supersedes Third Law, *any*
human being can use the law of obedience to overcome the law of self-
protection. He can order any robot to damage itself or even destroy itself
for any reason, or for no reason.

"Is this just? Would we treat an animal so? Even an inanimate object which has given us good service has a claim on our consideration. And
a robot is not insensible; it is not an animal. It can think well enough to enable it to talk to us, reason with us, joke with us. Can we treat them as
friends, can we work together with them, and not give them some of the
fruit of that friendship, some of the benefit of co-working?

"If a man has the right to give a robot any order that does not involve harm to a human being, he should have the decency never to give a
robot any order that involves harm to a robot, unless human safety absolutely requires it. With great power goes great responsibility, and if the
robots have Three Laws to protect men, is it too much to ask that men have
a law or two to protect robots?"

Andrew was right. It was the battle over public opinion that held the
key to courts and Legislature and in the end a law passed which set up
conditions under which robot-harming orders were forbidden. It was end-
lessly qualified and the punishments for violating the law were totally inadequate, but the principle was established. The final passage by the World
Legislature came through on the day of Little Miss's death.

That was no coincidence. Little Miss held on to life desperately
during the last debate and let go only when word of victory arrived. Her
last smile was for Andrew. Her last words were: "You have been good to
us, Andrew."

She died with her hand holding his, while her son and his wife and
children remained at a respectful distance from both.

12.

Andrew waited patiently while the receptionist disappeared into the inner office. He might have used the holographic chatterbox, but unquestionably it was unmanned (or perhaps unroboted) by having to deal with another robot rather than with a human being.

Andrew passed the time revolving the matter in his mind. Could "unroboted" be used as an analogue of "unmanned," or had "unmanned" become a metaphoric term sufficiently divorced from its original literal meaning to be applied to robots—or to women for that matter?

Such problems came frequently as he worked on his book on robots. The trick of thinking out sentences to express all complexities had undoubtedly increased his vocabulary.

Occasionally, someone came into the room to stare at him and he did not try to avoid the glance. He looked at each calmly, and each in turn looked away.

Paul Martin finally came out. He looked surprised, or he would have if Andrew could have made out his expression with certainty. Paul had taken to wearing the heavy makeup that fashion was dictating for both sexes and though it made sharper and firmer the somewhat bland lines of his face, Andrew disapproved. He found that disapproving of human beings, as long he did not express it verbally, did not make him very uneasy. He could even write the disapproval. He was sure it had not always been so.

Paul said, "Come in, Andrew. I'm sorry I made you wait but there was something I *had* to finish. Come in. You had said you wanted to talk to me, but I didn't know you meant here in town."

"If you are busy, Paul, I am prepared to continue to wait."

Paul glanced at the interplay of shifting shadows on the dial on the wall that served as timepiece and said, "I can make some time. Did you come alone?"

"I hired an automatobile."

"Any troubles?" Paul asked, with more than a trace of anxiety.

"I wasn't expecting any. My rights are protected."

Paul looked the more anxious for that. "Andrew, I've explained that the law is unenforceable, at least under most conditions. . . . And if you insist on wearing clothes, you'll run into trouble eventually—just like that first time."

"And only time, Paul. I'm sorry you are displeased."

"Well, look at it this way; you are virtually a living legend, Andrew, and you are too valuable in many different ways for you to have any right to take chances with yourself. . . . How's the book coming?"

"I am approaching the end, Paul. The publisher is quite pleased."

"Good!"

"I don't know that he's necessarily pleased with the book as a book. I think he expects to sell many copies because it's written by a robot and it's that that pleases him."

"Only human, I'm afraid."

"I am not displeased. Let it sell for whatever reason since it will mean money and I can use some."

"Grandmother left you—"

"Little Miss was generous, and I'm sure I can count on the family to help me out further. But it is the royalties from the book on which I am counting to help me through the next step."

"What next step is that?"

"I wish to see the head of U.S. Robots and Mechanical Men, Inc. I have tried to make an appointment, but so far I have not been able to reach him. The corporation did not cooperate with us in the writing of the book, so I am not surprised, you understand."

Paul was clearly amused. "Cooperation is the last thing you can expect. They didn't cooperate with us in our great fight for robot rights. Quite the reverse and you can see why. Give a robot rights and people may not want to buy them."

"Nevertheless," said Andrew, "If you call them, you may obtain an interview for me."

"I'm no more popular with them than you are, Andrew."

"But perhaps you can hint that by seeing me they may head off a campaign by Feingold and Martin to strengthen the rights of robots further."

"Wouldn't that be a lie, Andrew?"

"Yes, Paul, and I can't tell one. That is why you must call."

"Ah, you can't lie, but you can urge me to tell a lie, is that it? You're getting more human all the time, Andrew."

13.

It was not easy to arrange, even with Paul's supposedly weighted name.

But it was finally carried through and, when it was, Harley Smythe-Robertson, who, on his mother's side, was descended from the original founder of the corporation and who had adopted the hyphenation to indicate it, looked remarkably unhappy. He was approaching retirement age and his entire tenure as president had been devoted to the matter of robot rights. His gray hair was plastered thinly over the top of his scalp, his face was not made up, and he eyed Andrew with brief hostility from time to time.

Andrew said, "Sir, nearly a century ago, I was told by a Merton Mansky of this corporation that the mathematics governing the plotting of the positronic pathways was far too complicated to permit of any but approximate solutions and that therefore my own capacities were not fully predictable."

"That was a century ago." Smythe-Robertson hesitated, then said icily, "*Sir*. It is true no longer. Our robots are made with precision now and are trained precisely to their jobs."

"Yes," said Paul, who had come along, as he said, to make sure that the corporation played fair, "with the result that my receptionist must be guided at every point once events depart from the conventional, however slightly."

Smythe-Robertson said, "You would be much more displeased if it were to improvise."

Andrew said, "Then you no longer manufacture robots like myself which are flexible and adaptable."

"No longer."

"The research I have done in connection with my book," said Andrew, "indicates that I am the oldest robot presently in active operation."

"The oldest presently," said Smythe-Robertson, "and the oldest ever. The oldest that will ever be. No robot is useful after the twenty-fifth year. They are called in and replaced with newer models."

"No robot *as presently manufactured* is useful after the twenty-fifth year," said Paul pleasantly. "Andrew is quite exceptional in this respect."

Andrew, adhering to the path he had marked out for himself, said, "As the oldest robot in the world and the most flexible, am I not unusual enough to merit special treatment from the company?"

"Not at all," said Smythe-Robertson freezingly. "Your unusualness is an embarrassment to the company. If you were on lease, instead of having been a sale outright through some mischance, you would long since have been replaced."

"But that is exactly the point," said Andrew. "I am a free robot and I own myself. Therefore I come to you and ask you to replace me. You cannot do this without the owner's consent. Nowaday's, that consent is extorted as a condition of the lease, but in my time this did not happen."

Smythe-Robertson was looking both startled and puzzled, and for a moment there was silence. Andrew found himself staring at the holograph on the wall. It was a death mask of Susan Calvin, patron saint of all roboticists. She was dead nearly two centuries now, but as a result of writing his book Andrew knew her so well he could half persuade himself that he had met her in life.

Smythe-Robertson said, "How can I replace you for you? If I replace you as robot, how can I donate the new robot to you as owner since in the very act of replacement you cease to exist?" He smiled grimly.

"Not at all difficult," interposed Paul. "The seat of Andrew's personality is his positronic brain and it is the one part that cannot be replaced without creating a new robot. The positronic brain, therefore, is Andrew the owner. Every other part of the robotic body can be replaced without affecting the robot's personality, and those other parts are the brain's possessions. Andrew, I should say, wants to supply his brain with a new robotic body."

"That's right," said Andrew calmly. He turned to Smythe-Robertson. "You have manufactured androids, haven't you? Robots that have the outward appearance of humans complete to the texture of the skin?"

Smythe-Robertson said, "Yes, we have. They worked perfectly well, with their synthetic fibrous skins and tendons. There was virtually no metal anywhere except for the brain, yet they were nearly as tough as metal robots. They were tougher, weight for weight."

Paul looked interested. "I didn't know that. How many are on the market?"

"None," said Smythe-Robertson. "They were much more expensive than metal models and a market survey showed they would not be accepted. They looked too human."

Andrew said, "But the corporation retains its expertise, I assume. Since it does, I wish to request that I be replaced by an organic robot, an android."

Paul looked surprised. "Good Lord," he said.

Smythe-Robertson stiffened. "Quite impossible!"

"Why is it impossible?" asked Andrew. "I will pay any reasonable fee, of course."

Smythe-Robertson said, "We do not manufacture androids."

"You do not *choose* to manufacture androids," interposed Paul quickly. "That is not the same as being unable to manufacture them."

Smythe-Robertson said, "Nevertheless, the manufacture of androids is against public policy."

"There is no law against it," said Paul.

"Nevertheless, we do not manufacture them, and we will not."

Paul cleared his throat. "Mr. Smythe-Robertson," he said, "Andrew is a free robot who is under the purview of the law guaranteeing robot rights. You are aware of this, I take it?"

"Only too well."

"This robot, as a free robot, chooses to wear clothes. This results in his being frequently humiliated by thoughtless human beings despite the law against the humiliation of robots. It is difficult to prosecute vague offenses that don't meet with the general disapproval of those who must decide on guilt and innocence."

"U. S. Robots understood that from the start. Your father's firm unfortunately did not."

"My father is dead now," said Paul, "but what I see is that we have here a clear offense with a clear target."

"What are you talking about?" said Smythe-Robertson.

"My client, Andrew Martin—he has just become my client—is a free robot who is entitled to ask U.S. Robots and Mechanical Men, Inc., for the right of replacement, which the corporation supplies anyone who owns a robot for more than twenty-five years. In fact, the corporation insists on such replacement."

Paul was smiling and thoroughly at his ease. He went on, "The positronic brain of my client is the owner of the body of my client—which is certainly more than twenty-five years old. The positronic brain demands the replacement of the body and offers to pay any reasonable fee for an android body as that replacement. If you refuse the request, my client undergoes humiliation and we will sue.

"While public opinion would not ordinarily support the claim of a robot in such a case, may I remind you that U.S. Robots is not popular with the public generally. Even those who must use and profit from robots are suspicious of the corporation. This may be a hangover from the days when robots were widely feared. It may be resentment against the power and wealth of U.S. Robots which has a worldwide monopoly. Whatever the cause may be, the resentment exists and I think you will find that you would prefer not to withstand a lawsuit, particularly since my client is wealthy and will live for many more centuries and will have no reason to refrain from fighting the battle forever."

Smythe-Robertson had slowly reddened. "You are trying to force me to. . . ."

"I force you to do nothing," said Paul. "If you wish to refuse to accede to my client's reasonable request, you may by all means do so and we will leave without another word. . . . But we will sue, as is certainly our right, and you will find that you will eventually lose."

Smythe-Robertson said, "Well—" and paused.

"I see that you are going to accede," said Paul. "You may hesitate but you will come to it in the end. Let me assure you, then, of one further point. If, in the process of transferring my client's positronic brain from his present body to an organic one, there is any damage, however slight, then I will never rest till I've nailed the corporation to the ground. I will, if necessary, take every possible step to mobilize public opinion against the corporation if one brain path of my client's platinumiridium essence is scrambled." He turned to Andrew and said, "Do you agree to all this, Andrew?"

Andrew hesitated a full minute. It amounted to the approval of lying, of blackmail, of the badgering and humiliation of a human being. But not physical harm, he told himself, not physical harm.

He managed at last to come out with a rather faint "Yes."

14.

It was like being constructed again. For days, then for weeks, finally for months, Andrew found himself not himself somehow, and the simplest actions kept giving rise to hesitation.

Paul was frantic. "They've damaged you, Andrew. We'll have to institute suit."

Andrew spoke very slowly. "You mustn't. You'll never be able to prove—something—m-m-m-m—"

"Malice?"

"Malice. Besides, I grow stronger, better. It's the tr-tr-tr—"

"Tremble?"

"Trauma. After all, there's never been such an op-op-op—before."

Andrew could feel his brain from the inside. No one else could. He knew he was well and during the months that it took him to learn full coordination and full positronic interplay, he spent hours before the mirror.

Not quite human! The face was stiff—too stiff—and the motions were too deliberate. They lack the careless free flow of the human being, but perhaps that might come with time. At least he could wear clothes without the ridiculous anomaly of a metal face going along with it.

Eventually he said, "I will be going back to work."

Paul laughed and said, "That means you are well. What will you be doing? Another book?"

"No," said Andrew seriously. "I live too long for any one career to seize me by the throat and never let me go. There was a time when I was primarily an artist and I can still turn to that. And there was a time when I was a historian and I can still turn to that. But now I wish to be a robobiologist."

"A robopsychologist, you mean."

"No. That would imply the study of positronic brains and at the moment I lack the desire to do that. A robobiologist, it seems to me, would be concerned with the working of the body attached to that brain."

"Wouldn't that be a roboticist?"

"A roboticist works with a metal body. I would be studying an organic humanoid body, of which I have the only one, as far as I know."

"You narrow your field," said Paul thoughtfully. "As an artist, all conception is yours; as a historian, you dealt chiefly with robots; as a robobiologist, you will deal with yourself."

Andrew nodded. "It would seem so."

Andrew had to start from the very beginning, for he knew nothing of ordinary biology, almost nothing of science. He became a familiar sight in the libraries, where he sat at the electronic indices for hours at a time, looking perfectly normal in clothes. Those few who knew he was a robot in no way interfered with him.

He built a laboratory in a room which he added to his house, and his library grew, too.

Years passed, and Paul came to him one day and said, "It's a pity you're no longer working on the history of robots. I understand U.S. Robots is adopting a radically new policy."

Paul had aged, and his deteriorating eyes had been replaced with photoptic cells. In that respect, he had drawn closer to Andrew. Andrew said, "What have they done?"

"They are manufacturing central computers, gigantic positronic brains, really, which communicate with anywhere from a dozen to a thousand robots by microwave. The robots themselves have no brains at all. They are the limbs of the gigantic brain, and the two are physically separate."

"Is that more efficient?"

"U.S. Robots claims it is. Smythe-Robertson established the new direction before he died, however, and it's my notion that it's a backlash at you. U.S. Robots is determined that they will make no robots that will give them the type of trouble you have, and for that reason they separate brain and body. The brain will have no body to wish changed; the body will have no brain to wish anything."

"It's amazing, Andrew," Paul went on, "the influence you have had on the history of robots. It was your artistry that encouraged U.S. Robots to make robots more precise and specialized; it was your freedom that resulted in the establishment of the principle of robotic rights; it was your insistence on an android body that made U.S. Robots switch to brain-body separation."

Andrew said, "I suppose in the end the corporation will produce one vast brain controlling several billion robotic bodies. All the eggs will be in one basket. Dangerous. Not proper at all."

"I think you're right," said Paul, "but I don't suspect it will come to pass for a century at least and I won't live to see it. In fact, I may not live to see next year."

"Paul!" said Andrew, in concern.

Paul shrugged. "We're mortal, Andrew. We're not like you. It doesn't matter too much, but it does make it important to assure you on one point. I'm the last of the human Martins. There are collaterals descended from my great-aunt, but they don't count. The money I control personally will be left to the trust in your name and as far as anyone can foresee the future, you will be economically secure."

"Unnecessary," said Andrew, with difficulty. In all this time, he could not get used to the deaths of the Martins.

Paul said, "Let's not argue. That's the way it's going to be. What are you working on?"

"I am designing a system for allowing androids—myself—to gain energy from the combustion of hydrocarbons, rather than from atomic cells."

Paul raised his eyebrows. "So that they will breathe and eat?"

"Yes."

"How long have you been pushing in that direction?"

"For a long time now, but I think I have designed an adequate combustion chamber for catalyzed controlled breakdown."

"But why, Andrew? The atomic cell is surely infinitely better."

"In some ways, perhaps, but the atomic cell is inhuman."

15.

It took time, but Andrew had time. In the first place, he did not wish to do anything till Paul had died in peace.

With the death of the great-grandson of Sir, Andrew felt more nearly exposed to a hostile world and for that reason was the more determined to continue the path he had long ago chosen.

Yet he was not really alone. If a man had died, the firm of Feingold and Martin lived, for a corporation does not die any more than a robot does. The firm had its directions and it followed them soullessly. By way of the trust and through the law firm, Andrew continued to be wealthy. And in return for their own large annual retainer, Feingold and Martin involved themselves in the legal aspects of the new combustion chamber.

When the time came for Andrew to visit U.S. Robots and Mechanical Men, Inc., he did it alone. Once he had gone with Sir and once with Paul. This time, the third time, he was alone and manlike.

U.S. Robots had changed. The production plant had been shifted to a large space station, as had grown to be the case with more and more industries. With them had gone many robots. The Earth itself was becoming parklike, with its one-billion-person population stabilized and perhaps not more than thirty per cent of its at least equally large robot population independently brained.

The Director of Research was Alvin Magdescu, dark of complexion and hair, with a little pointed beard and wearing nothing above the waist but the breastband that fashion dictated. Andrew himself was well covered in the older fashion of several decades back.

Magdescu said, "I know you, of course, and I'm rather pleased to see you. You're our most notorious product and it's a pity old Smythe-Robinson was so set against you. We could have done a great deal with you."

"You still can," said Andrew.

"No, I don't think so. We're past the time. We've had robots on Earth for over a century, but that's changing. It will be back to space with them and those that stay here won't be brained."

"But there remains myself, and I stay on Earth."

"True, but there doesn't seem to be much of the robot about you. What new request have you?"

"To be still less a robot. Since I am so far organic, I wish an organic source of energy. I have here the plans—"

Magdescu did not hasten through them. He might have intended to at first, but he stiffened and grew intent. At one point he said, "This is remarkably ingenious. Who thought of all this?"

"I did," said Andrew.

Magdescu looked up at him sharply, then said, "It would amount to a major overhaul of your body, and an experimental one, since it has never been attempted before. I advise against it. Remain as you are."

Andrew's face had limited means of expression, but impatience showed plainly in his voice. "Dr. Magdescu, you miss the entire point. You have no choice but to accede to my request. If such devices can be built into my body, they can be built into human bodies as well. The tendency to lengthen human life by prosthetic devices has already been remarked on. There are no devices better than the ones I have designed and am designing.

"As it happens, I control the patents by way of the firm of Feingold and Martin. We are quite capable of going into business for ourselves and of developing the kind of prosthetic devices that may end by producing human beings with many of the properties of robots. Your own business will then suffer.

"If, however, you operate on me now and agree to do so under similar circumstances in the future, you will receive permission to make use of the patents and control the technology of both robots and the prosthetization of human beings. The initial leasing will not be granted, of course, until after the first operation is completed successfully, and after enough time has passed to demonstrate that it is indeed successful." Andrew felt scarcely any First Law inhibition to the stern conditions he was setting a human being. He was learning to reason that what seemed like cruelty might, in the long run, be kindness.

Magdescu looked stunned. He said, "I'm not the one to decide something like this. That's a corporate decision that would take time."

"I can wait a reasonable time," said Andrew, "but only a reasonable time." And he thought with satisfaction that Paul himself could not have done it better.

16.

It took only a reasonable time, and the operation was a success.

Magdescu said, "I was very much against the operation, Andrew, but not for the reasons you might think. I was not in the least against the experiment, if it had been on someone else. I hated risking *your* positronic brain. Now that you have the positronic pathways interacting with simulated nerve pathways, it might be difficult to rescue the brain intact if the body went bad."

"I had every faith in the skill of the staff at U.S. Robots," said Andrew. "And I can eat now."

"Well, you can sip olive oil. It will mean occasional cleanings of the combustion chamber, as we have explained to you. Rather an uncomfortable touch, I should think."

"Perhaps, if I did not expect to go further. Self-cleaning is not impossible. In fact, I am working on a device that will deal with solid food that may be expected to contain incombustible fractions—indigestible matter, so to speak, that will have to be discarded."

"You would then have to develop an anus."

"The equivalent."

"What else, Andrew?"

"Everything else."

"Genitalia, too?"

"Insofar as they will fit my plans. My body is a canvas on which I intend to draw—"

Magdescu waited for the sentence to be completed, and when it seemed that it would not be, he completed it himself. "A man?"

"We shall see," said Andrew.

Magdescu said, "It's a puny ambition, Andrew. You're better than a man. You've gone downhill from the moment you opted for organicism."

"My brain has not suffered."

"No, it hasn't. I'll grant you that. But, Andrew, the whole new breakthrough in prosthetic devices made possible by your patents is being marketed under your name. You're recognized as the inventor and you're honored for it—as you are. Why play further games with your body?"

Andrew did not answer.

The honors came. He accepted membership in several learned societies, including one which was devoted to the new science he had established; the one he had called robobiology but had come to be termed prosthetology.

On the one hundred and fiftieth anniversary of his construction, there was a testimonial dinner given in his honor at U.S. Robots. If Andrew saw irony in this, he kept it to himself.

Alvin Magdescu came out of retirement to chair the dinner. He was himself ninety-four years old and was alive because he had prosthetized devices that, among other things, fulfilled the function of liver and kidneys. The dinner reached its climax when Magdescu, after a short and emotional talk, raised his glass to toast "the Sesquicentennial Robot."

Andrew had had the sinews of his face redesigned to the point where he could show a range of emotions, but he sat through all the ceremonies solemnly passive. He did not like to be a Sesquicentennial Robot.

17.

It was prosthetology that finally took Andrew off the Earth. In the decades that followed the celebration of the Sesquicentennial, the Moon had come to be a world more Earth-like than Earth in every respect but its gravitational pull and in its underground cities there was a fairly dense population.

Prosthetized devices there had to take the lesser gravity into account and Andrew spent five years on the Moon working with local prosthetologists to make the necessary adaptations. When not at his work, he wandered among the robot population, every one of which treated him with the robotic obsequiousness due a man.

He came back to an Earth that was humdrum and quiet in comparison and visited the offices of Feingold and Martin to announce his return.

The current head of the firm, Simon DeLong, was surprised. He said, "We had been told you were returning, Andrew" (he had almost said "Mr. Martin"), "but we were not expecting you till next week."

"I grew impatient," said Andrew brusquely. He was anxious to get to the point. "On the Moon, Simon, I was in charge of a research team of twenty human scientists. I gave orders that no one questioned. The Lunar robots deferred to me as they would to a human being. Why, then, am I not a human being?"

A wary look entered DeLong's eyes. He said, "My dear Andrew, as you have just explained, you are treated as a human being by both robots and human beings. You are therefore a human being *de facto*."

"To be a human being *de facto* is not enough. I want not only to be treated as one, but to be legally identified as one. I want to be a human being *de jure*."

"Now that is another matter," said DeLong. "There we would run into human prejudice and into the undoubted fact that however much you may be like a human being, you are *not* a human being."

"In what way not?" said Andrew. "I have the shape of a human being and organs equivalent to those of a human being. My organs, in fact, are identical to some of those in a prosthetized human being. I have contributed artistically, literarily, and scientifically to human culture as much as any human being now alive. What more can one ask?"

"I myself would ask nothing more. The trouble is that it would take an act of the World Legislature to define you as a human being. Frankly, I wouldn't expect that to happen."

"To whom on the Legislature could I speak?"

"To the chairman of the Science and Technology Committee perhaps."

"Can you arrange a meeting?"

"But you scarcely need an intermediary. In your position, you can—"

"No. You arrange it." (It didn't even occur to Andrew that he was giving a flat order to a human being. He had grown accustomed to that on the Moon.) "I want him to know that the firm of Feingold and Martin is backing me in this to the hilt."

"Well, now—"

"To the hilt, Simon. In one hundred and seventy-three years I have in one fashion or another contributed greatly to this firm. I have been under obligation to individual members of the firm in times past. I am not now. It is rather the other way around now and I am calling in my debts."

DeLong said, "I will do what I can."

18.

The chairman of the Science and Technology Committee was of the East Asian region and she was a woman. Her name was Chee Li-Hsing and her transparent garments (obscuring what she wanted obscured only by their dazzle) made her look plastic-wrapped.

She said, "I sympathize with your wish for full human rights. There have been times in history when segments of the human population fought for full human rights. What rights, however, can you possibly want that you do not have?"

"As simple a thing as my right to life. A robot can be dismantled at any time."

"A human being can be executed at any time."

"Execution can only follow due process of law. There is no trial needed for my dismantling. Only the word of a human being in authority is needed to end me. Besides—besides—" Andrew tried desperately to allow no sign of pleading, but his carefully designed tricks of human expression and tone of voice betrayed him here. "The truth is, I want to be a man. I have wanted it through six generations of human beings."

Li-Hsing looked up at him out of darkly sympathetic eyes. "The Legislature can pass a law declaring you one—they could pass a law declaring a stone statue to be defined as a man. Whether they will actually do so is, however, as likely in the first case as the second. Congresspeople are as human as the rest of the population and there is always that element of suspicion against robots."

"Even now?"

"Even now. We would all allow the fact that you have earned the prize of humanity and yet there would remain the fear of setting an undesirable precedent."

"What precedent? I am the only free robot, the only one of my type, and there will never be another. You may consult U.S. Robots."

"'Never' is a long time, Andrew—or, if you prefer, Mr. Martin—since I will gladly give you my personal accolade as a man. You will find that most Congresspeople will not be willing to set the precedent, no matter how meaningless such a precedent might be. Mr. Martin, you have my sympathy, but I cannot tell you to hope. Indeed—"

She sat back and her forehead wrinkled. "Indeed, if the issue grows too heated, there might well arise a certain sentiment, both inside the Legislature and outside, for that dismantling you mentioned. Doing away with you could turn out to be the easiest way of resolving the dilemma. Consider that before deciding to push matters."

Andrew said, "Will no one remember the technique of prosthetology, something that is almost entirely mine?"

"It may seem cruel, but they won't. Or if they do, it will be remembered against you. It will be said you did it only for yourself. It will be said it was part of a campaign to roboticize human beings, or to humanify robots; and in either case evil and vicious. You have never been part of a political hate campaign, Mr. Martin, and I tell you that you will be the object of vilification of a kind neither you nor I would credit and there would be people who'll believe it all. Mr. Martin, let your life be." She arose and, next to Andrew's seated figure, she seemed small and almost childlike.

Andrew said, "If I decide to fight for my humanity, will you be on my side?"

She thought, then said, "I will be—insofar as I can be. If at any time such a stand would appear to threaten my political future, I may have to abandon you, since it is not an issue I feel to be at the very root of my beliefs. I am trying to be honest with you."

"Thank you, and I will ask no more. I intend to fight this through whatever the consequences, and I will ask you for your help only for as long as you can give it."

19.

It was not a direct fight. Feingold and Martin counseled patience and Andrew muttered grimly that he had an endless supply of that. Feingold and Martin then entered on a campaign to narrow and restrict the area of combat.

They instituted a lawsuit denying the obligation to pay debts to an individual with a prosthetic heart on the grounds that the possession of a robotic organ removed humanity, and with it the constitutional rights of human beings.

They fought the matter skillfully and tenaciously, losing at every step but always in such a way that the decision was forced to be as broad as possible, and then carrying it by way of appeals to the World Court.

It took years, and millions of dollars.

When the final decision was handed down, DeLong held what amounted to a victory celebration over the legal loss. Andrew was, of course, present in the company offices on the occasion.

"We've done two things, Andrew," said DeLong, "both of which are good. First of all, we have established the fact that no number of artifacts in the human body causes it to cease being a human body. Secondly, we have engaged public opinion in the question in such a way as to put it fiercely on the side of a broad interpretation of humanity since there is not a human being in existence who does not hope for prosthetics if that will keep him alive."

"And do you think the Legislature will now grant me my humanity?" asked Andrew.

DeLong looked faintly uncomfortable. "As to that, I cannot be optimistic. There remains the one organ which the World Court has used as the criterion of humanity. Human beings have an organic cellular brain and robots have a platinumiridium positronic brain if they have one at all—and you certainly have a positronic brain. . . . No, Andrew, don't get that look in your eye. We lack the knowledge to duplicate the work of a cellular brain in artificial structures close enough to the organic type to allow it to fall within the Court's decision. Not even you could do it."

"What ought we do, then?"

"Make the attempt, of course. Congresswoman Li-Hsing will be on our side and a growing number of other Congress people. The President will undoubtedly go along with a majority of the Legislature in this matter."

"Do we have a majority?"

"No, far from it. But we might get one if the public will allow its desire for a broad interpretation of humanity to extend to you. A small chance, I admit, but if you do not wish to give up, we must gamble for it."

"I do not wish to give up."

20.

Congresswoman Li-Hsing was considerably older than she had been when Andrew had first met her. Her transparent garments were long gone. Her hair was now close-cropped and her coverings were tubular. Yet still Andrew clung, as closely as he could within the limits of reasonable taste, to the style of clothing that had prevailed when he had first adopted clothing over a century before.

She said, "We've gone as far as we can, Andrew. We'll try once more after recess, but, to be honest, defeat is certain and the whole thing will have to be given up. All my most recent efforts have only earned me a certain defeat in the coming congressional campaign."

"I know," said Andrew, "and it distresses me. You said once you would abandon me if it came to that. Why have you not done so?"

"One can change one's mind, you know. Somehow, abandoning you became a higher price than I cared to pay for just one more term. As it is, I've been in the Legislature for over a quarter of a century. It's enough."

"Is there no way we can change minds, Chee?"

"We've changed all that are amenable to reason. The rest—the majority—cannot be moved from their emotional antipathies."

"Emotional antipathy is not a valid reason for voting one way or the other."

"I know that, Andrew, but they don't advance emotional antipathy as their reason."

Andrew said cautiously, "It all comes down to the brain, then, but must we leave it at the level of cells versus positrons? Is there no way of forcing a functional definition? Must we say that a brain is made of this or that? May we not say that a brain is something—anything—capable of a certain level of thought?"

"Won't work," said Li-Hsing. "Your brain is man-made, the human brain is not. Your brain is constructed, theirs developed. To any human being who is intent on keeping up the barrier between himself and a robot, those differences are a steel wall a mile high and a mile thick."

"If we could get at the source of their antipathy—the very source of—"

"After all your years," said Li-Hsing sadly, "you are still trying to reason out the human being. Poor Andrew, don't be angry, but it's the robot in you that drives you in that direction."

"I don't know, said Andrew. "If I could bring myself—"

1. (reprise)

If he could bring himself—

He had known for a long time it might come to that, and in the end he was at the surgeon's. He found one skillful enough for the job at hand, which meant a robot surgeon, for no human surgeon could be trusted in this connection, either in ability or in intention.

The surgeon could not have performed the operation on a human being, so Andrew, after putting off the moment of decision with a sad line of questioning that reflected the turmoil within himself, put the First Law to one side by saying, "I, too, am a robot."

He then said, as firmly as he had learned to form the words even at human beings over these past decades, "I order you to carry through the operation on me."

In the absence of the First Law, an order so firmly given from one who looked so much like a man activated the Second Law sufficiently to carry the day.

21.

Andrew's feeling of weakness was, he was sure, quite imaginary. He had recovered from the operation. Nevertheless, he leaned, as unobtrusively as he could manage, against the wall. It would be entirely too revealing to sit.

Li-Hsing said, "The final vote will come this week, Andrew. I've been able to delay it no longer, and we must lose. . . . And that will be it, Andrew."

Andrew said, "I am grateful for your skill at delay. It gave me the time I needed, and I took the gamble I had to."

"What gamble is this?" asked Li-Hsing with open concern.

"I couldn't tell you, or the people at Feingold and Martin. I was sure I would be stopped. See here, if it is the brain that is at issue, isn't the greatest difference of all the matter of immortality? Who really cares what a brain looks like or is built of or how it was formed? What matters is that brain cells die; *must* die. Even if every other organ in the body is maintained or replaced, the brain cells, which cannot be replaced without changing and therefore killing the personality, must eventually die.

"My own positronic pathways have lasted nearly two centuries without perceptible change and can last for centuries more. Isn't *that* the fundamental barrier? Human beings can tolerate an immortal robot, for it doesn't matter how long a machine lasts. They cannot tolerate an immortal human being, since their own mortality is endurable only so long as it is universal. And for that reason they won't make me a human being."

Li-Hsing said, "What is it you're leading up to, Andrew?"

"I have removed that problem. Decades ago, my positronic brain was connected to organic nerves. Now, one last operation has arranged that connection in such a way that slowly—quite slowly—the potential is being drained from my pathways."

Li-Hsing's finely wrinkled face showed no expression for a moment. Then her lips tightened. "Do you mean you've arranged to die, Andrew? You can't have. That violates the Third Law."

"No," said Andrew, "I have chosen between the death of my body and the death of my aspirations and desires. To have let my body live at the cost of the greater death is what would have violated the Third Law."

Li-Hsing seized his arm as though she were about to shake him. She stopped herself. "Andrew, it won't work. Change it back."

"It can't be. Too much damage was done. I have a year to live—more or less. I will last through the two hundredth anniversary of my construction. I was weak enough to arrange that."

"How can it be worth it? Andrew, you're a fool."

"If it brings me humanity, that will be worth it. If it doesn't, it will bring an end to striving and that will be worth it, too."

And Li-Hsing did something that astonished herself. Quietly, she began to weep.

22.

It was odd how that last deed caught at the imagination of the world. All that Andrew had done before had not swayed them. But he had finally accepted even death to be human and the sacrifice was too great to be rejected.

The final ceremony was timed, quite deliberately, for the two hundredth anniversary. The World President was to sign the act and make it law and the ceremony would be visible on a global network and would be beamed to the Lunar state and even to the Martian colony.

Andrew was in a wheelchair. He could still walk, but only shakily.

With mankind watching, the World President said, "Fifty years ago, you were declared a Sesquicentennial Robot, Andrew." After a pause, and in a more solemn tone, he said, "Today we declare you a Bicentennial Man, Mr. Martin."

And Andrew, smiling, held out his hand to shake that of the President.

23.

Andrew's thoughts were slowly fading as he lay in bed.

Desperately he seized at them. Man! He was a man! He wanted that to be his last thought. He wanted to dissolve—die—with that.

He opened his eyes one more time and for one last time recognized Li-Hsing waiting solemnly. There were others, but those were only shadows, unrecognizable shadows. Only Li-Hsing stood out against the deepening gray. Slowly, inchingly, he held out his hand to her and very dimly and faintly felt her take it.

She was fading in his eyes, as the last of his thoughts trickled away.

But before she faded completely, one last fugitive thought came to him and rested for a moment on his mind before everything stopped.

"Little Miss," he whispered too low to be heard.

3

Equality

A big fish overtook a little one and wanted to swallow him.
The little fish squeaked out: "It is unjust. I also want to live.
All fishes are equal before the law." The big fish answered:
"What's the matter? I won't discuss whether we are equal,
but if you don't want me to eat you, then do you please
swallow me if you can—swallow me, don't be afraid, I
shan't set on you." The little fish opened his mouth and
poked about trying to get the big fish in, sighed at last and
said: "You have it. Swallow me."

Equality
Fedor Sologub

The two groups who have struggled hardest for equality in the United States
are not robots like the Bicentennial Man, but blacks and women. In 1865
the Thirteenth Amendment to the Constitution abolished slavery and involuntary servitude. In 1920 the Nineteenth Amendment accorded women citizens the right to vote. Since those historic changes, many other groups—
homosexuals, the handicapped, specific ethnic groups, prisoners, the elderly—have demanded certain civil rights based on the notion of equality,
but the two most vocal groups are still women and blacks. The current emphasis of the debate focuses on employment and educational opportunities
and this has led to a controversy over the concept of "quotas." Apparently
intended to right prior wrongs, affirmative action has resulted in some
claims of reverse discrimination.

Although there is no agreed-upon definition of "quotas," the term
appears to embrace the notion that admissions and employment hiring policies should utilize a system in which fixed numbers of women and minorities are assured entry into the academic community and the work force regardless of the hardship it causes men and whites with stronger qualifications. Consider the following questions:

• If a group of people takes a test for a position, should a different
and easier test be administered to minorities and women on the basis of their
having been denied prior educational opportunities?

•   Should all applicants be given the same test with subsequent scaling of the test to bring the scores of the minorities and the women up to the level necessary to ensure a balanced academic community and work force?

•   Would the men and the whites competing against women and minorities under the aforesaid mentioned systems not have a legitimate legal cause based on reverse discrimination?

Any discussion of equality needs to address the controversial questions of whether or not all people are in fact equal and what "equal under the law" means. One area in which this controversy has raged is over the issue of women in combat. Those who oppose women in the traditionally male role raise the following objections:

•   Paternalism requires the exclusion of women from combat to save the women from having direct contact with the enemy and, in turn, to save them from the increased risk of capture.

•   Patriotism demands the protection of the citizens of the country from women in combat whose sex-linked biological differences—especially pregnancy, menstruation, and inferior physical strength—make it unsafe to rely on women in armed combat.

Proponents of women in combat state:

•   Sex-linked, biological differences are overstated and irrelevant given the nature of future warfare which is unlikely to be the traditional face-to-face armed combat of the past.

•   If the women *want* to serve, then paternalism has no place in the discussion and such specious arguments should be ignored.

•   The real issue is not about sex-linked biological differences but economic inequality: Women are denied armed-combat positions because these roles carry higher pay, higher military rank, and coveted career opportunities.

As the civil rights and equality debate continues, we should ask ourselves whether "equality" taken to the extreme would lead to a society like that painted by Kurt Vonnegut, Jr., in "Harrison Bergeron"—a society in which equality leads to its citizens being reduced to the lowest common denominator rather than being provided the opportunity to reach their full potential.

"The Lynching of Jube Benson," by Paul Laurence Dunbar, deals not only with the unequal treatment given to blacks because of existing prejudice, but it also pulls gently at the veil covering the psychological cause of such prejudice. The doctor in the story is acutely aware of Jube's devotion to Miss Annie, and praises Jube for the attention that he lavishes on the doctor during his sickness. Notice, however, how easily the doctor is swayed by the crowd into reading Jube's good-natured grin to be one of "slyness," leading the doctor to take a disastrous position for both Jube and the doctor—a position based on pure emotion and devoid of reason.

Harrison Bergeron
Kurt Vonnegut, Jr.

The year was 2081, and everybody was finally equal. They weren't only equal before God and the law. They were equal every which way. Nobody was smarter than anybody else. Nobody was better looking than anybody else. Nobody was stronger or quicker than anybody else. All this equality was due to the 211th, 212th, and 213th Amendments to the Constitution, and to the unceasing vigilance of agents of the United States Handicapper General.

Some things about living still weren't quite right, though. April, for instance, still drove people crazy by not being springtime. And it was in that clammy month that the H-G men took George and Hazel Bergeron's fourteen-year-old son, Harrison, away.

It was tragic, all right, but George and Hazel couldn't think about it very hard. Hazel had a perfectly average intelligence, which meant she couldn't think about anything except in short bursts. And George, while his intelligence was way above normal, had a little mental handicap radio in his ear. He was required by law to wear it at all times. It was tuned to a government transmitter. Every twenty seconds or so, the transmitter would send out some sharp noise to keep people like George from taking unfair advantage of their brains.

George and Hazel were watching television. There were tears on Hazel's cheeks, but she'd forgotten for the moment what they were about.

On the television screen were ballerinas.

A buzzer sounded in George's head. His thoughts fled in panic, like bandits from a burglar alarm.

"That was a real pretty dance, that dance they just did," said Hazel.

"Hugh?" said George.

"That dance—it was nice," said Hazel.

"Yup," said George. He tried to think a little about the ballerinas. They weren't really very good—no better than anybody else would have been anyway. They were burdened with sashweights and bags of birdshot, and their faces were masked, so that no one, seeing a free and graceful gesture or a pretty face, would feel like something the cat drug in. George was toying with the vague notion that maybe dancers shouldn't be handicapped. But he didn't get very far with it before another noise in his ear radio scattered his thoughts.

George winced. So did two of the eight ballerinas.

Hazel saw him wince. Having no mental handicap herself, she had to ask George what the latest sound had been.

"Sounded like somebody hitting a milk bottle with a ball peen hammer," said George.

"I'd think it would be real interesting, hearing all the different sounds," said Hazel, a little envious. "All the things they think up."

"Um," said George.

"Only, if I was Handicapper General, you know what I would do?" said Hazel. Hazel, as a matter of fact, bore a strong resemblance to the Handicapper General, a woman named Diana Moon Glampers. "If I was Diana Moon Glampers," said Hazel. "I'd have chimes on Sunday—just chimes. Kind of in honor of religion."

"I could think, if it was just chimes," said George.

"Well—maybe make 'em real loud," said Hazel. "I think I'd make a good Handicapper General."

"Good as anybody else," said George.

"Who knows better'n I do what normal is?" said Hazel.

"Right," said George. He began to think glimmeringly about his abnormal son who was now in jail, about Harrison, but a twenty-one-gun salute in his head stopped that.

"Boy!" said Hazel, "that was a doozy, wasn't it?"

It was such a doozy that George was white and trembling, and tears stood on the rims of his red eyes. Two of the eight ballerinas had collapsed to the studio floor, were holding their temples.

"All of a sudden you look so tired," said Hazel. "Why don't you stretch out on the sofa, so's you can rest your handicap bag on the pillows, honeybunch." She was referring to the forty-seven pounds of birdshot in a canvas bag, which was padlocked around George's neck. "Go on and rest the bag for a little while," she said. "I don't care if you're not equal to me for a while."

George weighted the bag with his hands. "I don't mind it," he said. "I don't notice it any more. It's just a part of me."

"You been so tired lately—kind of wore out," said Hazel. "If there was just some way we could make a little hole in the bottom of the bag, and just take out a few of them lead balls. Just a few."

"Two years in prison and two thousand dollars fine for every ball I took out," said George. "I don't call that a bargain."

"If you could just take a few out when you came home from work," said Hazel. "I mean—you don't compete with anybody around here. You just set around."

"If I tried to get away with it," said George, "then other people'd get away with it—and pretty soon we'd be right back to the dark ages again, with everybody competing against everybody else. You wouldn't like that, would you?"

"I'd hate it," said Hazel.

"There you are," said George. "The minute people start cheating on laws, what do you think happens to society?"

If Hazel hadn't been able to come up with an answer to this question, George couldn't have supplied one. A siren was going off in his head.

"Reckon it'd fall all apart," said Hazel.

"What would?" said George blankly.

"Society," said Hazel uncertainly. "Wasn't that what you just said?"

"Who knows?" said George.

The television program was suddenly interrupted for a news bulleting. It wasn't clear at first as to what the bulletin was about, since the announcer, like all announcers, had a serious speech impediment. For about half a minute, and in a state of high excitement, the announcer tried to say, "Ladies and gentlemen—"

He finally gave up, handed the bulletin to a ballerina to read.

"That's all right—" Hazel said of the announcer, "he tried. That's the big thing. He tried to do the best he could with what God gave him. He should get a nice raise for trying so hard."

"Ladies and gentlemen—" said the ballerina, reading the bulletin. She must have been extraordinarily beautiful, because the mask she wore was hideous. And it was easy to see that she was the strongest and most graceful of all the dancers, for her handicap bags were as big as those worn by two-hundred-pound men.

And she had to apologize at once for her voice, which was a very unfair voice for a woman to use. Her voice was a warm, luminous, timeless melody. "Excuse me—" she said, and she began again, making her voice absolutely uncompetitive.

"Harrison Bergeron, age fourteen," she said in a grackle squawk, "Has just escaped from jail, where he was held on suspicion of plotting to overthrow the government. He is a genius and an athlete, is underhandicapped, and should be regarded as extremely dangerous."

A police photograph of Harrison Bergeron was flashed on the screen upside down, then sideways, upside down again, then right side up. The picture showed the full length of Harrison against a background calibrated in feet and inches. He was exactly seven feet tall.

The rest of Harrison's appearance was Halloween and hardware. Nobody had ever borne heavier handicaps. He had outgrown hindrances faster than the H-G men could think them up. Instead of a little ear radio for a mental handicap, he wore a tremendous pair of earphones, and spectacles with thick wavy lenses. The spectacles were intended to make him not only half blind, but to give him whanging headaches besides.

Scrap metal was hung all over him. Ordinarily, there was a certain symmetry, a military neatness to the handicaps issued to strong people, but Harrison looked like a walking junkyard. In the race of life, Harrison carried three hundred pounds.

And to offset his good looks, the H-G men required that he wear at all times a red rubber ball for a nose, keep his eyebrows shaved off, and cover his even white teeth with black caps at snaggle-tooth random.

"If you see this boy," said the ballerina, "do not—I repeat, do not—try to reason with him."

There was the shriek of a door being torn from its hinges.

Screams and barking cries of consternation came from the television set. The photograph of Harrison Bergeron on the screen jumped again and again, as though dancing to the tune of an earthquake.

George Bergeron correctly identified the earthquake, and well he might have—for many was the time his own home had danced to the same crashing tune. "My god—" said George, "that must be Harrison!"

The realization was blasted from his mind instantly by the sound of an automobile collision in his head.

When George could open his eyes again, the photograph of Harrison was gone. A living, breathing Harrison filled the screen.

Clanking, clownish, and huge, Harrison stood in the center of the studio. The knob of the uprooted studio door was still in his hand. Ballerinas, technicians, musicians, and announcers cowered on their knees before him, expecting to die.

"I am the Emperor!" cried Harrison. "Do you hear? I am the Emperor! Everybody must do what I say at once!" He stamped his foot and the studio shook.

"Even as I stand here—" he bellowed, "crippled, hobbled, sickened—I am a greater ruler than any man who ever lived! Now watch me become what I can become!"

Harrison tore the straps of his handicap harness like wet tissue paper, tore straps guaranteed to support five thousand pounds.

Harrison's scrap-iron handicaps crashed to the floor.

Harrison thrust his thumbs under the bar of the padlock that secured his head harness. The bar snapped like celery. Harrison smashed his headphones and spectacles against the wall.

He flung away his rubber-ball nose, revealed a man that would have awed Thor, the god of thunder.

"I shall now select my Empress!" he said, looking down on the cowering people. "Let the first woman who dares rise to her feet claim her mate and her throne!"

A moment passed, and then a ballerina arose, swaying like a willow.

Harrison plucked the mental handicap from her ear, snapped off her physical handicaps with marvelous delicacy. Last of all, he removed her mask.

She was blindingly beautiful.

"Now—" said Harrison, taking her hand, "shall we show the people the meaning of the word dance? Music!" he commanded.

The musicians scrambled back into their chairs, and Harrison stripped them of their handicaps, too. "Play your best," he told them, "and I'll make you barons and dukes and earls."

The music began. It was normal at first—cheap, silly, false. But Harrison snatched two musicians from their chairs, waved them like batons as he sang the music as he wanted it played. He slammed them back into their chairs.

The music began again and was much improved.

Harrison and his Empress merely listened to the music for a while— listened gravely, as though synchronizing their heartbeats with it.

They shifted their weights to their toes.

Harrison placed his big hands on the girl's tiny waist, letting her sense the weightlessness that would soon be hers.

And then, in an explosion of joy and grace, into the air they sprang!

Not only were the laws of the land abandoned, but the law of gravity and the laws of motion as well.

They reeled, whirled, swiveled, flounced, capered, gamboled, and spun.

They leaped like deer on the moon.

The studio ceiling was thirty feet high, but each leap brought the dancers nearer to it.

It became their obvious intention to kiss the ceiling.

They kissed it.

And then, neutralizing gravity with love and pure will, they remained suspended in air inches below the ceiling, and they kissed each other for a long, long time.

It was then that Diana Moon Glampers, the Handicapper General, came into the studio with a double-barreled ten-gauge shotgun. She fired twice, and the Emperor and the Empress were dead before they hit the floor.

Diana Moon Glampers loaded the gun again. She aimed it at the musicians and told them they had ten seconds to get their handicaps back on.

It was then that the Bergerons' television tube burned out.

Hazel turned to comment about the blackout to George. But George had gone out into the kitchen for a can of beer.

George came back in with the beer, paused while a handicap signal shook him up. And then he sat down again. "You been crying?" he said to Hazel.

"Yup," she said.

"What about?" he said

"I forget," she said. "Something real sad on television."

"What was it?" he said.

"It's all kind of mixed up in my mind," said Hazel.

"Forget sad things," said George.

"I always do," said Hazel.

"That's my girl," said George. He winced. There was the sound of a rivetting gun in his head.

"Gee—I could tell that one was a doozy," said Hazel.

"You can say that again," said George.

"Gee—" said Hazel, "I could tell that one was a doozy."

The Lynching of Jube Benson
Paul Laurence Dunbar

Gordon Fairfax's library held but three men, but the air was dense with clouds of smoke. The talk had drifted from one topic to another much as the smoke wreaths had puffed, floated, and thinned away. Then Handon Gay, who was an ambitious young reporter, spoke of a lynching story in a recent magazine, and the matter of punishment without trial put new life into the conversation.

"I should like to see a real lynching," said Gay rather callously.

"Well, I should hardly express it that way," said Fairfax, "but if a real, live lynching were to come my way, I should not avoid it."

"I should," spoke the other from the depths of his chair, where he had been puffing in moody silence. Judged by his hair, which was freely sprinkled with gray, the speaker might have been a man of forty-five or fifty, but his face, though lined and serious, was youthful, the face of a man hardly past thirty.

"What! you, Dr. Melville? Why, I thought that you physicians wouldn't weaken at anything."

"I have seen one such affair," said the doctor gravely, "in fact, I took a prominent part in it."

"Tell us about it," said the reporter, feeling for his pencil and notebook, which he was, nevertheless, careful to hide from the speaker.

The men drew their chairs eagerly up to the doctor's, but for a minute he did not seem to see them, but sat gazing abstractedly into the fire, then he took a long draw upon his cigar and began:

"I can see it all very vividly now. It was in the summertime and about seven years ago. I was practising at the time down in the little town of Bradford. It was a small and primitive place, just the location for an impecunious medical man, recently out of college.

"In lieu of a regular office, I attended to business in the first of two rooms which I rented from Hiram Daly, one of the more prosperous of the townsmen. Here I boarded and here also came my patients—white and black—whites from every section, and blacks from 'nigger town,' as the west portion of the place was called.

"The people about me were most of them coarse and rough, but they were simple and generous, and as time passed on I had about abandoned my intention of seeking distinction in wider fields and determined to settle into the place of a modest country doctor. This was rather a strange conclusion for a young man to arrive at, and I will not deny that the presence in the house of my host's beautiful young daughter, Annie, had something to do with my decision. She was a beautiful young girl of seventeen or eighteen, and very far superior to her surroundings. She had a native grace and a pleasing way about her that made everybody that came under her spell her abject slave. White and black who knew her loved her, and none, I thought, more deeply and respectfully than Jube Benson, the black man of all work about the place.

"He was a fellow whom everybody trusted; an apparently steadygoing, grinning sort, as we used to call him. Well, he was completely under Miss Annie's thumb and would fetch and carry for her like a faithful dog. As soon as he saw that I began to care for Annie, and anybody could see that, he transferred some of his allegiance to me and became my faithful servitor also. Never did a man have a more devoted adherent in his wooing than did I, and many a one of Annie's tasks which he volunteered to do gave her an extra hour with me. You can imagine that I liked the boy, and you need not wonder any more that as both wooing and my practice waxed apace, I was content to give up my great ambitions and stay just where I was.

"It wasn't a very pleasant thing, then, to have an epidemic of typhoid break out in the town that kept me going so that I hardly had time for the courting that a fellow wants to carry on with his sweetheart while he is still young enough to call her his girl. I fumed, but duty was duty, and I kept to my work night and day. It was now that Jube proved how invaluable he was as coadjutor. He not only took messages to Annie, but brought sometimes little ones from her to me, and he would tell me little secret things that he had overheard her say that made me throb with joy and swear at him for repeating his mistress's conversation. But, best of all, Jube was a perfect Cerberus, and no one on earth could have been more effective in keeping away or deluding the other young fellows who visited the Dalys. He would tell me of it afterwards, chuckling softly to himself. 'An,' Doctah, I say to Mistah Hemp Stevens, '"Scuse us, Mistah Stevens, but Miss Annie, she des' gone out," an' den he go outer de gate lookin' moughty lonesome. When Sam Elkins come, I say, "Sh, Mistah Elkins, Miss Annie, she done tuk down," an' he say, "What, Jube, you don' reckon hit de—" Den he stop an' look skeert, an' I say, "I feared hit is, Mistah Elkins," an' sheks my haid ez solemn. He goes outer de gate lookin' lak his bes' frien' done daid, an' all de time Miss Annie behine de cu'tain ovah de po'ch des' a-laffin' fit to kill.'

"Jube was a most admirable liar, but what could I do? He knew that I was a young fool of a hypocrite, and when I would rebuke him for these deceptions, he would give way and roll on the floor in an excess of delighted laughter until from very contagion I had to join him—and, well, there was no need of my preaching when there had been no beginning to his repentance and when there must ensure a continuance of his wrong-doing.

"This thing went on for over three months, and then, pouf! I was down like a shot. My patients were nearly all up, but the reaction from overwork made me an easy victim of the lurking germs. Then Jube loomed up as a nurse. He put everyone else aside, and with the doctor, a friend of mine from a neighboring town, took entire charge of me. Even Annie herself was put aside, and I was cared for as tenderly as a baby. Tom, that was my physician and friend, told me all about it afterward with tears in his eyes. Only he was a big, blunt man, and his expressions did not convey all that he meant. He told me how my nigger had nursed me as if I were a sick kitten and he my mother. Of how fiercely he guarded his right to be the sole one to 'do' for me, as he called it, and how, when the crisis came, he hovered, weeping but hopeful, at my beside until it was safely passed, when they drove him, weak and exhausted, from the room. As for me, I knew little about it at the time, and cared less. I was too busy in my fight with death. To my chimerical vision there was only a black but gentle demon that came and went, alternating with a white fairy, who would insist on coming in on her head, growing larger and larger and then dissolving. But the pathos and devotion in the story lost nothing in my blunt friend's telling.

"It was during the period of a long convalescence, however, that I came to know my humble ally as he really was, devoted to the point of abjectness. There were times when, for very shame at his goodness to me, I would beg him to go away, to do something else. He would go, but before I had time to realize that I was not being ministered to, he would be back at my side, grinning and pottering just the same. He manufactured duties for the joy of performing them. He pretended to see desires in me that I never had, because he liked to pander to them, and when I became entirely exasperated and ripped out a good round oath, he chuckled with the remark, "Dah, now, you sholy is gittin' well. Nevah did hyeah a man anywhaih nigh Jo'dan's sho' cuss dat.'

"Why, I grew to love, him, love him, oh, yes, I loved him as well—oh, what am I saying? All human love and gratitude are damned poor things; excuse me, gentlemen, this isn't a pleasant story. The truth is usually a nasty thing to stand.

"It was not six months after that that my friendship to Jube, which he had been at such great pains to win, was put to too severe a test.

"It was in the summertime again, and, as business was slack, I had ridden over to see my friend, Dr. Tom. I had spent a good part of the day there, and it was past four o'clock when I rode leisurely into Bradford. I was in a particularly joyous mood and no premonition of the impending catastrophe oppressed me. No sense of sorrow, present or to come, forced itself upon me, even when I saw men hurrying through the almost deserted streets. When I got within sight of my home and saw a crowd surrounding it, I was only interested sufficiently to spur my horse into a jog trot, which brought me up to the throng, when something in the sullen, settled horror in the mens' faces gave a sudden, sick thrill. They whispered a word to me, and without a thought, save for Annie, the girl who had been so surely growing into my heart, I leaped from the saddle and tore my way through the people to the house.

"It was Annie, poor girl, bruised and bleeding, her face and dress torn from struggling. They were gathered round her with whites faces, and oh, with what terrible patience they were trying to gain from her fluttering lips the name of her murderer. They made way for me and I knelt at her side. She was beyond my skill, and my will merged with theirs. One thought was in our minds.

"'Who?' I asked.

"Her eyes half opened. 'That black—' She fell back into my arms dead.

"We turned and looked at each other. The mother had broken down and was weeping, but the face of the father was like iron.

"'It is enough,' he said; 'Jube has disappeared.' He went to the door and said to the expectant crowd, 'She is dead.'

"I heard the angry roar without swelling up like the noise of a flood, and then I heard the sudden movement of many feet as the men separated into searching parties, and laying the dead girl back upon her couch, I took my rifle and went out to join them.

"As if by intuition the knowledge had passed among the men that Jube Benson had disappeared, and he, by common consent, was to be the object of our search. Fully a dozen of the citizens had seen him hasten in toward the woods and noted his skulking air, but as he had grinned in his old good-natured way they had, at the time, thought nothing of it. Now, however, the diabolical reason of his slyness was apparent. He had been shrewd enough to disarm suspicion, and by now was far away. Even Mrs. Daly, who was visiting with a neighbor, had seen him stepping out by a back way, and had said with a laugh, 'I reckon that black rascal's arunning off somewhere.' Oh, if she had only known!

"'To the woods! To the woods!' that was the cry, and away we went, each with the determination not to shoot, but to bring the culprit alive into town, and then to deal with him as his crime deserved.

"I cannot describe the feelings I experienced as I went out that night to beat the woods for this human tiger. My heart smoldered within me like a coal, and I went forward under the impulse of a will that was half my own, half some more malignant power's. My throat throbbed drily, but water nor whisky would not have quenched my thirst. The thought has come to me since that now I could interpret the panther's desire for blood and sympathize with it, but then I thought nothing. I simply went forward, add watched, watched with burning eyes for a familiar form that I had looked for as often before with such different emotions.

"Luck or ill-luck, which you will, was with our party, and just as dawn was graying the sky, we came upon our quarry crouched in the corner of a fence. It was only half light, and we might have passed, but my eyes had caught sight of him, and I raised the cry. We levelled our guns and he rose and came toward us.

"'I t'ought you wa'n't gwine see me,' he said sullenly, 'I didn't mean no harm.'

"'Harm!'

"Some of the men took the word up with oaths, others were ominously silent.

"We gathered around him like hungry beasts, and I began to see terror dawning in his eyes. He turned to me, 'I's moughty glad you's heah, Doc,' he said, 'you ain't gwine let 'em whup me.'

"'Whip you, you hound,' I said, 'I'm going to see you hanged,' and in the excess of my passion I struck him full on the mouth. He made a motion as if to resent the blow against even such great odds, but controlled himself.

"'W'y, Doctah,' he exclaimed in the saddest voice I have ever heard, 'w'y, Doctah! I ain't stole nuffin' o' yo'n, an' I was comin' back. I only run off to see my gal, Lucy, ovah to de Centah.'

"'You lie!' I said, and my hands were busy helping others bind him upon a horse. Why did I do it? I don't know. A false education, I reckon, one false from the beginning. I saw his black face glooming there in the half light, and I could only think of him as a monster. It's tradition. At first I was told that the black man would catch me, and when I got over that, they taught me that the devil was black, and when I had recovered from the sickness of that belief, here were Jube and his fellows with faces of menacing blackness. There was only one conclusion: This black man stood for all the powers of evil, the result of whose machinations had been gathering in my mind from childhood up. But this has nothing to do with what happened.

"After firing a few shots to announce our capture, we rode back into town with Jube. The ingathering parties from all directions met us as we made our way up to the house. All was very quiet and orderly. There was no doubt that it was, as the papers would have said, a gathering of the best citizens. It was a gathering of stern, determined men, bent on a terrible vengeance.

"We took Jube into the house, into the room where the corpse lay. At the sight of it he gave a scream like an animal's and his face went the color of storm-blown water. This was enough to condemn him. We divined rather than heard his cry of 'Miss Ann, Miss Ann, oh, my God, doc, you don't t'ink I done it?'

"Hungry hands were ready. We hurried him out into the yard. A rope was ready. A tree was at hand. Well, that part was the least of it, save that Hiram Daly stepped aside to let me be the first to pull upon the rope. It was lax at first. Then it tightened, and I felt the quivering soft weight resist my muscles. Other hands joined, and Jube swung off his feet.

"No one was masked. We knew each other. Not even the culprit's face was covered, and the last I remember of him as he went into the air was a look of sad reproach that will remain with me until I meet him face to face again.

"We were tying the end of the rope to a tree, where the dead man might hang as a warning to his fellows, when a terrible cry chilled us to the marrow.

"'Cut 'im down, cut 'im down, he ain't guilty. We got de one. Cut him down, fu' Gawd's sake. Here's de man, we foun' him hidin' in de barn!'

"Jube's brother, Ben, and another Negro came rushing toward us, half dragging, half carrying a miserable-looking wretch between them. Someone cut the rope and Jube dropped lifeless to the ground.

"'Oh, my Gawd, he's daid, he's daid!' wailed the brother, but with blazing eyes he brought his captive into the center of the group, and we saw in the full light the scratched face of Tom Skinner—the worst white ruffian in town—but the face we saw was not as we were accustomed to see it, merely smeared with dirt. It was blackened to imitate a Negro's.

"God forgive me; I could not wait to try to resuscitate Jube. I knew he was already past help, so I rushed into the house and to the dead girl's side. In the excitement they had not yet washed or laid her out. Carefully, carefully, I searched underneath her broken fingernails. There was skin there. I took it out, the little curled pieces, and went with it to my office.

"There, determinedly, I examined it under a powerful glass, and read my own doom. It was the skin of a white man, and in it were embedded strands of short, brown hair or beard.

"How I went out to tell the waiting crowd I do not know, for something kept crying in my ears, 'Blood guilty! Blood guilty!'

"The men went away stricken into silence and awe. The new prisoner attempted neither denial nor plea. When they were gone, I would have helped Ben carry his brother in, but he waved me away fiercely. 'You he'ped murder my brothah, you dat was *his* frien', go 'way, go 'way! I'll tek him home myse'f.' I could only respect his wish, and he and his comrade took up the dead man and between them bore him up the street on which the sun was now shining full.

"I saw the few men who had not skulked indoors uncovered as they passed, and I—I—stood there between the two murdered ones, while all the while something in my ears kept crying, 'Blood guilty! Blood guilty!'"

The doctor's head dropped into his hands and he sat for some time in silence, which was broken by neither of the men, then he rose, saying, "Gentlemen, that was my last lynching."

4

Standards and Presumptions

If the law be [that] a murderer may always escape, if only he shall so mutilate the body of his victim as to make identification by direct evidence impossible; or shall so effectually conceal it that discovery is delayed until decomposition has taken away the possibility of personal recognition; . . . the Penal Code has opened a door of escape to that brutal courage which can mangle and burn the lifeless body, and has put a premium upon and offered a reward for that species of atrocity.

People v. Palmer
109 N.Y. 110 (1888)

The reasonable-doubt standard plays a vital role in the American scheme of criminal procedure. It is a prime instrument for reducing the risk of convictions resting on factual error. The standard provides concrete substance for the presumption of innocence—that bedrock "axiomatic and elementary" principle whose "enforcement lies at the foundation of the administration of our criminal law."

. . . .

In a criminal case . . . we do not view the social disutility of convicting an innocent man as equivalent to the disutility of acquitting someone who is guilty.

In re Winship
397 U.S. 358 (1970)

In establishing criminal laws, standards and presumptions are adopted in order to avoid the conviction of an innocent man—to avoid the sort of outcome which takes place in "The Lynching of Jube Benson." The standard of proof established under early common law in order to convict a party charged with murder came to be known as the Corpus Delicti. The judge in the following short story entitled "The Corpus Delicti," by Melville Davisson Post, states it thus:

> To warrant conviction of murder there must be direct proof
> either of the death, as of the finding and identification of the
> corpse, or of criminal violence adequate to produce death,
> and exerted in such a manner as to account for the disappear-
> ance of the body; and it is only when there is direct proof of
> the one that the other can be established by circumstantial
> evidence.

How could such a rule be justified if by its application it would allow a man like Samuel, a.k.a. Richard, a.k.a. Victor, to go free when the evidence is so clearly against him? Notice how the Court in *People v. Palmer* reeled against a standard that would require direct proof of a victim's identification before a conviction, since it would lead to punishment of only the less-con-niving and less-base criminal. Ironically, in "The Corpus Delicti" the bet-ter—or worse—the murderer is, the better chance he has of being acquitted. Is it safe to allow the use of circumstantial evidence of the death if there is direct proof of the violence?

FICTION: A man learns that his wife is having an adulterous af-fair. In a jealous rage he drives his wife to a public area, drags her out of the car, pulls out a loaded gun, and shoots her. Policemen who happen to be nearby disarm the irate husband and send the wounded wife to the hospi-tal where she quickly recovers. The husband is charged with, tried for, and convicted of attempted murder. He spends the next five years in a striped shirt making license plates, and his wife visits him faithfully every Wednes-day night. Upon his release, he returns to his wife.

Two months later he again drives his wife to a busy public place. He takes a gun from his pocket, shoots his wife through the windshield, then jumps into the car and drives away leaving an astonished crowd of onlookers. The police are called but to no avail. Neither the husband nor the wife is seen again for three weeks.

After three weeks, the husband returns to town alone, shows up for work in the car with the bullet hole in the windshield, and is arrested for murder. In spite of his protests that he did not kill his wife, he is found guilty and hanged until dead. The conviction seems justified. Knowing of a prior attempted murder and a bullet aimed at his wife and shot through the windshield of the car in which she was sitting, wouldn't any jury feel safe in convicting him of murder?

POSTSCRIPT: Two weeks after the hanging of the husband, the wife reappears. She states that her lover, who is an expoliceman, in-sisted that she wear a bulletproof vest for a while after her husband came out of prison. The policeman/boyfriend believed that the husband was ca-pable of another murder attempt if he discovered that the illicit relationship was continuing. After the husband shot the wife through the windshield and drove off, she feigned death until he stopped the car in the country and left to survey the area for a place to bury her. At that point, she fled over the hill, hitched a ride, called the boyfriend, and hid low until she heard that the husband was dead and she felt safe to come home again.

If you were not the reader watching every move of the murderer in "The Corpus Delicti," could you imagine a scenario in which it was possible for Nina San Croix to still be alive in spite of what the policemen saw and heard?

"The Benefit of the Doubt," by Jack London, looks at the presumption of innocence and the standard of proof beyond a reasonable doubt—a presumption and a standard often explored in stories of homicide. In London's story, though, the theme is applied to a story of criminal assault and battery.

"The Benefit of the Doubt" and "The Corpus Delicti" point to the problems inherent in striving to arrive at the truth through the judicial process. How can the legal system function adequately when witnesses like the murderer in "The Corpus Delicti" and Patsy and his friends commit perjury readily and without compunction and when the very political machine charged with finding the truth is itself at times corrupt?

The Corpus Delicti
Melville Davisson Post

I

"That man Mason," said Samuel Walcott, "is the mysterious member of this club. He is more than that; he is the mysterious man of New York."

"I was much surprised to see him," answered his companion, Marshall St. Clair, of the great law firm of Seward, St. Clair & De Muth. "I had lost track of him since he went to Paris as counsel for the American stockholders of the Canal Company. When did he come back to the States?"

"He turned up suddenly in his ancient haunts about four months ago," said Walcott, "as grand, gloomy, and peculiar as Napoleon ever was in his palmiest days. The younger members of the club called him 'Zanona Redivivus.' He wanders through the house usually late at night, apparently without noticing anything or anybody. His mind seems to be deeply and busily at work, leaving his bodily self to wander as it may happen. Naturally, strange stories are told of him; indeed, his individuality and his habit of doing some unexpected thing, and doing it in such a marvelously original manner that men who are experts at it look on in wonder, cannot fail to make him an object of interest.

"He has never been known to play at any game whatever, and yet one night he sat down to the chess table with old Admiral Du Brey. You know the admiral is the great champion since he beat the French and English officers in the tournament last winter. Well, you also know that the conventional openings at chess are scientifically and accurately determined. To the utter disgust of Du Brey, Mason opened the game with an unheard-of attack from the extremes of the board. The old admiral stopped and, in a kindly patronizing way, pointed out the weak and absurd folly of his move and asked him to begin again with some one of the safe openings. Mason smiled and answered that if one had a head that he could trust he could use it; if not, then it was the part of wisdom to follow blindly the dead forms of some man who had a head. Du Brey was naturally angry and set himself to demolish Mason as quickly as possible. The game was rapid for a few moments. Mason lost piece after piece. His opening was broken and destroyed and its utter folly apparent to the lookers-on. The admiral smiled and the game seemed all one-sided, when, suddenly, to his utter horror, Du Brey found that his king was in a trap. The foolish opening had been only a piece of shrewd strategy. The old admiral fought and cursed and sacrificed his pieces, but it was of no use. He was gone. Mason checkmated him in two moves and arose wearily.

"'Where in Heaven's name, man,' said the old admiral, thunder-struck, 'did you learn that master-piece?'

"'Just here,' replied Mason. 'To play chess, one should know his opponent. How could the dead masters lay down rules by which you could be beaten, sir? They had never seen you'; and thereupon he turned and left the room. Of course, St. Clair, such a strange man would soon become an object of all kinds of mysterious rumors. Some are true and some are not. At any rate, I know that Mason is an unusual man with a gigantic intellect. Of late he seems to have taken a strange fancy to me. In fact, I seem to be the only member of the club that he will talk with, and I confess that he startles and fascinates me. He is an original genius, St. Clair, of an unusual order."

"I recall vividly," said the younger man, "that before Mason went to Paris he was considered one of the greatest lawyers of this city and he was feared and hated by the bar at large. He came here, I believe, from Virginia and began with the high-grade criminal practice. He soon became famous for his powerful and ingenious defenses. He found holes in the law through which his clients escaped, holes that by the profession at large were not suspected to exist, and that frequently astonished the judges. His ability caught the attention of the great corporations. They tested him and found in him learning and unlimited resources. He pointed out methods by which they could evade obnoxious statutes, by which they could comply with the apparent letter of the law and yet violate its spirit, and advised them well in that most important of all things, just how far they could bend the law without breaking it. At the time he left for Paris he had a vast clientage and he was in the midst of a brilliant career. The day he took passage from New York, the bar lost sight of him. No matter how great a man may be, the wave soon closes over him in a city like this. In a few years Mason was forgotten. Now only the older practitioners would recall him, and they would do so with hatred and bitterness. He was a tireless, savage, uncompromising fighter, always a recluse."

"Well," said Walcott, "he reminds me of a great world-weary cynic, transplanted from some ancient mysterious empire. When I come into the man's presence I feel instinctively the grip of his intellect. I tell you, St. Clair, Randolph Mason is the mysterious man of New York."

At this moment a messenger boy came into the room and handed Mr. Walcott a telegram. "St. Clair," said the gentleman, rising, "the directors of the Elevated are in session, and we must hurry." The two men put on their coats and left the house.

Samuel Walcott was not a club man after the manner of the Smart Set, and yet he was in fact a club man. He was a bachelor in the latter thirties, and resided in a great silent house on the avenue. On the street he was a man of substance, shrewd and progressive, backed by great wealth. He had various corporate interests in the larger syndicates, but the basis and foundation of his fortune was real estate. His houses on the avenue were the best possible property, and his elevator row in the importers' quarter was indeed a literal gold mine. It was known that, many years before, his grandfather had died and left him the property, which, at that time, was of no great value. Young Walcott had gone out into the gold-fields and had been lost sight of and forgotten. Ten years afterward he had turned up suddenly in New York and taken possession of his property, then vastly increased in value. His speculations were almost phenomenally successful, and, backed by the now-enormous value of his real property, he was soon on a level with the merchant princes. His judgment was considered sound, and he had the full confidence of his business associates for safety and caution. Fortune heaped up riches around him with a lavish hand. He was unmarried and the halo of his wealth caught the keen eye of the matron with marriageable daughters. He was invited out, caught by the whirl of society, and tossed into its maelstrom. In a measure he reciprocated. He kept horses and a yacht. His dinners at Delmonico's and the club were above reproach. But with all he was a silent man with a shadow deep in his eyes, and seemed to court the society of his fellow, not because he loved them, but because he either hated or feared solitude. For years the strategy of the matchmaker had gone gracefully afield, but Fate is relentless. If she shields the victim from the traps of men, it is not because she wishes him to escape, but because she is pleased to reserve him for her own trap. So it happened that, when Virginia St. Clair assisted Mrs. Miriam Steuvisant at her midwinter reception, this same Samuel Walcott fell deeply and hopelessly and utterly in love, and it was so apparent to the beaten generals present that Mrs. Miriam Steuvisant applauded herself, so to speak, with encore after encore. It was good to see this courteous, silent man literally at the feet of the young debutante. He was there of right. Even the mothers of marriageable daughters admitted that. The young girl was brown-haired, brown-eyed, and tall enough, said the experts, and of the blue blood royal, with all the grace, courtesy, and inbred genius of such princely heritage.

Perhaps it was objected by the censors of the Smart Set that Miss St. Clair's frankness and honesty were a trifle old-fashioned, and that she was a shadowy bit of a puritan; and perhaps it was of these same qualities that Samuel Walcott received his hurt. At any rate the hurt was there and deep, and the new actor stepped up into the old, time-worn, semi-tragic drama, and began his role with a tireless, utter sincerity that was deadly dangerous if he lost.

II

Perhaps a week after the conversation between St. Clair and Walcott, Randolph Mason stood in the private writing-room of the club with his hands behind his back.

He was a man apparently in the middle forties; tall and reasonably broad across the shoulders; muscular without being either stout or lean. His hair was thin and of a brown color, with erratic streaks of gray. His forehead was broad and high and of a faint reddish color. His eyes were restless, inky black, and not over-large. The nose was big and muscular and bowed. The eyebrows were black and heavy, almost bushy. There were heavy furrows running from the nose downward and outward to the corners of the mouth. The mouth was straight and the jaw was heavy, and square.

Looking at the face of Randolph Mason from above, the expression in repose was crafty and cynical; viewed from below upward, it was savage and vindictive, almost brutal; while from the front, if looked squarely in the face, the stranger was fascinated by the animation of the man and at once concluded that his expression was fearless and sneering. He was evidently of Southern extraction and a man of unusual power.

A fire smoldered on the hearth. It was a crisp evening in the early fall, and with that far-off touch of melancholy which ever heralds the coming winter, even in the midst of a city. The man's face looked tired and ugly. His long white hands were clasped tight together. His entire figure and face wore every mark of weakness and physical exhaustion; but his eyes contradicted. They were red and restless.

In the private dining-room the dinner party was in the best of spirits. Samuel Walcott was happy. Across the table from him was Miss Virginia St. Clair, radiant, a tinge of color in her cheeks. On their side, Mrs. Miriam Steuvisant and Marshall St. Clair were brilliant and light-hearted. Walcott looked at the young girl and the measure of his worship was full. He wondered for the thousandth time how she could possibly love him and by what earthly miracle she had come to accept him, and how it would be always to have her across the table from him, his own table in his own house.

They were about to rise from the table when one of the waiters entered the room and handed Walcott an envelope. He thrust it quickly into his pocket. In the confusion of rising the others did not notice him, but his face was ash-white and his hands trembled violently as he placed the wraps around the bewitching shoulders of Miss St. Clair.

"Marshall," he said, and despite the powerful effort his voice was hollow, "you will see the ladies safely cared for, I am called to attend a grave matter."

"All right, Walcott," answered the young man, with cheery good-nature, "you are too serious, old man; trot along."

"The poor dear," murmured Mrs. Steuvisant, after Walcott had helped them to the carriage and turned to go up the steps of the club, "the poor dear is hard hit, and men are such funny creatures when they are hard hit."

Samuel Walcott, as his fate would, went direct to the private writing-room and opened the door. The lights were not turned on and in the dark he did not see Mason motionless by the mantel-shelf. He went quickly across the room to the writing-table, turned on one of the lights, and, taking the envelope from his pocket, tore it open. Then he bent down by the light to read the contents. As his eyes ran over the paper, his jaw fell. The skin drew away from his cheek-bones and his face seemed literally to sink in. His knees gave way under him and he would have gone down in a heap had it not been for Mason's long arms that closed around him and held him up. The human economy is ever mysterious. The moment the new danger threatened, the latent power of the man as an animal, hidden away in the centers of intelligence, asserted itself. His hand clutched the paper and, with a half slide, he turned in Mason's arms. For a moment he stared up at the ugly man whose thin arms felt like wire ropes.

"You are under the dead-fall, aye," said Mason. "The cunning of my enemy is sublime."

"Your enemy?" gasped Walcott. "When did you come into it? How in God's name did you know it? How your enemy?"

Mason looked down at the wide, bulging eyes of the man.

"Who should know better than I?" he said. "Haven't I broken through all the traps and plots that she could set?"

"She? She trap you?" The man's voice was full of horror.

"The old schemer," muttered Mason. "The cowardly old schemer, to strike in the back; but we can beat her. She did not count on my helping you—I, who know her so well."

Mason's face was red, and his eyes burned. In the midst of it all he dropped his hands and went over to the fire. Samuel Walcott arose, panting, and stood looking at Mason, with his hands behind him on the table. The naturally strong nature and the rigid school in which the man had been trained presently began to tell. His composure in part returned and he thought rapidly. What did this strange man know? Was he simply making shrewd guesses, or had he some mysterious knowledge of this matter? Walcott could not know that Mason meant only Fate, that he believed her to be his great enemy. Walcott had never before doubted his own ability to meet any emergency. This mighty jerk had carried him off his feet. He was unstrung and panic-stricken. At any rate this man had promised help. He would take it. He put the paper and envelope carefully into his pocket, smoothed out his rumpled coat, and going over to Mason touched him on the shoulder.

"Come," he said, "if you are to help me we must go."

The man turned and followed him without a word. In the hall Mason put on his hat and overcoat, and the two went out into the street. Walcott hailed a cab, and the two were driven to his house on the avenue. Walcott took out his latch-key, opened the door, and led the way into the library. He turned on the light and motioned Mason to seat himself at the table. Then he went into another room and presently returned with a bundle of papers and a decanter of brandy. He poured out a glass of the liquor and offered it to Mason. The man shook his head. Walcott poured the contents of the glass down his own throat. Then he set the decanter down and drew up a chair on the side of the table opposite Mason.

"Sir," said Walcott, in a voice deliberate, indeed, but as hollow as a sepulcher, "I am done for. God has finally gathered up the ends of the net, and it is knotted tight."

"Am I not here to help you?" said Mason, turning savagely. "I can beat Fate. Give me the details of her trap."

He bent forward and rested his arms on the table. His streaked gray hair was rumpled and on end, and his face was ugly. For a moment Walcott did not answer. He moved a little into the shadow; then he spread the bundle of old yellow papers out before him.

"To begin with," he said, "I am a living lie, a gilded, crime-made sham, every bit of me. There is not an honest piece anywhere. It is all lie. I am a liar and a thief before men. The property which I possess is not mine, but stolen from a dead man. The very name which I bear is not my own, but is the bastard child of a crime. I am more than all that—I am a murderer; a murderer before the law; a murderer before God; and worse than a murderer before the pure woman whom I love more than anything that God could make."

He paused for a moment and wiped the perspiration from his face.

"Sir," said Mason, "this is all drivel, infantile drivel. What you are is of no importance. How to get out is the problem, how to get out."

Samuel Walcott leaned forward, poured out a glass of brandy, and swallowed it.

"Well," he said, speaking slowly, "my right name is Richard Warren. In the spring of 1879 I came to New York and fell in with the real Samuel Walcott, a young man with a little money and some property which his grandfather had left him. We became friends, and concluded to go to the far west together. Accordingly we scraped together what money we could lay our hands on, and landed in the gold-mining regions of California. We were young and inexperienced, and our money went rapidly. One April morning we drifted into a little shack camp, away up in the Sierra Nevadas, called Hell's Elbow. Here we struggled and starved for perhaps a year. Finally, in utter desperation, Walcott married the daughter of a Mexican gambler, who ran an eating-house and a poker joint. With them we lived from hand to mouth in a wild, God-forsaken way for several years. After a time the woman began to take a strange fancy to me. Walcott finally noticed it, and grew jealous.

"One night, in a drunken brawl, we quarreled, and I killed him. It was late at night, and, beside the woman, there were four of us in the poker room—the Mexican gambler, a half-breed devil called Cherubim Pete, Walcott, and myself. When Walcott fell, the half-breed whipped out his weapon and fired at me across the table; but the woman, Nina San Croix, struck his arm, and, instead of killing me, as he intended, the bullet mortally wounded her father, the Mexican gambler. I shot the half-breed through the forehead and turned around, expecting the woman to attack me. On the contrary, she pointed to the window and bade me wait for her on the cross-trail below.

"It was fully three hours later before the woman joined me at the place indicated. She had a bag of gold dust, a few jewels that belonged to her father, and a package of papers. I asked her why she had stayed behind so long, and she replied that the men were not killed outright and that she had brought a priest to them and waited until they had died. This was the truth, but not all the truth. Moved by superstition or foresight, the woman had induced the priest to take down the sworn statements of the two dying men, seal it, and give it to her. This paper she brought with her. All this I learned afterward. At the time I knew nothing of this damning evidence.

"We struck out together for the Pacific coast. The country was lawless. The privations we endured were almost past belief. At times the woman exhibited cunning and ability that were almost genius; and through it all, often in the very fingers of death, her devotion to me never wavered. It was dog-like and seemed to be her only object on earth. When we reached San Francisco, the woman put these papers into my hands." Walcott took up the yellow package, and pushed it across the table to Mason.

"She proposed that I assume Walcott's name, and that we come boldly to New York and claim the property. I examined the papers, found a copy of a will by which Walcott inherited the property, a bundle of correspondence, and sufficient documentary evidence to establish his identity beyond the shadow of a doubt. Desperate gambler as I now was, I quailed before the daring plan of Nina San Croix. I urged that I, Richard Warren, would be known, that the attempted fraud would be detected and would result in investigation, and perhaps unearth the whole horrible matter.

"The woman pointed out how much I resembled Walcott, what vast changes ten years of such life as we had led would naturally be expected to make in men, how utterly impossible it would be to trace back the fraud to Walcott's murder at Hell's Elbow, in the wild passes of the Sierra Nevadas. She bade me remember that we were both outcasts, both crime-branded, both enemies of man's law and God's; that we had nothing to lose; we were both sunk to the bottom. Then she laughed, and said that she had not found me a coward until now, but that if I had turned chicken-hearted, that was the end of it, of course. The result was, we sold the gold dust and jewels in San Francisco, took on such evidences of civilization as possible, and purchased passage to New York on the best steamer we could find.

"I was growing to depend on the bold gambler spirit of this woman, Nina San Croix; I felt the need of her strong, profligate nature. She was of a queer breed and a queerer school. Her mother was the daughter of a Spanish engineer, and had been stolen by the Mexican, her father. She herself had been raised and educated as best as might be in one of the monasteries along the Rio Grande, and had there grown to womanhood before her father, fleeing into the mountains of California, carried her with him.

"When we landed in New York I offered to announce her as my wife, but she refused, saying that her presence would excite comment and perhaps attract the attention of Walcott's relatives. We therefore arranged that I should go alone into the city, claim the property, and announce myself as Samuel Walcott, and that she should remain under cover until such time as we could feel the ground safe under us.

"Every detail of the plan was fatally successful. I established my identity without difficulty and secured the property. It had increased vastly in value, and I, as Samuel Walcott, soon found myself a rich man. I went to Nina San Croix in hiding and gave her a large sum of money, with which she purchased a residence in a retired part of the city, far up in a northern suburb. Here she lived secluded and unknown while I remained in the city, living here as a wealthy bachelor.

"I did not attempt to abandon the woman, but went to her from time to time in disguise and under cover of the greatest secrecy. For a time everything ran smooth, the woman was still devoted to me above everything else, and thought always of my welfare first and seemed content to wait so long as I thought best. My business expanded. I was sought after and consulted and drawn into the higher life of New York, and more and more felt that the woman was an albatross on my neck. I put her off with one excuse after another. Finally she began to suspect me and demanded that I should recognize her as my wife. I attempted to point out the difficulties. She met them all by saying that we should both go to Spain, there I could marry her, and we could return to America and drop into my place in society without causing more than a passing comment.

"I concluded to meet the matter squarely once for all. I said that I would convert half of the property into money and give it to her, but that I would not marry her. She did not fly into a storming rage as I had expected, but went quietly out of the room and presently returned with two papers, which she read. One was the certificate of her marriage to Walcott duly authenticated; the other was the dying statement of her father, the Mexican gambler, and of Samuel Walcott, charging me with murder. It was in proper form and certified by the Jesuit priest.

"'Now,' she said, sweetly, when she had finished, 'which do you prefer, to recognize your wife or to turn all the property over to Samuel Walcott's widow and hang for his murder?'

"I was dumfounded and horrified. I saw the trap that I was in and I consented to do anything she should say if she would only destroy the papers. This she refused to do. I pleaded with her and implored her to destroy them. Finally she gave them to me with a great show of returning confidence, and I tore them into bits and threw them into the fire.

"That was three months ago. We arranged to go to Spain and do as she said. She was to sail this morning and I was to follow. Of course I never intended to go. I congratulated myself on the fact that all trace of evidence against me was destroyed and that her grip was now broken. My plan was to induce her to sail, believing that I would follow. When she was gone I would marry Miss St. Clair, and if Nina San Croix should return I would defy her and lock her up as a lunatic. But I was reckoning like an infernal ass, to imagine for a moment that I could thus hoodwink such a woman as Nina San Croix.

"Tonight I received this." Walcott took the envelope from his pocket and gave it to Mason. "You saw the effect of it; read it and you will understand why. I felt the death hand when I saw her writing on the envelope."

Mason took the paper from the envelope. It was written in Spanish and ran:

"Greeting to RICHARD WARREN.

"The great Señor does his Little Nina injustice to think she would go away to Spain and leave him to the beautiful America. She is not so thoughtless. Before she goes, she shall be, oh so very rich! and the dear Señor shall be, oh so very safe! The archbishop and the kind church hate murderers.

"*Nina San Croix.*

"Of course, fool, the papers you destroyed were copies.

"*N. San C.*"

To this was pinned a line in a delicate, aristocratic hand, saying that the archbishop would willingly listen to Madam San Croix's statement if she would come to him on Friday morning at eleven.

"You see," said Walcott, desperately, "there is no possible way out.

I know the woman—when she decides to do a thing that is the end of it. She has decided to do this."

Mason turned around from the table, stretched out his long legs, and thrust his hands deep into his pockets. Walcott sat with his head down, watching Mason hopelessly, almost indifferently, his face blank and sunken. The ticking of the bronze clock on the mantel shelf was loud, painfully loud. Suddenly Mason drew his knees in and bent over, put both his bony hands on the table, and looked at Walcott.

"Sir," he said, "this matter is in much shape that there is only one thing to do. This growth must be cut out at the roots, and cut out quickly. This is the first fact to be determined, and a fool would know it. The second fact is that you must do it yourself. Hired killers are like the grave and the daughters of the horse,—leech—they cry always, 'Give, Give.' They are only palliatives, not cures. By using them you swap perils. You simply take a stay of execution at best. The common criminal would know this. These are the facts of your problem. The master plotters of crime would see here but two difficulties to meet:

"A practical method for accomplishing the body of the crime.

"A cover for the criminal agent.

"They would see no farther, and attempt to guard no farther. After they had provided a plan for the killing and a means by which the killer could cover his trail and escape from the theater of the homicide, they would believe all the requirements of the problems met, and would stop. The greatest, the very giants among them, have stopped here and have been in great error.

"In every crime, especially in the great ones, there exists a third element, preeminently vital. This third element the master plotters have either overlooked or else have not had the genius to construct. They plan with rare cunning to baffle the victim. They plan with vast wisdom, almost genius, to baffle the trailer. But they fail utterly to provide any plan for baffling the punisher. Ergo, their plots are fatally defective and often result in ruin. Hence the vital necessity for providing the third element—the escape *ipso jure*."

Mason arose, walked around the table, and put his hand firmly on Samuel Walcott's shoulder. "This must be done tomorrow night," he continued; "you must arrange your business matters tomorrow and announce that you are going on a yacht cruise, by order of your physician, and may not return for some weeks. You must prepare your yacht for a voyage, instruct your men to touch at a certain point on Staten Island, and wait until six o'clock day after tomorrow morning. If you do not come aboard by that time, they are to go to one of the South American ports and remain until further orders. By this means your absence for an indefinite period will be explained. You will go to Nina San Croix in the disguise which you have always used, and from her to the yacht, and by this means step out of your real status and back into it without leaving traces. I will come here tomorrow evening and furnish you with everything that you shall need and give you full and exact instructions in every particular. These details you must execute with the greatest care, as they will be vitally essential to the success of my plan."

Through it all Walcott had been silent and motionless. Now he arose, and in his face there must have been some premonition of protest, for Mason stepped back and put out his hand. "Sir," he said, with brutal emphasis, "not a word. Remember that you are only the hand, and the hand does not think." Then he turned around abruptly and went out of the house.

III

The place which Samuel Walcott had selected for the residence of Nina San Croix was far up in a northern suburb of New York. The place was very old. The lawn was large and ill-kept; the house, a square old-fashioned brick, was set far back from the street and partly hidden by trees. Around it all was a rusty iron fence. The place had the air of genteel ruin, such as one finds in the Virginias.

On a Thursday of November, about three o'clock in the afternoon, a little man, driving a dray, stopped in the alley at the rear of the house. As he opened the back gate an old Negro woman came down the steps from the kitchen and demanded to know what he wanted. The drayman asked if the lady of the house was in. The old Negro answered that she was asleep at this hour and could not be seen.

"That is good," said the little man; "now there won't be any row. I brought up some cases of wine which she ordered from our house last week and which the boss told me to deliver at once, but I forgot it until today. Just let me put it in the cellar now, Auntie, and don't say a word to the lady about it and she won't ever know that it was not brought up on time."

The drayman stopped, fished a silver dollar out of his pocket, and gave it to the old Negro. "There now, Auntie," he said, "my job depends upon the lady not knowing about this wine; keep it mum."

"Dat's all right, honey," said the old servant, beaming like a May morning. "De cellar door is open, carry it all in and put it in de back part and nobody ain't never going to know how long it has been in dar."

The old Negro went back into the kitchen and the little man began to unload the dray. He carried in five wine cases and stowed them away in the back part of the cellar as the old woman had directed. Then, after having satisfied himself that no one was watching, he took from the dray two heavy paper sacks, presumably filled with flour, and a little bundle wrapped in an old newspaper; these he carefully hid behind the wine cases in the cellar. After a while he closed the door, climbed on his dray, and drove off down the alley.

About eight o'clock in the evening of the same day a Mexican sailor dodged in the front gate and slipped down to the side of the house. He stopped by the window and tapped on it with his finger. In a moment a woman opened the door. She was tall, lithe, and splendidly proportioned, with a dark Spanish face and straight hair. The man stepped inside. The woman bolted the door and turned round.

"Ah," she said, smiling, "it is you, Señor? How good of you."

The man started. "Whom else did you expect?" he said quickly.

"Oh!" laughed the woman, "perhaps the archbishop."

"Nina!" said the man, in a broken voice that expressed love, humility, and reproach. His face was white under the black sunburn.

For a moment the woman wavered. A shadow flitted over her eyes, then she stepped back. "No," she said, "not yet."

The man walked across to the fire, sank down in a chair, and covered his face with his hands. The woman stepped up noiselessly behind him and leaned over the chair. The man was either in great agony or else he was a superb actor, for the muscles of his neck twitched violently and his shoulders trembled.

"Oh," he muttered, as though echoing his thoughts, "I can't do it, I can't!"

The woman caught the words and leaped up as though some one had struck her in the face. She threw back her head. Her nostrils dilated and her eyes flashed.

"You can't do it!" she cried. "Then you do love her! You shall do it! Do you hear me? You shall do it! You killed him! You got rid of him! But you shall not get rid of me. I have the evidence, all of it. The archbishop will have it tomorrow. They shall hang you! Do you hear me? They shall hang you!"

The woman's voice rose, it was loud and shrill. The man turned slowly round without looking up, and stretched out his arms toward the woman. She stopped and looked down at him. The fire glittered for a moment and then died out of her eyes, her bosom heaved and her lips began to tremble. With a cry she flung herself into his arms, caught him around the neck, and pressed his face up against her cheek.

"Oh! Dick, Dick," she sobbed, "I do love you so! I can't live without you! Not another hour, Dick! I do want you so much, so much, Dick!"

The man shifted his right arm quickly, slipped a great Mexican knife out of his sleeve, and passed his fingers slowly up the woman's side until he felt the heart beat under his hand, then he raised the knife, gripped the handle tight, and drove the keen blade into the woman's bosom. The hot blood gushed out over his arm and down on his leg. The body, warm and limp, slipped down in his arms. The man got up, pulled out the knife, and thrust it into a sheath at his belt, unbuttoned the dress, and slipped it off of the body. As he did this a bundle of papers dropped upon the floor; these he glanced at hastily and put into his pocket. Then he took the dead woman up in his arms, went out into the hall, and started to go up the stairway. The body was relaxed and heavy, and for that reason difficult to carry. He doubled it up into an awful heap, with the knees against the chin, and walked slowly and heavily up the stairs and out into the bath-room. There he laid the corpse down on the tiled floor. Then he opened the window, closed the shutters, and lighted the gas. The bath-room was small and contained an ordinary steel tub, porcelain-lined, standing near the window and raised about six inches above the floor. The sailor went over to the tub, pried up the metal rim of the outlet with his knife, removed it, and fitted into its place a porcelain disk which he took from his pocket; to this disk was attached a long platinum wire, the end of which he fastened on the outside of the tub. After he had done this he went back to the body, stripped off its clothing, put it down in the tub, and began to dismember it with the great Mexican knife. The knife was strong and sharp as a razor. The man worked rapidly and with the greatest care.

When he had finally cut the body into as small pieces as possible, he replaced the knife in its sheath, washed his hands, and went out of the bathroom and downstairs to the lower hall. The sailor seemed perfectly familiar with the house. By a side door he passed into the cellar. There he lighted the gas, opened one of the wine cases, and taking up all the bottles that he could conveniently carry, returned to the bath-room. There he poured the contents into the tub on the dismembered body and then returned to the cellar with the empty bottles, which he replaced in the wine cases. This he continued to do until all the cases but one were emptied and the bathtub was more than half full of liquid. The liquid was sulfuric acid.

When the sailor returned to the cellar with the last empty wine bottles, he opened the fifth case, which really contained wine, took some of it out, and poured a little into each of the empty bottles in order to remove any possible odor of the sulfuric acid. Then he turned out the gas and brought up to the bath-room with him the two paper flour sacks and the little heavy bundle. These sacks were filled with nitrate of soda. He set them down by the door, opened the little bundle, and took out two long rubber tubes, each attached to a heavy gas burner, not unlike the ordinary burners of a small gas-stove. He fastened the tubes to two of the gas jets, put the burners under the tub, turned the gas on full, and lighted it. Then he threw into the tub the woman's clothing and the papers which he had found on her body, after which he took up the two heavy sacks of nitrate of soda and dropped them carefully into the sulfuric acid. When he had done this he went quickly out of the bath-room and closed the door.

The deadly acids at once attacked the body and began to destroy it; as the heat increased, the acids boiled and the destructive process was rapid and awful. From time to time the sailor opened the door of the bath-room cautiously and, holding a wet towel over his mouth and nose, looked in at his horrible work. At the end of a few hours there was only a swimming mass in the tub. When the man looked at four o'clock, it was all a thick, murky liquid. He turned off the gas quickly and stepped back out of the room. For perhaps half an hour he waited in the hall; finally, when the acids had cooled so that they no longer gave off fumes, he opened the door and went in, took hold of the platinum wire and, pulling the porcelain disk from the stop-cock, allowed the awful contents of the tub to run out. Then he turned on the hot water, rinsed the tub clean, and replaced the metal outlet. Removing the rubber tubes, he cut them into pieces, broke the porcelain disk, and rolling up the platinum wire, washed it all down the sewer pipe.

The fumes had escaped through the open window; this he now closed and set himself to putting the bath-room in order, and effectually removing every trace of his night's work. The sailor moved around with the very greatest degree of care. Finally, when he had arranged everything to his complete satisfaction, he picked up the two burners, turned out the gas, and left the bath-room, closing the door after him. From the bath-room he went directly to the attic, concealed the two rusty burners under a heap of rubbish, and then walked carefully and noiselessly down the stairs and the lower hall. As he opened the door and stepped into the room where he had killed the woman, two police officers sprang out and seized him. The man screamed like a wild beast taken in a trap, and sank down.

"Oh! oh!" he cried, "it was no use! It was no use to do it!" Then he recovered himself in a manner and was silent. The officers handcuffed him, summoned the patrol, and took him at once to the station-house. There he said he was a Mexican sailor and that his name was Victor Ancona; but he would say nothing further. The following morning he sent for Randolph Mason and the two were long together.

IV

The obscure defendant charged with murder has little reason to complain of the law's delays. The morning following the arrest of Victor Ancona, the newspapers published long sensational articles, denounced him as a fiend, and convicted him. The grand jury, as it happened, was in session. The preliminaries were soon arranged and the case was railroaded into trial. The indictment contained a great many counts and charged the prisoner with the murder of Nina San Croix by striking, stabbing, choking, poisoning, and so forth.

The trial had continued for three days and had appeared so overwhelmingly one-sided that the spectators who were crowded into the courtroom had grown to be violent and bitter partisans, to such an extent that the police watched them closely. The attorneys for the People were dramatic and denunciatory and forced their case with arrogant confidence. Mason, as counsel for the prisoner, was indifferent and listless. Throughout the entire trial he had sat almost motionless at the table, his gaunt form bent over, his long legs drawn up under his chair, and his weary, heavy-muscled face, with its restless eyes, fixed and staring out over the heads of the jury, was like a tragic mask. The bar, and even the judge, believed that the prisoner's counsel had abandoned his case.

The evidence was all in and the People rested. It had been shown that Nina San Croix had resided for many years in the house in which the prisoner was arrested; that she had lived by herself, with no other companion than an old Negro servant; that her past was unknown, and that she received no visitors, save the Mexican sailor, who came to her house at long intervals. Nothing whatever was shown tending to explain who the prisoner was or whence he had come. It was shown that on Tuesday preceding the killing the archbishop had received a communication from Nina San Croix, in which she said she desired to make a statement of the greatest import, and asking for an audience. To this the archbishop replied that he would willingly grant her a hearing if she would come to him at eleven o'clock on Friday morning. Two policemen testified that about eight o'clock on the night of Thursday they had noticed the prisoner slip into the gate of Nina San Croix's residence and go down to the side of the house, where he was admitted; that his appearance and seeming haste had attracted their attention; that they had concluded that it was some clandestine amour, and out of curiosity had both slipped down to the house and endeavored to find a position from which they could see into the room, but were unable to do so and were about to go back to the street when they heard a woman's voice cry out in great anger: "I know that you love her and that you want to get rid of me, but you shall not do it! You murdered him, but you shall not murder me! I have all the evidence to convict you of murdering him! The archbishop will have it tomorrow! They shall hang you! Do you hear me? They shall hang you for this murder!" That thereupon one of the policeman proposed that they should break into the house and see what was wrong, but the other had urged that it was only the usual lovers' quarrel and if they should interfere they would find nothing upon which a charge could be based and would only be laughed at by the chief; that they had waited and listened for a time, but hearing nothing further had gone back to the street and contented themselves with keeping a strict watch on the house.

The People proved further, that on Thursday evening Nina San Croix had given the old Negro domestic a sum of money and dismissed her, with the instruction that she was not to return until sent for. The old woman testified that she had gone directly to the house of her son, and later had discovered that she had forgotten some articles of clothing which she needed; that thereupon she had returned to the house and had gone up the back way to her room—this was about eight o'clock; that while there she had heard Nina San Croix's voice in great passion and remembered that she had used the words stated by the policeman; that these sudden, violent cries had frightened her greatly and she had bolted the door and been afraid to leave the room; shortly thereafter, she had heard heavy footsteps ascending the stairs, slowly and with great difficulty, as though someone were carrying a heavy burden; that therefore her fear had increased and that she had put out the light and hidden under the bed. She remembered hearing the footsteps moving about upstairs for many hours, how long she could not tell. Finally, about half-past four in the morning she crept out, opened the door, slipped downstairs, and ran out into the street. There she had found the policemen and requested them to search the house.

The two officers had gone to the house with the woman. She had opened the door and they had just had time to step back into the shadow when the prisoner entered. When arrested, Victor Ancona had screamed with terror and cried out, "It was no use! It was no use to do it!"

The chief of police had come to the house and instituted a careful search. In the room below, from which the cries had come, he found a dress which was identified as belonging to Nina San Croix and which she was wearing when last seen by the domestic, about six o'clock that evening. This dress was covered with blood, and had a slit about two inches long in the left side of the bosom, into which the Mexican knife, found on the prisoner, fitted perfectly. These articles were introduced in evidence, and it was shown that the slit would be exactly over the heart of the wearer, and that such a wound would certainly result in death. There was much blood on one of the chairs and on the floor. There was also blood on the prisoner's coat and the leg of his trousers, and the heavy Mexican knife was also bloody. The blood was shown by the experts to be human blood.

The body of the woman was not found, and the most rigid and tireless search failed to develop the slightest trace of the corpse, or the manner of its disposal. The body of the woman had disappeared as completely as though it had vanished into the air.

When counsel announced that he had closed for the People, the judge turned and looked gravely down at Mason. "Sir," he said, "the evidence for the defense may now be introduced."

Randolph Mason arose slowly and faced the judge.

"If your Honor please," he said, speaking slowly and distinctly, "the defendant has no evidence to offer." He paused while a murmur of astonishment ran over the court-room. "But, if your Honor please," he continued, "I move that the jury be directed to find the prisoner not guilty."

The crowd stirred. The counsel for the People smiled. The judge looked sharply at the speaker over his glasses. "On what ground?" he said curtly.

"On the ground," replied Mason, "that the *corpus delicti* has not been proven."

"Ah!" said the judge, for once losing his judicial gravity.

Mason sat down abruptly. The senior counsel for the prosecution was on his feet in a moment.

"What!" he said. "The gentleman bases his motion on a failure to establish the *corpus delicti*? Does he jest or has he forgotten the evidence? The term '*corpus delicti*' is technical, and means the body of the crime, or the substantial fact that a crime has been committed. Does anyone doubt it in this case? It is true that no one actually saw the prisoner kill the decedent, and that he has so successfully hidden the body that it has not been found, but the powerful chain of circumstances, clear and close-linked, proving motive, the criminal agency, and the criminal act, is overwhelming.

"The victim in this case is on the eve of making a statement that would prove fatal to the prisoner. The night before the statement is to be made he goes to her residence. They quarrel. Her voice is heard, raised high in the greatest passion, denouncing him, and charging that he is a murderer, that she has the evidence and will reveal it, that he shall be hanged and that he shall not be rid of her. Here is the motive for the crime, clear as light. Are not the bloody knife, the bloody dress, the bloody clothes of the prisoner, unimpeachable witnesses to the criminal act? The criminal agency of the prisoner has not the shadow of a possibility to obscure it. His motive is gigantic. The blood on him, and his despair when arrested, cry, 'Murder! murder!' with a thousand tongues.

"Men may lie, but circumstances cannot. The thousand hopes and fears and passions of men may delude, or bias the witness. Yet it is beyond the human mind to conceive that a clear, complete chain of concatenated circumstances can be in error. Hence it is that the greatest jurists have declared that such evidence, being rarely liable to delusion or fraud, is safest and most powerful. The machinery of human justice cannot guard against the remote and improbable doubt. The inference is persistent in the affairs of men. It is the only means by which the human mind reaches the truth. If you forbid the jury to exercise it, you bid them work after first striking off their hands. Rule out the irresistible inference, and the need of justice is come in this land; and you may as well leave the spider to weave his web through the abandoned court-room."

The attorney stopped, looked down at Mason with a pompous

sneer, and retired to his place at the table. The judge sat thoughtful and motionless. The jurymen leaned forward in their seats.

"If your Honor please," said Mason, rising, "this is a matter of law, plain, clear, and so well settled in the State of New York that even counsel for the People should know it. The question before your Honor is simple. If the *corpus delicti*, the body of the crime, has been proven, as required by the laws of the commonwealth, then this case should go to the jury. If not, then it is the duty of this court to direct the jury to find the prisoner not guilty. There is here no room for judicial discretion. Your Honor has but to recall and apply the rigid rule announced by our courts prescribing distinctly how the *corpus delicti* in murder must be proven.

"The prisoner here stands charged with the highest crime. The law demands, first, that the crime, as a fact, be established. The fact that the victim is indeed dead must first be made certain before anyone can be convicted of her killing, because, so long as there remains the remotest doubt as to the death, there can be no certainty as to the criminal agent, although the circumstantial evidence indicating the guilt of the accused may be positive, complete, and utterly irresistible. In murder, the *corpus delicti*, or body of the crime, is composed of two elements:

"Death, as a result.

"The criminal agency of another as the means.

"It is the fixed and immutable law of this state, laid down in the leading case of Ruloff v. The People, and binding upon this court, that both components of the *corpus delicti* shall not be established by circumstantial evidence. There must be direct proof of one or the other of the these two component elements of the *corpus delicti*. If one is proven by direct evidence, the other may be presumed; but both shall not be presumed from circumstances, no matter how powerful, how cogent, or how completely overwhelming the circumstances may be. In other words no man can be convicted of murder in the State of New York, unless the body of the victim be found and identified, or there be direct proof that the prisoner did some act adequate to produce death, and did it in such a manner as to account for the disappearance of the body."

The face of the judge cleared and grew hard. The members of the bar were attentive and alert; they were beginning to see the legal escape open up. The audience were puzzled; they did not yet understand. Mason turned to the counsel for the People. His ugly face was bitter with contempt.

"For three days," he said, "I have been tortured by this useless and expensive farce. If counsel for the People had been other than play-actors, they would have known in the beginning that Victor Ancona could not be convicted for murder, unless he were confronted in this courtroom with a living witness, who had looked into the dead face of Nina San Croix; or, if not that, a living witness who had seen him drive the dagger into her bosom.

"I care not if the circumstantial evidence in this case were so strong and irresistible as to be overpowering; if the judge on the bench, if the jury, if every man within sound of my voice, were convinced of the guilt of the prisoner to the degree of certainty that is absolute; if the circumstantial evidence left in the mind no shadow of the remotest improbable doubt; yet, in the absence of the eyewitnesses, this prisoner cannot be punished, and this court must compel the jury to acquit him."

The audience now understood, and they were dumfounded. Surely this was not the law. They had been taught that the law was common sense, and this—this was anything else.

Mason saw it all, and grinned. "In its tenderness," he sneered, "the law shields the innocent. The good law of New York reaches out its hand and lifts the prisoner out of the clutches of the fierce jury that would hang him."

Mason sat down. The room was silent. The jurymen looked at each other in amazement. The counsel for the People arose. His face was white with anger, and incredulous.

"Your Honor," he said, "this doctrine is monstrous. Can it be said that, in order to evade punishment, the murderer has only to hide or destroy the body of the victim or sink it into the sea? Then, if he is not seen to kill, the law is powerless and the murderer can snap his finger in the face of re-tributive justice. If this is the law, then the law for the highest crime is a dead letter. The great commonwealth winks at murder and invites every man to kill his enemy, provided he kill him in secret and hide him. I repeat, your Honor"—the man's voice was now loud and angry and rang through the court-room—"that this doctrine is monstrous!"

"So said Best, and Story, and many another," muttered Mason, "and the law remained."

"The court," said the judge, abruptly, "desires no further argument."

The counsel for the People resumed his seat. His face lighted up with triumph. The court was going to sustain him.

The judge turned and looked down at the jury. He was grave, and spoke with deliberate emphasis.

"Gentlemen of the jury," he said, "the rule of Lord Hale obtains in this state and is binding upon me. It is the law as stated by counsel for the prisoner: that to warrant conviction of murder there must be direct proof either of the death, as of the finding and identification of the corpse, or of criminal violence adequate to produce death, and exerted in such a manner as to account for the disappearance of the body; and it is only when there is direct proof of the one that the other can be established by circumstantial evidence. This is law, and cannot now be departed from. I do not presume to explain its wisdom. Chief-Justice Johnson has observed, in the leading case, that it may have its probable foundation in the idea that where direct proof is absent as to both the fact of the death and of criminal violence capable of producing death, no evidence can rise to the degree of moral certainty that the individual is dead by criminal intervention, or even lead by direct inference to this result; and that, where the fact of death is not certainly ascertained, all inculpatory circumstantial evidence wants the key necessary for its satisfactory interpretation, and cannot be depended on to furnish more than probable results. It may be, also, that such a rule has some reference to the dangerous possibility that a general preconception of guilt, or a general excitement of popular feeling, may creep in to supply the place of evidence, if, upon other than direct proof of death or a cause of death, a jury are permitted to pronounce a prisoner guilty.

"In this case the body has not been found and there is no direct proof of criminal agency on the part of the prisoner, although the chain of circumstantial evidence is complete and irresistible in the highest degree. Nevertheless, it is all circumstantial evidence, and under the laws of New York the prisoner cannot be punished. I have no right of discretion. The law does not permit a conviction in this case, although every one of us may be morally certain of the prisoner's guilt. I am, therefore, gentlemen of the jury, compelled to direct you to find the prisoner not guilty."

"Judge," interrupted the foreman, jumping up in the box, "we cannot find the verdict under our oath; we know that this man is guilty."

"Sir," said the judge, "this is matter of law in which the wishes of the jury cannot be considered. The clerk will write a verdict of not guilty, which you, as foreman, will sign."

The spectators broke out into a threatening murmur that began to grow and gather volume. The judge rapped on his desk and ordered the bailiffs promptly to suppress any demonstration on the part of the audience. Then he directed the foreman to sign the verdict prepared by the clerk. When this was done he turned to Victor Ancona; his face was hard and there was a cold glitter in his eyes.

"Prisoner at the bar," he said, "you have been put to trail before this tribunal on a charge of cold-blooded and atrocious murder. The evidence produced against you was of such powerful and overwhelming character that it seems to have left no doubt in the minds of the jury, nor indeed in the mind of any person present in this court-room.

"Had the question of your guilt been submitted to these twelve arbiters, a conviction would certainly have resulted and the death penalty would have been imposed. But the law, rigid, passionless, even-eyed, has thrust in between you and the wrath of your fellows and saved you from it. I do not cry out against the impotency of the law; it is perhaps as wise as imperfect humanity could make it. I deplore, rather, the genius of evil men who, by cunning design, are enabled to slip through the fingers of this law. I have no word of censure or admonition for you, Victor Ancona. The law of New York compels me to acquit you. I am only its mouthpiece, with my individual wishes throttled. I speak only those things which the law directs I shall speak.

"You are now at liberty to leave this court-room, not guiltless of the crime of murder, perhaps, but at least rid of its punishment. The eyes of men may see Cains' mark on your brow, but the eyes of the law are blind to it."

When the audience fully realized what the judge had said they were amazed and silent. They know as well as men could know that Victor Ancona was guilty of murder, and yet he was now going out of the courtroom free. Could it happen that the law protected only against the blundering rogue? They had heard always of the boasted completeness of the law which magistrates from time immemorial had labored to perfect, and now when the skillful villain sought to evade it, they saw how weak a thing it was.

V

The wedding march of Lohengrin floated out from the Episcopal Church of St. Mark, clear and sweet, and perhaps heavy with its paradox of warning. The theater of this coming contract before high heaven was a wilderness of roses worth the taxes of a country. The high caste of Manhattan, by the grace of the check-book, were present, clothed in Parisian purple and fine linen, cunningly and marvelously wrought.

Over in her private pew, ablaze with jewels and decked with fabrics from the deft hand of many a weaver, sat Mrs. Miriam Steuvisant as imperious and self-complacent as a queen. To her it was all a kind of triumphal procession, proclaiming her ability as a general. With her were a choice few of the *genus homo*, which obtains at the five-o'clock teas, instituted, say the sages, for the purpose of sprinkling the holy water of Lethe.

"Czarina," whispered Reggie Du Puyster, leaning forward, "I salute you. The ceremony *sub jugum* is superb."

"Walcott is an excellent fellow," answered Mrs. Steuvisant, "not a vice, you know, Reggie."

"Aye, Empress," put in the other, "a purist taken in the net. The clean-skirted one has come to the altar. *Vive la vertu!*"

Samuel Walcott, still sunburned from his cruise, stood before the chancel with the only daughter of the blue-blooded St. Clairs. His face was clear and honest and his voice firm. This was life and not romance. The lid of the sepulcher had closed and he had slipped from under it. And now, and ever after, the hand red with murder was clean as any.

The minister raised his voice, proclaiming the holy union before God, and this twain, half pure, half foul, now by divine ordinance one flesh, bowed down before it. No blood cried from the ground. The sunlight of high noon streamed down through the windowpanes like a benediction.

Back in the pew of Mrs. Miriam Steuvisant, Reggie Du Puyster turned down his thumb. "Habet!" he said.

The Benefit of the Doubt
Jack London

I

Carter Watson, a current magazine under his arm, strolled slowly along, gazing about him curiously. Twenty years had elapsed since he had been on this particular street, and the changes were great and stupefying. This Western city of three hundred thousand souls had contained but thirty thousand, when, as a boy, he had been wont to ramble along its streets. In those days the street he was now on had been a quiet residence street in the respectable working-class quarter. On this late afternoon he found that it had been submerged by a vast and vicious tenderloin. Chinese and Japanese shops and dens abounded, all confusedly intermingled with low white resorts and boozing kens. This quiet street of his youth had become the toughest quarter of the city.

He looked at his watch. It was half-past five. It was the slack time of the day in such a region, as he well knew, yet he was curious to see. In all his score of years of wandering and studying social conditions over the world, he had carried with him the memory of his old town as a sweet and wholesome place. The metamorphosis he now beheld was startling. He certainly must continue his stroll and glimpse the infamy to which his town had descended.

Another thing: Carter Watson had a keen social and civic consciousness. Independently wealthy, he had been loath to dissipate his energies in the pink teas and freak dinners of society, while actresses, race-horses, and kindred diversions had left him cold. He had the ethical bee in his bonnet and was a reformer of no mean pretension, though his work had been mainly in the line of contributions to the heavier reviews and quarterlies and to the publication over his name of brightly, cleverly written books on the working classes and the slum-dwellers. Among the twenty-seven to his credit occurred titles such as, "If Christ Came to New Orleans," "The Worked-out Worker," "Tenement Reform in Berlin," "The Rural Slums of England," "The People of the East Side," "Reform Versus Revolution," "The University Settlement as a Hot Bed of Radicalism" and "The Cave Man of Civilization."

But Carter Watson was neither morbid nor fanatic. He did not lose his head over the horrors he encountered, studied, and exposed. No hair-brained enthusiasm branded him. His humor saved him, as did his wide experience and his conservative philosophic temperament. Nor did he have any patience with lightning change reform theories. As he saw it, society would grow better only through the painfully slow and arduously painful processes of evolution. There were no short cuts, no sudden regenerations. The betterment of mankind must be worked out in agony and misery just as all past social betterments had been worked out.

But on this late summer afternoon, Carter Wilson was curious. As he moved along he paused before a gaudy drinking place. The sign above read, "The Vendome." There were two entrances. One evidently led to the bar. This he did not explore. The other was a narrow hallway. Passing through this he found himself in a huge room, filled with chair-encircled tables and quite deserted. In the dim light he made out a piano in the distance. Making a mental note that he would come back some time and study the class of persons that must sit and drink at those multitudinous tables, he proceeded to circumnavigate the room.

Now, at the rear, a short hallway led off to a small kitchen, and here, at a table, alone, sat Patsy Horan, proprietor of the Vendome, consuming a hasty supper ere the evening rush of business. Also, Patsy Horan was angry with the world. He had got out of the wrong side of bed that morning, and nothing had gone right all day. Had his barkeepers been asked, they would have described his mental condition as a grouch. But Carter Watson did not know this. As he passed the little hallway, Patsy Horan's sullen eyes lighted on the magazine he carried under his arm. Patsy did not know Carter Wilson, nor did he know that what he carried under his arm was a magazine. Patsy, out of the depths of his grouch, decided that this stranger was one of those pests who marred and scarred the halls of his back rooms by tacking up or pasting up advertisements. The color on the front cover of the magazine convinced him that it was such an advertisement. Thus the trouble began. Knife and fork in hand, Patsy leaped for Carter Watson.

"Out wid yeh!" Patsy replied. "I know yer game!"

Carter Watson was startled. The man had come upon him like the eruption of a jack-in-the-box.

"A defacin' me walls," cried Patsy, at the same time emitting a string of vivid and vile, rather than virile, epithets of opprobrium.

"If I have given any offense I did not mean to—"

But that was as far as the visitor got. Patsy interrupted.

"Get out wid yeh; yeh talk too much wid yer mouth," quoted Patsy, emphasizing his remarks with flourishes of the knife and fork.

Carter Watson caught a quick vision of that eating-fork inserted uncomfortably between his ribs, knew that it would be rash to talk further with his mouth, and promptly turned to go. The sight of his meekly retreating back must have further enraged Patsy Horan, for that worthy, dropping the table implements, sprang upon him.

Patsy weighed one hundred and eighty pounds. So did Watson. In this they were equal. But Patsy was a rushing, rough-and-tumble saloon-fighter, while Watson was a boxer. In this the latter had the advantage, for Patsy came in wide open, swinging his right in a perilous sweep. All

Watson had to do was to straight-left him an escape. But Watson had another advantage. His boxing, and his experience in the slums and ghettos of the world, had taught him restraint.

He pivoted on his feet, and, instead of striking, ducked the other's winging blow and went into a clinch. But Patsy, charging like a bull, had the momentum of his rush, while Watson, whirling to meet him, had no momentum. As a result, the pair of them went down, with all their three hundred and sixty pounds of weight, in a long crashing fall, Watson underneath. He lay with his head touching the rear wall of the large room. The street was a hundred and fifty feet away, and he did some quick thinking. His first thought was to avoid trouble. He had no wish to get into the papers of this, his childhood town, where many of his relatives and family friends still lived.

So it was that he locked his arms around the man on top of him, held him close, and waited for the help to come that must come in response to the crash of the fall. The help came—that is, six men ran in from the bar and formed about in a semi-circle.

"Take him off, fellows," Watson said. "I haven't struck him, and I don't want any fight."

But the semi-circle remained silent. Watson held on and waited. Patsy, after various vain efforts to inflict damage, made an overture.

"Leggo o' me an' I'll get off o' yeh," said he.

Watson let go, but when Patsy scrambled to his feet he stood over his recumbent foe, ready to strike.

"Get up," Patsy commanded.

His voice was stern and implacable, like the voice of God calling to judgment, and Watson knew there was no mercy there.

"Stand back and I'll get up," he countered.

"If yer a gentleman, get up," quoth Patsy, his pale blue eyes aflame with wrath, his fist ready for a crushing blow.

At the same moment he drew his foot back to kick the other in the face. Watson blocked the kick with his crossed arms and sprang to his feet so quickly that he was in a clinch with his antagonist before the latter could strike. Holding him, Watson spoke to the onlookers:

"Take him away from me, fellows. You see I am not striking him. I don't want to fight. I want to get out of here."

The circle did not move nor speak. Its silence was ominous and sent a chill to Watson's heart. Patsy made an effort to throw him, which culminated in his putting Patsy on his back. Tearing loose from him, Watson sprang to his feet and made for the door. But the circle of men was interposed like a wall. He noticed the white, pasty faces, the kind that never see the sun, and knew that the men who barred his way were the night prowlers and preying beasts of the city jungle. By them he was thrust back upon the pursuing, bull-rushing Patsy.

Again it was a clinch, in which, in momentary safety, Watson appealed to the gang. And again his words fell on deaf ears. Then it was that he knew fear. For he had known of many similar situations, in low dens like this, when solitary men were manhandled, their ribs and features caved in, themselves beaten and kicked to death. And he knew, further, that if he were to escape he must neither strike his assailant nor any of the men who opposed him.

Yet in him was righteous indignation. Under no circumstances could seven to one be fair. Also, he was angry, and there stirred in him the fighting beast that is in all men. But he remembered his wife and children, his unfinished book, the ten thousand rolling acres of the up-country ranch he loved so well. He even saw in flashing visions the blue of the sky, the golden sun pouring down on his flower-spangled meadows, the lazy cattle knee-deep in the brooks, and the flash of trout in the riffles. Life was good—too good for him to risk it for a moment's sway of the beast. In short, Carter Watson was cool and scared.

His opponent, locked by his masterly clinch, was striving to throw him. Again Watson put him on the floor, broke away, and was thrust back by the pasty-faced circle to duck Patsy's swinging right and effect another clinch. This happened many times. And Watson grew even cooler, while the baffled Patsy, unable to inflict punishment, raged wildly and more wildly. He took to batting with his head in the clinches. The first time, he landed his forehead flush on Watson's nose. After that, the latter, in the clinches, buried his face in Patsy's breast. But the enraged Patsy batted on, striking his own eye and nose and cheek on the top of the other's head. The more he was thus injured, the more and the harder did Patsy bat.

This one-sided contest continued for twelve or fifteen minutes. Watson never struck a blow, and strove only to escape. Sometimes, in the free moments, circling about among the tables as he tried to win the door, the pasty-faced men gripped his coat-tails and flung him back at the winging right of the on-rushing Patsy. Time upon time, and times without end, he clinched and put Patsy on his back, each time first whirling him around and putting him down in the direction of the door and gaining toward that goal by the length of the fall.

In the end, hatless, dishevelled, with streaming nose and one eye closed, Watson won to the sidewalk and into the arms of a policeman.

"Arrest that man," Watson panted.

"Hello, Patsy," said the policeman. "What's the mix-up?"

"Hello, Charley," was the answer. "This guy comes in—"

"Arrest that man, officer," Watson repeated.

"G'wan! Beat it!" said Patsy.

"Beat it!" added the policeman. "If you don't I'll pull you in."

"Not unless you arrest that man. He has committed a violent and unprovoked assault on me."

"Is it so, Patsy?" was the officer's query.

"Nah. Lemme tell you, Charley, an' I got the witnesses to prove it, so help me God. I was settin' in me kitchen eatin' a bowl of soup, when this guy comes in an' gets gay wid me. I never seen him in me born days before. He was drunk—"

"Look at me, officer," protested the indignant sociologist. "Am I drunk?"

The officer looked at him with sullen, menacing eyes and nodded to Patsy to continue.

"This guy gets gay wid me. 'I'm Tim McGrath,' says he, 'an' I can

do the like to you,' says he. 'Put up yer hands.' I smiles, an' wid that, biff
biff, he lands me twice an' spills me soup. Look at me eye. I'm fair murdered."

"What are you going to do officer?" Watson demanded.

"Go on, beat it," was the answer, "or I'll pull you sure."

Then the civic righteousness of Carter Watson flamed up.

"Mr. Officer, I protest—"But at that moment the policeman grabbed
his arm with a savage jerk that nearly overthrew him.

"Come on, you're pulled."

"Arrest him, too," Watson demanded.

"Nix on that play," was the reply. "What did you assault him for,
him a peacefully eatin' his soup?"

II

Carter Watson was genuinely angry. Not only had he been wantonly assaulted, badly battered, and arrested, but the morning papers without exception came out with lurid accounts of his drunken brawl with the
proprietor of the notorious Vendome. Not one accurate or truthful line was
published. Patsy Horan and his satellites described the battle in detail. The
one incontestible thing was that Carter Watson had been drunk. Thrice he
had been thrown out of the place and into the gutter, and thrice he had come
back, breathing blood and fire and announcing that he was going to clean
out the place. **"EMINENT SOCIOLOGIST JAGGED AND
JUGGED,"** was the first head-line he read, on the front page, accompanied by a large portrait of himself. Other headlines were: **"CARTER
WATSON ASPIRED TO CHAMPIONSHIP HONORS";
"CARTER WATSON GETS HIS"; "NOTED SOCIOLOGIST
ATTEMPTS TO CLEAN OUT A TENDERLOIN CAFE";** and
**"CARTER WATSON KNOCKED OUT BY PATSY HORAN IN
THREE ROUNDS."**

At the police court, next morning, under bail, appeared Carter
Watson to answer the complaint of the People Versus Carter Watson for the
latter's assault and battery on one Patsy Horan. But first, the Prosecuting
Attorney, who was paid to prosecute all offenders against the People, drew
him aside and talked with him privately.

"Why not let it drop?" said the Prosecuting Attorney. "I tell you
what you do, Mr. Watson: Shake hands with Mr. Horan and make it up,
and we'll drop the case right here. A word to the Judge, and the case
against you will be dismissed."

"But I don't want it dismissed," was the answer. "Your office being what it is, you should be prosecuting me instead of asking me to make
up with this—this fellow."

"Oh, I'll prosecute you all right," retorted the Prosecuting Attorney.

"Also you will have to prosecute this Patsy Horan," Watson advised; "for I shall now have him arrested for assault and battery."

"You'd better shake and make up," the Prosecuting Attorney repeated, and this time there was almost a threat in his voice.

The trials of both men were set for a week later, on the same morning, in police Judge Witberg's court.

"You have no chance," Watson was told by an old friend of his boyhood, the retired manager of the biggest paper in the city. "Everybody knows you were beaten up by this man. His reputation is most unsavory. But it won't help you in the least. Both cases will be dismissed. This will be because you are you. Any ordinary man would be convicted."

"But I do not understand," objected the perplexed sociologist. "Without warning I was attacked by this man and badly beaten. I did not strike a blow. I—"

"That has nothing to do with it," the other cut him off.

"Then what is there that has anything to do with it?"

"I'll tell you. You are now up against the local police and political machine. Who are you? You are not even a legal resident in this town. You live up in the country. You haven't a vote of your own here. Much less do you swing any votes. This dive proprietor swings a string of votes in his precinct—a mighty long string."

"Do you mean to tell me that this Judge Witberg will violate the sacredness of his office and oath by letting this brute off?" Watson demanded.

"Watch him," was the grim reply. "Oh, he'll do it nicely enough. He will give an extra-legal, extra-judicial decision, abounding in every word in the dictionary that stands for fairness and right."

"But there are the newspapers," Watson cried.

"They are not fighting the administration at present. They'll give it to you hard. You see what they have already done to you."

"Then these snips of boys on the police detail won't write the truth?"

"They will write something so near like the truth that the public will believe it. They write their stories under instruction, you know. They have their orders to twist and color, and there won't be much left of you when they get done. Better drop the whole thing right now. You are in bad."

"But the trails are set."

"Give the word and they'll drop them now. A man can't fight a machine unless he has a machine behind him."

III

But Carter Watson was stubborn. He was convinced that the machine would beat him, but all his days he had sought social experience, and this was certainly something new.

The morning of the trial the Prosecuting Attorney made another attempt to patch up the affair.

"If you feel that way, I should like to get a lawyer to prosecute the case," said Watson.

"No you don't," said the Prosecuting Attorney. "I am paid by the People to prosecute, and prosecute I will. But let me tell you. You have no chance. We shall lump both cases into one, and you watch out."

Judge Witberg looked good to Watson. A fairly young man, short, comfortably stout, smooth-shaven and with an intelligent face, he seemed a very nice man indeed. This good impression was added to by the smiling lips and the wrinkles of laughter in the corners of his black eyes. Looking at him and studying him, Watson felt almost sure that his old friend's prognostication was wrong.

But Watson was soon to learn. Patsy Horan and two of his satellites testified to almost colossal aggregation of perjuries. Watson could not have believed it possible without having experienced it. They denied the existence of the other four men. And of the two that testified, one claimed to have been in the kitchen, a witness to Watson's unprovoked assault on Patsy, while the other, remaining in the bar, had witnessed Watson's second and third rushes into the place as he attempted to annihilate the unoffending Patsy. The vile language ascribed to Watson was so voluminously and unspeakably vile, that he felt they were injuring their own case. It was so impossible that he should utter such things. But when they described the brutal blows he had rained on poor Patsy's face, and the chair he demolished when he vainly attempted to kick Patsy, Watson waxed secretly hilarious and at the same time sad. The trial was a farce, but such lowness of life was depressing to contemplate when he considered the long upward climb humanity must make.

Watson could not recognize himself, nor could his worst enemy have recognized him, in the swashbuckling, rough-housing picture that was painted of him. But, as in all cases of complicated perjury, rifts and contradictions in the various stories appeared. The Judge somehow failed to notice them, while the Prosecuting Attorney and Patsy's attorney shied off from them gracefully. Watson had not bothered to get a lawyer for himself, and he was now glad that he had not.

Still, he retained a semblance of faith in Judge Witberg when he went himself on the stand and started to tell his story.

"I was strolling casually along the street, your Honor," Watson began, but was interrupted by the Judge.

"We are not here to consider your previous actions," bellowed Judge Witberg. "Who struck the first blow?"

"Your Honor," Watson pleaded, "I have no witnesses of the actual fray, and the truth of my story can only be brought out by telling the story fully—"

Again he was interrupted.

"We do not care to publish any magazines here," Judge Witberg roared, looking at him so fiercely and malevolently that Watson could scarcely bring himself to believe that this was the same man he had studied a few minutes previously.

"Who struck the first blow?" Patsy's attorney asked.

The Prosecuting Attorney interposed, demanding to know which of the two cases lumped together this was, and by that right Patsy's lawyer, at that stage of the proceedings, should take the witness. Patsy's attorney fought back. Judge Witberg interfered, professing no knowledge of any two cases being lumped together. All this had to be explained. Battle royal raged terminating in both attorneys apologizing to the Court and to each other. And so it went, and to Watson it had the seeming of a group of pickpockets ruffling and bustling an honest man as they took his purse. The machine was working, that was all.

"Why did you enter this place of unsavory reputation?" was asked him.

"It has been my custom for many years, as a student of economics and sociology, to acquaint myself—"

But this was as far as Watson got.

"We want none of your ologies here," snarled Judge Witberg. "It is a plain question. Answer it plainly. Is it true or not true that you were drunk? That is the gist of the question."

When Watson attempted to hell how Patsy had injured his face in his attempts to bat with his head, Watson was openly scouted and flouted, and Judge Witberg again took him in hand.

"Are you aware of the solemnity of the oath you took to testify to nothing but the truth on this witness stand?" the Judge demanded. "This is a fairy story you are telling. It is not reasonable that a man would so injure himself, and continue to injure himself, by striking the soft and sensitive parts of his face against your head. You are a sensible man. It is unreasonable is it not?"

"Men are unreasonable when they are angry," Watson answered meekly.

Then it was that Judge Witberg was deeply outraged and righteously wrathful.

"What right have you to say that?" he cried. "It is gratuitous. It has no bearing on the case. You are here as a witness, sir, of events that have transpired. The Court does not wish to hear any expressions of opinion from you at all."

"I but answered your question, your Honor," Watson protested humbly.

"You did nothing of the sort," was the next blast. "And let me warn you, sir, let me warn you, that you are laying yourself liable to contempt by such insolence. And I will have you know that we know how to observe the law and the rules of courtesy down here in this little courtroom. I am ashamed of you."

And, while the next punctilious legal wrangle between the attorneys interrupted his tale of what happened in the Vendome, Carter Watson, without bitterness, amused and at the same time sad, saw rise before him the machine, large and small, that dominated his country, the unpunished and shameless grafts of a thousand cities perpetrated by the spidery and vermin-like creatures of the machines. Here it was before him, a courtroom and a judge, bowed down in subservience by the machine to a dive-keeper who swung a string of votes. Petty and sordid as it was, it was one face of the many-faced machine that loomed colossally, in every city and state, in a thousand guises over-shadowing the land.

A familiar phrase rang in his ears: "It is to laugh." At the height of the wrangle, he giggled, once, aloud, and earned a sullen frown from Judge Witberg. Worse, a myriad times, he decided, were these bullying lawyers and this bullying judge than the bucko mates in first quality hellships, who not only did their own bullying but protected themselves as well. These petty rapscallions, on the other hand, sought protection behind the majesty of the law. They struck, but no one was permitted to strike back, for behind them were the prison cells and the clubs of the stupid policemen—paid and professional fighters and beaters-up of men. Yet he was not bitter. The grossness and the sliminess of it was forgotten in the simple grotesqueness of it, and he had the saving sense of humor.

Nevertheless, hectored and heckled though he was, he managed in the end to give a simple, straightforward version of the affair, and, despite a belligerant cross-examination, his story was not shaken in any particular. Quite different it was from the perjuries that had shouted aloud through the stories of Patsy and his two witnesses.

Both Patsy's attorney and the Prosecuting Attorney rested their cases, letting everything go before the Court without argument. Watson protested against this, but was silenced when the Prosecuting Attorney told him that he was the Public Prosecutor and knew his business.

"Patrick Horan has testified that he was in danger of his life and that he was compelled to defend himself," Judge Witberg's verdict began. "Mr. Watson has testified to the same thing. Each has sworn that the other struck the first blow; each has sworn that the other made an unprovoked assault on him. It is an axiom of the law that the defendant should be given the benefit of the doubt. A very reasonable doubt exists. Therefore, in the case of the People Versus Carter Watson the benefit of the doubt is given to said Carter Watson and he is herewith ordered discharged from custody. The same reasoning applies to the case of the People Versus Patrick Horan. He is given the benefit of the doubt and discharged from custody. My recommendation is that both defendants shake hands and make up."

In the afternoon papers the first headline that caught Watson's eye was: **"CARTER WATSON ACQUITTED."** In the second paper it was: **"CARTER WATSON ESCAPES A FINE."** But what capped everything was the one beginning: **"CARTER WATSON A GOOD FELLOW."** In the text he read how Judge Witberg had advised both fighters to shake hands, which they promptly did. Further, he read:

"'Let's have a nip on it,' said Patsy Horan.

"'Sure,' said Carter Watson.

"And, arm in arm, they ambled for the nearest saloon."

IV

Now, from the whole adventure, Watson carried away no bitterness. It was a social experience of a new order, and it led to the writing of another book, which he entitled, **"POLICE COURT PROCEDURE: A TENTATIVE ANALYSIS."**

One summer morning a year later, on his ranch, he left his horse and himself clambered on through a miniature canyon to inspect some rock ferns he had planted the previous winter. Emerging from the upper end of the canyon, he came out on one of his flower-spangled meadows, a delightful isolated spot, screened from the world by low hills and clumps of trees. And here he found a man, evidently on a stroll from the summer hotel down at the little town of a mile away. They met face to face and the recognition was mutual. It was Judge Witberg. Also, it was a clear case of trespass, for Watson had trespass signs upon his boundaries, though he never enforced them.

Judge Witberg held out his hand, which Watson refused to see. "Oh, yes, I see your hand, but I don't care to take it. The papers said I shook hands with Patsy Horan after the trial. You know I didn't, but let me tell you that I'd a thousand times rather shake hands with him and his vile following of curs, than with you."

Judge Witberg was painfully flustered, and as he hemmed and hawed and essayed to speak, Watson, looking at him, was struck by a sudden whim, and he determined on a grim and facetious antic.

"I should scarcely expect any animus from a man of your acquirements and knowledge of the world," the Judge was saying.

"Animus?" Watson replied. "Certainly not. I haven't such a thing in my nature. And to prove it, let me show you something curious, something you have never seen before." Casting about him, Watson picked up a rough stone the size of his fist. "See this. Watch me."

So saying, Carter Watson tapped himself a sharp blow on the cheek. The stone laid the flesh open to the bone and the blood spurted forth.

"The stone was too sharp," he announced to the astounded police judge, who thought he had gone mad. "I must bruise it a trifle. There is nothing like being realistic in such matters."

Whereupon Carter Watson found a smooth stone and with it pounded his cheek nicely several times.

"Ah," he cooed. "That will turn beautifully green and black in a few hours. It will be most convincing."

"You are insane," Judge Witberg quavered.

"Don't use such vile language to me," said Watson. "You see my bruised and bleeding face? You did that, with that right hand of yours. You hit me twice—biff biff. It is a brutal and unprovoked assault. I am in danger of my life. I must protect myself."

Judge Witberg backed away in alarm before the menacing fists of the other.

"If you strike me I'll have you arrested," Judge Witberg threatened.

"That is what I told Patsy," was the answer. "And do you know what he did when I told him that?"

"No."

"That!"

And at the same moment Watson's right fist landed flush on Judge Witberg's nose, putting that legal gentleman over on his back on the grass.

"Get up!" commanded Watson. "If you are a gentleman, get up— that's what Patsy told me, you know."

Judge Witberg declined to rise, and was dragged to his feet by the coat-collar, only to have one eye blacked and be put on his back again. After that it was a red Indian massacre. Judge Witberg was humanely and scientifically beaten up. His cheeks were boxed, his ears cuffed, and his face was rubbed in the turf. And all the time Watson exposited the way Patsy Horan had done it. Occasionally, and very carefully, the facetious sociologist administered a real bruising blow. Once, dragging the poor Judge to his feet, he deliberately bumped his own nose on the gentleman's head. The nose promptly bled.

"See that!" cried Watson, stepping back and deftly shedding his blood all down his own shirt front. "You did it. With your fist you did it. It is awful. I am fair murdered. I must again defend myself."

And once more Judge Witberg impacted his features on a fist and was sent to grass.

"I will have you arrested," he sobbed as he lay.

"That's what Patsy said."

"A brutal—sniff, sniff,—and unprovoked—sniff, sniff—assault."

"That's what Patsy said."

"I will surely have you arrested."

"Speaking slangily, not if I can beat you to it."

And with that, Carter Watson departed down the canyon, mounted his horse, and rode to town.

An hour later, as Judge Witberg limped up the grounds to his hotel, he was arrested by a village constable on a charge of assault and battery preferred by Carter Watson.

V

"Your Honor," Watson said next day to the village Justice, a well to do farmer and graduate, thirty years before, from a cow college, "since this Sol Witberg has seen fit to charge me with battery, following upon my charge of battery against him, I would suggest that both cases be lumped together. The testimony and the facts are the same in both cases.

To this the Justice agreed, and the double case proceeded. Watson, as prosecuting witness, first took the stand and told his story.

"I was picking flowers," he testified. "Picking flowers on my own land, never dreaming of danger. Suddenly this man rushed upon me from behind the trees. 'I am the Dodo,' he says, 'and I can do you to a frazzle. Put up your hands.' I smiled, but with that, biff biff, he struck me, knocking me down and spilling my flowers. The language he used was frightful. It was an unprovoked and brutal assault. Look at my cheek. Look at my nose. I could not understand it. He must have been drunk. Before I recovered from my surprise he had administered this beating. I was in danger of my life and was compelled to defend myself. That is all, Your Honor, though I must say, in conclusion, that I cannot get over my perplexity. Why did he say he was the Dodo? Why did he so wantonly attack me?"

And thus was Sol Witberg given a liberal education in the art of perjury. Often, from his high seat, he had listened indulgently to police court perjuries in cooked-up cases; but for the first time perjury was directed against him, and he no longer sat above the court, with the bailiffs, the policemen's clubs, and the prison cells behind him.

"Your Honor," he cried, "never have I heard such a pack of lies told by so bare-faced a liar—"

Watson here sprang to his feet.

"Your Honor, I protest. It is for your Honor to decide truth or falsehood. The witness is on the stand to testify to actual events that have transpired. His personal opinion upon things in general, and upon me, has no bearing on the case whatever."

The Justice scratched his head and waxed phlegmatically indignant.

"The point is well taken," he decided. "I am surprised at you, Mr. Witberg, claiming to be a judge and skilled in the practice of the law, and yet being guilty of such unlawyerlike conduct. Your manner, sir, and your methods, remind me of a shyster. This is a simple case of assault and battery. We are here to determine who struck the first blow, and we are not interested in your estimates of Mr. Watson's personal character. Proceed with your story."

Sol Witberg would have bitten his bruised and swollen lip in chagrin had it not hurt so much. But he contained himself and told a simple, straightforward, truthful story.

"Your Honor," Watson said, "I would suggest that you ask him what he was doing on my premises."

"A very good question. What were you doing, sir, on Mr. Watson's premises?"

"I did not know they were his premises."

"It was a trespass, your Honor," Watson cried. "The warnings are posted conspicuously."

"I saw no warnings," said Sol Witberg.

"I have seen them myself," snapped the Justice. "They are very conspicuous. And I would warn you, sir, that if you palter with the truth in such little matters you may darken your more important statements with suspicion. Why did you strike Mr. Watson?"

"Your Honor, as I have testified, I did not strike a blow."

The Justice looked at Carter Watson's bruised and swollen visage, and turned to glare at Sol Witberg.

"Look at that man's cheek!" he thundered. "If you did not strike a blow how comes it that he is so disfigured and injured?"

"As I testified—"

"Be careful," the Justice warned.

"I will be careful, sir. I will say nothing but the turth. He struck himself with a rock. He struck himself with two different rocks."

"Does it stand to reason that a man, any man not a lunatic, would so injure himself, and continue to injure himself, by striking the soft and sensitive parts of his face with a stone?" Carter Watson demanded.

"It sounds like a fairy story," was the Justice's comment. "Mr. Witberg, had you been drinking?"

"No, sir."

"Do you never drink?"

"On occasion."

The Justice meditated on this answer with an air of astute profundity.

Watson took advantage of the opportunity to wink at Sol Witberg, but that much-abused gentleman saw nothing humorous in the situation.

"A very peculiar case, a very peculiar case," the Justice announced, as he began his verdict.

"The evidence of the two parties is flatly contradictory. There are no witnesses outside the two principals. Each claims the other committed the assault, and I have no legal way of determining the truth. But I have my private opinion, Mr. Witberg, and I would recommend that henceforth you keep off of Mr. Watson's premises and keep away from this section of the country—"

"This is an outrage!" Sol Witberg blurted out.

"Sit down, sir!" was the Justice's thundered command. "If you interrupt the Court in this manner again, I shall fine you for contempt. And I warn you I shall fine you heavily—you, a judge yourself, who should be conversant with the courtesy and dignity of courts. I shall now give my verdict.

"It is a rule of law that the defendant shall be given the benefit of the doubt. As I have said, and I repeat, there is no legal way for me to determine who struck the first blow. Therefore, and much to my regret,"—here he paused and glared at Sol Witberg—"in each of these cases I am compelled to give the defendant the benefit of the doubt. Gentlemen, you are both dismissed."

"Let us have a nip on it," Watson said to Witberg, as they left the courtroom; but that outraged person refused to lock arms and amble to the nearest saloon.

Part Two
The Judicial System

5

Finding the Truth

Truth, nowhere, lies yet everywhere in these—
Not absolutely in a portion, yet
Evolvable from the whole.

The Ring and the Book
Robert Browning

When you have eliminated the impossible,
whatever remains, however *improbable*,
must be the truth.

The Sign of Four
Sir Arthur Conan Doyle

Robert Browning's preoccupation with the abstract idea of truth manifests itself in his 21,116 line poem *The Ring and the Book*, which is in the form of a dramatic monologue. Browning believed that although truth may seem different to each of those wrestling to find it, truth *is* ultimately "evolvable" and amounts to something real—it is not only perceived truth.

In the last section we noted that standards and presumptions are incorporated into the law in order to help ensure that no one is convicted of a crime that he or she has not committed. In "The Corpus Delicti," Richard Warren commits a murder, yet the legal system is unable to convict him because the standard of proof required to prove his guilt is not met. We feel that we "know the truth" as we read "The Benefit of the Doubt," but the presumption of innocence and the standard of the benefit of the doubt as applied by that particular judge leads to a faulty perception of the truth. Justice Harlan in a concurring opinion in *In re Winship*, 397 U.S. 358 (1970), states: "I view the requirement of proof beyond a reasonable doubt in a criminal case as bottomed on a fundamental value determination of our society that it is far worse to convict an innocent man than to let a guilty man go free." Yet, if each judicial action or proceeding resulted in the discovery of the ultimate truth, then the legal system would have no need of standards and presumptions, which often allow a guilty person to escape conviction. The guilty person would emerge wearing a sign like the scarlet letter worn by Hester Prynne.

Literary scholars and other readers study the point of view of short stories, novels, plays, movies, and poems, to help them discover the truth of the narratives with which they are presented. In relation to the point of view, we ask: Who is telling the story? Can we trust the narrator? In choosing the point of view, the author controls how much and in what form the "truth" is revealed to the reader. The three most common choices of point of view are:

- **Omniscient.** The reader is let into the minds of all of the characters and knows what they are thinking.

- **Limited Omniscient.** The reader sees into the mind of only one character or into the minds of a select number of characters.

- **Objective.** The characters talk and interact with each other, but the reader is never allowed to know what they are thinking. They may *say* what they are thinking, but we need to evaluate whether or not they are telling the truth.

In the judicial framework, the lawyers, judges, and jury are given only an objective view of the story. They are not privy to the innermost thoughts of the players. Again, it should be stressed that an accused murderer who claims self-defense by saying: "I thought *he* was going to kill *me*" might not necessarily be giving us a truthful picture of his thought process. Each statement has to be weighed and evaluated. To help discover the truth, we observe the speaker's body language, dress, disposition, what others say, what he or she says about others, prior actions, and habits. Yet, even if we detect general character traits in that person, we need to ask: On the occasion in question, did this person step out of character? If so, was the resulting behavior somehow justified or provoked?

"In a Grove," by Ryunosuke Akutagawa, clearly demonstrates the problems involved in discovering the truth. As the woodcutter, the Buddhist priest, the policeman, the old woman, Tajomaru, and the wife tell their stories, the reader—placed in the position of a judge or a member of a jury—strives to reconstruct the facts and glean the truth from the contradictory stories which are told; but even if the reader feels fairly confident that the truth can be determined by the end of the wife's confession, the introduction of the story of the murdered man, as told through a medium, only serves, once again, to change and challenge any perceived "truth" which has so far emerged, leaving the reader further confused and uncertain as to the reliability of the various narrators. Would a judge or jury be able to convict anyone given only the testimony before the reader in this story?

The short story "Story of the Chief of Old Cairo," from *The Arabian Nights*, presents a real twist to the idea of finding the truth by some fair means of judicial process. Is this a story in which God sees the truth, but does not wait?

In a Grove
Ryunosuke Akutagawa

THE TESTIMONY OF A WOODCUTTER QUESTIONED
BY A HIGH POLICE COMMISSIONER

Yes, sir. Certainly, it was I who found the body. This morning, as usual, I went to cut my daily quota of cedars, when I found the body in a grove in a hollow in the mountains. The exact location? About 150 meters off the Yamashina stage road. It's an out-of-the way grove of bamboo and cedars.

The body was lying flat on its back dressed in a bluish silk kimono and a wrinkled head-dress of the Kyoto style. A single sword-stroke had pierced the breast. The fallen bamboo-blades around it were stained with bloody blossoms. No, the blood was no longer running. The wound had dried up, I believe. And also, a gad-fly was stuck fast there, hardly noticing my footsteps.

You ask me if I saw a sword or any such thing?

No, nothing, sir. I found only a rope at the root of a cedar near by. And . . . well, in addition to a rope, I found a comb. That was all. Apparently he must have made a battle of it before he was murdered, because the grass and fallen bamboo-blades had been trampled down all around.

"A horse was near by?"

No, sir. It's hard enough for a man to enter, let alone a horse.

THE TESTIMONY OF A TRAVELING BUDDHIST PRIEST
QUESTIONED BY A HIGH POLICE COMMISSIONER

The time? Certainly, it was about noon yesterday, sir. The unfortunate man was on the road from Sekiyama to Yamashina. He was walking toward Sekiyama with a woman accompanying him on horseback, who I have since learned was his wife. A scarf hanging from her head hid her face from view. All I saw was the color of her clothes, a lilac-colored suit. Her horse was a sorrel with a fine mane. The lady's height? Oh, about four feet five inches. Since I am a Buddhist priest, I took little notice about her details. Well, the man was armed with a sword as well as a bow and arrow. And I remember that he carried some twenty odd arrows in his quiver.

Little did I expect that he would meet such a fate. Truly human life is as evanescent as the morning dew or a flash of lightning. My words are inadequate to express my sympathy for him.

THE TESTIMONY OF A POLICEMAN QUESTIONED BY A HIGH POLICE COMMISSIONER

The man that I arrested? He is a notorious brigand called Tajomaru. When I arrested him, he had fallen off his horse. He was groaning on the bridge at Awataguchi. The time? It was in the early hours of last night. For the record, I might say that the other day I tried to arrest him, but unfortunately he escaped. He was wearing a dark blue silk kimono and a large plain sword. And, as you see, he got a bow and arrows somewhere. You say that this bow and these arrows look like the ones owned by the dead man? Then Tajomaru must be the murderer. The bow wound with leather strips, the black lacquered quiver, the seventeen arrows with hawk feathers —these were all in his possession I believe. Yes, sir, the horse is, as you say, a sorrel with a fine mane. A little beyond the stone bridge I found the horse grazing by the roadside, with his long rein dangling. Surely there is some providence in his having been thrown by the horse.

Of all the robbers prowling around Kyoto, this Tajomaru has given the most grief to the women in town. Last autumn a wife who came to the mountain back of the Pindora of the Toribe Temple, presumably to pay a visit, was murdered, along with a girl. It has been suspected that it was his doing. If this criminal murdered the man, you cannot tell what he may have done with the man's wife. May it please your honor to look into this problem as well.

THE TESTIMONY OF AN OLD WOMAN QUESTIONED BY A HIGH POLICE COMMISSIONER

Yes, sir, that corpse is the man who married my daughter. He does not come from Kyoto. He was a samurai in the town of Kokufu in the province of Wakasa. His name was Kanazawa no Takehiko, and his age was twenty-six. He was of a gentle disposition, so I am sure he did nothing to provoke the anger of others.

My daughter? Her name is Masago, and her age is nineteen. She is a spirited, fun-loving girl, but I am sure she has never known any man except Takehiko. She has a small, oval, dark-complected face with a mole at the corner of her left eye.

Yesterday Takehiko left for Wakasa with my daughter. What bad luck it is that things should have come to such a sad end! What has become of my daughter? I am resigned to giving up my son-in-law as lost, but the fate of my daughter worries me sick. For heaven's sake leave no stone unturned to find her. I hate that robber Tajomaru, or whatever his name is. Not only my son-in-law, but my daughter . . . (Her later words were drowned in tears.)

TAJOMARU'S CONFESSION

I killed him, but not her. Where's she gone? I can't tell. Oh, wait a minute. No torture can make me confess what I don't know. Now things have come to such a head, I won't keep anything from you.

Yesterday a little past noon I met that couple. Just then a puff of wind blew, and raised her hanging scarf, so that I caught a glimpse of her face. Instantly it was again covered from my view. That may have been one reason; she looked like a Bodhisattva. At that moment I made up my mind to capture her even if I had to kill her man.

Why? To me killing isn't a matter of such great consequence as you might think. When a woman is captured, her man has to be killed anyway. In killing, I use the sword I wear at my side. Am I the only one who kills people? You, you don't use your swords. You kill people with your power, with your money. Sometimes you kill them on the pretext of working for their good. It's true they don't bleed. They are in the best of health, but all the same you've killed them. It's hard to say who is a greater sinner, you or me. (An ironical smile.)

But it would be good if I could capture a woman without killing her man. So, I made up my mind to capture her, and do my best not to kill him. But it's out of the question on the Yamashina stage road. So I managed to lure the couple into the mountains.

It was quite easy. I became their travelling companion, and I told them there was an old mound in the mountain over there, and that I had dug it open and found many mirrors and swords. I went on to tell them I'd buried the things in a grove behind the mountain, and that I'd like to sell them at a low price to anyone who would care to have them. Then . . . you see, isn't greed terrible? He was beginning to be moved by my talk before he knew it. In less than half an hour they were driving their horse toward the mountain with me.

When they came in front of the grove, I told them that the treasures were buried in it, and I asked them to come and see. The man had no objection—he was blinded by greed. The woman said she would wait on horseback. It was natural for her to say so, at the sight of a thick grove. To tell you the truth, my plan worked just as I wished, so I went into the grove with him, leaving her behind alone.

The grove is only bamboo for some distance. About fifty yards ahead there's a rather open clump of cedars. It was a convenient spot for my purpose. Pushing my way through the grove, I told him a plausible lie that the treasures were buried under the cedars. When I told him this, he pushed his laborious way toward the slender cedar visible through the grove. After a while the bamboo thinned out, and we came to where a number of cedars grew in a row. As soon as we got there, I seized him from behind. Because he was a trained, sword-bearing warrior, he was quite strong, but he was taken by surprise, so there was no help for him. I soon tied him up to the root of a cedar. Where did I get a rope? Thank heaven, being a robber, I had a rope with me, since I might have to scale a wall at any moment. Of course it was easy to stop him from calling out by gagging his mouth with fallen bamboo leaves.

When I disposed of him, I went to his woman and asked her to come and see him, because he seemed to have been suddenly taken sick. It's needless to say that this plan also worked well. The woman, her sedge hat off, came into the depths of the grove, where I led her by the hand. The instant she caught sight of her husband, she drew a small sword. I've never seen a woman of such violent temper. If I'd been off guard, I'd have got a thrust in my side. I dodged, but she kept on slashing at me. She might have wounded me deeply or killed me. But I'm Tajomaru. I managed to strike down her small sword without drawing my own. The most spirited woman is defenseless without a weapon. At last I could satisfy my desire for her without taking her husband's life.

Yes, . . . without taking his life. I had no wish to kill him. I was about to run away from the grove, leaving the woman behind in tears, when she frantically clung to my arm. In broken fragments of words, she asked that either her husband or I die. She said it was more trying than death to have her shame known to two men. She gasped out that she wanted to be the wife of whichever survived. Then a furious desire to kill him seized me. (Gloomy excitement.)

Telling you in this way, no doubt I seem a crueler man than you. But that's because you didn't see her face. Especially her burning eyes at that moment. As I saw her eye to eye, I wanted to make her my wife even if I were to be struck by lightning. I wanted to make her my wife . . . this single desire filled my mind. This was not only lust, as you might think. At that time if I'd had no other desire than lust, I'd surely not have minded knocking her down and running away. Then I wouldn't have stained my sword with his blood. But the moment I gazed at her face in the dark grove, I decided not to leave there without killing him.

But I didn't like to resort to unfair means to kill him. I untied him and told him to cross swords with me. (The rope that was found at the root of the cedar is the rope I dropped at the time.) Furious with anger, he drew his thick sword. And quick as thought, he sprang at me ferociously, without speaking a word. I needn't tell you how our fight turned out. The twenty-third stroke . . . please remember this. I'm impressed with this fact still. Nobody under the sun has ever clashed swords with me twenty strokes. (A cheerful smile.)

When he fell, I turned toward her, lowering my blood-stained sword. But to my great astonishment she was gone. I wondered to where she had run away. I looked for her in the clump of cedars. I listened, but heard only a groaning sound from the throat of the dying man.

As soon as we started to cross swords, she may have run away through the grove to call for help. When I thought of that, I decided it was a matter of life and death to me. So, robbing him of his sword, and bow and arrows, I ran out to the mountain road. There I found her horse still grazing quietly. It would be a mere waste of words to tell you the later details, but before I entered town I had already parted with the sword. That's all my confession. I know that my head will be hung in chains anyway, so put me down for the maximum penalty. (A defiant attitude.)

THE CONFESSION OF A WOMAN WHO HAS
COME TO THE *SHIMIZU* TEMPLE

That man in the blue silk kimono, after forcing me to yield to him, laughed mockingly as he looked at my bound husband. How horrified my husband must have been! But no matter how hard he struggled in agony, the rope cut into him all the more tightly. In spite of myself I ran stumblingly toward his side. Or rather I tried to run toward him, but the man instantly knocked me down. Just at that moment I saw an indescribable light in my husband's eyes. Something beyond expression . . . his eyes make me shudder even now. That instantaneous look of my husband, who couldn't speak a word, told me all his heart. The flash in his eyes was neither anger or sorrow . . . only a cold light, a look of loathing. More struck by the look in his eyes than by the blow of the thief, I called out in spite of myself and fell unconscious.

In the course of time I came to, and found that the man in blue silk was gone. I saw only my husband still bound to the root of the cedar. I raised myself from the bamboo-blades with difficulty, and looked into his face, but the expression in his eyes was just the same as before.

Beneath the cold contempt in his eyes, there was hatred. Shame, grief, and anger . . . I don't know how to express my heart at that time. Reeling to my feet, I went up to my husband.

"Takehiko," I said to him, "since the things have come to this pass, I cannot live with you. I'm determined to die, ... but you must die, too. You saw my shame. I can't leave you alive as you are."

This was all I could say. Still he went on gazing at me with loathing and contempt. My heart breaking, I looked for his sword. It must have been taken by the robber. Neither his sword nor his bow and arrows were to be seen in the grove. But fortunately my small sword was lying at my feet. Raising it over head, once more I said, "Now give me your life. I'll follow you right away."

When he heard these words, he moved his lips with difficulty. Since his mouth was stuffed with leaves, of course his voice could not be heard at all. But at a glance I understood his words. Despising me, his look said only, "Kill me." Neither conscious nor unconscious, I stabbed the small sword through the lilac-colored kimono into his breast.

Again at this time I must have fainted. By the time I managed to look up, he had already breathed his last—still in bonds. A streak of sinking sunlight streamed through the clump of cedars and bamboos, and shone on his pale face. Gulping down my sobs, I untied the rope from his dead body. And . . . and what has become of me since I have no more strength to tell you. Anyway I hadn't the strength to die. I stabbed my own throat with the small sword, I threw myself into a pond at the foot of the mountain, and I tried to kill myself in many ways. Unable to end my life, I am still living in dishonor. (A lonely smile.) Worthless as I am, I must have been forsaken even by the most merciful Kwannon. I killed my own husband. I was violated by the robber. Whatever can I do? Whatever can I . . . I . . . (Gradually, violent sobbing.)

THE STORY OF THE MURDERED MAN, AS TOLD
THROUGH A MEDIUM

After violating my wife, the robber, sitting there, began to speak comforting words to her. Of course I couldn't speak. My whole body was tied fast to the root of a cedar. But meanwhile I winked at her many times, as much as to say "Don't believe the robber." I wanted to convey some such meaning to her. But my wife, sitting dejectedly on the bamboo leaves, was looking hard at her lap. To all appearance, she was listening to his words. I was agonized by jealousy. In the meantime the robber went on with his clever talk, from one subject to another. The robber finally made his bold, brazen proposal. "Once your virtue is stained, you won't get along well with your husband, so won't you be my wife instead? It's my love for you that made me be violent toward you."

While the criminal talked, my wife raised her face as if in a trance. She had never looked so beautiful as at that moment. What did my beautiful wife say in answer to him while I was sitting bound there? I am lost in space, but I have never thought of her answer without burning with anger and jealousy. Truly she said, . . . "Then take me away with you wherever you go."

This is not the whole of her sin. If that were all, I would not be tormented so much in the dark. When she was going out of the grove as if in a dream, her hand in the robber's, she suddenly turned pale, and pointed at me tied to the root of the cedar, and said, "Kill him! I cannot marry you as long as he lives." "Kill him!" she cried many times, as if she had gone crazy. Even now these words threaten to blow me headlong into the bottomless abyss of darkness. Has such a hateful thing come out of a human mouth ever before? Have such cursed words ever struck a human ear, even once? Even once such a . . . (A sudden cry of scorn.) At these words the robber himself turned pale. "Kill him," she cried, clinging to his arms. Looking hard at her, he answered neither yes nor no . . . but hardly had I thought about his answer before she had been knocked down into the bamboo leaves. (Again a cry of scorn.) Quietly folding his arms, he looked at me and said, "What will you do with her? Kill her or save her? You have only to nod. Kill her?" For these words alone I would like to pardon his crime.

While I hesitated, she shrieked and ran into the depths of the grove. The robber instantly snatched at her, but he failed even to grasp her sleeve.

After she ran away, he took up my sword, and my bow and arrows. With a single stroke he cut one of my bonds. I remember his mumbling, "My fate is next." Then he disappeared from the grove. All was silent after that. No, I heard someone crying. Untying the rest of my bonds, I listened carefully, and I noticed that it was my own crying. (Long silence.)

I raised my exhausted body from the root of the cedar. In front of me there was shining the small sword which my wife had dropped. I took it up and stabbed it into my breast. A bloody lump rose to my mouth, but I didn't feel any pain. When my breast grew cold, everything was as silent as the dead in their graves. What profound silence! Not a single bird-note was heard in the sky over this grave in the hollow of the mountains. Only a lonely light lingered on the cedars and mountain. By and by the light gradually grew fainter, till the cedars and bamboo were lost to view. Lying there, I was enveloped in deep silence.

Then someone crept up to me. I tried to see who it was. But darkness had already been gathering round me. Someone . . . that someone drew the small sword softly out of my breast in its invisible hand. At the same time once more blood flowed into my mouth. And once and for all I sank down into the darkness of space.

Story of the
Chief of Old Cairo
From The Arabian Nights

I once hanged ten thieves each on his own gibbet, and especially charged
the guards to watch them and hinder the folk from taking any one of them
down. Next morning when I came to look at them, I found two bodies
hanging from one gallows and said to the guards, "Who did this, and where
is the tenth gibbet?" But they denied all knowledge of it, and I was about to
beat them till they owned the truth, when they said, "Know, O Emir, that
we fell asleep last night, and when we awoke, we found that some one had
stolen one of the bodies, gibbet and all; so we were alarmed and feared thy
wrath. But, behold, up came a peasant-fellow driving his ass; whereupon
we laid hands on him and killed him and hanged his body upon this gallows, in the stead of the thief who had been stolen." Now when I heard
this, I marvelled and asked them, "What had he with him?"; and they answered, "He had a pair of saddlebags on the ass." Quoth I, "What was in
them?"; quoth they, "We know not." So I said, "Bring them hither"; and
when they brought them to me I bade open them, behold, therein was the
body of a murdered man, cut in pieces. Now as soon as I saw this, I marvelled at the case and said in myself, "Glory to God! The cause of the
hanging of this peasant was none other but his crime against this murdered
man; and thy lord is not unjust toward His servants."

6

The Jury System

All tryalls shall be by verdict of twelve men as neer as may
be peers or equals from the neighborhood and in the country, shire or division where the fact shall arise or grow
whether the same be by indictment, infermaction, declaration
or otherwise, and the person offencer or defendant.

The New York Charter of
Liberties and Privileges
1683

In all criminal prosecutions, the accused shall enjoy the right
to a speedy and public trial, by an impartial jury of the State
and district wherein the crime shall have been committed.

The Constitution of the
United States, Amendment VI
1791

In the short story "The Lynching of Jube Benson," a man is hung for a
murder that he did not commit, and his indictment takes place without a trial
and without a jury. If Jube *had* received a trial with an *impartial* jury con-
sisting of members of his peers, which members of society would have
comprised that jury? Webster's dictionary defines "peer" as: "1. an equal;
one of the same rank, value, quality, ability, etc.; as, he was tried by a jury
of his *peers*." Should Jube have been tried by a group of poor, uneducated
black slaves from the same country as he came from? Should an accused
murderer have a jury of other accused murderers? Or should we have jurors
who are educated, intelligent, capable of reason, unbiased, and impartial?

Consider a medical malpractice case in which the jury is subjected to
nine days of expert testimony on the standard of care in doing bypass
surgery. How can we provide the doctor accused of malpractice with a jury
of his peers? Should we give the doctor a jury of physicians? Or consider a
products liability case in which the lengthy testimony of engineering experts
centers around the safety of a newly designed airbag system which met the
specifications and standards of the industry before installation but subsequently malfunctioned. Should we give the automobile manufacturer a jury
of his manufacturing competitors?

In a jury trial the judge decides issues of law and the jury decides issues of fact; therefore, the lawyer frames legal issues in language that the judge and the lawyer are trained to understand, while, at the same time, he addresses the jury in layman's terms. Would it be better if the members of the jury had legal training, becoming professional jurors and spending their time on a jury circuit, deciding issues within a legal framework?

Some of the other relevant questions concerning the jury system are as follows:

- Who should serve?
- Who should be exempt?
- Who should be excused?
- Should we demand a unanimous verdict? In a criminal case? In a civil case? In all cases?
- Just what does *impartial* mean?

In 1951 Solomon Asch conducted an experiment in which subjects were asked to compare the length of lines on a display. In one experiment, subjects were asked to tell the experimenter which of the three lines on the right matched the length of the line on the left. Only one member of the group of eight people participating in the experiment as "subjects" was not a confederate of the experimenter. As each of the confederates gave a wrong response to the stimulus and the real subject answered last, there was extreme pressure to conform to the group. In 32 percent of all the trials performed by Solomon Asch, the one real subject conformed to the group and gave a clearly incorrect statement regarding the length of the lines. This conformity was drastically reduced if one of the confederates gave a correct response—in that case the rate of conformity was reduced from 32 percent to 5 percent. This phenomenon of conformity to group pressure is evident in the dynamics of the jury as the members argue, cajole, persuade, and reason in an attempt to get the other jurors to vote with them. "Beyond Any Doubt" by Robert O'Neil Bristow clearly demonstrates this conformity in the jury process and also challenges the notion of an impartial jury.

Susan Glaspell's "A Jury of Her Peers" also addresses the jury process. Would there be fewer convictions if each accused person had a *real* jury of his or her peers, such as Minnie Foster's jury, which truly empathized with the accused and thoroughly understood her motivation?

Beyond Any Doubt
Robert O'Neil Bristow

Tom Howell stubbed his cigarette in the cluttered ash tray on the table. As he did so, he looked thoughtfully from face to face, at the eleven men seated around the table. They were solemn faces. Intense and resentful. The men were tired, some of them growing angry from the exhaustion of deliberation in the jury room. On the wall the second hand of the clock moved silently, relentlessly, in its course. The vote was eleven for death. One for acquittal. The single dissenting vote had been cast by Tom Howell.

Now strenuously urged by the judge to reach a decision, the eleven men concentrated their attention on the single vote that stood between Jack Echols and the electric chair.

Tom reached for another cigarette, sighing deeply. He very desperately wished he was back on the job at the drug store he managed. Or better still, at home with Jane, his wife, and Randy their eleven year old son, perhaps sitting comfortably on the lawn with a cool drink in his hand. There his responsibility was limited to his family. He disliked having the power to save or destroy another man's life by a single irrevocable decision.

Tom Howell was a small, very lean man. As the result of a mine explosion on Guadalcanal, he wore thick-lensed glasses which gave him 20/40 vision. While the other men in the jury room were dressed in suits and ties, Tom Howell wore no jacket. His clean white shirt was frayed at the collar, his tie was inexpensive.

The foreman was Doctor McNair, a heavy man of florid complexion, and a man of some standing in the small midwestern city. He was tolerant and diplomatic by nature. His vote had been cast for death. The others, several of them successful businessmen, had also voted for death on the first ballot.

The acknowledged leader for the death penalty group was Carl Purvis, a wealthy man who owned land and had other interests, including the hardware store where Tom Howell had formerly worked. Carl Purvis had fired Tom in a fit of anger over a mixup in a wholesale order. Carl Purvis was fifty-five years old, a political power in the county, an abrupt egocentric. He was impatient and intolerant of opposition of any kind.

Dr. McNair's voice interrupted the uncomfortable silence. "Tom," he said, making an effort to smile. "We want to reach a decision tonight. We've been over and over the case. Now . . . again I'd like to ask you to repeat your stand."

Tom Howell loosened his tie and ran his forefinger around the irritated flesh on his neck where the frayed edge of collar had rubbed. He cleared his throat, and as he began to speak, his voice cracked.

"The Judge said that if there was a reasonable doubt of guilt, we should not give the death penalty. That's why I can't vote for death. I think there is a doubt that Echols killed the man."

"Oh, *for God's sake!*" The voice was Carl Purvis'. He slammed a heavy fist against the table and muttered to himself.

"The evidence," Tom went on, ignoring Purvis, "that the State emphasized, was the fact that Echols was apprehended in the middle of a robbery, with the gun that had killed a policeman three months earlier. I'm not arguing that it wasn't the gun at all. The ballistics expert showed that to be true. But Echols said he bought the gun from a man he hardly knew after they met in a bar. He swore he didn't own the gun at the time of the killing. I'm saying there is some doubt whether or not he did have the gun when the police officer was killed."

"For God's sake, Howell," Carl Purvis shouted, "do you think Echols would admit he owned the gun at that time? What the hell would *you* do?"

"I don't know. I repeat that there is simply no proof that Echols had the gun before the killing. Certainly he had it when he robbed the supermarket, but I can't believe a man who had killed a policeman would *keep* the gun. He'd know if he was caught, the murder would be traced to him. To me that would be stupid."

"It would be stupid!" Purvis said. "It would be damned stupid, but just how smart do you think this Echols is? He's spent half of his life behind bars. He doesn't have the brilliant mind that you have. . . ." Purvis's voice ended with a tone of heavy sarcasm.

"If he was a confirmed criminal," Tom said evenly, his jaws growing tense, "it seems to me that he'd have even more reason to get rid of the gun if he'd used it to kill the policeman. A first offender might not consider that, but a confirmed criminal like Echols would dispose of the gun. I think Echols bought the gun from the killer, with no idea that it had been used to murder a lawman."

Carl Purvis cursed and stood up, moving angrily away from the table.

"I think Mr. Purvis has a point," Dr. McNair said diplomatically. "The defendant wasn't very smart or he'd never have been in prison on so many counts. Do you know he raped a girl when he was seventeen?"

"Doctor!" Tom said suddenly, "We aren't trying this man for rape."

"Of course. Yes. But he had no alibi in this case. Tom, he could not prove. . . ."

"He said he was in his room at the Majestic Hotel."

"He said that," the doctor agreed, "but was he? Surely someone would have seen him enter and leave. The hotel clerk testified that he hadn't seen Echols all day. He said he thought he was gone at the time."

"Did he go look? Did he know for sure?" Tom asked.

"Howell, it's a small hotel. A flop house. If Echols had been there, the clerk would have known."

"Echols said he was drunk. He said he didn't even go out to eat that night."

Carl Purvis wheeled around and paced to the table, standing angrily over Tom Howell.

"You're pretty naive, son. You didn't expect that killer to stand in the box and tell the truth, did you? Don't you know he's been in and out of trouble all his life?"

Tom Howell adjusted his glasses nervously. This was becoming a terrible strain. Several times he had been almost prepared to tell them that if they were so certain, he'd go along with the death penalty. But at the moment, when he might have changed his vote, something had held him back. He was tempted now, but once again he resisted, although less forcefully than before.

"Mr. Purvis," Dr. McNair said, "why don't you come sit down and we'll talk this over some more."

Carl Purvis, casting an angry glance at Tom, returned to his seat, mumbling profanity.

"There was the identification by the other police officer," Dr. McNair said. "He positively identified Echols as the man who wounded him."

"True," Tom admitted. "Officer Tolliver was directing traffic when the killer drove through a light at the intersection. Officer Tolliver fired two shots and the killer fired back, hitting him in the leg. That's the way they said it happened. But the defense attorney showed that the killer's car was doing forty-five miles an hour. Officer Tolliver saw him for just an instant. I think the defense attorney was right when he reasoned that it simply wasn't possible, in a hail of bullets, to positively identify a man while he's traveling that fast in a car. The officer saw only the face, the killer was wearing a hat. I think the officer is honest, but I can't believe that he can make a positive identification." Tom Howell mopped his forehead with his handkerchief. He shook his head. "From all that testimony we heard," he said wearily, "and our discussion . . . I still think there is a doubt."

"That's right," Carl Purvis snapped, "and there's a doubt if the sun will come up tomorrow too. But it's a pretty thin doubt. You're hiding behind it, Howell."

"Gentlemen, please," Dr. McNair said.

"He should have disqualified himself for jury duty," Purvis shouted. "He isn't holding out because he thinks the man is innocent. He's holding out because he hasn't got the guts to give death. He's never had any guts. I ought to know."

"Sit down, please, Mr. Purvis," Dr. McNair said.

Carl Purvis glared and remained standing.

How often Tom had asked himself if he could serve on a jury when a death penalty was possible. He let his mind slip back to the morning after he had been subpoenaed. Jane had put his toast and eggs on the table, but he had left them untouched, uneaten and cold.

"You're worrying about it too much, Tom," she said.

"Ummmmm . . . it's not just the jury duty. I can spare the time for that. It's the death penalty. They'll ask me and I'm not sure what to say.

Who wants to have that responsibility. . . . I mean really *wants* it? And yet *somebody* is going to qualify. Maybe several of those self-righteous zealots. Can't you hear them after they've given him death, describing how troubled they were, how tremendous a decision it was? I can see it. In fact, I could name a dozen right off hand."

"But that doesn't answer your question, does it, Tom?"

He had smiled. "No . . . that doesn't make me any more certain whether or not I should disqualify myself." He pushed the eggs away. "I'm sorry," he said. He lighted a cigarette and smoked thoughtfully. "I *could* give death. I would. But I'd have to be sure. I'd have to be so damned sure I could turn over and fall asleep every night without thinking back and wondering. Does that qualify me?"

Jane had taken the cigarette from his fingers and drawn on it, returning it to him. "It's your decision," she said. "*You* know."

Tom coughed and was aware of the gnawing fear, the uncertainty in his mind. Could he change now? Should he change? Let them have it the way they saw it . . . could he hold out? He looked around the jury room.

"Look . . . I'm not eager to send a man to death. I admit that. But maybe that's because I saw too much of it. I saw hundreds of men die and I had a hand in it. No, I'm going to be very careful before I send a man to the electric chair."

He noticed several eyebrows raise. Had he admitted that he thought they might be right after all? Was this the first sign of surrender?

"Maybe I shouldn't be on this jury," he said. "I don't know. I wish now that I hadn't been called. But let me say this. If I'm not eager to give death and should not be here for that reason, I think that there are some of us here who are just a little bit too eager to give him death, and they don't belong on this jury any more than I do. This is supposed to be a group of impartial men . . . and I wonder if, after all the newspaper publicity, the pictures of the policeman's widow and all. . . . I wonder if any of us came here with completely impartial minds."

"See there!" Carl Purvis shouted, "He's admitting he doesn't belong on this jury."

Dr. McNair was showing frustration. "Please, gentlemen," he said. "Let's be sensible."

And for several moments the terrible silence again returned and the second hand of the clock moved, and moved.

Somewhat more restrained in tone, Carl Purvis spoke. "Howell, you used to work for me. You didn't like me and I never cared much for you. I want to say this. I think you're holding out because I fired you, and I'm on the other side. I think it has nothing to do with this case at all. You're just trying to take out your resentment against me, in this cheap, filthy way."

For the first time, Tom stood to speak, and if he had ever felt hate, he felt it then.

"You couldn't be more right," he said loudly. "I don't like you. I think you're a bigoted, egotistical slob." He was breathing hard now and he was surprised to find it so difficult to draw air into his lungs. "But I wouldn't pardon a guilty man just because I resent you. You, Mr. Purvis, are the *least* important part of this whole rotten mess. I wouldn't like you even if you were voting for acquittal. Not one damned bit. But . . ." he paused to get his breath, "I'm voting this way because I feel there is a doubt. I see that man out there waiting for a decision whether we kill him or let him live. I couldn't care less about your personal feelings for me or mine for you."

"This discussion has gotten out of hand," Dr. McNair said, "This is neither the time nor the place for personality conflicts, and I ask you not to let personal antagonism enter into this deliberation."

Tom sat and buried his face in his hands, emotionally exhausted. He remembered Carl Purvis' fit of rage, that day in the hardware store, his face growing dark, menacing, his voice loud, uncontrolled.

In the presence of the other clerks, Carl Purvis had fired him not even learning all the facts about the mistake in the wholesale order. Not caring.

It had not been easy for Tom to get another job because the whispering that followed his dismissal hinted vaguely at dishonesty. He refused to leave town to take another position with another hardware firm.

"No," he argued, "if I run, they'll believe I did something wrong. I'll make out and eventually people will know that Carl Purvis made an impulsive, hot-headed decision."

Tom had stuck. In two years he had added another thousand dollars to his savings. He was all right now. He had recently talked to the banker, and if his loan came through as he expected, he would soon open his own store, a fishing and hardware specialty house, on a small scale at first. But it would grow, Tom felt sure.

Tom glanced up from the table. The room had been silent for some time. It seemed uncomfortably crowded, all of them watching him warily, impatiently.

Tom recognized the deep resentment he felt against Carl Purvis. With studied honesty, he asked himself if it *was* possible that he was holding out because of his hatred for Purvis. Did he really doubt that Echols was guilty. Again the wave of uncertainty swept over him. It would be easy to stop now, to go along with the other eleven. He considered it very seriously.

"Tom," Dr. McNair said, "look at it the other way. If you can, just look at the evidence. We are dealing with a known criminal. He's been in jail for years. He never got past the third grade. He raped a girl when he was seventeen. He beat her. He showed that he could be cruel, even kill perhaps, if necessary. He went into a liquor store with a mask and held the place up. Then he got in the car and started off. The policeman reached the scene, and when he tried to stop the criminal, he was shot down. The killer then made an escape, wounding the traffic officer as he fled. Later . . . Echols was arrested in possession of the gun that had killed the officer. He was checked out carefully and he could give no alibi at all. Echols didn't deny owning the gun. He said he bought it from a man and described that man vaguely. He couldn't even give the man's first name. The traffic officer who tried to stop him identified Echols as the man who shot him in the leg. Now, our point is this . . . if Echols could prove that he had been in his room . . . or if he could prove that he had bought the gun from someone, and provided a name, it might be different. If the police officer had even said that he was *almost* sure that Echols was the killer . . . then Tom, we feel there would be doubt. As it is, Echols has failed to clear himself, on any single point. Nobody really wants to send a man to his execution. It would take a neurotic sadist to enjoy that.

"And yet . . . can we turn men like Echols free? Are our police officers to go out and patrol, knowing that they may be killed, if the people they are protecting do not in turn protect the officers? Tom, please . . . we have a responsibility here. Eleven of us are deeply convinced that Echols was the killer. We have no doubt. Don't you think, as a medical man dedicated to saving lives, that if there was any doubt, I'd be the first to vote against the death penalty?"

"I think you would," Tom agreed.

"Very well. As foreman, I'm calling a coffee break. Let's all relax and reconsider the facts. After the break, we will take another ballot. Someone rap on the door and send out for coffee."

One of the jurymen went to the door and ordered. Then, splitting up into groups, the jurymen talked softly to one another, leaving Tom alone at the end of the table.

Tom overheard the high-pitched tenor of the music teacher as he discussed the case, the talented hands gesturing in jerky movements.

"Well . . . if you want to know what I think. . . . I think this criminal is not *worth* salvaging. I frankly don't have any doubt, but if I did, I think I'd just take into consideration that he isn't worth the risk he poses to good decent people. Now, I mean that's just my idea, but he's simply *nothing*. Nothing!"

Tom removed his glasses and wiped them clean with his handkerchief. He discounted what the music teacher said. It was only to be expected from an overly emotional man. But Dr. McNair, he thought, was an honest, level-headed, decent man. He was committed to the saving of lives. Certainly he would be the last to condemn a man to death if there was any doubt. The concise, simple way he had presented the argument left Tom with less conviction that Echols was innocent. If only he could remove that lingering uncertainty. Could he be right, when all the others were so thoroughly convinced? He wondered if perhaps, in his feeling for the underdog, he had given too much credence to the presentation by the defense. He didn't want to send a man to death, and yet, if Echols was guilty, he knew that he had to make the decision.

The gun, the lack of an alibi, the identification of the police officer . . . it was damning enough. Yet, somehow he couldn't find it conclusive.

He remembered the looks on the faces of the townspeople after he had been fired at the hardware store. Some of them, on the basis of circumstances, were ready to believe that he had been dishonest, that he had been fired for that reason.

There had been no way to defend himself against these unspoken accusations. There were the long nights, lying awake, projecting their faces on the shadowy ceiling, mentally gauging their distrust of him.

Tom wondered if he was unwilling to believe that Echols was guilty because of his own experience. *Was he in reality only defending himself now? Or was there a genuine doubt?* He wondered.

None of the other men were in question. The music teacher. The football coach. The businessmen. They all knew. They found no agony, no doubt, in rendering a decision. Tom lighted a cigarette, and while it tasted raw in his mouth, he smoked it thoughtfully. If *they* were so certain, he reasoned that he must be wrong. If only one of them had been in doubt, it would have made a difference.

But they had not shown such doubt. He was alone. He had never been so thoroughly alone in his life. He considered how easy it would be on the next ballot to write *guilty*. A word. A single word that would relieve him of all responsibility. He took a slip of paper and wrote the word, speculatively. He studied his writing. It was not as difficult as he had imagined. If he put his faith in the other eleven men, it would not be hard. If he did not, he was again very much alone. He told himself to stop the fight now. *Vote guilty. Vote for death.*

It would be easy. Or would it? Maybe it didn't stop there. It was just possible that if he appeased these men here, he might appease them outside the courtroom. *Go along with the crowd. Don't be a dissenter. The way to get ahead is to go along. Sell out.*

He glanced up as Carl Purvis drew a chair beside him. "Tom . . . I'm a blunt man," he said levelly, without anger, "and I know you've been to the bank to borrow money to start a hardware store in competition with me. That doesn't bother me. I can take competition. There's room enough for both of us. I said I was blunt, and I am. I have a strong vote on the board of directors at the bank. It comes down to this. If you vote with us, you get the loan. If you don't, I'll stop it. The rest of us are convinced. Now just face the truth and go along. You'll have your loan and a lousy rapist criminal will go to the chair. If we don't give it to him, he'll kill somebody else before it's over. He'll go there one way or another. All you do is ease off and go along. That shouldn't be too hard."

"You mean that?" Tom asked. "About the loan? You really do?"

Carl Purvis spoke softly, but with strength. "I mean it. You can yell your head off and I'll deny ever saying it, but, boy, you'll know!"

Carl Purvis pushed his chair away and joined the others as coffee was brought into the room.

Tom drank slowly, very thoughtfully. He refused to allow himself to grow angry. Not now. What Purvis had said was undeniably true. He was in a position to block the loan. And yet, perhaps, considering the testimony, Echols *was* guilty. If so, he should face the death penalty. Then there was also Dr. McNair's studied decision. Tom respected that. There were the facts as they had seen them. Echols was a confirmed criminal. Freed of this crime, he might go on to commit another that would inevitably lead him to the electric chair. Eleven against one. Were they right? He considered his long-cherished hope for a business of his own. This too was in the balance. Was he so certain that Echols was innocent that he would sacrifice his own future?

Dr. McNair hesitated as he reached Tom's chair. Tom felt the doctor's hand on his shoulder. "Tell me, Tom," McNair said, "do you really have a doubt? Or is it too difficult to back down?"

Tom looked up into the doctor's face. He was very tired. "Have you asked yourself the same thing?" he said.

"What do you mean?"

"With the comfort of ten others, it might be hard for you to change too."

Dr. McNair did not reply.

"I know how I *feel*. I feel like he's guilty," Tom said.

Dr. McNair raised an eyebrow and leaned closer. "Go on," he said.

"But . . . they didn't prove that in court. They left some doubts. Not for the others, but for me."

"Yet, you feel . . ."

"Yes, I feel he's guilty. Do you want me to vote what I feel or what I know?"

Dr. McNair shook his head slowly.

"Maybe sometime—I don't really know—but maybe you had a patient and you felt certain that you had diagnosed the trouble. Maybe you treated it and later, when the patient died, you found that it was something else. Maybe some of these men just don't want to doubt. You probably don't even understand . . ."

Dr. McNair looked about the room thoughtfully. "We'd better start," he said softly. He took his place at the head of the table. The others followed quickly. "Gentlemen, in a spirit of deep sincerity," I ask you to draw a paper and pencil and cast a ballot."

The men wrote quickly and folded the one-word messages as Dr. McNair passed the plate. Tom studied them before writing. He considered the prisoner waiting below. He considered his wife and Randy. The small business he wanted so badly. And before he wrote, he considered the facts in the case—those controversial facts that were so strangely elastic in interpretation. Was there really any doubt? The key word. *Doubt.*

Tom was the last to drop his paper in the place. He had written thoughtfully. The plate was then handed to the foreman.

The doctor announced seven guilty votes before he paused. "Not guilty." Dr. McNair read, and dropped the paper on the table.

Tom Howell stood slowly. His voice was so subdued that the others leaned toward him to hear him.

"Once and for all," he said, his eyes growing damp behind his thick glasses, "I vote for acquittal. As I do so, I know the very great responsibility I have taken. I can tell you now that if we sit here and deliberate until the world ends, I will not change my vote. I will under no circumstances change my vote. Not to please you, . . . nor help you get this over with."

Tom sat down. Dr. McNair shuffled through the ballots. Tom glanced quickly at Carl Purvis. Perhaps what hopes he had had for the bank loan were destroyed by his brief announcement. He suspected that it was just possible that the board of directors would ask Purvis not to cast a vote, since the loan involved a business competitive to his. It did not matter. Tom would get the money somehow, someday.

He knew also that if he was deeply disappointed in this, still he had acted in good faith. He would not have to live without respect for himself.

"That wasn't really necessary, Tom," Dr. McNair said gently. He gestured with the ballots. "I had not finished counting." The men sat silently. Dr. McNair lighted a cigarette. "The vote has changed," he said, "It is now two for acquittal, ten guilty."

Tom let his eyes move quickly from man to man. He saw the surprise register in the face of the music teacher. It was not so comfortable now with two votes opposing him. His narrow face was troubled. Tom saw indecision there, a weakening. He glanced at the coach. He looked as though he might be ready to call another play before it was too late.

And Tom heard Dr. McNair's voice, coaxing, and sensed that it was he who had changed his vote.

" . . . not what we feel, but what we know for fact. This is the basis, and if there is doubt—as two of us believe now—"

Tom detected the change that had taken place in the room. Even Purvis was nodding with McNair.

Tom Howell adjusted his glasses as the weariness began to leave him. He was feeling better. When the time came, he had rewarded himself with human dignity by standing alone. This was enough.

The music teacher raised his hand, like a schoolboy, and asked for another vote. Tom smiled and reached for his pencil. It would be over soon.

A Jury of Her Peers
Susan Glaspell

When Martha Hale opened the storm door and got a cut of the north wind, she ran back for her big woolen scarf. As she hurriedly wound that round her head her eye made a scandalized sweep of her kitchen. It was no ordinary thing that called her away—it was probably farther from ordinary than anything that had ever happened in Dickson County. But what her eye took in was that her kitchen was in no shape for leaving: her bread all ready for mixing, half the flour sifted and half unsifted.

She hated to see things half-done; but she had been at that when the team from town stopped to get Mr. Hale, and then the sheriff came running in to say his wife wished Mrs. Hale would come too—adding, with a grin, that he guessed she was getting scary and wanted another woman along. So she had dropped everything right where it was.

"Martha!" now came her husband's impatient voice. "Don't keep folks waiting out here in the cold."

She again opened the storm door, and this time joined the three men and the one woman waiting for her in the big two-seated buggy.

After she had the robes tucked around her she took another look at the woman who sat beside her on the back seat. She had met Mrs. Peters the year before at the county fair, and the thing she remembered about her was that she didn't seem like a sheriff's wife. She was small and thin and didn't have a strong voice. Mrs. Gorman, the sheriff's wife before Gorman went out and Peters came in, had a voice that somehow seemed to be backing up the law with every word. But if Mrs. Peters didn't look like a sheriff's wife, Peters made it up in looking like a sheriff. He was to a dot the kind of man who could get himself elected sheriff—a heavy man with a big voice, who was particularly genial with the law-abiding, as if to make it plain that he knew the difference between criminals and noncriminals. And right there it came into Mrs. Hale's mind, with a stab, that this man who was so pleasant and lively with all of them was going to the Wrights' now as a sheriff.

"The country's not very pleasant this time of year," Mrs. Peters at last ventured, as if she felt they ought to be talking as well as the men.

Mrs. Hale scarcely finished her reply, for they had gone up a little hill and could see the Wright place now, and seeing it did not make her feel like talking. It looked very lonesome this cold March morning. It had always been a lonesome-looking place. It was down in a hollow, and the poplar trees around it were lonesome-looking trees. The men were looking at it and talking about what had happened. The county attorney was bending to one side of the buggy, and kept looking steadily at the place as they drew up to it.

"I'm glad you came with me," Mrs. Peters said nervously, as the two women were about to follow the men in through the kitchen door.

Even after she had her foot on the doorstep, her hand on the knob, Martha Hale had a moment of feeling she could not cross that threshold. And the reason it seemed she couldn't cross it now was simply because she hadn't crossed it before. Time and time again it had been in her mind, "I ought to go over and see Minnie Foster"—she still thought of her as Minnie Foster, though for twenty years she had been Mrs. Wright. And then there was always something to do and Minnie Foster would go from her mind. But *now* she could come.

The men went over to the stove. The women stood close together by the door. Young Henderson, the county attorney, turned around and said:

"Come up to the fire, ladies."

Mrs. Peters took a step forward, then stopped. "I'm not—cold," she said.

The men talked for a minute about what a good thing it was the sheriff had sent his deputy out that morning to make a fire for them, and then Sheriff Peters stepped back from the stove, unbuttoned his outer coat, and leaned his hands on the kitchen table in a way that seemed to make the beginning of official business. "Now, Mr. Hale," he said in a sort of semiofficial voice, "before we move things about, you tell Mr. Henderson just what it was you saw when you came here yesterday morning."

The county attorney was looking around the kitchen.

"By the way," he said, "has anything been moved?" He turned to the sheriff. "Are things just as you left them yesterday?"

Peters looked from cupboard to sink; from that to a small worn rocker a little to one side of the kitchen table.

"It's just the same."

"Somebody should have been left here yesterday," said the county attorney.

"Oh—yesterday," returned the sheriff, with a little gesture as of yesterday having been more than he could bear to think of. "When I had to send Frank to Morris Center for that man who went crazy—let me tell you, I had my hands full *yesterday*. I knew you could get back from Omaha by today, George, and as long as I went over everything here myself. . . ."

"Well, Mr. Hale," said the county attorney, in a way of letting what was past and gone go, "tell just what happened when you came here yesterday morning."

Mrs. Hale, still leaning against the door, had that sinking feeling of the mother whose child is about to speak a piece. Lewis often wandered along and got things mixed up in a story. She hoped he would tell this straight and plain, and not say unnecessary things that would just make things harder for Minnie Foster. He didn't begin at once, and she noticed

that he looked queer—as if standing in that kitchen and having to tell what
he had seen there yesterday morning made him almost sick.

"Harry and I had started to town with a load of potatoes," Mrs.
Hale's husband began.

Harry was Mrs. Hale's oldest boy. He wasn't with them now, for
the very good reason that those potatoes never got to town yesterday and he
was taking them this morning, so he hadn't been home when the sheriff
stopped to say he wanted Mr. Hale to come over to the Wright place and tell
the county attorney his story there, where he could point it all out.

"We came along this road," Hale was going on, with a motion of his
hand to the road over which they had just come, "and as we got in sight of
the house I says to Harry, 'I'm goin' to see if I can't get John Wright to
take a telephone.' You see," he explained to Henderson, "unless I can get
somebody to go in with me they won't come out this branch road except for
a price I can't pay. I'd spoke to Wright about it once before; but he put me
off, saying folks talked too much anyway, and all he asked was peace and
quiet—guess you know about how much he talked himself. But I thought
maybe if I went to the house and talked about it before his wife, and said all
the womenfolks liked the telephones, and that in this lonesome stretch of
road it would be a good thing—well, I said to Harry that that was what I
was going to say—though I said at the same time that I didn't know as what
his wife wanted made much difference to John . . ."

Now, there he was!—saying things he didn't need to say. Mrs.
Hale tried to catch her husband's eye, but fortunately the county attorney
interrupted with:

"Let's talk about that a little later, Mr. Hale. I do want to talk about
that, but I'm anxious now to get along to just exactly what happened when
you got here."

When he began this time, it was very deliberately and carefully:

"I didn't see or hear anything. I knocked at the door. And still it
was all quiet inside. I knew they must be up—it was past eight o'clock. So
I knocked again, louder, and I thought I heard somebody say, 'Come in.' I
wasn't sure—I'm not sure yet. But I opened the door—this door," jerking
a hand toward the door by which the two women stood, "and there, in that
rocker"—pointing to it—"sat Mrs. Wright."

Everyone in the kitchen looked at the rocker. It came into Mrs.
Hale's mind that the rocker didn't look in the least like Minnie Foster—the
Minnie Foster of twenty years before. It was a dingy red, with wooden
rungs up the back, and the middle rung was gone, and the chair sagged to
one side.

"How did she—look?" the county attorney was inquiring.

"Well," said Hale, "she looked—queer."

"How do you mean—queer?"

As he asked it he took out a notebook and pencil. Mrs. Hale did not
like the sight of that pencil. She kept her eye fixed on her husband, as if to
keep him from saying unnecessary things that would go into that notebook
and make trouble.

Hale did speak guardedly, as if the pencil had affected him too.

"Well, as if she didn't know what she was going to do next. And kind of—done up."

"How did she seem to feel about your coming?"

"Why, I didn't think she minded—one way or other. She didn't pay much attention. I said, 'Ho' do, Mrs. Wright? It's cold, ain't it?' And she said, 'Is it?'—and went on pleatin' at her apron.

"Well, I was surprised. She didn't ask me to come up to the stove, or to sit down, but just set there, not even lookin' at me. And so I said: 'I want to see John.' And then she laughed. I guess you would call it a laugh.

"I thought of Harry and the team outside, so I said, a little sharp, 'Can I see John?' 'No,' says she—kind of dull-like. 'Ain't he home?' says I. Then she looked at me. 'Yes,' says she, 'he's home.' 'Then why can't I see him?' I asked her, out of patience with her now. ''Cause he's dead,' says she, just as quiet and dull—and fell to pleatin' her apron. 'Dead?' says I, like you do when you can't take in what you've heard.

"She just nodded her head, not getting a bit excited, but rockin' back and forth.

"'Why—where is he?' says I, not knowing *what* to say.

"She just pointed upstairs—like this"—pointing to the room above.

"I got up, with the idea of going up there myself. By this time I— didn't know what to do. I walked from there to here; then I says: 'Why, what did he die of?'

"'He died of a rope round his neck,' says she; and just went on pleatin' at her apron."

Hale stopped speaking and stood staring at the rocker, as if he were still seeing the woman who had sat there the morning before. Nobody spoke; it was as if everyone were seeing the woman who had sat there the morning before.

"And what did you do then?" the county attorney at last broke the silence.

"I went out and called Harry. I thought I might—need help. I got Harry in, and we went upstairs." His voice fell almost to a whisper. "There he was—lying over the . . ."

"I think I'd rather have you go into that upstairs," the attorney interrupted, "where you can point it all out. Just go on now with the rest of the story."

"Well, my first thought was to get that rope off. It looked . . ."

He stopped, his face twitching.

"But Harry, he went up to him, and he said, 'No, he's dead all right, and we'd better not touch anything.' So we went downstairs. She was still sitting that same way. 'Has anybody been notified?' I asked. 'No,' said she, unconcerned.

"'Who did this, Mrs. Wright?' said Harry. He said it business-like, and she stopped pleatin' at her apron. 'I don't know,' she says. 'You don't *know*?' says Harry. 'Weren't you sleepin' in the bed with him?' 'Yes,' says she, 'but I was on the inside.' 'Somebody slipped a rope round his neck and strangled him, and you didn't wake up?' says Harry. 'I didn't wake up,' she said after him.

"We may have looked as if we didn't see how that could be, for after a minute she said, 'I sleep sound.'

"Harry was going to ask her more questions, but I said maybe that weren't our business; maybe we ought to let her tell her story first to the coroner or the sheriff. So Harry went fast as he could over to High Road—the Rivers' place, where there's a telephone."

"And what did she do when she knew you had gone for the coroner?" The attorney got his pencil in his hand all ready for writing.

"She moved from that chair to this one over here"—Hale pointed to a small chair in the corner—"and just sat there with her hands held together and looking down. I got a feeling that I ought to make some conversation, so I said I had come in to see if John wanted to put in a telephone; and at that she started to laugh, and then she stopped and looked at me—scared."

At the sound of a moving pencil the man who was telling the story looked up.

"I dunno—maybe it wasn't scared," he hastened; "I wouldn't like to say it was. Soon Harry got back, and then Dr. Lloyd came, and you, Mr. Peters, and so I guess that's all I know that you don't."

He said that last with relief, and moved a little, as if relaxing. Everyone moved a little. The county attorney walked toward the stair door.

"I guess we'll go upstairs first—then out to the barn and around."

He paused and looked around the kitchen.

"You're convinced there was nothing important here?" he asked the sheriff. "Nothing that would—point to any motive?"

The sheriff too looked all around, as if to reconvince himself.

"Nothing here but kitchen things," he said, with a little laugh for the insignificance of kitchen things.

The county attorney was looking at the cupboard—a peculiar, ungainly structure, half closet and half cupboard, the upper part of it being built in the wall, and the lower part just the old-fashioned kitchen cupboard. As if its queerness attracted him, he got a chair and opened the upper part and looked in. After a moment he drew his hand away sticky.

"Here's a nice mess," he said resentfully.

The two women had drawn nearer, and now the sheriff's wife spoke.

"Oh—her fruit," she said, looking to Mrs. Hale for sympathetic understanding. She turned back to the county attorney and explained: "She worried about that when it turned so cold last night. She said the fire would go out and her jars burst."

Mrs. Peters' husband broke into a laugh.

"Well, can you beat the women! Held for murder, and worrying about her preserves!"

The young attorney set his lips.

"I guess before we're through she may have something more serious than preserves to worry about."

"Oh, well," said Mrs. Hale's husband, with good-natured superiority, "women are used to worrying over trifles."

The two women moved a little closer together. Neither of them spoke. The county attorney seemed suddenly to remember his manners—and think of his future.

"And yet," said he, with the gallantry of a young politician, "for all their worries, what would we do without the ladies?"

The women did not speak; did not unbend. He went to the sink and began washing his hands. He turned to wipe them on the roller towel— whirled it for a cleaner place.

"Dirty towels! Not much of a housekeeper, would you say, ladies?" He kicked his foot against some dirty pans under the sink.

"There's a great deal of work to be done on a farm," said Mrs. Hale stiffly.

"To be sure. And yet"—with a little bow to her—"I know there are some Dickson County farmhouses that do not have such roller towels."

"Those towels get dirty awful quick. Men's hands aren't always as clean as they might be."

"Ah, loyal to your sex, I see," he laughed. He stopped and gave her a keen look. "But you and Mrs. Wright were neighbors. I suppose you were friends, too."

Martha Hale shook her head.

"I've seen little enough of her of late years. I've not been in this house—it's more than a year."

"And why was that? You didn't like her?"

"I liked her well enough," she replied with spirit. "Farmers' wives have their hands full, Mr. Henderson. And then . . ." she looked around the kitchen.

"Yes?" he encouraged.

"It never seemed a very cheerful place," said she, more to herself than to him.

"No," he agreed; "I don't think anyone would call it cheerful. I shouldn't say she had the homemaking instinct."

"Well, I don't know as Wright had, either," she muttered.

"You mean they didn't get on very well?" he was quick to ask.

"No; I don't mean anything," she answered, with decision. As she turned a little away from him, she added: "But I don't think a place would be any the cheerfuller for John Wright's bein' in it."

"I'd like to talk to you about that a little later, Mrs. Hale," he said. "I'm anxious to get the lay of things upstairs now."

He moved toward the stair door, followed by the two men.

"I suppose anything Mrs. Peters does'll be all right?" the sheriff inquired. "She was to take in some clothes for her, you know—and a few little things. We left in such a hurry yesterday."

The county attorney looked at the two women whom they were leaving alone there among the kitchen things.

"Yes—Mrs. Peters," he said, his glance resting on the woman who was not Mrs. Peters, the big farmer woman who stood behind the sheriff's wife. "Of course Mrs. Peters is one of us," he said, in a manner of entrusting responsibility. "And keep your eye out, Mrs. Peters, for anything that might be of use. No telling; you women might come upon a clue to the motive—and that's the thing we need."

Mr. Hale rubbed his face after the fashion of a showman getting ready for a pleasantry.

"But would the women know a clue if they did come upon it?" he said; and having delivered himself of this, he followed the others through the stair door.

The women stood motionless and silent, listening to the footsteps, first upon the stairs, then in the room above.

Then, as if releasing herself from something strange, Mrs. Hale began to arrange the dirty pans under the sink, which the county attorney's disdainful push of the foot had deranged.

"I'd hate to have men comin' into my kitchen," she said testily—"snoopin' round and criticizin'."

"Of course it's no more than their duty," said the sheriff's wife, in her manner of timid acquiescence.

"Duty's all right," replied Mrs. Hale bluffly; "but I guess that deputy sheriff that come out to make the fire might have got a little of this on." She gave the roller towel a pull. "Wish I'd thought of that sooner! Seems mean to talk about her for not having things slicked up, when she had to come away in such a hurry."

She looked around the kitchen. Certainly it was not "slicked up." Her eye was held by a bucket of sugar on a low shelf. The cover was off the wooden bucket, and beside it was a paper bag—half full.

Mrs. Hale moved toward it.

"She was putting this in there," she said to herself—slowly.

She thought of the flour in her kitchen at home—half sifted. She had been interrupted, and had left things half done. What had interrupted Minnie Foster? Why had that work been left half done? She made a move as if to finish it—unfinished things always bothered her—and then she glanced around and saw that Mrs. Peters was watching her—and she didn't want Mrs. Peters to get that feeling she had got of work begun and then—for some reason—not finished.

"It's a shame about her fruit," she said, and walked toward the cupboard that the county attorney had opened, and got on the chair, murmuring: "I wonder if it's all gone."

It was a sorry enough looking sight, but "Here's one that's all right," she said at last. She held it toward the light. "This is cherries, too." She looked again. "I declare I believe that's the only one."

With a sigh, she got down from the chair, went to the sink, and wiped off the bottle.

"She'll feel awful bad, after all her hard work in the hot weather. I remember the afternoon I put up my cherries last summer."

She set the bottle on the table, and, with another sigh, started to sit down in the rocker. But she did not sit down. Something kept her from sitting down in that chair. She straightened—stepped back, and, half turned away, stood looking at it, seeing the woman who had sat there "pleatin' at her apron."

The thin voice of the sheriff's wife broke in upon her: "I must be getting those things from the front room closet." She opened the door into the other room, started in, stepped back. "You coming with me, Mrs. Hale?" she asked nervously. "You—you could help me get them."

They were soon back—the stark coldness of that shut-up room was not a thing to linger in.

"My!" said Mrs. Peters, dropping the things on the table and hurrying to the stove.

Mrs. Hale stood examining the clothes the woman who was being detained in town had said she wanted.

"Wright was close!" she exclaimed, holding up a shabby black skirt that bore the marks of much making over. "I think maybe that's why she kept so much to herself. I s'pose she felt she couldn't do her part; and then, you don't enjoy things when you feel shabby. She used to wear pretty clothes and be lively—when she was Minnie Foster, one of the town girls, singing in the choir. But that—oh, that was twenty years ago."

With a carefulness in which there was something tender, she folded the shabby clothes and piled them at one corner of the table. She looked up at Mrs. Peters, and there was something in the other woman's look that irritated her.

"She don't care," she said to herself. "Much difference it makes to her whether Minnie Foster had pretty clothes when she was a girl."

Then she looked again, and she wasn't so sure; in fact, she hadn't at any time been perfectly sure about Mrs. Peters. She had that shrinking manner, and yet her eyes looked as if they could see a long way into things.

"This all you was to take in?" asked Mrs. Hale.

"No," said the sheriff's wife; "she said she wanted an apron. Funny thing to want," she ventured in her nervous little way, "For there's not much to get you dirty in jail, goodness knows. But I suppose just to make her feel more natural. If you're used to wearing an apron—She said they were in the bottom drawer of this cupboard. Yes—here they are. And then her little shawl that always hung on the stair door."

She took the small gray shawl from behind the door leading upstairs.

Suddenly Mrs. Hale took a quick step toward the other woman.

"Mrs. Peters!"

"Yes, Mrs. Hale?"

"Do you think she—did it?"

A frightened look blurred the other thing in Mrs. Peters' eyes.

"Oh, I don't know," she said, in a voice that seemed to shrink away from the subject.

"Well, I don't think she did," affirmed Mrs. Hale stoutly. "Asking for an apron and her little shawl. Worryin' about her fruit."

"Mr. Peters says . . ." Footsteps were heard in the room above; she stopped, looked up, then went on in a lowered voice: "Mr. Peters says—it looks bad for her. Mr. Henderson is awful sarcastic in a speech, and he's going to make fun of her saying she didn't—wake up."

For a moment Mrs. Hale had no answer. Then, "Well, I guess John Wright didn't wake up—when they was slippin that rope under his neck," she muttered.

"No, its *strange*," breathed Mrs. Peters. "They think it was such a—funny way to kill a man."

"That's just what Mr. Hale said," said Mrs. Hale, in a resolutely natural voice. "There was a gun in the house. He says that's what he can't understand."

Mr. Henderson said, coming out, that what was needed for the case was a motive. Something to show anger—or sudden feeling."

"Well, I don't see any signs of anger around here," said Mrs. Hale. "I don't . . ."

She stopped. It was as if her mind tripped on something. Her eye was caught by a dish towel in the middle of the kitchen table. Slowly she moved toward the table. One half of it was wiped clean, the other half messy. Her eyes made a slow, almost unwilling turn to the bucket of sugar and the half-empty bag beside it. Things begun—and not finished.

After a moment she stepped back, and said, in that manner of releasing herself: "Wonder how they're finding things upstairs? I hope she had it a little more red up there. You know"—she paused, and feeling gathered— "it seems kind of *sneaking*: locking her up in town and coming out here to get her own house to turn against her?"

"But, Mrs. Hale," said the sheriff's wife, "the law is the law."

"I s'pose 'tis," answered Mrs. Hale shortly.

She turned to the stove, worked with it a minute, and when she straightened up she said aggressively:

"The law is the law—and a bad stove is a bad stove. How'd you like to cook on this?"—pointing with the poker to the broken lining. She opened the oven door and started to express her opinion of the oven; but she was swept into her own thoughts, thinking of what it would mean, year after year, to have that stove to wrestle with. The thought of Minnie Foster trying to bake in that oven—and the thought of her never going over to see Minnie Foster . . ."

She was startled by hearing Mrs. Peters say:

"A person gets discouraged—and loses heart."

The sheriff's wife had looked from the stove to the pail of water which had been carried in from outside. The two women stood there, silent, above them the footsteps of the men who were looking for evidence against the woman who had worked in that kitchen. That look of seeing into things, of seeing through a thing to something else, was in the eyes of the sheriff's wife now. When Mrs. Hale next spoke to her, it was gently:

"Better loosen up your things, Mrs. Peters. We'll not feel them when we go out."

Mrs. Peters went to the back of the room to hang up the fur tippet she was wearing. A moment later she exclaimed, "Why, she was piecing a quilt," and held up a large sewing basket piled high with quilt pieces.

Mrs. Hale spread some of the blocks out on the table.

"Its' log-cabin pattern," she said, putting several of them together. "Pretty, isn't it?"

They were so engaged with the quilt that they did not hear the footsteps on the stairs. Just as the stair door opened Mrs. Hale was saying:

"Do you suppose she was going to quilt it or just knot it?"

The sheriff threw up his hands.

"They wonder whether she was going to quilt it or just knot it!" he cried.

There was a laugh for the ways of women, a warming of hands over the stove, and then the county attorney said briskly:

"Well, let's go right out to the barn and get that cleared up."

"I don't see as there's anything so strange," Mrs. Hale said resentfully, after the outside door had closed on the three men—"our taking up our time with little things while we're waiting for them to get the evidence. I don't see as it's anything to laugh about."

"Of course they've got awful important things on their minds," said the sheriff's wife apologetically.

They returned to an inspection of the block for the quilt. Mrs. Hale was looking at the fine, even sewing, and was preoccupied with thoughts of the woman who had done that sewing, when she heard the sheriff's wife say, in a queer tone:

"Why, look at this one."

She turned to take the block held out to her.

"The sewing," said Mrs. Peters, in a troubled way. "All the rest of them have been so nice and even—but—this one. Why, it looks as if she didn't know what she was about!"

Their eyes met—something flashed to life, passed between them; then, as if with an effort, they seemed to pull away from each other. A moment Mrs. Hale sat there, her hands folded over that sewing which was so unlike all the rest of the sewing. Then she had pulled a knot and drawn the threads.

"Oh, what are you doing, Mrs. Hale?" asked the sheriff's wife.

"Just pulling out a stitch or two that's not sewed very good," said Mrs. Hale mildly.

"I don't think we ought to touch things," Mrs. Peters said, a little helplessly.

"I'll just finish up this end," answered Mrs. Hale, still in that mild, matter-of-fact fashion.

She threaded a needle and started to replace bad sewing with good. For a little while she sewed in silence. Then, in that thin, timid voice, she heard:

"Mrs. Hale!"

"Yes, Mrs. Peters?"

"What do you suppose she was so—nervous about?"

"Oh, *I* don't know," said Mrs. Hale, as if dismissing a thing not important enough to spend much time on. "I don't know as she was—nervous. I sew awful queer sometimes when I'm just tired."

She cut a thread, and out of the corner of her eye looked up at Mrs. Peters. The small, lean face of the sheriff's wife seemed to have tightened up. Her eyes had that look of peering into something. But next moment she moved, and said in her indecisive way:

"Well, I must get those clothes wrapped. They may be through sooner than we think. I wonder where I could find a piece of paper—and string."

"In that cupboard, maybe," suggested Mrs. Hale, after a glance around.

One piece of the crazy sewing remained unripped. Mrs. Peters' back turned, Martha Hale now scrutinized that piece, compared it with the dainty, accurate sewing of the other blocks. The difference was startling. Holding this block made her feel queer, as if the distracted thoughts of the woman who had perhaps turned to it to try to quiet herself were communicating themselves to her.

Mrs. Peters' voice roused her.

"Here's a birdcage," she said. "Did she have a bird, Mrs. Hale?"

"Why, I don't know whether she did or not." She turned to look at the cage Mrs. Peters was holding up. "I've not been here in so long." She sighed. "There was a man last year selling canaries cheap—but I don't know as she took one. Maybe she did. She used to sing real pretty herself."

"Seems kind of funny to think of a bird here." She half laughed— an attempt to put up a barrier. "But she must have had one—or why would she have a cage? I wonder what happened to it."

"I suppose maybe the cat got it," suggested Mrs. Hale, resuming her sewing.

"No; she didn't have a cat. She's got that feeling some people have about cats—being afraid of them. When they brought her to our house yesterday, my cat got in the room, and she was real upset and asked me to take it out."

"My sister Bessie was like that." Mrs. Hale laughed.

The sheriff's wife did not reply. The silence made Mrs. Hale turn around. Mrs. Peters was examining the birdcage.

"Look at this door," she said slowly. "It's broke. One hinge has been pulled apart."

Mrs. Hale came nearer.

"Looks as if someone must have been—rough with it."

Again their eyes met—startled, questioning, apprehensive. For a moment neither spoke nor stirred. Then Mrs. Hale, turning away, said brusquely:

"If they're going to find any evidence, I wish they'd be about it. I don't like this place."

"But I'm awful glad you came with me, Mrs. Hale." Mrs. Peters put the birdcage on the table and sat down. "It would be lonesome for me—sitting here alone."

"Yes, it would, wouldn't it?" agreed Mrs. Hale, a certain very determined naturalness in her voice. She had picked up the sewing, but now it dropped in her lap, and she murmured in a different voice: "But I tell you what I *do* wish, Mrs. Peters. I wish I had come over sometimes when she was here. I wish—I had."

"But of course you were awful busy, Mrs. Hale. Your house—and your children."

"I could've come," retorted Mrs. Hale shortly. "I stayed away because it weren't cheerful—and that's why I ought to have come. I"—she looked around—"I've never liked this place. Maybe because it's down in a hollow and you don't see the road. I don't know what it is, but it's a lonesome place, and always was. I wish I had come over to see Minnie Foster sometimes. I can see now—" She did not put it into words.

"Well, you mustn't reproach yourself," counseled Mrs. Peters. "Somehow, we just don't see how it is with other folks till—something comes up."

"Not having children makes less work," mused Mrs. Hale, after a silence, "but it makes a quiet house—and Wright out to work all day—and no company when he did come in. Did you know John Wright, Mrs. Peters?"

"Not to know him. I've seen him in town. They say he was a good man."

"Yes—good," conceded John Wright's neighbor grimly. "He didn't drink, and kept his word as well as most, I guess, and paid his debts. But he was a hard man, Mrs. Peters. Just to pass the time of day with him—" She stopped, shivered a little. "Like a raw wind that gets to the bone." Her eye fell upon the cage on the table before her, and she added, almost bitterly, "I should think she would've wanted a bird!"

Suddenly she leaned forward, looking intently at the cage. "But what do you s'pose went wrong with it?"

"I don't know," returned Mrs. Peters; "unless it got sick and died."

But after she said it she reached over and swung the broken door. Both women watched it as if somehow held by it.

"You didn't know—her?" Mrs. Hale asked, a gentler note in her voice.

"Not till they brought her yesterday," said the sheriff's wife.

"She—come to think of it, she was kind of like a bird herself. Real sweet and pretty, but kind of timid and—fluttery. How—she—did—change."

That held her for a long time. Finally, as if struck with a happy thought and relieved to get back to everyday things, she exclaimed:

"Tell you what, Mrs. Peters, why don't you take the quilt in with you? It might take up her mind."

"Why, I think that's a real nice idea, Mrs. Hale," agreed the sheriff's wife, as if she too were glad to come into the atmosphere of a simple kindness. "There couldn't possibly be any objection to that, could there? Now, just what will I take? I wonder if her patches are in here—and her things."

They turned to the sewing basket.

"Here's some red," said Mrs. Hale, bringing out a roll of cloth. Underneath that was a box. "Here, maybe her scissors are in here—and her things." She held it up. "What a pretty box! I'll warrant that was something she had a long time ago—when she was a girl."

She held it in her hand a moment; then, with a little sigh, opened it.

Instantly her hand went to her nose.

"Why . . . !"

Mrs. Peters drew nearer—then turned away.

"There's something wrapped up in this piece of silk," faltered Mrs. Hale.

Her hand not steady, Mrs. Hale raised the piece of silk. "Oh, Mrs. Peters!" she cried, "It's . . ."

Mrs. Peters bent closer.

"It's the bird," she whispered.

"But, Mrs. Peters!" cried Mrs. Hale. "*Look* at it! Its *neck*—look at its neck! It's all—other side *to*."

The sheriff's wife again bent closer.

"Somebody wrung its neck," said she, in a voice that was slow and deep.

And then again the eyes of the two women met—this time clung together in a look of dawning comprehension, of growing horror. Mrs. Peters looked from the dead bird to the broken door of the cage. Again their eyes met. And just then there was a sound at the outside door.

Mrs. Hale slipped the box under the quilt pieces in the basket and sank into the chair before it. Mrs. Peters stood holding to the table. The county attorney and the sheriff came in.

"Well, ladies," said the county attorney, as one turning from serious things to little pleasantries, "have you decided whether she was going to quilt it or knot it?"

"We think," began the sheriff's wife in a flurried voice, "that she was going to—knot it."

He was too preoccupied to notice the change that came in her voice on that last.

"Well, that's very interesting, I'm sure," he said tolerantly. He caught sight of the cage. "Has the bird flown?"

"We think that the cat got it," said Mrs. Hale in a voice curiously even.

He was walking up and down, as if thinking something out.

"Is there a cat?" he asked absently.

Mrs. Hale shot a look up at the sheriff's wife.

"Well, not *now*," said Mrs. Peters. "They're superstitious, you know; they leave."

The county attorney did not heed her. "No sign at all of anyone having come in from the outside," he said to Peters, in the manner of continuing an interrupted conversation. "Their own rope. Now let's go upstairs again and go over it, piece by piece. It would have to have been someone who knew just the . . ."

The stair door closed behind them and their voices were lost.

The two women sat motionless, not looking at each other, but as if peering into something and at the same time holding back. When they spoke now it was as if they were afraid of what they were saying, but as if they could not help saying it.

"She liked the bird," said Martha Hale, low and slowly. "She was going to bury it in the pretty box."

"When I was a girl," said Mrs. Peters, under her breath, "my kitten —there was a boy took a hatchet, and before my eyes—before I could get there—" She covered her face an instant. "If they hadn't held me back I would have"—she caught herself, looked upstairs where footsteps were heard, and finished weakly—"hurt him."

Then they sat without speaking or moving.

"I wonder how it would seem," Mrs. Hale at last began, as if feeling her way over strange ground—"never to have had any children around."

Her eyes made a slow sweep of the kitchen, as if seeing what that kitchen had meant through all the years. "No, Wright wouldn't like the bird," she said after that—"a thing that sang. She used to sing. He killed that too." Her voice tightened.

Mrs. Peters moved easily.

"Of course we don't know who killed the bird."

"I knew John Wright," was Mrs. Hale's answer.

"It was an awful thing was done in this house that night, Mrs. Hale," said the sheriff's wife. "Killing a man while he slept—slipping a thing round his neck that choked the life out of him."

Mrs. Hale's hand went out to the birdcage.

"His neck, choked the life out of him."

"We don't *know* who killed him," whispered Mrs. Peters wildly. "We don't *know*."

Mrs. Hale had not moved. "If there had been years and years of—nothing, then a bird to sing to you, it would be awful—still—after the bird was still."

It was as if something within her, not herself, had spoken, and it found in Mrs. Peters something she did not know as herself.

"I know what stillness is," she said, in a queer, monotonous voice. "When we homesteaded in Dakota, and my first baby died—after he was two years old—and me with no other then . . ."

Mrs. Hale stirred.

"How soon do you suppose they'll be through looking for the evidence?"

"I know what stillness is," repeated Mrs. Peters, in just that same way. Then she too pulled back. "The law has got to punish crime, Mrs. Hale," she said in her tight little way.

"I wish you'd seen Minnie Foster," was the answer, "when she wore a white dress with blue ribbon, and stood up there in the choir and sang."

The picture of that girl, the fact that she had lived neighbor to that girl for twenty years, and had let her die for lack of life, was suddenly more than she could bear.

"Oh, I *wish* I'd come over here once in a while!" she cried. "That was a crime! That was a crime! Who's going to punish that?"

"We mustn't take on," said Mrs. Peters, with a frightened look toward the stairs.

"I might 'a' *known* she needed help! I tell you, its *queer*, Mrs. Peters. We live close together, and we live far apart. We all go through the same things—it's all just a different kind of the same thing! If it weren't—why do you and I *understand*? Why do we *know*—what we know this minute?"

She dashed her hand across her eyes. Then, seeing the jar of fruit on the table, she reached for it and choked out:

"If I was you I wouldn't *tell* her her fruit was gone! Tell her it *ain't*. Tell her it's all right—all of it. Here—take this in to prove it to her! She—she may never know whether it was broke or not."

Mrs. Peters reached out for the bottle of fruit as if she were glad to take it—as if touching a familiar thing, having something to do, could keep her from something else. She got up, looked about for something to wrap the fruit in, took a petticoat from the pile of clothes she had brought from the front room, and nervously started winding that round the bottle.

"My!" she began, in a high, false voice, "it's a good thing the men couldn't hear us! Getting all stirred up over a little thing like a—dead canary." She hurried over that. "As if that could have anything to do with—with—My, wouldn't they *laugh*?"

Footsteps were heard on the stairs.

"Maybe they would," muttered Mrs. Hale—"maybe they wouldn't."

"No, Peters," said the county attorney incisively; "it's all perfectly clear, except the reason for doing it. But you know juries when it comes to women. If there was some definite thing—something to show. Something to make a story about. A thing that would connect up with this clumsy way of doing it."

In a covert way Mrs. Hale looked at Mrs. Peters. Mrs. Peters was looking at her. Quickly they looked away from each other. The outer door opened and Mr. Hale came in.

"I've got the team round now," he said. "Pretty cold out there."

"I'm going to stay here awhile by myself," the county attorney suddenly announced. "You can send Frank out for me, can't you?" he asked the sheriff. "I want to go over everything. I'm not satisfied we can't do better."

Again, for one brief moment, the two women's eyes found one another.

The sheriff came up to the table.

"Did you want to see what Mrs. Peters was going to take in?"

The county attorney picked up the apron. He laughed. "Oh, I guess they're not very dangerous things the ladies have picked out."

Mrs. Hale's hand was on the sewing basket in which the box was concealed. She felt that she ought to take her hand off the basket. She did not seem able to. He picked up one of the quilt blocks which she had piled on to cover the box. Her eyes felt like fire. She had a feeling that if he took up the basket she would snatch it from him.

But he did not take it up. With another little laugh, he turned away.

"No; Mrs. Peters doesn't need supervising. For that matter, a sheriff's wife is married to the law. Ever think of it that way, Mrs. Peters?"

Mrs. Peters was standing beside the table. Mrs. Hale shot a look up at her; but she could not see her face. Mrs. Peters had turned away. When she spoke, her voice was muffled.

"Not—just that way," she said.

"Married to the law!" chuckled Mrs. Peters' husband. He moved toward the door into the front room and said to the county attorney:

"I just want you to come in here a minute, George. We ought to take a look at these windows."

"Oh—windows," said the county attorney scoffingly.

"We'll be right out, Mr. Hale," said the sheriff to the farmer.

Hale went to look after the horses. The sheriff followed the county attorney into the other room. Again—for one final moment—the two women were alone in that kitchen.

Martha Hale sprang up, her hands tight together, looking at that other woman, with whom it rested. At first she could not see her eyes, for the sheriff's wife had not turned back since she turned away at that suggestion of being married to the law. But now Mrs. Hale made her turn back. Her eyes made her turn back. Slowly, unwillingly, Mrs. Peters turned her head until her eyes met the eyes of the other woman. There was a moment when they held each other in a steady, burning look in which there was no evasion nor flinching.

Then Martha Hale's eyes pointed the way to the basket in which was hidden the thing that would make certain the conviction of the other woman—that woman who was not there and yet who had been there with them all through that hour.

For a moment Mrs. Peters did not move. And then she did it. With a rush forward, she threw back the quilt pieces, got the box, tried to put it in her handbag. It was too big. Desperately she opened it, started to take the bird out. But there she broke—she could not touch the bird. She stood there helpless, foolish.

There was the sound of a knob turning in the inner door. Martha Hale snatched the box from the sheriff's wife, and got it in the pocket of her big coat just as the sheriff and the county attorney came back.

"Well, Henry," said the county attorney facetiously, "at least we found out that she was not going to quilt it. She was going to—what is it you call it, ladies?"

Mrs. Hale's hand was against the pocket of her coat.

"We call it—knot it, Mr. Henderson."

7

Trial Lawyers in Action

I know you lawyers can, with ease,
Twist words and meaning as you please;
That language, by your skill made pliant,
Will bend to favor every client;
That 'tis the fee directs the sense,
To make out either side's pretense,
When you peruse the clearest case,
You see it with a double face,
For scepticism is your profession;
You hold there's doubt in all expression.

Fables
John Gay

This first thing we do, let's kill all the lawyers.

Henry VI
William Shakespeare

In the last section we considered the difficult challenge faced by the jury in having to determine guilt or innocence based upon conflicting testimony. Such testimony and supporting evidence are presented to the jury through an adversarial proceeding in which witnesses are guided and controlled by the lawyers who take a pivotal role in the judicial process. The lawyer is trained to argue persuasively on both sides of an issue, and although some lawyers resist taking cases that they feel they cannot win, others are often faced with the weakest side of the case. Even so, they are expected to prepare for trial with the ultimate goal of winning in mind. The lawyer's art of rhetoric is, therefore, his sharpest tool.

"Colonel Starbottle for the Plaintiff" by Bret Harte deals with some of the practices engaged in by a vigorous attorney for the plaintiff. First, Colonel Starbottle has superior oratorical abilities and is a sympathetic pleader to the jury—the members of which laugh, weep, and become impassioned by the colonel's rhetoric. Where is the truth of the case if the outcome depends on the skills of the lawyer? In many instances, only one party is able to afford an experienced and qualified attorney. Should the state ensure that both parties are not only *adequately* but *equally* represented?

Second, when the colonel is asked to take a breach of promise case, his first consideration is what the reaction of the jury will be if he has to read love letters to them. At this point, he considers whether he might be publicly humiliated and the possibility that this will be a losing case. Should lawyers choose only cases which they feel they can win? If so, should this decision be made on the basis of ego, on maintaining reputation, or on the lawyer's ability to adequately represent clients?

Third, the colonel is asked to "tell the whole story [his] own way." The inference is that the lawyer can present the facts in such a way as to persuade the jury that his client is the innocent and injured party. How much leeway should the lawyer have in presenting the facts to the jury? Remember that the lawyer cannot allow his client to perjure himself and has an obligation to report any such perjury to the judge. This is in conflict with the notion that there exists an attorney/client privilege which makes statements made to the attorney by the client confidential unless the client waives that privilege. What is the lawyer to do? Does he instruct the client not to tell him anything that may be harmful to the client if elicited by opposing counsel on cross-examination? That way, the attorney would not know if the client was perjuring himself. In presenting the facts in the most favorable light, isn't the attorney really shading the truth?

Fourth, an attorney needs to be careful that he doesn't have a conflict of interest between two clients. Here, the colonel has represented the upcoming defendant in a previous case. By his own admission, Starbottle considers Mr. Hotchkiss to be a client although the prior litigation has been completed. Other than the fact that the relationship between Mr. Hotchkiss and Starbottle would be wrecked by the colonel's representation of Zaidee, is there any other reason why he should not take this case?

Finally, at one point the colonel develops his own "theory of the case," speculates on what opposing counsel will argue, and develops his own arguments in opposition. The lawyer's training in arguing both sides of the case enables the lawyer, like the colonel, to anticipate every eventuality of the trial. Would the attorney be able to do this successfully if the client withheld information from his own attorney? Surely the attorney needs to know everything that the client knows in order to adequately represent the client. Once again, the attorney is presented with the double bind between knowing and not knowing.

When we think about trial lawyers we usually think about litigators such as Clarence Darrow, William M. Kunstler, or F. Lee Bailey, but the judicial system has a provision that allows a party to appear *pro se*, that is, a party may appear on his or her own behalf. Contemplation of the *pro se* party brings to mind visions of a poor plaintiff or defendant arguing against a skillful, smooth, and sophisticated lawyer for the opposition. There are times, however, when clients represent themselves with ultimate success, such as the protagonist in Irwin Shaw's delightful short story "Triumph of Justice" does. Mike Pilato seeks and finds "justice." Naive Mike believes that lawyers are only needed by the party who is the wrongdoer. Ironically, the judge instructs Victor—antagonist and prevaricator of the truth—that he can "tell the truth without any danger." The danger is, of course, that if

Victor tells the truth, he will be found to be the guilty party and a perjurer. Rather than admonish Mike to retain a lawyer for any possible future proceeding, should not the judge have admonished Victor for his patent perjury?

Colonel Starbottle
for the Plaintiff
Bret Harte

It had been a day of triumph for Colonel Starbottle. First, for his personality, as it would have been difficult to separate the Colonel's achievements from his individuality; second, for his oratorical abilities as a sympathetic pleader; and third, for his functions as the leading legal counsel for the Eureka Ditch Company versus the State of California. On his strictly legal performances in this issue I prefer not to speak; there were those who denied them, although the jury had accepted them in the face of the ruling of the half-amused, half-cynical Judge himself. For an hour they had laughed with the Colonel, wept with him, been stirred to personal indignation or patriotic exaltation by his passionate and lofty periods,—what else could they do than give him their verdict? If it was alleged by some that the American eagle, Thomas Jefferson, and the Resolutions of '98 had nothing whatever to do with the contest of a ditch company over a doubtfully worded legislative document; that whole-sale abuse of the State Attorney and his political motives had not the slightest connection with the legal question raised—it was, nevertheless, generally accepted that the losing party would have been only too glad to have the Colonel on their side. And Colonel Starbottle knew this, as, perspiring, florid, and panting he rebuttoned the lower buttons of his blue frock-coat, which had become loosed in an oratorical spasm, and readjusted his old-fashioned, spotless shirt frill above it as he strutted from the court-room amidst the hand shakings and acclamations of his friends.

And there an unprecedented thing occurred. The Colonel absolutely declined spirituous refreshment at the neighboring Palmetto Saloon, and declared his intention of proceeding directly to his office in the adjoining square. Nevertheless, the Colonel quitted the building alone, and apparently unarmed, except for his faithful gold-headed stick, which hung as usual from his forearm. The crowd gazed after him with undisguised admiration of this new evidence of his pluck. It was remembered also that a mysterious note had been handed to him at the conclusion of his speech,— evidently a challenge from the State Attorney. It was quite plain that the Colonel—a practiced duelist—was hastening home to answer it.

But herein they were wrong. The note was in a female hand, and simply requested the Colonel to accord an interview with the writer at the Colonel's office as soon as he left the court. But it was an engagement that the Colonel—and devoted to the fair sex as he was to the "code"—was no less prompt in accepting. He flicked away the dust from his spotless white trousers and varnished boots with his handkerchief, and settled his black cravat under his Byron collar as he neared his office. He was surprised, however, on opening the door of his private office, to find his visitor already there; he was still more startled to find her somewhat past middle age and plainly attired. But the Colonel was brought up in a school of Southern politeness, already antique in the republic, and his bow of courtesy belonged to the epoch of his shirt frill and strapped trousers. No one could have detected his disappointment in his manner, albeit his sentences were short and complete. But the colonel's colloquial speech was apt to be fragmentary incoherencies of his larger oratorical utterances.

"A thousand pardons—for—er—having kept a lady waiting—er! But—er—congratulations of friends—and—er—courtesy due to them—er—interfered with—though perhaps only heightened—by procrastination—the pleasure of—ha!" And the Colonel completed his sentence with a gallant wave of his fat but white and well-kept hand.

"Yes! I came to see you along o' that speech of yours. I was in court. When I heard you gettin' it off on that jury, I says to myself, 'That's the kind o' lawyer I want. A man that's flowery and convincin'! Just the man to take up our case.'"

"Ah! It's a matter of business, I see," said the Colonel, inwardly relieved, but externally careless. "And—er—may I ask the nature of the case?"

"Well! it's a breach-o'-promise suit," said the visitor calmly.

If the colonel had been surprised before, he was now really startled, and with an added horror that required all his politeness to conceal. Breach-of-promise cases were his peculiar aversion. He had always held them to be a kind of litigation which could have been obviated by the prompt killing of the masculine offender—in which case he would have gladly defended the killer. But a suit of damages,—*damages!*—with the reading of love-letters before a hilarious jury and court, was against all his instincts. His chivalry was outraged; his sense of humor was small, and in the course of his career he had lost one or two important cases through an unexpected development of this quality in a jury.

The woman had evidently noticed his hesitation, but mistook its cause. "It ain't me—but my darter."

The Colonel recovered his politeness. "Ah! I am relieved, my dear madam! I could hardly conceive a man ignorant enough to—er—er—throw away such evident good fortune—or base enough to deceive the trustfulness of womanhood—mature and experienced only in the chivalry of our sex, ha!"

The woman smiled grimly. "Yes!—it's my darter, Zaidee Hooker—so ye might spare some of them pretty speeches for *her*—before the jury."

The Colonel winced slightly before this doubtful prospect, but smiled. "Ha! Yes!—certainly—the jury. But—er—my dear lady, need we go as far as that? Cannot this affair be settled—er—out of court? Could not this—er—individual—be admonished—told that he must give satisfaction—personal satisfaction—for his dastardly conduct—to—er—near relative—or even valued personal friend? The—er—arrangements necessary for that purpose I myself would undertake."

He was quite sincere; indeed, his small black eyes shone with that fire which a pretty woman or an "affair of honor" could alone kindle. The visitor stared vacantly at him, and said slowly, "And what good is that goin' to do *us*?"

"Compel him to—er—perform his promise," said the Colonel, leaning back in his chair.

"Ketch him doin' it!" she exclaimed scornfully. "No—that ain't wot we're after. We must make him *pay*! Damages—and nothin' short o' *that*."

The Colonel bit his lip. "I suppose," he said gloomily, "you have documentary evidence—written promises and protestations—er—er—love-letters, in fact?"

"No—nary a letter! Ye see, that's jest it—and that's where *you* come in. You've got to convince that jury yourself. You've got to show what it is—tell the whole story your own way. Lord! to a man like you that's nothin'."

Startling as this admission might have been to any other lawyer, Starbottle was absolutely relieved by it. The absence of any mirth-provoking correspondence, and the appeal solely to his own powers of persuasion, actually struck his fancy. He lightly put aside the compliment with a wave of his white hand.

"Of course," he said confidently, "there is strongly presumptive and corroborative evidence? Perhaps you can give me—er—a brief outline of the affair?"

"Zaidee kin do that straight enough, I reckon," said the woman; "what I want to know first is, kin you take the case?"

The Colonel did not hesitate; his curiosity was piqued. "I certainly can. I have no doubt your daughter will put me in possession of sufficient facts and details—to constitute what we call—er—a brief."

"She kin be brief enough—or long enough—for the matter of that," said the woman, rising. The Colonel accepted this implied witticism with a smile.

"And when may I have the pleasure of seeing her?" he asked politely.

"Well, I reckon as soon as I can trot out and call her. She's just outside, meanderin' in the road—kinder shy, ye know, at first."

She walked to the door. The astounded Colonel nevertheless gallantly accompanied her as she stepped out into the street and called shrilly, "You Zaidee!"

A young girl here apparently detached herself from a tree and the ostentatious perusal of an old election poster, and sauntered down towards the office door. Like her mother, she was plainly dressed; unlike her, she had a pale, rather refined face, with a demure mouth and downcast eyes. This was all the Colonel saw as he bowed profoundly and led the way into his office, for she accepted his salutations without lifting her head. He helped her gallantly to a chair, on which she seated herself sideways, somewhat ceremoniously, with her eyes following the point of her parasol as she traced a pattern on the carpet. A second chair offered to the mother, that lady, however, declined. "I reckon to leave you and Zaidee together to talk it out," she said; turning to her daughter, she added, "Jest you tell him all, Zaidee," and before the Colonel could rise again, disappeared from the room. In spite of his professional experience, Starbottle was for a moment embarrassed. The young girl, however, broke the silence without looking up.

"Adoniram K. Hotchkiss," she began, in a monotonous voice, as if it were a recitation addressed to the public, "first began to take notice of me a year ago. Arter that—off and on"—

"One moment," interrupted the astounded Colonel; "do you mean Hotchkiss the President of the Ditch Company?" He had recognized the name of a prominent citizen—a rigid, ascetic, taciturn, middle-aged man—a deacon—and more than that, the head of the company he had just defended. It seemed inconceivable.

"That's him," she continued, with eyes still fixed on the parasol and without changing her monotonous tone—"off and on ever since. Most of the time at the Free-Will Baptist Church—at morning service, prayer-meetings, and such. And at home—outside—er—in the road."

"Is it this gentleman—Mr. Adoniram K. Hotchkiss—who—er—promised marriage?" stammered the Colonel.

"Yes."

The Colonel shifted uneasily in his chair. "Most extraordinary! for—you see—my dear young lady—this becomes a—er—most delicate affair."

"That's what maw said," returned the young woman simply, yet with the faintest smile playing around her demure lips and downcast cheek.

"I mean," said the Colonel, with a pained yet courteous smile, "that this—er—gentleman—is in fact—er—one of my clients."

"That's what maw said too, and of course your knowing him will make it all the easier for you."

A slight flush crossed the Colonel's cheek as he returned quickly and a little stiffly, "On the contrary—er—it may make it impossible for me to—er—act in this matter."

The girl lifted her eyes. The Colonel held his breath as the long lashes were raised to his level. Even to an ordinary observer that sudden revelation of her eyes seemed to transform her face with subtle witchery. They were large, brown, and soft, yet filled with an extraordinary penetration and prescience. They were the eyes of an experienced woman of thirty fixed in the face of a child. What else the Colonel saw there Heaven only knows! He felt his inmost secrets plucked from him—his whole soul laid bare—his vanity, belligerency, gallantry—even his medieval chivalry, penetrated, and yet illuminated, in that single glance. And when the eyelids fell again, he felt that a greater part of himself had been swallowed up in them.

"I beg your pardon," he said hurriedly, "I mean—this matter may be arranged—er—amicably. My interest with—and as you wisely say—my—er—knowledge of my client—er—Mr. Hotchkiss—may effect—a compromise."

"And damages," said the young girl, readdressing her parasol, as if she had never looked up.

The Colonel winced. "And—er—undoubtedly compensation—if you do not press a fulfillment of the promise. Unless," he said, with an attempted return to his former easy gallantry, which, however, the recollection of her eyes made difficult, "it is a question of—er—the affections."

"Which?" asked his fair client softly.

"If you still love him?" explained the Colonel, actually blushing.

Zaidee again looked up; again taking the Colonel's breath away with eyes that expressed not only the fullest perception of what he had said, but of what he thought and had not said, and with an added subtle suggestion of what he might have thought. "That's tellin'," she said, dropping her long lashes again.

The Colonel laughed vacantly. Then feeling himself growing imbecile, he forced an equally weak gravity. "Pardon me—I understand there are no letters; may I know the way in which he formulated his declaration and promises?"

"Hymn-books."

"I beg your pardon," said the mystified lawyer.

"Hymn-books—marked words in them with pencil—and passed 'em on to me," repeated Zaidee. "Like 'love,' 'dear,' 'precious,' 'sweet,' and 'blessed,'" she added, accenting each word with a push of her parasol on the carpet. "Sometimes a whole line outer Tate and Brady—and Solomon's Song, you know, and sich."

"I believe," said the Colonel loftily, "that the—er—phrases of sacred psalmody lend themselves to the langauge of the affections. But in regard to the distinct promise of marriage—was there—er—no other expression?"

"Marriage Service in the prayer-book—lines and words outer that— all marked," Zaidee replied.

The Colonel nodded naturally and approvingly. "Very good. Were others cognizant of this? Were there any witnesses?"

"Of course not," said the girl. "Only me and him. It was generally at church-time—or prayer-meeting. Once, in passing the plate, he slipped one o' them peppermint lozenges with the letters stamped on it 'I love you' for me to take."

The Colonel coughed slightly, "And you have the lozenge?"

"I ate it."

"Ah," said the Colonel. After a pause he added delicately, "but were these attentions—er—confined to—er—sacred precincts? Did he meet you elsewhere?"

"Useter pass our house on the road," returned the girl, dropping into her monotonous recital, "and useter signal."

"Ah, signal?" repeated the Colonel approvingly.

"Yes! He'd say 'Keerow,' and I'd say 'Keeree.' Suthing like a bird, you know."

Indeed, as she lifted her voice in imitation of the call, the Colonel thought it certainly very sweet and birdlike. At least as she gave it. With his remembrance of the grim deacon he had doubts as to the melodiousness of his utterance. He gravely made her repeat it.

"And after that signal?" he added suggestively.

"He'd pass on."

The Colonel again coughed slightly, and tapped his desk with his penholder.

"Were there any endearments—er—caresses—er—such as taking your hand—er—clasping your waist?" he suggested, with a gallant yet respectful sweep of his white hand and bowing of his head; "er—slight pressure of your fingers in the changes of a dance—I mean," he corrected himself, with an apologetic cough—"in the passing of the plate?"

"No; he was not what you'd call 'fond,'" returned the girl.

"Ah! Adoniram K. Hotchkiss was not 'fond' in the ordinary acceptance of the word," noted the Colonel, with professional gravity.

She lifted her disturbing eyes, and again absorbed his in her own. She also said "Yes," although her eyes in their mysterious prescience of all he was thinking disclaimed the necessity of any answer at all. He smiled vacantly. There was a long pause; on which she slowly disengaged her parasol from the carpet pattern, and stood up.

"I reckon that's about all," she said.

"Er—yes—but one moment," began the Colonel vaguely. He would have liked to keep her longer, but with her strange premonition of him he felt powerless to detain her, or explain his reason for doing so. He instinctively knew she had told him all; his professional judgment told him that a more hopeless case had never come to his knowledge. Yet he was not daunted, only embarrassed. "No matter," he said. "Of course I shall have to consult with you again."

Her eyes again answered that she expected he would, and she added simply, "When?"

"In the course of a day or two," he replied quickly. "I will send you word."

She turned to go. In his eagerness to open the door for her, he upset his chair, and with some confusion, that was actually youthful, he almost impeded her movements in the hall, and knocked his broad-brimmed Panama hat from his bowing hand in a final gallant sweep. Yet as her small, trim, youthful figure, with its simple Leghorn straw hat confined by a blue bow under her round chin, passed away before him, she looked more like a child than ever.

The Colonel spent that afternoon in making diplomatic inquiries. He found his youthful client was the daughter of a widow who had a small ranch on the cross-roads, near the new Free-Will Baptist Church—the evident theatre of this pastoral. They led a secluded life, the girl being little known in the town, and her beauty and fascination apparently not yet being a recognized fact. The Colonel felt a pleasurable relief at this, and a general satisfaction he could not account for. His few inquires concerning Mr. Hotchkiss only confirmed his own impressions of the alleged lover,—a serious-mined, practically abstracted man, abstentive of youthful society, and the last man apparently capable of levity of the affections or serious flirtation. The Colonel was mystified, but determined of purpose, whatever that purpose might have been.

The next day he was at his office at the same hour. He was alone—

as usual—the Colonel's office being really his private lodgings, disposed in connecting rooms, a single apartment reserved for consultation. He had no clerk, his papers and briefs being taken by his faithful body-servant and ex-slave "Jim" to another firm who did his office work since the death of Major Stryker, the Colonel's only law partner, who fell in a duel some years previous. With a fine constancy the Colonel still retained his partner's name on his doorplate, and, it was alleged by the superstitious, kept a certain invincibility also through the *manes* of the lamented and somewhat feared man.

The Colonel consulted his watch, whose heavy gold case still showed the marks of a providential interference with a bullet destined for its owner, and replaced it with some difficulty and shortness of breath in his fob. At the same moment he heard a step in the passage, and the door opened to Adoniram K. Hotchkiss. The Colonel was impressed; he had a duelist's respect for punctuality.

The man entered with a nod and the expectant inquiring look of a busy man. As his feet crossed the sacred threshold the Colonel became all courtesy; he placed a chair for his visitor, and too, his hat from his half-reluctant hand. He then opened a cupboard and brought out a bottle of whiskey and two glasses.

"A—er—slight refreshment, Mr. Hotchkiss," he suggested politely.

"I never drink," replied Hotchkiss, with the severe attitude of a total abstainer.

"Ah—er—not the finest Bourbon whiskey, selected by a Kentucky friend? No? pardon me! A cigar, then—the mildest Havana."

"I do not use tobacco nor alcohol in any form," repeated Hotchkiss ascetically. "I have no foolish weaknesses."

The Colonel's moist, beady eyes swept silently over his client's sallow face. He leaned back comfortably in his chair, and half closing his eyes as in dreamy reminiscence, said slowly: "Your reply, Mr. Hotchkiss, reminds me of—er—sing'lar circumstance that—er—occurred, in point of fact—at the St. Charles Hotel, New Orleans. Pinky Hornblower—personal friend—invited Senator Doolittle to join him in a social glass. Received, sing'larly enough reply similar to yours. 'Don't drink nor smoke?' said Pinkey. 'Gad, sir, you must be mighty sweet on the ladies.' Ha!" The Colonel paused long enough to allow the faint flush to pass from Hotchkiss's cheek, and went on, half closing his eyes: "'I allow no man, sir, to discuss my personal habits,' declared Doolittle, over his shirt collar. 'Then I reckon shootin' must be one of those habits,' said Pinkey coolly. Both men drove out on the Shell Road back of cemetery next morning. Pinkey put a bullet at twelve paces through Doolittle's temple. Poor Doo never spoke again. Left three wives and seven children, they say—two of 'em black."

"I got a note from you this morning," said Hotchkiss, with badly concealed impatience. "I suppose in reference to our case. You have taken judgment, I believe."

The Colonel, without replying, slowly filled a glass of whiskey and water. For a moment he held it dreamily before him, as if still engaged in gentle reminiscences called up by the act. Then tossing it off, he wiped his lips with a large white handkerchief, and leaning back comfortably in his chair, said, with a wave of his hand, "The interview I requested, Mr. Hotchkiss, concerns a subject—which I may say is—er—er—at present *not* of a public or business nature—although *later* it might become—er—er— both. It is an affair of some—er—delicacy."

The Colonel paused, and Mr. Hotchkiss regarded him with increased impatience. The Colonel, however, continued, with unchanged deliberation: "It concerns—er—er—a young lady—a beautiful, high-souled creature, sir, who, apart from her personal loveliness—er—er—I may say is one of the first families of Missouri, and—er—not remotely connected by marriage with one of—er—er—my boyhood's dearest friends." The latter, I grieve to say, was a pure invention of the Colonel's—an oratorical addition to the scanty information he had obtained the previous day. "The young lady," he continued blandly, "enjoys the further distinction of being the object of such attention from you as would make this interview— really—a confidential matter—er—er—among friends and—er—er— relation in present and future. I need not say that the lady I refer to is Miss Zaidee Juno Hooker, only daughter of Almira Ann Hooker, relict of Jefferson Brown Hooker, formerly of Boone County, Kentucky, and latterly of—er—Pike County, Missouri."

The sallow, ascetic hue of Mr. Hotchkiss's face had passed through a livid and then a greenish shade, and finally settled into a sullen red. "What's all this about?" he demanded roughly.

The least touch of belligerent fire came into Starbottle's eye, but his bland courtesy did not change. "I believe," he said politely, "I have made myself clear as between—er—gentlemen, though perhaps not as clear as I should to—er—er—jury."

Mr. Hotchkiss was apparently struck with some significance in the lawyer's reply. "I don't know," he said, in a lower and more cautious voice, "what you mean by what you call 'my attentions' to—any one—or how it concerns you. I have not exchanged half a dozen words with—the person you name—have never written her a line—nor even called at her house."

He rose with an assumption of ease, pulled down his waistcoat, buttoned his coat, and took up his hat. The Colonel did not move.

"I believe I have already indicated my meaning in what I have called 'your attentions,'" said the Colonel blandly, "and given you my 'concern' for speaking as—er—er—mutual friend. As to your statement of your relations with Miss Hooker, I may state that it is fully corroborated by the statement of the young lady herself in this very office yesterday."

"Then what does this impertinent nonsense mean? Why am I summoned her?" demanded Hotchkiss furiously.

"Because," said the Colonel deliberately, "that statement is infamously—yes, damnably to your discredit, sir!"

Mr. Hotchkiss was here seized by one of those impotent and inconsistent rages which occasionally betray the habitually cautious and timid man. He caught up the Colonel's stick, which was laying on the table. At the same moment the Colonel, without any apparent effort, grasped it by the handle. To Mr. Hotchkiss's astonishment, the stick separated in two pieces, leaving the handle and about two feet of narrow glittering steel in the Colonel's hand. The man recoiled, dropping the useless fragment. The Colonel picked it up, fitted the shining blade in it, clicked the spring, and then rising with a face of courtesy yet of unmistakably genuine pain, and with even a slight tremor in his voice, said gravely,—

"Mr. Hotchkiss, I owe you a thousand apologies, sir, that—er—a weapon should be drawn by me—even through your own inadvertence— under the sacred protection of my roof, and upon an unarmed man. I beg your pardon, sir, and I even withdraw the expressions which provoked that inadvertence. Nor does this apology prevent you from holding me respon- sible—personally responsible—elsewhere for an indiscretion committed in behalf of a lady—my—er—client."

"Your client? Do you mean you have taken her case? You, the counsel for the Ditch Company?" asked Mr. Hotchkiss, in trembling indig- nation.

"Having won your case, sir," replied the Colonel coolly, "the—er— usages of advocacy do not prevent me from espousing the cause of the weak and unprotected."

"We shall see, sir," said Hotchkiss, grasping the handle of the door and backing into the passage. "There are other lawyers who"—

"Permit me to see you out," interrupted the Colonel, rising politely.

—"will be ready to resist the attacks of blackmail," continued Hotchkiss, retreating along the passage.

"And then you will be able to repeat your remarks to me in the street," continued the Colonel, bowing, as he persisted in following his visitor to the door.

But here Mr. Hotchkiss quickly slammed it behind him, and hurried away. The Colonel returned to his office, and sitting down, took a sheet of letter-paper bearing the inscription "Starbottle and Stryker, Attorneys and Counselors," and wrote the following lines:—

HOOKER *versus* HOTCHKISS.

DEAR MADAM,—Having had a visit from the defendant in above, we should be pleased to have an interview with you at two p.m. tomorrow.

Your obedient servants,
STARBOTTLE AND STRYKER.

This he sealed and dispatched by his trusted servant Jim, and then devoted a few moments to reflection. It was the custom of the Colonel to act first, and justify the action by reason afterwards.

He knew that Hotchkiss would at once lay the matter before rival counsel. He knew that they would advise him that Miss Hooker had "no case"—that she would be nonsuited on her own evidence, and he ought not to compromise, but be ready to stand trial. He believed, however, that Hotchkiss feared such exposure, and although his own instincts had been at first against this remedy, he was now instinctively in favor of it. He re- membered his own power with a jury; his vanity and his chivalry alike approved of this heroic method; he was bound by no prosaic facts—he had his own theory of the case, which no mere evidence could gainsay. In fact, Mrs. Hooker's admission that he was to "tell the story in his own way" actually appeared to him an inspiration and a prophecy.

Perhaps there was something else, due possibly to the lady's wonderful eyes, of which he had thought much. Yet it was not her simplicity that affected him solely; on the contrary, it was her apparent intelligent reading of the character of her recreant lover—and of his own! Of all the Colonel's previous "light" or "serious" loves, none had ever before flattered him in that way. And it was this, combined with the respect which he had held for their professional relations, that precluded his having a more familiar knowledge of his client, through serious questioning or playful gallantry. I am not sure it was not part of the charm to have a rustic *femme incomprise* as a client.

Nothing could exceed the respect with which he greeted her as she entered his office the next day. He even affected not to notice that she had put on her best clothes, and, he made no doubt, appeared as when she had first attracted the mature yet faithless attentions of Deacon Hotchkiss at church. A white virginal muslin was belted around her slim figure by a blue ribbon, and her Leghorn hat was drawn around her oval cheek by a bow of the same color. She had a Southern girls' narrow feet, encased in white stockings and kid slippers, which were crossed primly before her as she sat in a chair, supporting her arm by her faithful parasol planted firmly on the floor. A faint odor of southern wood exhaled from her, and, oddly enough, stirred the Colonel with a far-off recollection of a pine-shaded Sunday-school on a Georgia hillside, and of his first love, aged ten, in a short starched frock. Possibly it was the same recollection that revived something of the awkwardness she had felt then.

He, however, smiled vaguely, and sitting down, coughed slightly, and placed his finger-tips together. "I have had an—er—interview with Mr. Hotchkiss, but—I—er—regret to say there seems to be no prospect of—er—compromise."

He paused, and to his surprise her listless "company" face lit up with an adorable smile. "Of course!—ketch him!" she said. "Was he mad when you told him?" She put her knees comfortably together and leaned forward for a reply.

For all that, wild horses could not have torn from the Colonel a word about Hotchkiss's anger. "He expressed his intention of employing counsel—and defending a suit," returned the Colonel, affably basking in her smile.

She dragged her chair nearer his desk. "Then you'll fight him tooth and nail?" she asked eagerly; "you'll show him up? You'll tell the whole story your own way? You'll give him fits?—and you'll make him pay? Sure?" she went on breathlessly.

"I—er—will," said the Colonel almost as breathlessly.

She caught his fat white hand, which was lying on the table, between her own and lifted it to her lips. He felt her soft young fingers even through the lisle-thread gloves that encased them, and the warm moisture of her lips upon his skin. He felt himself flushing—but was unable to break the silence or change his position. The next moment she had scuttled back with her chair to her old position.

"I—er—certainly shall do my best," stammered the Colonel, in an attempt to recover his dignity and composure.

"That's enough! You'll do it," said she enthusiastically. "Lordy! Just you talk for me as ye did for his old Ditch Company, and you'll fetch it—every time! Why, when you made that jury sit up the other day—when you got that off about the Merrikan flag waving equally over the rights of honest citizens banded together in peaceful commercial pursuits, as well as over the fortress of official proflig—"

"Oligarchy," murmured the Colonel courteously.

—"oligarchy," repeated the girl quickly, "my breath was just took away. I said to maw, 'Ain't he too sweet for anything!' I did, honest Injin! And when you rolled it all off at the end—never missing a word (you didn't need to mark 'em in a lesson-book, but had 'em all ready on your tongue)— and walked out—Well! I didn't know you nor the Ditch Company from Adam, but I could have just run over and kissed you there before the whole court!"

She laughed, with her face glowing, although her strange eyes were cast down. Alack! the Colonel's face was equally flushed, and his own beady eyes were on his desk. To any other woman he would have voiced the banal gallantry that he should now, himself, look forward to that reward, but her words never reached his lips. He laughed, coughed slightly, and when he looked up again she had fallen into the same attitude as on her first visit, with her parasol point on the floor.

"I must ask you to—er—direct your memory to—er—another point: the breaking off of the—er—er—er—engagement. Did he—er—give any reason for it? Or show any cause?"

"No; he never said anything," returned the girl.

"Not in his usual way?—er—no reproaches out of the hymn-book?—or the sacred writings?"

"No; he just *quit*."

"Er—ceased his attentions," said the Colonel gravely. "And naturally you—er—were not conscious of any cause for his doing so."

The girl raised her wonderful eyes so suddenly and so penetratingly without replying in any other way that the Colonel could only hurriedly say: "I see! None, of course!"

At which she rose, the Colonel rising also. "We—shall begin proceedings at once. I must, however, caution you to answer no questions, nor say anything about this case to any one until you are in court."

She answered his request with another intelligent look and a nod. He accompanied her to the door. As he took her proffered hand, he raised the lisle-thread fingers to his lips with old-fashioned gallantry. As if that act had condoned for his first omissions and awkwardness, he became his old-fashioned self again, buttoned his coat, pulled out his shirt frill, and strutted back to his desk.

A day or two later it was known throughout the town that Zaidee Hooker had sued Adoniram Hotchkiss for breach of promise, and that the damages were laid at five thousand dollars. As in those bucolic days the

Western press was under the secure censorship of a revolver, a cautious tone of criticism prevailed, and any gossip was confined to personal expression, and even then at the risk of the gossiper. Nevertheless, the situation provoked the intensest curiosity. The Colonel was approached—until his statement that he should consider any attempt to overcome his professional secrecy a personal reflection withheld further advances. The community were left to the more ostentatious information of the defendant's counsel, Messrs. Ketcham and Bilser, that the case was "ridiculous" and "rotten," that the plaintiff would be nonsuited, and the fire-eating Starbottle would be taught a lesson that he could not "bully" the law, and there were some dark hints of a conspiracy. It was even hinted that the "case" was the revengeful and preposterous outcome of the refusal of Hotchkiss to pay Starbottle an extravagant fee for his late services to the Ditch Company. It is unnecessary to say that these words were not reported to the Colonel. It was, however, an unfortunate circumstance for the calmer, ethical consideration of the subject that the Church sided with Hotchkiss, as this provoked an equal adherence to the plaintiff and Starbottle on the part of the larger body of non-church-goes, who were delighted at a possible exposure of the weakness of religious rectitude. "I've allus had my suspicions o' them early candle-light meetings down at that gospel shop," said one critic, "and I reckon Deacon Hotchkiss didn't rope in the gals to attend jest for psalm-singing." "Then for him to get up and leave the board afore the game's finished and try to sneak out of it," said another,—"I suppose that's what they call *religious.*"

It was therefore not remarkable that the court-house three weeks later was crowded with an excited multitude of the curious and sympathizing. The fair plaintiff, with her mother, was early in attendance, and under the Colonel's advice appeared in the same modest garb in which she had first visited his office. This and her downcast, modest demeanor were perhaps at first disappointing to the crowd who had evidently expected a paragon of loveliness in this Circe of that grim, ascetic defendant, who sat beside his counsel. But presently all eyes were fixed on the Colonel who certainly made up in *his* appearance any deficiency of his fair client. His portly figure was clothed in a blue dress coat with brass buttons, a buff waistcoat which permitted his frilled shirt-front to become erectile above it, a black satin stock which confined a boyish turned-down collar around his full neck, and immaculate drill trousers, strapped over varnished boots. A murmur ran round the court. "Old 'Personally Responsible' has got his war-paint on"; "The Old War-Horse is smelling powder," were whispered comments. Yet for all that, the most irreverent among them recognized vaguely, in this bizarre figure, something of an honored part in their country's history and possibly felt the spell of old deeds and old names that had once thrilled their boyish pulses. The new District Judge returned Colonel Starbottle's profoundly punctilious bow. The Colonel was followed by his negro servant, carrying a parcel of hymn-books and Bibles, who, with a courtesy evidently imitated from his master, placed one before the opposite counsel. This, after a first curious glance, the lawyer somewhat superciliously tossed aside. But when Jim, proceeding to the jury-box, placed with equal politeness the remaining copies before the jury, the opposite counsel sprang to his feet.

"I want to direct the attention of the court to this unprecedented tampering with the jury, by this gratuitous exhibition of matter impertinent and irrelevant to the issue."

The Judge cast an inquiring look at Colonel Starbottle.

"May it please the court," returned Colonel Starbottle with dignity ignoring the counsel, "the defendant's counsel will observe that he is already furnished with the matter—which I regret to say he has treated—in the presence of the Court—and of his client, a deacon of the church—with—er—great superciliousness. When I state to your Honor that the books in question are hymn-book and copies of the Holy Scriptures, and that they are for the instruction of the jury, to whom I shall have to refer them in the course of my opening, I believe I am within my rights."

"The act is certainly unprecedented," said the Judge dryly, "but unless the counsel for the plaintiff expects the jury to *sing* from these hymn-books, their introduction is not improper, and I cannot admit the objection. As defendant's counsel are furnished with copies also, they cannot plead 'surprise,' as in the introduction of new matter, and as plaintiff's counsel relies evidently upon the jury's attention to his opening, he would not be the first person to distract it." After a pause he added, addressing the Colonel, who remained standing, "The Court is with you, sir; proceed."

But the Colonel remained motionless and statuesque with folded arms.

"I have overruled the objection," repeated the Judge "you may go on."

"I am waiting, your Honor, for the—er—withdrawal by the defendant's counsel of the word 'tampering,' as refers to myself, and of 'impertinent,' as refers to the sacred volumes."

"The request is a proper one, and I have no doubt will be acceded to," returned the Judge quietly. The defendant's counsel rose and mumbled a few words of apology and the incident closed. There was, however, a general feeling that the Colonel had in some way "scored," and if his object had been to excite the greatest curiosity about the books, he had made his point.

But impassive of his victory, he inflated his chest, with his right hand in the breast of his buttoned coat, and began. His usual high color had paled slightly, but the small pupils of his prominent eyes glittered like steel. The young girl leaned forward in her chair with an attention so breathless, a sympathy so quick, and an admiration so artless and unconscious that in an instant she divided with the speaker the attention of the whole assemblage. It was very hot; the court was crowded to suffocation; even the open windows revealed a crowd of faces outside the building, eagerly following the Colonel's words.

He would remind the jury that only a few weeks ago he stood there as the advocate of a powerful Company, then represented by the present defendant. He spoke then as the champion of strict justice against legal oppression; no less should he to-day champion the cause of the unprotected and the comparatively innocent—even though the plaintiff of yesterday was the defendant of to-day. As he approached the court a moment ago he had raised his eyes and beheld the starry flag flying from its dome, and he knew that glorious banner was a symbol of the perfect equality, under the Constitution, of the rich and the poor, the strong and the weak—an equality which made the simple citizen taken from the plough in the field, the pick in the gulch, or from behind the counter in the mining town, who served on that jury, the equal arbiters of justice with that highest legal luminary whom they were proud to welcome on the bench to-day. The Colonel paused, with a stately bow to the impassive Judge. It was this, he continued, which lifted his heart as he approached the building. And yet—he had entered it with an uncertain—he might almost say—a timid step. And why? He knew, gentlemen, he was about to confront a profound—ay! a sacred responsibility! Those hymn-books and holy writings handed to the jury were not, as his Honor had surmised, for the purpose of enabling the jury to indulge in—er—preliminary choral exercise! He might, indeed, say, "Alas, not!" They were the damning, incontrovertible proofs of the perfidy of the defendant. And they would prove as terrible a warning to him as the fatal characters upon Belshazzar's wall. There was a strong sensation. Hotchkiss turned a sallow green. His lawyers assumed a careless smile.

It was his duty to tell them that this was not one of those ordinary "breach-of-promise" cases which were too often the occasion of ruthless mirth and indecent levity in the court-room. The jury would find nothing of that there. There were no love-letters with the epithets of endearment, nor those mystic crosses and ciphers which, he had been credibly informed chastely hid the exchange of those mutual caresses known as "kisses." There was no cruel tearing of the veil from those sacred privacies of the human affection; there was no forensic shouting out of those fond confidences meant only for *one*. But there was, he was shocked to say, a new sacrilegious intrusion. The weak pipings of Cupid were mingled with the chorus of the saints,—the sanctity of the temple known as the "meeting-house" was desecrated by proceedings more in keeping with the shrine of Venus; and the inspired writings themselves were used as the medium of amatory and wanton flirtation by the defendant in his sacred capacity as deacon.

The Colonel artistically paused after this thunderous denunciation. The jury turned eagerly to the leaves of the hymn-books, but the larger gaze of the audience remained fixed upon the speaker and the girl, who sat in rapt admiration of his periods. After the hush, the Colonel continued in a lower and sadder voice: "There are, perhaps, a few of us here, gentlemen,—with the exception of the defendant,—who can arrogate to themselves the title of regular church-goers, or to whom these humbler functions of the prayer-meeting, the Sunday-school, and the Bible-class are habitually familiar. Yet"—more solemnly—"down in our hearts is the deep conviction of our shortcomings and failings, and a laudable desire that others, at least, should profit by the teachings we neglect. Perhaps," he continued, closing his eyes dreamily, "there is not a man here who does not recall the happy days of his boyhood, the rustic village spire, the lessons shared with some artless village maiden, with whom he later sauntered, hand in hand, through the woods, as the simple rhyme rose upon their lips,—

'Always make it a point to have it a rule,
Never to be late at the Sabbath-school.'

He would recall the strawberry feasts, the welcome annual picnic, redolent with hunks of gingerbread and sarsaparilla. How would they feel to know that these sacred recollections were now forever profaned in their memory by the knowledge that the defendant was capable of using such occasions to make love to the larger girls and teachers, whilst his artless companions were innocently—the Court will pardon me for introducing what I am credibly informed is the local expression—'doing gooseberry?'" The tremulous flicker of a smile passed over the faces of the listening crowd, and the Colonel slightly winced. But he recovered himself instantly, and continued,—

"My client, the only daughter of a widowed mother—who has for years stemmed the varying tides of adversity, in the western precincts of this town—stands before you to-day invested only in her own innocence. She wears no—er—rich gifts of her faithless admirer—is panoplied in no jewels, rings, nor mementos of affection such as lovers delight to hang upon the shrine of their affections; hers is not the glory with which Solomon decorated the Queen of Sheba, though the defendant, as I shall show later, clothed her in the less expensive flowers of the king's poetry. No, gentlemen! The defendant exhibited in this affair a certain frugality of—er—pecuniary investment, which I am willing to admit may be commendable in his class. His only gift was characteristic alike of his methods and his economy. There is, I understand, a certain not unimportant feature of religious exercise known as 'taking a collection.' The defendant, on this occasion, by the mute presentation of a tin plate covered with baize, solicited the pecuniary contributions of the faithful. On approaching the plaintiff, however, he himself slipped a love-token upon the plate and pushed it towards her. That love-token was a lozenge—a small disk, I have reason to believe, concocted of peppermint and sugar, bearing upon its reverse surface the simple words, 'I love you!' I have since ascertained that these disks may be bought for five cents a dozen—or at considerably less than one half cent for the single lozenge. Yes, gentlemen, the words 'I love you!'—the oldest legend of all; the refrain 'when the morning stars sang together'—were presented to the plaintiff by a medium so insignificant that there is, happily, no coin in the republic low enough to represent its value.

"I shall prove to you, gentlemen of the jury," said the Colonel solemnly, drawing a Bible from his coat-tail pocket, "that the defendant for the last twelve months conducted an amatory correspondence with the plaintiff by means of underlined words of Sacred Writ and church psalmody, such as 'beloved,' 'precious,' and 'dearest,' occasionally appropriating whole passages which seemed apposite to his tender passion. I shall call your attention to one of them. The defendant, while professing to be a total abstainer,—a man who, in my own knowledge, has refused spirituous refreshment as an inordinate weakness of the flesh,—with shameless hypocrisy underscores with his pencil the following passage, and presents it to the plaintiff. The gentlemen of the jury will find it in the Song of Solomon, page 548 chapter ii., verse 5." After a pause in which the rapid rustling of leaves was heard in the jury-box, Colonel Starbottle declaimed in a pleading, stentorian voice, "'Stay me with—er—*flagons*, comfort me with—er—apples—for—er—sick of love.' Yes, gentlemen!—yes, you may well turn from those accusing pages and look at the double-faced defendant. He desires—to—er—be—'stayed with flagons'! I am not aware at present what kind of liquor is habitually dispensed at these meetings, and from which the defendant so urgently clamored; but it will be my duty, before this trial is over, to discover it, if I have to summon every barkeeper in this district. For the moment I will simply call your attention to the *quantity*. It is not a single drink that the defendant asks for—not a glass of light and generous wine, to be shared with his inamorata, but a number of flagons or vessels, each possibly holding a pint measure—*for himself*!"

The smile of the audience had become a laugh. The Judge looked up warningly, when his eye caught the fact that the Colonel had again winced at this mirth. He regarded him seriously. Mr. Hotchkiss's counsel had joined in the laugh affectedly, but Hotchkiss himself sat ashy pale. There was also a commotion in the jury-box, a hurried turning over of leaves, and an excited discussion.

"The gentlemen of the jury," said the Judge, with official gravity, "will please keep order and attend only to the speeches of counsel. Any discussion here is irregular and premature, and must be reserved for the jury-room after they have retired."

The foreman of the jury struggled to his feet. He was a powerful man, with a good-humored face, and, in spite of his unfelicitous nickname of "The Bone-Breaker," had a kindly, simple but somewhat emotional nature. Nevertheless, it appeared as if he were laboring under some powerful indignation.

"Can we ask a question, Judge?" he said respectfully, although his voice had the unmistakable Western American ring in it, as of one who was unconscious that he could be addressing any but his peers.

"Yes," said the Judge good-humoredly.

"We're finding in this yere piece, out o' which the Kernel hes just bin a-quotin', some language that me and my pardner allow hadn't orter to read out afore a young lady in court, and we want to know of you—ez a fa'r-minded and impartial man—ef this is the reg'lar kind o' book given to gals and babies down at the meetin'-house."

"The jury will please follow the counsel's speech without comment," said the Judge briefly, fully aware that the defendant's counsel would spring to his feet, as he did promptly.

"The Court will allow us to explain to the gentlemen that the language they seem to object to has been accepted by the best theologians for the last thousand years as being purely mystic. As I will explain later, those are merely symbols of the Church"—

"Of wot?" interrupted the foreman, in deep scorn.

"Of the Church!"

"We ain't askin' any questions o' *you*, and we ain't takin' any answers," said the foreman, sitting down abruptly.

"I must insist," said the Judge sternly, "that the plaintiff's counsel be allowed to continue his opening without interruption. You" (to defendant's counsel) "will have your opportunity to reply later."

The counsel sank down in his seat with the bitter conviction that the jury was manifestly against him, and the case as good as lost. But his face was scarcely as disturbed as his client's, who, in great agitation, had begun to argue with him wildly, and was apparently pressing some point against the lawyer's vehement opposal. The Colonel's murky eyes brightened as he still stood erect, with his hand thrust in his breast.

"It will be put to you, gentlemen, when the counsel on the other side refrains from mere interruption and confines himself to reply, that my unfortunate client has no action—no remedy at law—because there was no spoken words of endearment. But, gentlemen, it will depend upon *you* to say what are and what are not articulate expressions of love. We all know that among the lower animals, with whom you may possibly be called upon to classify the defendant, there are certain signals more or less harmonious, as the case may be. The ass brays, the horse neighs, the sheep bleats—the feathered denizens of the grove call to their mates in more musical roundelays. These are recognized facts, gentlemen, which you yourselves, as dwellers among nature in this beautiful land, are all cognizant of. They are facts that no one would deny—and we should have a poor opinion of the ass who, at—er—such a supreme moment, would attempt to suggest that his call was unthinking and without significance. But, gentlemen, I shall prove to you that such was the foolish, self-convicting custom of the defendant. With the greatest reluctance, and the—er—greatest pain, I succeeded in wrestling from the maidenly modesty of my fair client the innocent confession that the defendant had induced her to correspond with him in these methods. Picture to yourself, gentlemen, the lonely moonlight road beside the widow's humble cottage. It is a beautiful night, sanctified to the affections, and the innocent girl is leaning from her casement. Presently there appears upon the road a slinking, stealthy figure, the defendant on his way to church. True to the instruction she has received from him, her lips part in the musical utterance" (the Colonel lowered his voice in a faint falsetto, presumably in fond imitation of his fair client), "'Keeree!' Instantly the night becomes resonant with the impassioned reply" (the Colonel here lifted his voice in stentorian tones), "'Keerow.' Again, as he passes, rises the soft 'Keeree'; again, as his form is lost in the distance, comes back the deep 'Keerow.'"

A burst of laughter, long, loud, and irrepressible, struck the whole court-room, and before the Judge could lift his half-composed face and take his handkerchief from his mouth, a faint "Keeree" from some unrecognized obscurity of the court-room was followed by a loud "Keerow" from some opposite locality. "The Sheriff will clear the court," said the Judge sternly; but, alas! as the embarrassed and choking officials rushed hither and thither, a soft "Keeree" from the spectators at the window, outside the court-house, was answered by a loud chorus of "Keerows" from the opposite windows, filled with onlookers. Again the laughter arose everywhere,—even the fair plaintiff herself sat convulsed behind her handkerchief.

The figure of Colonel Starbottle alone remained erect—white and rigid. And then the Judge, looking up, saw—what no one else in the court had seen—that the Colonel was sincere and in earnest; that what he had conceived to be the pleader's most perfect acting and most elaborate irony were the deep, serious mirthless convictions of a man without the least sense of humor. There was the respect of this conviction in the Judge's voice as he said to him gently, "You may proceed, Colonel Starbottle."

"I thank your Honor," said the Colonel slowly, "for recognizing and doing all in your power to prevent an interruption that, during my thirty years' experience at the bar, I have never been subject to without the privilege of holding the instigators thereof responsible—personally responsible. It is possibly my fault that I have failed, oratorically, to convey to the gentlemen of the jury the full force and significance of the defendant's signals. I am aware that my voice is singularly deficient in producing either the dulcet tones of my fair client or the impassioned vehemence of the defendant's response. I will," continued the Colonel, with a fatigued but blind fatuity that ignored the hurriedly knit brows and warning eyes of the Judge, "try again. The note uttered by my client" (lowering his voice to the faintest of falsettos) "was 'Keeree'; the response was 'Keerow-ow.'" And the Colonel's voice fairly shook the dome above him.

Another uproar of laughter followed this apparently audacious repetition, but was interrupted by an unlooked-for incident. The defendant rose abruptly, and tearing himself away from the withholding hand and pleading protestations of his counsel, absolutely fled from the court-room, his appearance outside being recognized by a prolonged "Keerow" from the bystanders, which again and again followed him in the distance.

In the momentary silence which followed, the Colonel's voice was heard saying, "We rest here, your Honor," and he sat down. No less white, but more agitated, was the face of the defendant's counsel, who instantly rose.

"For some unexplained reason, your Honor, my client desires to suspend further proceedings, with a view to effect a peaceable compromise with the plaintiff. As he is a man of wealth and position, he is able and willing to pay liberally for the privilege. While I, as his counsel, am still convinced of his legal irresponsibility, as he has chosen publicly to abandon his rights here, I can only ask your Honor's permission to suspend further proceedings until I can confer with Colonel Starbottle."

"As far as I can follow the pleadings," said the Judge gravely, "the case seems to be hardly one for litigation, and I approve of the defendant's course, while I strongly urge the plaintiff to accept it."

Colonel Starbottle bent over his fair client. Presently he rose, unchanged in look or demeanor. "I yield, your Honor, to the wishes of my client, and—er—lady. We accept."

Before the court adjourned that day it was known throughout the town that Adoniram K. Hotchkiss had compromised the suit for four thousand dollars and costs.

Colonel Starbottle had so far recovered his equanimity as to strut jauntily towards his office, where he was to meet his fair client. He was surprised, however, to find her already there, and in company with a somewhat sheepish-looking young man—a stranger. If the Colonel had any disappointment in meeting a third party to the interview, his old-fashioned courtesy did not permit him to show it. He bowed graciously, and politely motioned them each to a seat.

"I reckoned I'd bring Hiram around wit me," said the young lady, lifting her searching eyes, after a pause, to the Colonel's, "though he was awful shy, and allowed that you didn't know him from Adam, or even suspect his existence. But I said, 'That's just where you slip up, Hiram; a pow'ful man like the Colonel knows everything—and I've seen it in his eyes.' Lordy!" she continued, with a laugh, leaning forward over her parasol, as her eyes again sought the Colonel's, "don't you remember when you asked me if I loved that old Hotchkiss, and I told you, 'That's tellin',' and you looked at me—Lordy! I knew then you suspected there was a Hiram *somewhere*, as good as if I'd told you. Now you jest get up, Hiram, and give the Colonel a good handshake. For if it wasn't for *him* and *his* searchin' ways, and *his* awful power of language, I wouldn't hev got that four thousand dollars out o' that flirty fool Hotchkiss—enough to buy a farm, so as you and me could get married! That's what you owe to *him*. Don't stand there like a stuck fool starin' at him. He won't eat you—though he's killed many a better man. Come, have I got to do *all* the kissin'?"

It is of record that the Colonel bowed so courteously and so profoundly that he managed not merely to evade the proffered hand of the shy Hiram, but to only lightly touch the franker and more impulsive finger-tips of the gentle Zaidee. "I—er—offer my sincerest congratulations—though I think you—er—overestimate—my—er—powers of penetration. Unfortunately, a pressing engagement, which may oblige me also to leave town tonight, forbids my saying more. I have—er—left the—er—business settlement of this—er—case in the hands of the lawyers who do my office work, and who will show you every attention. And now let me wish you a very good afternoon."

Nevertheless, the Colonel returned to his private room, and it was nearly twilight when the faithful Jim entered, to find him sitting meditatively before his desk. "'Fo' God! Kernel, I hope dey ain't nuffin de matter, but you's lookin' mighty solemn! I ain't seen you look dat way, Kernel, since de day poor Massa Stryker was fetched home shot froo de head."

"Hand me down the whiskey, Jim," said the Colonel, rising slowly.

The negro flew to the closet joyfully, and brought out the bottle. The Colonel poured out a glass of the spirit and drank it with his old deliberation.

"You're quite right, Jim," he said, putting down his glass, "but I'm—er—getting old—and—somehow—I am missing poor Stryker damnably!"

Triumph of Justice
Irwin Shaw

Mike Pilato purposefully threw open the door of Victor's shack. Above him the sign that said, "Lunch, Truckmen Welcome," shook a little, and the pale shadows its red bulbs threw in the twilight waved over the State Road.

"Victor," Mike said, in Italian.

Victor was leaning on the counter, reading Walter Winchell in a spread-out newspaper. He smiled amiably. "Mike," he said, "I am so glad to see you."

Mike slammed the door. "Three hundred dollars, Victor," he said, standing five feet tall, round and solid as a pumpkin against the door. "You owe me three hundred dollars, Victor, and I am here tonight to collect."

Victor shrugged slightly and closed the paper on Walter Winchell.

"As I've been telling you for the past six months," he said, "Business is bad. I work and I work and at the end . . ." He shrugged again. "Barely enough to feed myself."

Mike's cheeks, farmer-brown, and wrinkled deeply by wind and sun, grew dark with blood. "Victor, you are lying in my face," he said slowly, his voice desperately even. "For six months, each time it comes time to collect the rent you tell me, 'Business is bad.' What do I say? I say 'All right, Victor, don't worry, I know how it is.'"

"Frankly, Mike," Victor said sadly, "there has been no improvement this month."

Mike's face grew darker than ever. He pulled harshly at the ends of his iron-gray mustache, his great hands tense and swollen with anger, repressed but terrible. "For six months, Victor," Mike said, "I believed you. Now I no longer believe you."

"Mike," Victor said reproachfully.

"My friends, my relatives," Mike said, "they prove it to me. Your business is wonderful, ten cars an hour stop at your door; you sell cigarettes to every farmer between here and Chicago; on your slot machine alone . . ." Mike waved a short thick arm at the machine standing invitingly against a wall, its wheels stopped at two cherries and a lemon. Mike swallowed hard, stood breathing heavily, his deep chest rising and falling sharply against his sheepskin coat. "Three hundred dollars!" he shouted. "Six months at fifty dollars! I built this shack with my own hands for you, Victor. I didn't know what kind of a man you were. You were an Italian, I trusted you! Three hundred dollars or get out tomorrow! Finish! That's my last word."

Victor smoothed his newspaper down delicately on the counter, his hands making a dry brushing sound in the empty lunchroom. "You misunderstand," he said gently.

"I misunderstand nothing!" Mike yelled. "You are on my land in my shack and you owe me three hundred dollars. . . ."

"I don't owe you anything," Victor said, looking coldly at Mike. "That is what you misunderstand. I have paid you every month, the first day of the month, fifty dollars."

"Victor!" Mike whispered, his hands dropping to his sides. "Victor, what are you saying . . ?"

"I have paid the rent. Please do not bother me any more." Calmly, Victor turned his back on Mike and turned two handles on the coffee urn. Steam, in a thin little plume, hissed up for a moment.

Mike looked at Victor's narrow back, with the shoulder blades jutting far out, making limp wings in the white shirt. There was finality in Victor's pose, boredom, easy certainty. Mike shook his head slowly, pulling hard at his mustache. "My wife," Mike said, to the disdainful back, "she told me not to trust you. My wife knew what she was talking about, Victor." Then, with a last flare of hope, "Victor, do you really mean it when you said you paid me?"

Victor didn't turn around. He flipped another knob on the coffee urn. "I mean it."

Mike lifted his arm, as though to say something, pronounce warning. Then he let it drop and walked out of the shack, leaving the door open. Victor came out from behind the counter, looked at Mike moving off with his little rolling limp down the road and across the cornfield. Victor smiled and closed the door and went back and opened the paper to Walter Winchell.

Mike walked slowly among the cornstalks, his feet crunching unevenly in the October earth. Absently he pulled at his mustache. Dolores, his wife, would have a thing or two to say. "No," she had warned him, "do not build a shack for him. Do not permit him onto your land. He travels with bad men; it will turn out badly. I warn you!" Mike was sure she would not forget this conversation and would repeat it to him word for word when he got home. He limped along unhappily. Farming was better than being a landlord. You put seed into the earth and you knew what was coming out. Corn grew from corn, and the duplicity of Nature was expected and natural. Also no documents were signed in the compact with Nature, no leases and agreements necessary, a man was not at a disadvantage if he couldn't read or write. Mike opened the door to his house and sat down heavily in the parlor, without taking his hat off. Rosa came and jumped on his lap, yelling, "Poppa, Poppa, tonight I want to go to the movies, Poppa, take me to the movies!"

Mike pushed her off. "No movies," he said harshly. Rosa stood in a corner and watched him reproachfully.

The door from the kitchen opened and Mike sighed as he saw his wife coming in, wiping her hands on her apron. She stood in front of

Mike, round, short, solid as a plow horse, canny, difficult to deceive.

"Why're you sitting in the parlor?" she asked.

"I feel like sitting in the parlor," Mike said.

"Every night you sit in the kitchen," Dolores said. "Suddenly you change."

"I've decided," Mike said loudly, "that it's about time I made some use of this furniture. After all, I paid for it, I might as well sit in it before I die."

"I know why you're sitting in the parlor," Dolores said.

"Good! You know!"

"You didn't get the money from Victor," Dolores wiped the last bit of batter from her hands. "It's as plain as the shoes on your feet."

"I smell something burning," Mike said.

"Nothing is burning. Am I right or wrong?" Dolores sat in the upright chair opposite Mike. She sat straight, her hands neatly in her lap, her head forward and cocked a little to one side, her eyes staring directly and accusingly into his. "Yes or no?"

"Please attend to your own department," Mike said miserably. "I do the farming and attend to the business details."

"Huh!" Dolores said disdainfully.

"Are you starving?" Mike shouted. "Answer me, are you starving?"

Rosa started to cry because her father was shouting.

"Please, for the love of Jesus," Mike screamed at her, "don't cry!"

Dolores enfolded Rosa in her arms. . . . "Baby, baby," she crooned, "I will not let him harm you."

"Who offered to harm her?" Mike screamed, banging on a table with his fist like a mallet. "Don't lie to her!"

Dolores kissed the top of Rosa's head soothingly. "There, there," she crooned. "There." She looked coldly at Mike. "Well. So he didn't pay."

"He . . ." Mike started loudly. Then he stopped, spoke in a low, reasonable voice. "So, to be frank with you, he didn't pay. That's the truth."

"What did I tell you?" Dolores said as Mike winced. "I repeat the words. 'Do not permit him onto your land. He travels with bad men; it will turn out badly. I warn you!' Did I tell you?"

"You told me," Mike said wearily.

"We will never see that money again," Dolores said, smoothing Rosa's hair. "I have kissed it goodbye."

"Please," said Mike. "Return to the kitchen. I am hungry for dinner. I have made plans already to recover the money."

Dolores eyed him suspiciously. "Be careful, Mike," she said. "His friends are gangsters and he plays poker every Saturday night with men who carry guns in their pocket."

"I am going to the law," Mike said. "I'm going to sue Victor for the three hundred dollars."

Dolores started to laugh. She pushed Rosa away and stood up and laughed.

"What's so funny?" Mike asked angrily. "I tell you I'm going to sue a man for money he owes me, you find it funny! Tell me the joke."

Dolores stopped laughing. "Have you got any papers? No! You trust him, he trusts you, no papers. Without papers you're lost in a court. You'll make a fool of yourself. They'll charge you for the lawyers. Please, Mike, go back to your farming."

Mike's face set sternly, his wrinkles harsh in his face with the gray stubble he never managed completely to shave. "I want my dinner, Dolores," he said coldly, and Dolores discreetly moved into the kitchen, saying, "It is not my business, my love; truly, I merely offer advice."

Mike walked back and forth in the parlor, limping, rolling a little from side to side, his eyes on the floor, his hands plunged into the pockets of his denims like holstered weapons, his mouth pursed with thought and determination. After a while he stopped and looked at Rosa, who prepared to weep once more.

"Rosa, baby," he said, sitting down and taking her gently on his lap. "Forgive me."

Rosa snuggled to him. They sat that way in the dimly lit parlor.

"Poppa," Rosa said finally.

"Yes," Mike said.

"Will you take me to the movies tonight, Poppa?"

"All right," Mike said. "I'll take you to the movies."

The next day Mike went into town, dressed in his neat black broadcloth suit and his black soft hat and his high brown shoes. He came back to the farm like a businessman in the movies, bustly, preoccupied, sober, but satisfied.

"Well?" Dolores asked him, in the kitchen.

He kissed her briskly, kissed Rosa, sat down, took his shoes off, rubbed his feet luxuriously, said paternally to his son who was reading *Esquire* near the window, "That's right, Anthony, study."

"Well?" asked Dolores.

"I saw Dominic in town," Mike said, watching his toes wiggling. "They're having another baby."

"Well," asked Dolores. "The case? The action?"

"All right," Mike said. "What is there for dinner?"

"Veal," Dolores said. "What do you mean 'all right'?"

"I've spoken to Judge Collins. He is filling out the necessary papers for me and he will write me a letter when I am to appear in court. Rosa, have you been a good girl?"

Dolores threw up her hands. "Lawyers. We'll throw away a fortune on lawyers. Good money after bad. We could put in an electric pump with the money."

"Lawyers will cost us nothing." Mike stuffed his pipe elaborately. "I have different plans. Myself. I will take care of the case myself." He lit up, puffed deliberately.

Dolores sat down across the table from him, spoke slowly, carefully. "Remember, Mike," she said. "This is in English. They conduct the court in English."

"I know," said Mike. "I am right. Justice is on my side. Why should I pay a lawyer fifty, seventy-five dollars to collect my own money?

There is one time you need lawyers—when you are wrong. I am not wrong. I will be my own lawyer."

"What do you know about the law?" Dolores challenged him.

"I know Victor owes me three hundred dollars." Mike puffed three times, quickly, on his pipe. "That's all I need to know."

"You can hardly speak English, you can't even read or write, nobody will be able to understand you. They'll all laugh at you, Mike."

"Nobody will laugh at me. I can speak English fine."

"When did you learn?" Dolores asked. "Today?"

"Dolores!" Mike shouted. "I tell you my English is all right."

"Say Thursday," Dolores said.

"I don't want to say it," Mike said, banging the table. "I have no interest in saying it."

"Aha," Dolores crowed. "See? He wants to be a lawyer in an American court, he can't even say Thursday."

"I can," Mike said. "Keep quiet, Dolores."

"Say Thursday." Dolores put her head to one side, spoke coquettishly, slyly, like a girl asking her lover to say he loved her.

"Stirday," Mike said, as he always said. "There!"

Dolores laughed, waving her hand. "And he wants to conduct a law case! Holy Mother! They will laugh at you!"

"Let them laugh!" Mike shouted. "I will conduct the case! Now I want to eat dinner! Anthony!" he yelled. "Throw away that trash and come to the table."

On the day of the trial, Mike shaved closely, dressed carefully in his black suit, put his black hat squarely on his head, and with Dolores seated grimly beside him drove early into town in the 1933 family Dodge.

Dolores said nothing all the way into town. Only after the car was parked and they were entering the courthouse, Mike's shoes clattering bravely on the legal marble, did Dolores speak. "Behave yourself," she said. Then she pinched his arm. Mike smiled at her, braced his yoke-like shoulders, took off his hat. His rough gray hair sprang up like steel wool when his hat was off, and Mike ran his hand through it as he opened the door to the courtroom. There was a proud, important smile on his face as he sat down next to his wife in the first row and patiently waited for his case to be called.

When Victor came, Mike glared at him, but Victor, after a quick look, riveted his attention on the American flag behind the Judge's head.

"See," Mike whispered to Dolores. "I have him frightened. He doesn't dare look at me. Here he will have to tell the truth."

"Sssh!" hissed Dolores. "This is a court of law."

"Michael Pilato," the clerk called, "versus Victor Fraschi."

"Me!" Mike said loudly, standing up.

"Sssh," said Dolores.

Mike put his hat in Dolores' lap, moved lightly to the little gate that separated the spectators from the principals in the proceedings. Politely, with a deep ironic smile, he held the gate open for Victor and his lawyer. Victor passed through without looking up.

"Who's representing you, Mr. Pilato?" the Judge asked when they were all seated. "Where's your lawyer?"

Mike stood up and spoke in a clear voice. "I represent myself. I am my lawyer."

"You ought to have a lawyer," the Judge said.

"I do not need a lawyer," Mike said loudly. "I am not trying to cheat anybody." There were about forty people in the courtroom and they all laughed. Mike turned and looked at them, puzzled. "What did I say?"

The Judge rapped with his gavel and the case was opened. Victor took the stand, while Mike stared, coldly accusing, at him. Victor's lawyer, a young man in a blue pinstripe suit and a starched tan shirt, questioned him. Yes, Victor said, he had paid each month. No, there were no receipts, Mr. Pilato could neither read nor write and they had dispensed with all formalities of that kind. No, he did not understand on what Mr. Pilato based his claim. Mike looked incredulously at Victor, lying under solemn oath, risking Hell for three hundred dollars.

Victor's lawyer stepped down and waved to Mike gracefully. "Your witness."

Mike walked dazedly past the lawyer and up to the witness stand, round, neat, his bull neck, deep red-brown and wrinkled, over his pure white collar, his large scrubbed hands politely but awkwardly held at his sides. He stood in front of Victor, leaning over a little toward him, his face close to Victor's.

"Victor," he said, his voice ringing through the courtroom, "tell the truth, did you pay me the money?"

"Yes," said Victor.

Mike leaned closer to him. "Look in my eye, Victor," Mike said, his voice clear and patient, "and answer me. Did you pay me the money?"

Victor lifted his head and looked unflinchingly into Mike's eyes. "I paid you the money."

Mike leaned even closer. His forehead almost touched Victor's now. "Look me *straight* in the eye, Victor."

Victor looked bravely into Mike's eyes, less than a foot away now.

"Now, Victor," Mike said, his eyes narrowed, cold, the light in them small and flashing and gray, "DID YOU PAY ME THE MONEY?"

Victor breathed deeply, "Yes," he said.

Mike took half a step back, almost staggering, as though he had been hit. He stared incredulously into the perjurer's eyes, as a man might stare at a son who has just admitted he has killed his mother, beyond pity, beyond understanding, outside all the known usage of human life. Mike's face worked harshly as the tides of anger and despair and vengeance rolled up in him.

"You're a goddam liar, Victor!" Mike shouted terribly. He leapt down from the witness platform, seized a heavy oak armchair, raised it murderously above Victor's head.

"Mike, oh, Mike!" Dolores' wail floated above the noise of the courtroom.

"Tell the truth, Victor!" Mike shouted, his face brick red, his teeth white behind his curled lips, almost senseless with rage, for the first time in his life threatening a fellow-creature with violence. "Tell it fast!"

He stood, the figure of Justice, armed with the chair, the veins pulsing in his huge wrists, the chair quivering high above Victor's head in his huge gnarled hands, his tremendous arms tight and bulging in their broad cloth sleeves. "Immediately, Victor!"

"Pilato!" shouted the Judge. "Put that chair down!"

Victor sat stonily, his eyes lifted in dumb horror to the chair above his head.

"Pilato," the Judge shouted, "you can be sent to jail for this!" He banged sternly but helplessly on his desk. "Remember, this is a court of law!"

"Victor?" Mike asked, unmoved, unmoving. "Victor? Immediately, please."

"No," Victor screamed, cringing in his seat, his hands now held in feeble defense before his eyes. "I didn't pay! I didn't!"

"Pilato," screamed the Judge, "This is not evidence!"

"You were lying?" Mike said inexorably, the chair still held, ax-like, above him.

"Mike, oh, Mike," wailed Dolores.

"It was not my idea," Victor babbled. "As God is my judge, I didn't think it up. Alfred Lotti, he suggested it, and Johnny Nolan. I am under the influence of corrupt men. Mike, for the love of God, please don't kill me, Mike, it would never have occurred to me myself, forgive me, forgive me. . . ."

"Guiness!" the Judge called to the court policeman. "Are you going to stand there and let this go on? Why don't you do something?"

"I can shoot him," Guiness said. "Do you want me to shoot the plaintiff?"

"Shut up," the Judge said.

Guiness shrugged and turned his head toward the witness stand, smiling a little.

"You were lying?" Mike asked, his voice low, patient.

"I was lying," Victor cried.

Slowly, with magnificent calm, Mike put the chair down neatly in its place. With a wide smile he turned to the Judge. "There," he said.

"Do you know any good reason," the Judge shouted, "why I shouldn't have you locked up?"

Victor was crying with relief on the witness stand, wiping the tears away with his sleeve.

"There is no possible excuse," the Judge said, "for me to admit this confession as evidence. We are a court of law in the State of Illinois, in the United States. We are not conducting the Spanish Inquisition, Mr. Pilato."

"Huh?" Mike asked, cocking his head.

"There are certain rules," the Judge went on, quickly, his voice high, "which it is customary to observe. It is not the usual thing, Mr. Pilato," he said harshly, "to arrive at evidence by bodily threatening to brain witnesses with a chair."

"He wouldn't tell the truth," Mike said simply.

"At the very least, Mr. Pilato," the Judge said, "you should get thirty days."

"Oh, Mike," wept Dolores.

"Mr. Fraschi," the Judge said, "I promise you that you will be protected. That nobody will harm you."

"I did it," sobbed Victor, his hands shaking uncontrollably in a mixture of fear, repentance, religion, joy at delivery from death. "I did it. I will not tell a lie. I'm a weak man and influenced by loafers. I owe him three hundred dollars. Forgive me, Mike, forgive me. . . ."

"He will not harm you," the Judge said patiently. "I guarantee it. You can tell the truth without any danger. Do you owe Mr. Pilato three hundred dollars?"

"I owe Mr. Pilato three hundred dollars," Victor said, swallowing four times in a row.

The young lawyer put three sheets of paper into his briefcase and snapped the lock.

The Judge sighed and wiped his brow with a handkerchief as he looked at Mike. "I don't approve of the way you conducted this trial, Mr. Pilato," he said. "It is only because you're a working man who has many duties to attend to on his land that I don't take you and put you away for a month to teach you more respect for the processes of law."

"Yes, sir," Mike said faintly.

"Hereafter," the Judge said, "kindly engage an attorney when you appear before me in this court."

"Yes, sir," Mike said.

"Mr. Pilato," the Judge said, "It is up to you to decide when and how he is to pay you."

Mike turned and walked back to Victor. Victor shrank into his chair. "Tomorrow morning, Victor," Mike said, waving his finger under Victor's nose, "at eight-thirty o'clock, I am coming into your store. The money will be there."

"Yes," said Victor.

"Is that all right?" Mike asked the Judge.

"Yes," said the Judge.

Mike strode over to the young lawyer. "And you," he said, standing with his hands on his hips in front of the young man with the pinstripe suit. "Mr. Lawyer. You knew he didn't pay me. A boy with an education. You should be ashamed of yourself." He turned to the Judge, smiled broadly, bowed. "Thank you." he said. "Good morning." Then, triumphantly, smiling broadly, rolling like a sea captain as he walked, he went through the little gate. Dolores was waiting with his hat. He took the hat, put Dolores' arm through his, marched down the aisle, nodding, beaming to the spectators. Someone applauded and by the time he and Dolores got to the door all the spectators were applauding.

He waited until he got outside, in the bright morning sunshine down the steps of the courthouse, before he said anything to Dolores. He put his hat on carefully, turned to her, grinning. "Well," he said, "did you observe what I did?"

"Yes," she said. "I was never so ashamed in my whole life!"

"Dolores!" Mike was shocked. "I got the money. I won the case."

"Acting like that in a court of law!" Dolores started bitterly toward the car. "What are you, a red Indian?"

    Dolores got into the car and slammed the door and Mike limped slowly around and got into the other side. He started the car without a word and shaking his head from time to time, drove slowly toward home.

8

The Judicial Process

Judges are apt to be naïf, simple-minded men, and they need
something of Mephistopheles. We too need education in the
obvious—to learn to transcend our own convictions and to
leave room for much that we hold dear to be done away with
short of revolution by the orderly change of law.

Law and the Court
Oliver Wendell Holmes, Jr.

What has once been settled by a precedent will not be unset-
tled overnight, for certainty and uniformity are gains not
lightly to be sacrificed. Above all is this true when honest
men have shaped their conduct on the pronouncement.

The Paradoxes of Legal Science
Benjamin Nathan Cardozo

"Triumph of Justice" illustrates the various roles that the judge assumes to
keep the court in order—he ensures that the players follow the rules of evidence, he admonishes the witnesses to tell the truth, and he calls on the
bailiff for assistance in removing a particularly hostile or aggressive participant. In maintaining such control, the judge has wide discretion to hold any
participant in contempt by leveling a fine or a prison sentence; on occasion,
the judge will resort to other extreme measures to control the behavior of
those in the courtroom. Such measures were taken by Federal Judge Julius
J. Hoffman during the trial of the Chicago Seven—seven defendants, and
Black Panther leader Bobby Seale, were charged with crossing state lines to
riot or to conspire to use interstate commerce to induce rioting. Frustrated
by Seale's outbursts, the judge ordered him bound and gagged until the
public made such an outcry over the judge's courtroom tactics that the judge
declared a mistrial in the case. During the trial, Judge Hoffman sentenced
all eight defendants and attorneys Weinglass and Kunstler for contempt.
Kunstler received a sentence of four years and thirteen days for the fourteen
instances in which he was held in contempt. Since that trial federal judges
are now limited to summary contempt charges to be used for the purposes
of courtroom order only, and any substantial punitive contempt charges re-

quire a formal hearing and the presentation of evidence before an unbiased tribunal.

Important as the role of the peacemaker is, the judge also faces the more difficult challenge of impartiality. Unlike the attorneys for the parties, the judge is said to be totally objective; but he is *not* a mediator—at least not during the trial. In reality, in pretrial conferences, the judge will cajole, pressure, and attempt to persuade the attorneys to strive for a settlement; at times, the judge will even suggest the terms for negotiation. During such pretrial conferences, the judge often asks what offers and counteroffers have been made. Ironically, such offers of compromise are not allowed into evidence at any subsequent trial. If that trial is a jury trial, the fact that the judge has heard such offers might do no harm; on the other hand, if the trial is to be decided by the judge only, then he has already received such forbidden information.

Once the pretrial conferences are over, if a settlement is not reached, the attorneys present the facts of the case to the jury in the light most favorable to their clients. They then proceed to present the law to the judge—through the cases, statutes, constitutions, and subsequent interpretation of those documents—in the same favorable light. When the attorneys rest their respective cases, the judge must decide the case on the law. In deciding the law the judge is said to be constrained in his decision and in his charge to the jury by precedent; that is, he is to be guided by the totality and evolution of a prior body of law. The judicial response to this body of law known as precedent has led to a lively debate among scholars as to just how much the judges are constrained. Some people argue that judges interpret legal texts; that is, adjudication is interpretation. Others argue that the law is determinate and objective, and adjudication is not interpretation. There are also those who take the middle ground and argue that each text has numerous meanings from which the interpreter chooses only one. While legal philosophers debate the intricacies of such theories, let it just be said that if judges are involved in interpretation at all, then it would be to their advantage, and to the advantage of the lawyers who must argue for an interpretation of each text, to learn to read a text critically.

In the short story "How the Pretty Maid of Portillon Convinced Her Judge," by Honoré de Balzac, a judge is engaged in the following practices that would not be condoned in any of our judges:

- The judge is not impartial and is influenced initially by the maiden's good looks. This absence of impartiality is further evident in his change of position when he learns who the defendant would be if he allowed the maiden to bring her case.

- The judge remarks that he is interested in "the case, not the justice of it."

- The judge demonstrates a sexist attitude toward the maiden by accusing her of inciting Monseigneur du Fou before the judge hears any testimony.

This is a story of sexual assault and it contains many of the issues which are raised in our present-day rape trials. Should the past behavior of the plaintiff be considered? Would you be convinced by this maiden's story that she was sexually abused? Without corroboration, should it be possible to get a conviction without medical evidence of an attack? Finally, what is implied by the author's tone? In utilizing satire, the author intentionally pokes fun at a serious subject, but we ought to guard against assuming that the author's position is the same as that of any particular character. In "How the Pretty Maid of Portillon Convinced Her Judge," is Balzac satirizing the plight of the maiden or is he satirizing the judicial process?

"A Wasted Day," by Richard Harding Davis, presents a judge who is the antithesis of the judge in "How the Pretty Maid of Portillon Convinced Her Judge." Notice that the judge says of the law: It "is not vindictive. . . . It wishes only to be just."

How the Pretty Maid of Portillon Convinced Her Judge

Honoré de Balzac

The maid of Portillon, who became, as everyone knows, La Tascherette, was, before she became a dyer, a laundress at the said place of Portillon, from which she took her name. If any there be who do not know Tours, it may be as well to state that Portillon is down the Loire, on the same side as St. Cyr, about as far from the bridge which leads to the cathedral of Tours as the said bridge is distant from Marmoutier, since the bridge is in the center of the embankment between Portillon and Marmoutier. Do you thoroughly understand?

Yes? Good! Now the maid had there her wash-house, from which she ran to the Loire with her washing in a second, and took the ferry-boat to get to St. Martin, which was on the other side of the river, for she had to deliver the greater part of her work in Chateauneuf and other places. About Midsummer day, seven years before marrying old Taschereau, she had just reached the right age to be loved. As she was a merry girl she allowed herself to be loved, without making a choice from any of the lads who pursued her with their intentions. Although there used to come to the bench under her window the son of Rabelais, who had seven boats on the Loire, Jehan's eldest, Marchandeau the tailor, and Peccard the ecclesiastical goldsmith, she made fun of them all, because she wished to be taken to church before burthening herself with a man, which proves that she was an honest woman until she was wheedled out of her virtue. She was one of those girls who take great care not to be contaminated, but who, if by chance they get deceived, let things take their course, thinking that for one stain or for fifty a good polishing up is necessary. These characters demand our indulgence.

A young noble of the court perceived her one day when she was crossing the water in the glare of the noonday sun, which lit up her ample charms, and seeing her, asked who she was. An old man, who was working on the banks, told him she was called the Pretty Maid of Portillon, a laundress, celebrated for her merry ways and her virtue. This young lord, besides ruffles to starch, had many precious linen draperies and things; he resolved to give the custom of his house to this girl, whom he stopped on the road. He was thanked by her and heartily, because he was the Sire Du Fou, the king's chamberlain. This encounter made her so joyful that her mouth was full of his name. She talked about it a great deal to the people of St. Martin, and when she got back to her washhouse was still full of it, and on the morrow at her work her tongue went nineteen to the dozen, and all on the same subject, so that as much was said concerning my Lord du Fou in Portillon as of God in a sermon; that is, a great deal too much.

"If she works like that in cold water, what will she do in warm?" said an old washerwoman. "She wants du Fou; he'll give her du Fou!"

The first time this giddy wench, with her head full of Monsieur du Fou, had to deliver the linen at his hotel, the chamberlain wished to see her, and was very profuse in praises and compliments concerning her charms, and wound up by telling her that she was not at all silly to be beautiful, and therefore he would give her more than she expected. The deed followed the word, for the moment his people were out of the room, he began to caress the maid, who thinking he was about to take out the money from his purse, dared not look at the purse, but said, like a girl ashamed to take her wages, "It will be for the first time."

"It will be soon," said he.

Some people say that he had great difficulty in forcing her to accept what he offered her, and hardly forced her at all; others that he forced her badly, because she came out, like an army flagging on the route, crying and groaning, and came to the judge. It happened that the judge was out. La Portillone awaited his return in his room, weeping and saying to the servant that she had been robbed, because Monseigneur du Fou had given her nothing but his mischief; whilst a canon of the chapter used to give her large sums for that which M. du Fou wanted for nothing. If she loved a man she would think it wise to do things for him for nothing, because it would be a pleasure to her; but the chamberlain had treated her roughly, and not kindly and gently, as he should have done, and that therefore he owed her the thousand crowns of the canon. The judge came in, saw the wench, and wished to kiss her, but she put herself on guard, and said she had come to make a complaint. The judge replied that certainly she could have the offender hanged if she liked, because he was most anxious to serve her. The injured maiden replied that she did not wish the death of her man, but that he should pay her a thousand gold crowns, because she had been robbed against her will.

"Ha! ha!" said the judge, "what he took was worth more than that."

"For the thousand crowns I'll cry quits, because I shall be able to live without washing."

"He who has robbed you, is he well off?"

"Oh, yes."

"Then he shall pay dearly for it. Who is it?"

"Monseigneur du Fou."

"Oh, that alters the case," said the judge.

"But justice?" said she.

"I said the case, not the justice of it," replied the judge. "I must know how the affair occurred."

Then the girl related naïvely how she was arranging the young lord's ruffles in his wardrobe, when he began to play with her skirts, and she turned round, saying—

"Go on with you!"

"You have no case," said the judge, "for by the speech he thought that you gave him leave to go on. Ha! ha!"

Then she declared that she had defended herself, weeping and crying out, and that that constitutes an assault.

"A wench's antics to incite him," said the judge.

Finally, La Portillone declared that against her will she had been taken round the waist and thrown, although she had kicked and cried and struggled, but that seeing no help at hand, she had lost courage.

"Good! Good!" said the judge. "Did you take pleasure in the affair?"

"No," said she. "My anguish can only be paid for with a thousand crowns."

"My dear," said the judge, "I cannot receive your complaint, because I believe no girl can be thus treated against her will."

"Hi! hi! hi! Ask your servant," said the little laundress, sobbing, "and hear what she'll tell you."

The servant affirmed that there were pleasant assaults and unpleasant ones; that if La Portillone had received neither amusement nor money, either one or the other was due her. This wise counsel threw the judge into a state of great perplexity.

"Jacqueline," said he, "before I sup I'll get to the bottom of this. Now go and fetch my needle and the red thread that I sew the legal paper bags with."

Jacqueline came back with a big needle, pierced with a pretty little hole, and a big red thread, such as the judges use. Then she remained standing to see the question decided, very much disturbed, as was also the complainant at these mysterious preparations.

"My dear," said the judge, "I am going to hold the bodkin, of which the eye is sufficiently large, to put this thread into it without trouble. If you do put it in, I will take up your case, and will make Monseigneur offer you a compromise."

"What's that?" said she. "I will not allow it."

"It is a word used in justice to signify an agreement."

"A compromise is then agreeable with justice?" said La Portillone.

"My dear, this violence has also opened your mind. Are you ready?"

"Yes," said she.

The waggish judge gave the poor nymph fair play, holding the eye steady for her; but when she wished to slip in the thread that she had twisted to make straight, he moved a little, and the thread went on the other side. She suspected the judge's argument, wetted the thread, stretched it, and came back again. The judge moved, twisted about, and wriggled like a bashful maiden; still the cursed thread would not enter. The girl kept trying at the eye, and the judge kept fidgeting. The marriage of the thread could not be consummated, the bodkin remained virgin, and the servant began to laugh, saying to La Portillone that she knew better how to endure than to perform. Then the roguish judge laughed too, and the fair Portillone cried for her golden crowns.

"If you don't keep still," cried she, losing patience; "if you keep moving about I shall never be able to put the thread in."

"Then, my dear, if you had done the same, Monseigneur would

have been unsuccessful too. Think, too, how easy is the one affair, and how difficult the other."

The pretty wench, who declared she had been forced, remained thoughtful, and sought to find a means to convince the judge by showing how she had been compelled to yield, since the honor of all poor girls liable to violence was at stake.

"Monseigneur, in order that the bet may be fair, I must do exactly as the young lord did. If I had only had to move I should be moving still, but he went through other performances."

"Let us hear them," replied the judge.

Then La Portillone straightens the thread; and rubs it in the wax of the candle, to make it firm and straight; then she looks towards the eye of the bodkin, held by the judge, slipping always to the right or to the left. Then she began making endearing little speeches, such as, "Ah, the pretty little bodkin! What a pretty mark to aim at! Never did I see such a little jewel! What a pretty little eye! Let me put this little thread into it! Ah! You will hurt my poor thread, my nice little thread! Keep still! Come, my love of a judge, judge of my love! Won't the thread go nicely into this iron gate, which makes good use of the thread, for it comes out very much out of order?" Then she burst out laughing, for she was better up in this game than the judge, who laughed too, so saucy and comical and arch was she, pushing the thread backwards and forwards. She kept the poor judge with the case in his hand until seven o'clock, keeping on fidgeting and moving about like a schoolboy let loose; but as La Portillone kept on trying to put the thread in, he could not help it. As, however, his joint was burning, and his wrist was tired, he was obliged to rest himself for a minute on the side of the table; then very dexterously the fair maid of Portillon slipped the thread in, saying—

"That's how the thing occurred."

"But my joint was burning."

"So was mine," said she.

The judge, convinced, told La Portillone that he would speak to Monseigneur du Fou, and would himself carry the affair through, since it was certain the young lord had embraced her against her will, but that for valid reasons he would keep the affair dark. On the morrow the judge went to the Court and saw the Monseigneur du Fou, to whom he recounted the young woman's complaint, and how she had set forth her case. This complaint lodged in Court, tickled the king immensely. Young du Fou having said that there was some truth in it, the king asked if he had much difficulty, and as he replied, innocently, "No." The king declared the girl was quite worth a hundred gold crowns, and the chamberlain gave them to the judge, in order not to be taxed with stinginess, and said that starch would be a good income to La Portillone. The judge came back to La Portillone, and said, smiling, that he had raised a hundred gold crowns for her. But if she desired the balance of the thousand, there were at that moment in the king's apartments certain lords who, knowing the case, had offered to make up the sum for her with her consent. The little hussy did not refuse this offer, saying, that in order to do no more washing in the future she did not mind doing a little hard work now. She gratefully acknowledged the trouble the good judge had taken, and gained her thousand crowns in a month. From this came the falsehoods and jokes concerning her because out of these ten lords jealousy made a hundred, whilst, differently from young men, La Portillone settled down to a virtuous life directly she had her thousand crowns. Even a duke, who would have counted out five hundred crowns, would have found this girl rebellious, which proves she was niggardly with her property. It is true that the king caused her to be sent for to his retreat of Rue Quinquangrogne, on the mall of Chardonneret, found her extremely pretty, exceedingly affectionate, enjoyed her society, and forbade the servants to interfere with her in any way whatever. Seeing she was so beautiful, Nicole Beaupertuis, the king's mistress, gave her a hundred gold crowns to go to Orléans, in order to see if the color of the Loire was the same there as at Portillon. She went there, and the more willingly because she did not care very much for the king. When the good man came who confessed the king in his last hour, and was afterwards canonized, La Portillone went to him to polish up her conscience, did penance, and founded a bed in the leper-house of St. Lazare-les-Tours. Many ladies whom you know have been assaulted by more than two lords, and have founded no other beds than those of their own houses. It is well to relate this fact in order to cleanse the reputation of this honest girl, who herself once washed dirty things, and who afterwards became famous for her clever tricks and her wit. She gave a proof of her merit in marrying Taschereau, whom she cuckolded right merrily, as has been related in the story of *The Reproach*. This proves to us most satisfactorily that with strength and patience justice itself can be violated.

A Wasted Day
Richard Harding Davis

When its turn came, the private secretary, somewhat apologetically, laid the letter in front of the Wisest Man in Wall Street.

"From Mrs. Austin, probation officer, Court of General Sessions," he explained. "Wants a letter about Spear. He's been convicted of theft. Comes up for sentence Tuesday."

"Spear?" repeated Arnold Thorndike.

"Young fellow, stenographer, used to do your letters last summer going in and out on the train."

The great man nodded. "I remember. What about him?"

The habitual gloom of the private secretary was lightened by a grin.

"Went on the loose; had with him about five hundred dollars belonging to the firm; he's with Isaacs & Sons now, shoe people on Sixth Avenue. Met a woman and woke up without the money. The next morning he offered to make good, but Isaacs called in the policeman. When they looked into it, they found the boy had been drunk. They tried to withdraw the charge, but he'd been committed. Now, the probation officer is trying to get the judge to suspend sentence. A letter from you, sir, would—"

It was evident the mind of the great man was elsewhere. Young men who, drunk or sober, spent the firm's money on women who disappeared before sunrise did not appeal to him. Another letter submitted that morning had come from his art agent in Europe. In Florence he had discovered the Correggio he had been sent to find. It was undoubtedly genuine, and he asked to be instructed by cable. The price was forty thousand dollars. With one eye closed, and the other keenly regarding the inkstand, Mr. Thorndike decided to pay the price; and with the facility of long practice dismissed the Correggio, and snapped his mind back to the present.

"Spear had a letter from us when he left, didn't he?" he asked. "What he has developed into, *since* he left us—" he shrugged his shoulders. The secretary withdrew the letter and slipped another in its place.

"Homer Firth, the landscape man," he chanted, "wants permission to use blue flint on the new road, with turf gutters, and to plant silver firs each side. Says it will run to about five thousand dollars a mile."

"No!" protested the great man firmly, "blue flint makes a country place look like a cemetery. Mine looks too much like a cemetery now. Landscape gardeners!" he exclaimed impatiently. "Their only idea is to insult nature. The place was better the day I bought it, when it was running wild; you could pick flowers all the way to the gates." Pleased that it should have recurred to him, the great man smiled. "Why, Spear," he exclaimed, "always took in a bunch of them for his mother. Don't you remember, we used to see him before breakfast wandering around the grounds picking flowers?" Mr. Thorndike nodded briskly. "I liked his taking flowers to his mother."

"He *said* it was to his mother," suggested the secretary gloomily.

"Well, he picked the flowers, anyway," laughed Mr. Thorndike. "He didn't pick our pockets. And he had the run of the house in those days. As far as we know," he dictated, "he was satisfactory. Don't say more than that."

The secretary scribbled a mark with his pencil. "And the landscape man?"

"Tell him," commanded Thorndike, "I want a wood road, suitable to a farm; and to let the trees grow where God planted them."

As his car slid downtown on Tuesday morning the mind of Arnold Thorndike was occupied with such details of daily routine as the purchase of a railroad, the Japanese loan, the new wing to his art gallery, and an attack that morning, in his own newspaper, upon his pet trust. But his busy mind was not too occupied to return the salutes of the traffic policemen who cleared the way for him. Or, by some genius of memory, to recall the fact that it was on this morning young Spear was to be sentenced for theft. It was a charming morning. The spring was at full tide, and the air was sweet and clean. Mr. Thorndike considered whimsically that to send a man to jail with the memory of such a morning clinging to him was adding a year to his sentence. He regretted he had not given the probation officer a stronger letter. He remembered the young man now, and favorably. A shy, silent youth, deft in work, and at other times conscious and embarrassed. But that, on the part of a stenographer, in the presence of the Wisest Man in Wall Street, was not unnatural. On occasions Mr. Thorndike had put even royalty—frayed, impecunious royalty, on the lookout for a loan—at its ease.

The hood of the car was down, and the taste of the air, warmed by the sun, was grateful. It was at this time, a year before, that young Spear picked the spring flowers to take to his mother. A year from now where would young Spear be?

It was characteristic of the great man to act quickly, so quickly that his friends declared he was a slave to impulse. It was these same impulses, leading so invariably to success, that made his enemies call him the Wisest Man. He leaned forward and touched the chauffeur's shoulder. "Stop at the Court of General Sessions," he commanded. What he proposed to do would take but a few minutes. A word, a personal word from him to the district attorney, or the judge, would be enough. He recalled that a Sunday Special had once calculated that the working time of Arnold Thorndike brought him in two hundred dollars a minute. At that rate, keeping Spear out of prison would cost a thousand dollars.

Out of the sunshine Mr. Thorndike stepped into the gloom of an echoing rotunda, shut in on every side, hung by balconies, lit, many stories overhead, by a dirty skylight. The place was damp, the air acrid with the smell of stale tobacco juice, and foul with the presence of many unwashed humans. A policeman, chewing stolidly, nodded toward an elevator shaft, and other policemen nodded him further on to the office of the district attorney. There Arnold Thorndike breathed more freely. He was again among his own people. He could not help but appreciate the dramatic qualities of the situation; that the richest man in Wall Street should appear in person to plead for a humble and weaker brother. He knew he could not escape recognition, his face was too well known, but, he trusted, for the sake of Spear, the reporters would make no display of his visit. With a deprecatory laugh, he explained why he had come. But the outburst of approbation he had anticipated did not follow.

The district attorney ran his finger briskly down a printed card. "Henry Spear," he exclaimed, "that's your man. Part Three, Judge Fallon. Andrews is in that court." He walked to the door of his private office. "Andrews!" he called.

He introduced an alert, broad-shouldered young man of years of much indiscretion and with a charming and inconsequent manner.

"Mr. Thorndike is interested in Henry Spear, coming up for sentence in Part Three this morning. Wants to speak for him. Take him over with you."

The district attorney shook hands quickly, and retreated to his private office. Mr. Andrews took out a cigarette and, as he crossed the floor, lit it.

"Come with me," he commanded. Somewhat puzzled, slightly annoyed, but enjoying withal the novelty of the environment and the curtness of his reception, Mr. Thorndike followed. He decided that, in his ignorance, he had wasted his own time and that of the prosecuting attorney. He should at once have sent in his card to the judge. As he understood it, Mr. Andrews was now conducting him to that dignitary, and, in a moment, he would be free to return to his own affairs, which were the affairs of two continents. But Mr. Andrews led him to an office, bare and small, and offered him a chair, and handed him a morning newspaper. There were people waiting in the room; strange people, only like those Mr. Thorndike had seen on ferry boats. They leaned forward toward young Mr. Andrews, fawning, their eyes wide with apprehension.

Mr. Thorndike refused the newspaper. "I thought I was going to see the judge," he suggested.

"Court doesn't open for a few minutes yet," said the assistant district attorney. "Judge is always late, anyway."

Mr. Thorndike suppressed an exclamation. He wanted to protest, but his clear mind showed him that there was nothing against which, with reason, he could protest. He could not complain because these people were not apparently aware of the sacrifice he was making. He had come among them to perform a kindly act. He recognized that he must not stultify it by a show of irritation. He had precipitated himself into a game of which he did not know the rules. That was all. Next time he would know better. Next time he would send a clerk. But he was not without a sense of humor, and the situation as it now was forced upon him struck him as amusing. He laughed good-naturedly and reached for the desk telephone.

"May I use this?" he asked. He spoke to the Wall Street office. He explained he would be a few minutes late. He directed what should be done if the market opened in a certain way. He gave rapid orders on many different matters, asked to have read to him a cablegram he expected from Petersburg, and one from Vienna.

"They answer each other," was his final instruction. "It looks like peace."

Mr. Andrews with genial patience had remained silent. Now he turned upon his visitors. A Levantine, burly, unshaven, and soiled, towered truculently above him. Young Mr. Andrews with his swivel chair tilted back, his hands clasped behind his head, his cigarette hanging from his lips, regarded the man dispassionately.

"You gotta hell of a nerve to come to see me," he commented cheerfully. To Mr. Thorndike, the form of greeting was novel. So greatly did it differ from the procedure of his own office that he listened with interest.

"Was it you," demanded young Andrews, in a puzzled tone, "or your brother who tried to knife me?" Mr. Thorndike, unaccustomed to cross the pavement to his office unless escorted by bank messengers and plain-clothesmen, felt the room growing rapidly smaller; the figure of the truculent Greek loomed to heroic proportions. The hand of the banker went vaguely to his chin, and from there fell to his pearl pin, which he hastily covered.

"Get out!" said young Andrews, "and don't show your face here—"

The door slammed upon the flying Greek. Young Andrews swung his swivel chair so that, over his shoulder, he could see Mr. Thorndike. "I don't like his face," he explained.

A kindly eyed, sad woman with a basket on her knee smiled upon Andrews with the familiarity of an old acquaintance.

"Is that woman going to get a divorce from my son," she asked, "now that he's in trouble?"

"Now that he's in Sing Sing?" corrected Mr. Andrews. "I *hope* so! She deserves it. That son of yours, Mrs. Bernard," he declared emphatically, "is no good."

The brutality shocked Mr. Thorndike. For the woman he felt a thrill of sympathy, but at once saw that it was superfluous. From the secure and lofty heights of motherhood, Mrs. Bernard smiled down upon the assistant district attorney as upon a naughty child. She did not even deign a protest. She continued merely to smile. The smile reminded Thorndike of the smile on the face of a mother in a painting by Murillo he had lately presented to the chapel in the college he had given to his native town.

"That son of yours," repeated young Andrews, "is a leech. He's robbed you, robbed his wife. Best thing I ever did for *you* was to send him up the river."

The mother smiled upon him beseechingly.

"Could you give me a pass?" she said.

Young Andrews flung up his hands and appealed to Thorndike.

"Isn't that just like a mother?" he protested. "That son of hers has broken her heart, tramped on her, cheated her, hasn't left her a cent; and she comes to me for a pass, so she can kiss him through the bars! And I'll bet she's got a cake for him in that basket!"

The mother laughed happily; she knew now she would get the pass.

"Mothers," explained Mr. Andrews, from the depth of his wisdom, "are all like that; your mother, my mother. If you went to jail, your mother would be just like that."

Mr. Thorndike bowed his head politely. He had never considered going to jail, or whether, if he did, his mother would bring him cake in a basket. Apparently there were many aspects and accidents of life not included in his experience.

Young Andrews sprang to his feet, and, with the force of a hose flushing a gutter, swept his soiled visitors into the hall.

"Come on," he called to the Wisest Man, "the court is open."

In the corridors were many people, and with his eyes on the broad shoulders of the assistant district attorney, Thorndike pushed his way through them. The people who blocked his progress were of the class unknown to him. Their looks were anxious, furtive, miserable. They stood in little groups, listening eagerly to a sharp-faced lawyer, or, in sullen despair, eying each other. At a door a tipstaff laid his hand roughly on the arm of Mr. Thorndike.

"That's all right, Joe," called young Mr. Andrews, "he's with *me*." They entered the court and passed down an aisle to a railed enclosure in which were high oak chairs. Again, in his effort to follow, Mr. Thorndike was halted, but the first tipstaff came to his rescue. "All right," he signaled, "he's with Mr. Andrews."

Mr. Andrews pointed to one of the oak chairs. "You sit there," he commanded, "it's reserved for members of the bar, but it's all right. You're with *me*."

Distinctly annoyed, slightly bewildered, the banker sank between the arms of a chair. He felt he had lost his individuality. Andrews had become his sponsor. Because of Andrews he was tolerated. Because Andrews had a pull he was permitted to sit as an equal among police-court lawyers. No longer was he Arnold Thorndike. He was merely the man "with Mr. Andrews."

Then even Andrews abandoned him. "The judge'll be here in a minute, now," said the assistant district attorney, and went inside a railed enclosure in front of the judge's bench. There he greeted another assistant district attorney whose years were those of even greater indiscretion than the years of Mr. Andrews. Seated on the rail, with their hands in their pockets and their backs turned to Mr. Thorndike, they laughed and talked together. The subject of their discourse was one Mike Donlin, as he appeared in vaudeville.

To Mr. Thorndike it was evident that young Andrews had entirely forgotten him. He arose and touched his sleeve. With infinite sarcasm Mr. Thorndike began: "My engagements are not pressing, but—"

A court attendant beat with his palm upon the rail.

"Sit down!" whispered Andrews. "The judge is coming."

Mr. Thorndike sat down.

The court attendant droned loudly words Mr. Thorndike could not distinguish. There was a rustle of silk, and from a door behind him the judge stalked past. He was a young man, the type of the Tammany politician. On his shrewd, alert, Irish-American features was an expression of unnatural gloom. With a smile Mr. Thorndike observed that it was as little suited to the countenance of the young judge as was the robe to his shoulders. Mr. Thorndike was still smiling when young Andrews leaned over the rail.

"Stand up!" he hissed. Mr. Thorndike stood up.

After the court attendant had uttered more unintelligible words, every one sat down; and the financier again moved hurriedly to the rail.

"I would like to speak to him now before he begins," he whispered. "I can't wait."

Mr. Andrews stared in amazement. The banker had not believed the young man could look so serious.

"Speak to him *now*!" exclaimed the district attorney. "You've got to wait till your man comes up. If you speak to the judge, *now*—" The voice of Andrews faded away in horror.

Not knowing in what way he had offended, but convinced that it was only by the grace of Andrews he had escaped a dungeon, Mr. Thorndike retreated to his armchair.

The clock on the wall showed him that, already, he had given to young Spear one hour and a quarter. The idea was preposterous. No one better than himself knew what his time was really worth. In half an hour there was a board meeting; later he was to hold a post-mortem on a railroad; at every moment questions were being asked by telegraph, by cable, questions that involved the credit of individuals, of firms, of even the country. And the one man who could answer them was risking untold sums only that he might say a good word for an idle apprentice. Inside the railed enclosure a lawyer was reading a typewritten speech. He assured his honor that he must have more time to prepare his case. It was one of immense importance. The name of a most respectable business house was involved, and a sum of no less than nine hundred dollars. Nine hundred dollars! The contrast struck Mr. Thorndike's sense of humor full in the center. Unknowingly, he laughed and found himself as conspicuous as though he had appeared suddenly in his nightclothes. The tipstaffs beat upon the rail, the lawyer he had interrupted uttered an indignant exclamation, Andrews came hurriedly toward him, and the young judge slowly turned his head.

"Those persons," he said, "who cannot respect the dignity of this court will leave it." As he spoke, with his eyes fixed on those of Mr. Thorndike, the latter saw that the young judge had suddenly recognized him. But the fact of his identity did not cause the frown to relax or the rebuke to halt unuttered. In even, icy tones the judge continued: "And it is well they should remember that the law is no respecter of persons and that the dignity of this court will be enforced, no matter who the offender may happen to be."

Andrews slipped into the chair beside Mr. Thorndike and grinned sympathetically.

"Sorry!" he whispered. "Should have warned you. We won't be long now," he added encouragingly. "As soon as this fellow finishes his argument, the judge'll take up the sentences. Your man seems to have other friends; Isaacs & Sons are here, and the typewriter firm who taught him; but what *you* say will help most. It won't be more than a couple of hours now."

"A couple of hours!" Mr. Thorndike raged inwardly. A couple of hours in this place where he had been publicly humiliated. He smiled, a thin, sharklike smile. Those who made it their business to study his expression, on seeing it, would have fled. Young Andrews, not being acquainted with the moods of the great man, added cheerfully: "By one o'clock, anyway."

Mr. Thorndike began grimly to pull on his gloves. For all he cared now young Spear could go hang. Andrews nudged his elbow.

"See that old lady in the front row?" he whispered. "That's Mrs. Spear. What did I tell you; mothers are all alike. She's not taken her eyes off you since court opened. She knows you're her one best bet."

Impatiently Mr. Thorndike raised his head. He saw a little white-haired woman who stared at him. In her eyes was the same look he had seen in the eyes of men who, at times of panic, fled to him, beseeching, entreating, forcing upon him what was left of the wreck of their fortunes, if only he would save their honor.

"And here come the prisoners," Andrews whispered. "See Spear? Third man from the last." A long line, guarded in front and rear, shuffled into the courtroom, and, as ordered, ranged themselves against the wall. Among them were old men and young boys, well dressed, clever-looking rascals, collarless tramps, fierce-eyed aliens, smooth-shaven, thin-lipped Broadwayards—and Spear.

Spear, his head hanging, with lips white and cheeks ashen, and his eyes heavy with shame.

Mr. Thorndike had risen, and, in farewell, was holding out his hand to Andrews. He turned, and across the courtroom the eyes of the financier and the stenographer met. At the sight of the great man Spear flushed crimson, and then his look of despair slowly disappeared; and into his eyes there came incredulously hope and gratitude. He turned his head suddenly to the wall.

Mr. Thorndike stood irresolute and then sank back into his chair.

The first man in the line was already at the railing, and the questions put to him by the judge were being repeated to him by the other assistant district attorney and a court attendant. His muttered answers were in turn repeated to the judge.

"Says he's married, naturalized citizen, Lutheran Church, diecutter by profession."

The probation officer, her hands filled with papers, bustled forward and whispered.

"Mrs. Austin says," continued the district attorney, "she's looked into this case and asks to have the man turned over to her. He has a wife and three children; has supported them for five years."

"Is the wife in court?" the judge said.

A thin, washed-out, pretty woman stood up and clasped her hands in front of her.

"Has this man been a good husband to you, madam?" asked the young judge.

The woman broke into vehement assurances. No man could have been a better husband. Would she take him back? Indeed she would take him back. She held out her hands as though she would physically drag her husband from the pillory.

The judge bowed toward the probation officer, and she beckoned the prisoner to her.

Other men followed, and in the fortune of each Mr. Thorndike found himself, to his surprise, taking a personal interest. It was as good as a play. It reminded him of the Sicilians he had seen in London in their little sordid tragedies. Only these actors were appearing in their proper persons in real dramas of a life he did not know, but which appealed to something that had been long untouched, long in disuse. It was an uncomfortable sensation that left him restless because, as he appreciated, it needed expression, an outlet. He found this, partially, in praising, through Andrews, the young judge who had publicly rebuked him. Mr. Thorndike found him astute, sane; his queries intelligent, his comments just. And this probation officer, she, too, was capable, was she not? Smiling at his interest in what to him was an old story, the younger man nodded.

"I like her looks," whispered the great man. "Like her clear eyes and clean skin. She strikes me as able, full of energy, and yet womanly. These men when they come under her charge," he insisted, eagerly, "need money to start again, don't they?" He spoke anxiously. He believed he had found the clue to his restlessness. It was a desire to help; to be of use to these failures who had fallen and who were being lifted to their feet. Andrews looked at him curiously. "Anything you give her," he answered, "would be well invested."

"If you tell me her name and address?" whispered the banker. He was much given to charity, but it had been perfunctory, it was extended on the advice of his secretary. In helping here he felt a genial glow of personal pleasure. It was much more satisfactory than giving an Old Master to his private chapel.

In the rear of the courtroom there was a scuffle that caused every one to turn and look. A man, who had tried to force his way past the tipstaffs, was being violently ejected, and, as he disappeared, he waved a paper toward Mr. Thorndike. The banker recognized him as his chief clerk. Andrews rose anxiously. "That man wanted to get to you. I'll see what it is. Maybe it's important."

Mr. Thorndike pulled him back.

"Maybe it is," he said dryly. "but I can't see him now, I'm busy."

Slowly the long line of derelicts, of birds of prey, of sorry, weak failures, passed before the seat of judgment. Mr. Thorndike had moved into a chair nearer to the rail, and from time to time made a note upon the back of an envelope. He had forgotten the time or had chosen to disregard it. So great was his interest that he had forgotten the particular derelict he had come to serve, until Spear stood almost at his elbow.

Thorndike turned eagerly to the judge and saw that he was listening to a rotund, gray little man with beady, birdlike eyes who, as he talked, bowed and gesticulated. Behind him stood a younger man, a more modern edition of the other. He also bowed and, behind gold eyeglasses, smiled ingratiatingly.

The judge nodded and, leaning forward, for a few moments fixed his eyes upon the prisoner.

"You are a very fortunate young man," he said. He laid his hand upon a pile of letters. "When you were your own worst enemy, your friends came to help you. These letters speak for you; your employers, whom you robbed, have pleaded with me in your favor. It is urged, in your behalf, that at the time you committed the crime of which you are found guilty, you were intoxicated. In the eyes of the law, that is no excuse. Some men can drink and keep their senses. It appears you cannot. When you drink you are a menace to yourself—and, as is shown by this crime, to the community. Therefore, you must not drink. In view of the good character to which your friends have testified, and on the condition that you do not touch liquor, I will not sentence you to jail, but will place you in charge of the probation officer."

The judge leaned back in his chair and beckoned to Mr. Andrews. It was finished. Spear was free, and from different parts of the courtroom people were moving toward the door. Their numbers showed that the friends of the young man had been many. Mr. Thorndike felt a certain twinge of disappointment. Even though the result relieved and pleased him, he wished, in bringing it about, he had had some part.

He begrudged to Isaacs & Sons the credit of having given Spear his liberty. His morning had been wasted. He had neglected his own interests, and in no way assisted those of Spear. He was moving out of the railed enclosure when Andrews called him by name.

"His Honor," he said impressively, "wishes to speak to you."

The judge leaned over his desk and shook Mr. Thorndike by the hand. Then he made a speech. The speech was about public-spirited citizens who, to the neglect of their own interest, came to assist the ends of justice and fellow creatures in misfortune. He purposely spoke in a loud voice, and everyone stopped to listen.

"The law, Mr. Thorndike, is not vindictive," he said. "It wishes only to be just. Nor can it be swayed by wealth or political or social influences. But when there is good in a man, I, personally, want to know it, and when gentlemen like yourself, of your standing in this city, come here to speak a good word for a man, we would stultify the purpose of justice if we did not listen. I thank you for coming, and I wish more of our citizens were as unselfish and public-spirited."

It was all quite absurd and most embarrassing, but inwardly Mr. Thorndike glowed with pleasure. It was a long time since any one had had the audacity to tell him he had done well. From the friends of Spear there was a ripple of applause, which no tipstaff took it upon himself to suppress, and to the accompaniment of this, Mr. Thorndike walked to the corridor.

He was pleased with himself and his fellow man. He shook hands with Isaacs & Sons and congratulated them upon their public spirit, and the typewriter firm upon their public spirit. And then he saw Spear standing apart regarding him doubtfully.

Spear did not offer his hand, but Mr. Thorndike took it and shook it and said, "I want to meet your mother."

And when Mrs. Spear tried to stop sobbing long enough to tell him how happy she was, and how grateful, he instead told her what a fine son she had, and that he remembered when Spear used to carry flowers to town for her. And she remembered it, too, and thanked him for the flowers. And he told Spear, when Isaacs & Sons went bankrupt, which at the rate they were giving away their money to the Hebrew Hospital would be very soon, Spear must come back to him. And Isaacs & Sons were delighted at the great man's pleasantry and afterward repeated it many times, calling upon each other to bear witness, and Spear felt as though some one had given him a new backbone, and Andrews, who was guiding Thorndike out of the building, was thinking to himself what a great confidence man had been lost when Thorndike became a banker.

The chief clerk and two bank messengers were waiting by the automobile with written calls for help from the office. They pounced upon the banker and almost lifted him into the car.

"There's still time!" panted the chief clerk.

"There is not!" answered Mr. Thorndike. His tone was rebellious, defiant. It carried all the authority of a spoiled child of fortune. "I've wasted most of this day," he declared, "and I intend to waste the rest of it. Andrews," he called, "jump in, and I'll give you a lunch at Sherry's."

The vigilant protector of the public dashed back into the building.

"Wait till I get my hat!" he called.

As the two truants rolled up the avenue the spring sunshine warmed them, the sense of duties neglected added zest to their holiday, and young Mr. Andrews laughed aloud.

Mr. Thorndike raised his eyebrows inquiringly.

"I was wondering," said Andrews, "how much it cost you to keep Spear out of jail?"

"I don't care," said the great man guiltily; "it was worth it."

Part Three
Punishment

9

Theories of Punishment

> Although we usually call reward and punishment the two
> hinges upon which all government turns, yet I could never
> observe this maxim to be put into practice by any nation, ex-
> cept that of Lilliput. . . . And these people thought it a
> prodigious defect of policy among us when I told them that
> our laws were enforced only by penalties, without any men-
> tion of reward. It is upon this account that the image of Jus-
> tice, in their courts of judicature, is formed with six eyes,
> two before, as many behind, and on each side one, to sig-
> nify circumspection; with a bag full of gold open in her right
> hand, and a sword sheathed in her left, to show she is more
> disposed to reward than to punish.
>
> *The Laws of the Lilliputians*
> Jonathan Swift

In the previous section, we saw that judges play many roles in the judicial
process—one of those roles is in establishing the payment to be extracted
from the guilty defendant for his or her crime. For the most part, the
judge's discretion is once again constrained—this time by statutes within
which he must work in issuing prison terms, setting fines, ordering probation, or insisting on some kind of civic duty in the way of community
involvement or attendance at classes designed to remedy past undesirable
behavior. Implicit in the legislative statutes to be used as guidelines for sentencing, and evident in the discretion which the judge exercises in applying
those statutes, is our justification for punishment. Some theories of such
justification are:

• **Protection of Society.** If protection of society is the primary
aim of punishment, then the obvious solution would be to lock up all of
those who pose a threat to others.

• **Reform of the Offender.** If reform is the goal, then perhaps
we need to adopt the Lilliputian notion of stressing rewards over punishments. The prisoners would be allowed to participate in a token economy
earning credit—in the form of special privileges, spending money, early re-

lease time—for good behavior. This would be followed up with a system of rewards which would encourage the released prisoner to stay out of trouble and away from crime.

• **Deterrence.** Deterrence has a twofold purpose—to deter the repeat offender and to deter others by their observation of the punishment given to the criminal. The major problem with the deterrence theory as it applies to repeat offenders is the fact that sociologists, psychologists, and psychiatrists have shown repeatedly by their research that sociopathic personalities—those who tend to be the repeat offender—do not learn by punishment. No matter how severe the punishment, the sociopath will come back again, and again, and again.

Deterrence of others taken to the logical extreme suggests that we should engage in some kind of public activity analogous to the placing of prisoners in the stocks on the village square for all the world to see. In our society this might take the form of school visits to prisons and televised executions.

How might a system of rewards work as a deterrent to both the repeat offender and others who have not yet, but might, commit a crime? Think of an imaginary line on the left side of which are all of the citizens who did not violate any of the laws last year, and on the right side of which are those who are perpetrators of some crime. If we were to reward all of those citizens on the left, would the inference be that conformity to the laws is difficult and not expected without the issuance of rewards which are not only in order but also necessary? Would this send the wrong signal to the public? Would we be able to make the rewards lucrative enough to discourage potential criminals?

• **Retribution.** If retribution is the goal of punishment and the "eye for an eye and a tooth for a tooth" philosophy of Hammurabi's code is at the core of the theory of punishment, who should administer such punishment? The State or the person wronged? Should the thief have his property taken away or his hands cut off? Or is it sufficient retribution if we lock up the offender for life? What should the institutional facilities be like for someone committed to an institution for life—color television and a recreation room, three meals a day and a clean well-lighted place to sleep? Or does a murderer deserve only bread and water in a dirty cell with one hour of exercise per day?

In Sir Walter Scott's short story "The Two Drovers," the judge deliberates on primitive man's acceptance of revenge as a defense to crime—retribution by the aggrieved party rather than by the State—but he concludes that a mistaken notion of honor cannot absolve the wrongdoer in a court of law, especially when so much time has passed between the provocation and the act that "crime of passion" cannot be pleaded. The judge's main objective in the charge to the jury is to ensure that the punishment of Robin Oig is a deterrent to others so that a thousand daggers are not unsheathed "between the Land's End and the Orkneys." His ultimate aim is to maintain social order. Also, Oig is nonrepentant, although he does espouse a primitive philosophy when he states that his life is given for the life which he took.

Leo Tolstóy's short story "Too Dear" raises many questions concerning the nature and purpose of punishment. Most of those questions relate to the role of economics in the sentencing and housing of a prisoner:

*   Should the citizens have a say in the choice of the punishment of the criminal when their taxes are used to finance the judicial system and its workings?

*   Would we be justified in changing a life sentence to a death sentence because it would be economically efficient?

*   Should the age of the criminal be taken into account in sentencing? Would it be more justifiable to hang a younger man than an older man on the basis of economics?

*   How do we expect prisoners to fit into society after a lengthy prison term if, in addition to a prison record, they have no work skills?

*   Should prisoners continue to earn Social Security credits while they are in prison so that they will have a pension when they *retire*?

The Two Drovers
Sir Walter Scott

CHAPTER I

It was the day after Doune Fair when my story commences. It had been a brisk market: several dealers had attended from the northern and midland counties in England, and English money had flown so merrily about as to gladden the hearts of the Highland farmers. Many large droves were about to set off for England, under the protection of their owners, or of the topsmen whom they employed in the tedious, laborious, and responsible office of driving the cattle for many hundred miles, from the market where they had been purchased to the fields or farm-yards where they were to be fattened for the shambles.

The Highlanders, in particular, are masters of this difficult trade of driving, which seems to suit them as well as the trade of war. It affords exercise for all their habits of patient endurance and active exertion. They are required to know perfectly the drove-roads, which lie over the wildest tracts of the country, and to avoid as much as possible the highways, which distress the feet of the bullocks, and the turnpikes, which annoy the spirit of the drover; whereas on the broad green or grey track, which leads across the pathless moor, the herd not only move at ease and without taxation, but, if they mind their business, may pick up a mouthful of food by the way. At night, the drovers usually sleep along with their cattle, let the weather be what it will; and many of these hardy men do not once rest under a roof during a journey on foot from Lochaber to Lincolnshire. They are paid very highly, for the trust reposed is of the last importance, as it depends on their prudence, vigilance, and honesty whether the cattle reach the final market in good order, and afford a profit to the grazier. But, as they maintain themselves at their own expense, they are especially economical in that particular. At the period we speak of, a Highland drover was victualled for his long and toilsome journey with a few handfuls of oatmeal and two or three onions, renewed from time to time, and a ram's horn filled with whisky, which he used regularly, but sparingly, every night and morning. His dirk, or *skenedhu* (i.e. black knife), so worn as to be concealed beneath the arm, or by the folds of the plaid, was his only weapon, excepting the cudgel with which he directed the movements of the cattle. A Highlander was never so happy as on these occasions. There was a variety in the whole journey which exercised the Celt's natural curiosity and love of motion; there were the constant change of place and scene, the petty adventures incidental to the traffic, and the intercourse with the various farmers, graziers, and traders, intermingled with occasional merrymakings, not the less acceptable to Donald that they were void of expense; and there was the consciousness of superior skill: for the Highlander, a child amongst flocks, is a prince amongst herds, and his natural habits induce him to disdain the shepherd's slothful life, so that he feels himself nowhere more at home than when following a gallant drove of his country cattle in the character of their guardian.

Of the number who left Doune in the morning, and with the purpose we have described, not a *glunamie* of them all cocked his bonnet more briskly, or gartered his tartan hose under knee over a pair of more promising *spiogs* (legs), than did Robin Oig M'Combich, called familiarly Robin Oig, that is, Young, or the Lesser, Robin. Though small of stature, as the epithet Oig implies, and not very strongly limbed, he was as light and alert as one of the deer of his mountains. He had an elasticity of step which, in the course of a long march, made many a stout fellow envy him; and the manner in which he busked his plaid and adjusted his bonnet argued a consciousness that so smart a John Highlandman as himself would not pass unnoticed among the Lowland lasses. The ruddy cheek, red lips, and white teeth set off a countenance which had gained by exposure to the weather a healthful and hardy rather than a rugged hue. If Robin Oig did not laugh, or even smile, frequently, as indeed is not the practice among his countrymen, his bright eyes usually gleamed from under his bonnet with an expression of cheerfulness ready to be turned into mirth.

The departure of Robin Oig was an incident in the little town, in and near which he had many friends, male and female. He was a topping person in his way, transacted considerable business on his own behalf, and was entrusted by the best farmers in the Highlands, in preference to any other drover in that district. He might have increased his business to any extent had he condescended to manage it by deputy; but, except a lad or two, sister's sons of his own, Robin rejected the idea of assistance, conscious, perhaps, how much his reputation depended upon his attending in person to the practical discharge of his duty in every instance. He remained, therefore, contented with the highest premium given to persons of his description, and comforted himself with the hopes that a few journeys to England might enable him to conduct business on his own account in a manner becoming his birth. For Robin Oig's father, Lachlan M'Combich, or 'son of my friend' (his actual clansurname being M'Gregor), had been so called by the celebrated Rob Roy, because of the particular friendship which had subsisted between the grandsire of Robin and that renowned cateran. Some people even say that Robin Oig derived his Christian name from one as renowned in the wilds of Loch Lomond as ever was his namesake, Robin Hood, in the precincts of merry Sherwood. 'Oh such ancestry,' as James Boswell says, 'who would not be proud?' Robin Oig was proud accordingly; but his frequent visits to England and to the Lowlands had given him tact enough to know that pretensions which still gave him a little right to distinction in his own lonely glen might be both obnoxious and ridiculous if preferred elsewhere. The pride of birth, therefore, was like the miser's treasure, the secret subject of his contemplation, but never exhibited to strangers as a subject of boasting.

Many were the words of gratulation and good-luck which were bestowed on Robin Oig. The judges commended his drove, especially Robin's own property, which were the best of them. Some thrust out their snuff-mulls for the parting pinch; others tendered the *doch-an-dorroch*, or parting-cup. All cried—'Good-luck travel out with you and come back home with you. Give you luck in the Saxon market—brave notes in the *leabhar-dhu* (black pocket-book) and plenty of English gold in the *sporran'* (pouch of goat-skin).

The bonny lasses made their adieus more modestly, and more than one, it was said, would have given her best brooch to be certain that it was upon her that his eye last rested as he turned towards the road.

Robin Oig had just given the preliminary 'Hoo-hoo!' to urge forward the loiterers of the drove, when there was a cry behind him.

'Stay, Robin—bide a blink. Here is Janet of Tomahourich—auld Janet, your father's sister.'

'Plague on her, for an auld Highland witch and spae-wife,' said a farmer from the Carse of Stirling; 'she'll cast some of her cantrips on the cattle.'

'She canna do that,' said another sapient of the same profession: 'Robin Oig is no the lad to leave any of them without tying St. Mungo's knot on their tails, and that will put to her speed the best witch that ever flew over Dimayet upon a broomstick.'

It may not be indifferent to the reader to know that the Highland cattle are peculiarly liable to be 'taken,' or infected, by spells and witchcraft, which judicious people guard against by knitting knots of peculiar complexity on the tuft of hair which terminates the animal's tail.

But the old woman, who was the object of the farmer's suspicion, seemed only busied about the drover, without paying any attention to the drove. Robin, on the contrary, appeared rather impatient of her presence.

'What auld-world fancy,' he said, 'has brought you so early from the ingle-side this morning, muhme? I am sure I bid you good-even, and had your God-speed, last night.'

'And left me more siller than the useless old woman will use till you come back again, bird of my bosom,' said the sibyl. 'But it is little I would care for the food that nourishes me, or the fire that warms me, or for God's blessed sun itself, if aught but weal should happen to the grandson of my father. So let me walk the *deasil* round you, that you may go safe out into the far foreign land, and come safe home.'

Robin Oig stopped, half-embarrassed, half-laughing, and signing to those around that he only complied with the old woman to sooth her humour. In the meantime, she traced around him, with wavering steps, the propitiation, which some have thought has been derived from the Druidical mythology. It consists, as is well known, in the person who makes the *deasil* walking three times round the person who is the object of the ceremony, taking care to move according to the course of the sun. At once, however, she stopped short, and exclaimed, in a voice of alarm and horror, 'Grandson of my father, there is blood on your hand.'

'Hush, for God's sake, aunt,' said Robin Oig; 'you will bring more trouble on yourself with this *taishataragh* (second sight) than you will be able to get out of for many a day.'

The old woman only repeated, with a ghastly look, 'There is blood on your hand, and it is English blood. The blood of the Gael is richer and redder. Let us see—let us—'

Ere Robin Oig could prevent her, which, indeed, could only have been by positive violence, so hasty and peremptory were her proceedings, she had drawn from his side the dirk which lodged in the folds of his plaid, and held it up, exclaiming, although the weapon gleamed clear and bright in the sun, 'Blood, blood—Saxon blood again. Robin Oig M'Combich, go not this day to England!'

'Prutt, trutt,' answered Robin Oig, 'that will never do neither; it would be next thing to running the country. For shame, muhme, give me the dirk. You cannot tell by the colour the difference betwixt the blood of a black bullock and a white one, and you speak of knowing Saxon from Gaelic blood. All men have their blood from Adam, muhme. Give me my skene-dhu, and let me go on my road. I should have been half-way to Stirling brig by this time. Give me my dirk, and let me go.'

'Never will I give it to you,' said the old woman—'never will I quit my hold on your plaid, unless you promise me not to wear that unhappy weapon.'

The women around him urged him also, saying, few of his aunt's words fell to the ground; and as the Lowland farmers continued to look moodily on the scene, Robin Oig determined to close it at any sacrifice.

'Well, then,' said the young drover, giving the scabbard of the weapon to Hugh Morrison, 'you Lowlanders care nothing for these freats. Keep my dirk for me. I cannot give it you, because it was my father's; but your drove follows ours, and I am content it should be in your keeping, not in mine. Will this do, muhme?'

'It must,' said the old woman—'that is, if the Lowlander is mad enough to carry the knife.'

The strong Westlandman laughed aloud.

'Goodwife,' said he, 'I am Hugh Morrison from Glenae, come of the Manly Morrisons of auld langsyne, that never took short weapon against a man in their lives. And neither needed they: they had their broad-swords, and I have this bit supple,' showing a formidable cudgel; 'for dirking ower the board, I leave that to John Highlandman. Ye needna snort, none of you Highlandmen, and you in especial, Robin. I'll keep the bit knife, if you are feared for the auld spaewife's tale, and give it back to you whenever you want it.'

Robin was not particularly pleased with some part of Hugh Morrison's speech; but he had learned in his travels more patience than belonged to his Highland constitution originally, and he accepted the service of the descendant of the Manly Morrisons, without finding fault with the rather deprecating manner in which it was offered.

'If he had not had his morning in his head, and been but a Dumfriesshire hog into the boot, he would have spoken more like a gentleman. But you cannot have more of a sow than a grumph. It's shame my father's knife should ever slash a haggis for the like of him.'

Thus saying, but saying it in Gaelic, Robin drove on his cattle, and waved farewell to all behind him. He was in the greater haste, because he expected to join at Falkirk a comrade and brother in profession, with whom he proposed to travel in company.

Robin Oig's chosen friend was a young Englishman, Harry Wakefield by name, well known at every northern market, and in his way as much famed and honoured as our Highland driver of bullocks. He was nearly six feet high, gallantly formed to keep the rounds at Smithfield, or maintain the ring at a wrestling-match; and although he might have been overmatched, perhaps, among the regular professors of the fancy, yet, as a yokel or rustic, or a chance customer, he was able to give a bellyful to any amateur of the pugilistic art. Doncaster races saw him in his glory, betting his guinea, and generally successfully; nor was there a main fought in Yorkshire, the feeders being persons of celebrity, at which he was not to be seen, if business permitted. But though a 'sprack' lad, and fond of pleasure and its haunts, Harry Wakefield was steady, and not the cautious Robin Oig M'Combich himself was more attentive to the main chance. His holidays were holidays indeed; but his days of work were dedicated to steady and persevering labour. In countenance and temper, Wakefield was the model of Old England's merry yeomen, whose clothyard shafts, in so many hundred battles, asserted her superiority over the nations, and whose good sabres, in our own time, are her cheapest and most assured defence. His mirth was readily excited; for, strong in limb and constitution, and fortunate in circumstances, he was disposed to be pleased with everything about him; and such difficulties as he might occasionally encounter were, to a man of his energy, rather matter of amusement than serious annoyance. With all the merits of a sanguine temper, our young English drover was not without his defects. He was irascible, sometimes to the verge of being quarrelsome; and perhaps not the less inclined to bring his disputes to a pugilistic decision, because he found few antagonists able to stand up to him in the boxing-ring.

It is difficult to say how Harry Wakefield and Robin Oig first became intimates; but it is certain a close acquaintance had taken place betwixt them, although they had apparently few common subjects of conversation or of interest, so soon as their talk ceased to be of bullocks. Robin Oig, indeed, spoke the English language rather imperfectly upon any other topics but stots and kyloes, and Harry Wakefield could never bring his broad Yorkshire tongue to utter a single word of Gaelic. It was in vain Robin spent a whole morning, during a walk over Minch Moor, in attempting to teach his companion to utter, with true precision, the shibboleth *llhu*, which is the Gaelic for a calf. From Traquair to Murder Cairn, the hill rung with the discordant attempts of the Saxon upon the unmanageable monosyllable, and the heartfelt laugh which followed every failure. They had, however, better modes of awakening the echoes; for Wakefield could sing many a ditty to the praise of Moll, Susan, and Cicely, and Robin Oig had a particular gift at whistling interminable pibrochs through all their involutions, and, what was more agreeable to his companion's southern ear, knew many of the northern airs, both lively and pathetic, to which Wakefield learned to pipe a bass. Thus, though Robin could hardly have comprehended his companion's stories about horse-racing, and cock-fighting, or fox-hunting, and although his own legends of clan-fights and creaghs, varied with talk of Highland goblins and fairy folk, would have been caviare to his companion, they contrived nevertheless to find a degree of pleasure in each other's company, which had for three years back induced them to join company and travel together, when the direction of their journey permitted. Each, indeed, found his advantage in this companionship; for where could the Englishman have found a guide through the Western Highlands like Robin Oig M'Combich? and when they were on what Harry called the *right* side of the Border, his patronage, which was extensive, and his purse, which was heavy, were at all times at the service of his Highland friend, and on many occasions his liberality did him genuine yeoman's service.

CHAPTER II

Were ever two such loving friends!—
How could they disagree?
O thus it was, he loved him dear,
    And thought how to requite him,
And having no friend left but he,
    He did resolve to fight him.

Duke upon Duke.

The pair of friends had traversed with their usual cordiality the grassy wilds of Liddesdale, and crossed the opposite part of Cumberland, emphatically called The Waste. In these solitary regions the cattle under the charge of our drovers derived their subsistence chiefly by picking their food as they went along the drove-road, or somtimes by the tempting opportunity of a 'start and owerloup,' or invasion of the neighbouring pasture, where an occasion presented itself. But now the scene changed before them; they were descending towards a fertile and inclosed country, where no such liberties could be taken with impunity, or without a previous arrangement and bargain with the possessors of the ground. This was more especially the case, as a great northern fair was upon the eve of taking place, where both the Scotch and English drover expected to dispose of a part of their cattle, which it was desirable to produce in the market rested and in good order. Fields were therefore difficult to be obtained, and only upon high terms. This necessity occasioned a temporary separation betwixt the two friends, who went to bargain, each as he could, for the separate accommodation of his herd. Unhappily it chanced that both of them, unknown to each other, thought of bargaining for the ground they wanted on the property of a country gentleman of some fortune, whose estate lay in the neighbourhood. The English drover applied to the bailiff on the property, who was known to him. It chanced that the Cumbrian squire, who had entertained some suspicions of his manager's honesty, was taking occasional measures to ascertain how far they were well founded, and had desired that any inquiries about his inclosures, with a view to occupy them for a temporary purpose, should be referred to himself. As, however, Mr. Ireby had gone the day before upon a journey of some miles' distance to the northward, the bailiff chose to consider the check upon his full powers as for the time removed, and concluded that he should best consult his master's interest, and perhaps his own, in making an agreement with Harry Wakefield.

Meanwhile, ignorant of what his comrade was doing, Robin Oig, on his side, chanced to be overtaken by a good-looking smart little man upon a pony, most knowingly hogged and cropped, as was then the fashion, the rider wearing tight leather breeches and long-necked bright spurs. This cavalier asked one or two pertinent questions about markets and the price of stock. So Robin, seeing him a well-judging, civil gentleman, took the freedom to ask him whether he could let him know if there was any grass-land to be let in that neighbourhood, for the temporary accommodation of his drove. He could not have put the question to more willing ears. The gentleman of the buckskins was the proprietor with whose bailiff Harry Wakefield had dealt, or was in the act of dealing.

'Thou art in good luck, my canny Scott,' said Mr. Ireby, 'to have spoken to me, for I see thy cattle have done their day's work, and I have at my disposal the only field within three miles that is to be let in these parts.'

'The drove can pe gang two, three, four miles very pratty weel indeed,' said the cautious Highlander; 'put what would his honour pe axing for the peasts pe the head, if she was to tak the park for twa or three days?'

'We won't differ, Sawney, if you let me have six stots for winterers, in the way of reason.'

'And which peasts wad your honour pe for having?'

'Why, let me see—the two black—the dun one—yon doddy—him with the twisted horn—the brockit. How much by the head?'

'Ah,' said Robin, 'your honour is a shudge—a real shudge: I couldna have set off the pest six peasts petter mysell, me that ken them as if they were my pairns, puir things.'

'Well, how much per head, Sawney,' continued Mr. Ireby.

'It was high markets at Doune and Falkirk,' answered Robin.

And thus the conversation proceeded, until they had agreed on the *prix juste* for the bullocks, the squire throwing in the temporary accommodation of the inclosure for the cattle into the boot, and Robin making, as he thought, a very good bargain, provided the grass was but tolerable. The squire walked his pony alongside of the drove, partly to show him the way, and see him put into possession of the field, and partly to learn the latest news of the northern markets.

They arrived at the field, and the pasture seemed excellent. But what was their surprise when they saw the bailiff quietly inducting the cattle of Harry Wakefield into the grassy Goshen which had just been assigned to those of Robin Oig M'Combich by the proprietor himself! Squire Ireby set spurs to his horse, dashed up to his servant, and learning what had passed between the parties, briefly informed the English drover that his bailiff had let the ground without his authority, and that he might seek grass for his cattle wherever he would, since he was to get none there. At the same time he rebuked his servant severely for having transgressed his commands, and ordered him instantly to assist in ejecting the hungry and weary cattle of Harry Wakefield, which were just beginning to enjoy a meal of unusual plenty, and to introduce those of his comrade, whom the English drove now began to consider as a rival.

The feelings which arose in Wakefield's mind would have induced him to resist Mr. Ireby's decision; but every Englishman has a tolerably accurate sense of law and justice, and John Fleecebumpkin, the bailiff, having acknowledged that he had exceeded his commission, Wakefield saw nothing else for it than to collect this hungry and disappointed charge, and drive them on to seek quarters elsewhere. Robin Oig saw what had happened with regret, and hastened to offer to his English friend to share with him the disputed possession. But Wakefield's pride was severely hurt, and he answered disdainfully, 'Take it all, man—take it all; never make two bites of a cherry. Thou canst talk over the gentry, and blear a plain man's eye. Out upon you, man; I would not kiss any man's dirty latchets for leave to bake in his own.'

Robin Oig, sorry but not surprised at his comrade's displeasure, hastened to entreat his friends to wait but an hour till he had gone to the squire's house to receive payment for the cattle he had sold, and he would come back and help him to drive the cattle into some convenient place of rest, and explain to him the whole mistake they had both of them fallen into.

But the Englishman continued indignant. 'Thou hast been selling, hast thou? Ay—ay, thou is a cunning lad for kenning the hours of bargaining. Go to the devil with thyself, for I will ne'er see thy fause loon's visage again; thou should be ashamed to look me in the face.'

'I am ashamed to look no man in the face,' said Robin Oig, something moved; 'and, moreover, I will look you in the face this blessed day, if you will bide at the clachan down yonder.'

'Mayhap you had as well keep away,' said his comrade; and turning his back on his former friend, he collected his unwilling associates, assisted by the bailiff, who took some real and some affected interest in seeing Wakefield accommodated.

After spending some time in negotiating with more than one of the neighbouring farmers, who could not, or would not, afford the accommodation desired, Henry Wakefield at last, and in his necessity, accomplished his point by means of the landlord of the alehouse at which Robin Oig and he had agreed to pass the night, when they first separated from each other. Mine host was content to let him turn his cattle on a piece of barren moor, at a price little less than the bailiff had asked for the disputed inclosure; and the wretchedness of the pasture, as well as the price paid for it, were set down as exaggerations of the breach of faith and friendship of his Scottish crony. This turn of Wakefield's passions was encouraged by the bailiff, who had his own reasons for being offended against poor Robin, as having been the unwitting cause of his falling into disgrace with his master, as well as by the innkeeper, and two or three chance guests, who stimulated the drover in his resentment against his quondam associate—some from the ancient grudge against the Scots, which, when it exists anywhere, is to be found lurking in the Border counties, and some from the general love of mischief, which characterises mankind in all ranks of life, to the honour of Adam's children be it spoken. Good John Barleycorn also, who always heightens and exaggerates the prevailing passions, be they angry or kindly, was not wanting in his offices on this occasion; and confusion to false friends and hard masters was pledged in more than one tankard.

In the meanwhile, Mr. Ireby found some amusement in detaining the northern drover at his ancient hall. He caused a cold round of beef to be placed before the Scot in the butler's pantry, together with a foaming tankard of home-brewed, and took pleasure in seeing the hearty appetite with which these unwonted edibles were discussed by Robin Oig M'Combich. The squire himself, lighting his pipe, compounded between his patrician dignity and his love of agricultural gossip, by walking up and down while he conversed with his guest.

'I passed another drove,' said the squire, 'with one of your countrymen behind them; they were something less beasts than your drove, doddies most of them; a big man was with them—none of your kilts though, but a decent pair of breeches. D'ye know who he may be?'

'Hout aye, that might, could, and would be Hughie Morrison; I didna think he could hae peen sae weel up. He has made a day on us; but his Argyleshires will have wearied shanks. How far was he pehind?'

'I think about six or seven miles,' answered the squire, 'for I passed them at the Christenbury Craq, and I overtook you at the Hollan Bush. If his beasts be leg-weary, he will be maybe selling bargains.'

'Na—na, Hughie Morrison is no the man for pargains; ye maun come to some Highland body like Robin Oig hersell for the like of these. Put I maun pe wishing you goot-night, and twenty of them let alane ane, and I maun down to the clachan to see if the lad Harry Waakfelt is out of his humdudgeons yet.'

The party at the alehouse were still in full talk, and the treachery of Robin Oig still the theme of conversation, when the supposed culprit entered the apartment. His arrival, as usually happens in such a case, put an instant stop to the discussion of which he had furnished the subject, and he was received by the company assembled with that chilling silence which, more than a thousand exclamations, tells an intruder that he is unwelcome. Surprised and offended, but not appalled, by the reception which he experienced, Robin entered with an undaunted and even a haughty air, attempted no greeting, as he saw he was received with none, and placed himself by the side of the fire, a little apart from a table at which Harry Wakefield, the bailiff, and two or three other persons were seated. The ample Cumbrian kitchen would have afforded plenty of room, even for a larger separation.

Robin, thus seated, proceeded to light his pipe and call for a pint of two penny.

'We have no twopence ale,' answered Ralph Heskett, the landlord; 'but, as thou find'st thy own tobacco, it's like thou mayst find thy own liquor too; it's the wont of thy country, I wot.'

'Shame, goodman,' said the landlady, a blythe, bustling housewife, hastening herself to supply the guest with liquor. 'Thou knowest well enow what the strange man wants, and it's thy trade to be civil, man. Thou shouldst know, that if the Scot likes a small pot, he pays a sure penny.'

Without taking any notice of this nuptial dialogue, the Highlander took the flagon in his hand, and addressing the company generally, drank the interesting toast of 'Good markets,' to the party assembled.

'The better that the wind blew fewer dealers from the north,' said one of the farmers, 'and fewer Highland runts to eat up the English meadows.'

'Saul of my pody, put you are wrang there, my friend,' answered Robin, with composure; 'it is your fat Englishmen that eat up our Scots cattle, puir things.'

'I wish there was a summat to eat up their drovers,' said another; 'a plain Englishman canna make bread within a kenning of them.'

'Or an honest servant keep his master's favour, but they will come sliding in between him and the sunshine,' said the bailiff.

'If these pe jokes,' said Robin Oig, with the same composure, 'there is ower mony jokes upon one man.'

'It is no joke, but downright earnest,' said the bailiff. 'Harkye, Mr. Robin Ogg, or whatever is your name, it's right we should tell you that we are all of one opinion, and that is, that you, Mr. Robin Ogg, have behaved to our friend, Mr. Harry Wakefield here, like a raff and a blackguard.'

'Nae doubt—nae doubt,' answered Robin, with great composure; 'and you are a set of very pretty judges, for whose prains or pehaviour I wad not gie a pinch of sneeshing. If Mr. Harry Waakfelt kens where he is wranged, he kens where he may be righted.'

'He speaks truth,' said Wakefield, who had listened to what passed, divided between the offence which he had taken at Robert's late behaviour and the revival of his habitual feelings of regard.

He now rose and went towards Robin, who got up from his seat as he approached, and held out his hand.

'That's right, Harry—go it—serve him out,' resounded on all sides—'tip him the nailer—show him the mill.'

'Hold your peace all of you, and be—,' said Wakefield; and then addressing his comrade, he took him by the extended hand, with something alike of respect and defiance. 'Robin,' he said, 'thou hast used me ill enough this day; but if you mean like a frank fellow, to shake hands, and take a tussle for love on the sod, why, I'll forgie thee, man, and we shall be better friends than ever.'

'And would it not pe petter to pe cood friends without more of the matter?' said Robin; 'we will be much petter friendships with our panes hale than proken.'

Harry Wakefield dropped the hand of his friend, or rather threw it from him.

'I did not think I had been keeping company for three years with a coward.'

'Coward pelongs to none of my name,' said Robin, whose eyes began to kindle, but keeping the command of his temper. 'It was no coward's lege or hands, Harry Waakfelt, that drew you out of the fords of Frew, when you was drifting ower the plack rock and every eel in the river expected his share of you.'

'And that is true enough, too,' said the Englishman, struck by the appeal.

'Adzooks!' exclaimed the bailiff; 'sure Harry Wakefield, the nattiest lad at Whiteson Tryste, Wooler Fair, Carlisle Sands, or Stagehaw Bank, is not going to show white feather? Ah, this comes of living so long with kilts and bonnets; men forget the use of their daddles.'

'I may teach you, Master Fleecebumpkin, that I have not lost the use of mine,' said Wakefield, and then went on—'This will never do, Robin. We must have a turn-up, or we shall be the talk of the countryside. I'll be d-d if I hurt thee. I'll put on the gloves gin thou like. Come, stand forward like a man.'

'To be peaten like a dog,' said Robin; 'is there any reason in that? If you think I have done you wrong, I'll go before your shudge, though I neither know his law nor his language.'

A general cry of 'No, no—no law, no lawyer! A bellyful and be friends!' was echoed by the bystanders.

'But,' continued Robin, 'if I am to fight, I have no skill to fight like a jackanapes, with hands and nails.'

'How would you fight, then?' said his antagonist; 'though I am thinking it would be hard to bring you to the scratch anyhow.'

'I would fight with proad swords, and sink point on the first plood drawn, like a gentlemans.'

A loud shout of laughter followed the proposal, which indeed had rather escaped from poor Robin's swelling heart than been the dictate of his sober judgment.

'Gentlemen, quotha!' was echoed on all sides, with a shout of un-extinguishable laughter; 'a very pretty gentleman, God wot. Canst get two swords for the *gentleman* to fight with, Ralph Heskett?'

'No, but I can send to the armoury at Carlisle, and lend them two forks, to be making shift with in the meantime.'

'Tush, man,' said another, 'the bonny Scots come into the world with the blue bonnet on their heads, and dirk and pistol at their belt.'

'Best send post,' said Mr. Fleecebumpkin, 'to the squire of Corby Castle, to come and stand second to the *gentleman*.'

In the midst of this torrent of general ridicule, the Highlander in-stinctinvely griped beneath the folds of his plaid.

'But it's better not,' he said in his own language. 'A hundred curses on the swine-eaters, who know neither decency nor civility!'

'Make room the pack of you,' he said, advancing to the door.

But his former friend interposed his sturdy bulk, and opposed his leaving the house; and when Robin Oig attempted to make his way by force, he hit him down on the floor, with as much ease as a boy bowls down a nine-pin.

'A ring—a ring!' was now shouted, until the dark rafters, and the hams that hung on them, trembled again, and the very platters on the 'bink' clattered against each other. 'Well done, Harry'—'Give it him home, Harry'—'Take care of him now, he sees his own blood!'

Such were the exclamations, while the Highlander, starting from the ground, all his coldness and caution lost in frantic rage, sprung at his antag-onist with the fury, the activity, and the vindictive purpose of an incensed tiger-cat. But when could rage encounter science and temper? Robin Oig again went down in the unequal contest; and as the blow was necessarily a severe one, he lay motionless on the floor of the kitchen.

The landlady ran to offer some aid; but Mr. Fleecebumpkin would not permit her to approach. 'Let him alone,' he said, 'he will come to within time, and come up to the scratch again. He has not got half his broth yet.'

'He has got all I mean to give him, though,' said his antagonist, whose heart began to relent towards his old associate; 'and I would rather by half give the rest to yourself, Mr. Fleecebumpkin, for you pretend to know a thing or two, and Robin had not art enough even to peel before setting to, but fought with his plaid dangling about him. Stand up, Robin, my man, all friends now, and let me hear the man that will speak a word against you, or your country, for your sake.'

Robin Oig was still under the dominion of his passion, and eager to renew the onset; but being withheld on the one side by the peacemaking Dame Heskett, and on the other aware that Wakefield no longer meant to renew the combat, his fury sank into gloomy sullenness.

'Come—come, never grudge so much at it, man,' said the brave-spirited Englishman, with the placability of his country; 'shake hands, and we will be better friends than ever.'

'Friends!' exclaimed Robin Oig with strong emphasis—'friends! Never. Look to yourself, Harry Waakfelt.'

'Then the curse of Cromwell on your proud Scots stomach, as the man says in the play, and you may do your worst, and be d-d; for one man can say nothing more to another after a tussle, than that he is sorry for it.'

On these terms the friends parted. Robin Oig drew out, in silence, a piece of money, threw it on the table, and then left the alehouse. But, burning at the door, he shook his hand at Wakefield, pointing with his forefinger upwards, in a manner which might imply either a threat or a caution. He then disappeared in the moonlight.

Some words passed after his departure between the bailiff, who piqued himself on being a little of a bully, and Harry Wakefield, who, with generous inconsistency, was now not indisposed to begin a new combat in defence of Robin Oig's reputation, 'although he could not use his daddles like an Englishman, as it did not come natural to him.'

But Dame Heskett prevented this second quarrel from coming to a head by her peremptory interference. 'There should be no more fighting in her house,' she said; 'there had been too much already. And you, Mr. Wakefield, may live to learn,' she added, 'what it is to make a deadly enemy out of a good friend.'

'Pshaw, dame! Robin Oig is an honest fellow, and will never keep malice.'

'Do not trust to that: you do not know the dour temper of the Scots, though you have dealt with them so often. I have a right to know them, my mother being a Scot.'

'And so is well seen on her daughter,' said Ralph Heskett.

This nuptial sarcasm gave the discourse another turn; fresh customers entered the taproom or kitchen, and others left it. The conversation turned on the expected markets, and the report of prices from different parts both of Scotland and England; treaties were commenced, and Harry Wakefield was lucky enough to find a chap for a part of his drove, and at a very

considerable profit—an event of consequence more than sufficient to blot
out all remembrances of the unpleasant scuffle in the earlier part of the day.

But there remained one party from whose mind that recollection
could not have been wiped away by the possession of every head of cattle
betwixt Esk and Eden. This was Robin Oig M'Combich. 'That I should
have had no weapon,' he said, 'and for the first time in my life! Blighted be
the tongue that bids the Highlander part with the dirk. The dirk—ha! the
English blood! My muhme's word—when did her word fall to the
ground?'

The recollection of the fatal prophecy confirmed the deadly intention
which instantly sprang up in his mind.

'Ha! Morrison cannot be many miles behind; and if it were a hundred, what then?'

His impetuous spirit had now a fixed purpose and motive of action,
and he turned the light foot of his country towards the wilds, through which
he knew, by Mr. Ireby's report, that Morrison was advancing. His mind
was wholly engrossed by the sense of injury—injury sustained from a
friend, and by the desire of vengeance on one whom he now accounted his
most bitter enemy. The treasured ideas of self-importance and self-
opinion—of ideal birth and quality, had become more precious to him, like
the hoard to the miser, because he could only enjoy them in secret. But that
hoard was pillaged; the idols which he had secretly worshipped had been
desecrated and profaned. Insulted, abused, and beaten, he was no longer
worthy, in his own opinion, of the name he bore, or the lineage which he
belonged to; nothing was left to him—nothing but revenge; and, as the reflection added a galling spur to every step, he determined it should be as
sudden and signal as the offence.

When Robin Oig left the door of the alehouse, seven or eight English miles at least lay betwixt Morrison and him. The advance of the former was slow, limited by the sluggish pace of his cattle; the last left behind
him stubble-field and hedgerow, crag and dark heath, all glittering with
frost-rime in the broad November moonlight at the rate of six miles an hour.
And now the distant lowing of Morrison's cattle is heard; and now they are
seen creeping like moles in size and slowness of motion on the broad face
of the moor; and now he meets them, passes them, and stops their conductor.

'May good betide us,' said the Southlander. 'Is this you, Robin
M'Combich, or your wraith?'

'It is Robin Oig M'Combich,' answered the Highlander, 'and it is
not. But never mind that, put pe giving me the skene-dhu.'

'What! you are for back to the Highlands. The devil! Have you selt
all off before the fait? This beats all for quick markets.'

'I have not sold—I am not going north. May pe I will never go
north again. Give me pack my dirk, Hugh Morrison, or there will pe words
petween us.'

'Indeed, Robin, I'll be better advised before I gie it back to you; it is
a wanchancy weapon in a Highlandman's hand, and I am thinking you will
be about some barns-breaking.'

'Prutt, trutt! let me have my weapon,' said Robin Oig, impatiently.

'Hooly and fairly,' said his well-meaning friend. 'I'll tell you what will do better than these dirking doings. Ye ken Highlander, and Lowlander, and Bordermen are a' ae man's bairns when you are over the Scots dyke. See, the Eskdale callants, and fighting Charlie of Liddesdale, and the Lockerby lads, and the four Dandies of Lustruther, and a wheen mair grey plaids are coming up behind; and if you are wranged, there is the hand of a Manly Morrison, we'll see you righted, if Carlisle and Stanwix baith took up the feud.'

'To tell you the truth,' said Robin Oig, desirous of eluding the suspicions of his friend, 'I have enlisted with a party of the Black Watch, and must march off tomorrow morning.'

'Enlisted! Were you mad or drunk? You must buy yourself off. I can lend you twenty notes, and twenty to that, if the drove sell.'

'I thank you—thank ye, Hughie; but I go with goodwill the gate that I am going; so the dirk—the dirk!'

'There it is for you then, since less wunna serve. But think in what I was saying. Waes me, it will be sair news in the braes of Balquidder, that Robin Oig M'Combich should have run an ill gate, and ta'en on.'

'Ill news in Balquidder, indeed!' echoed poor Robin; 'but Cot speed you, Hughie, and send you good marcats. Ye winna meet with Robin Oig again, either at tryste or fair.'

So saying, he shook hastily the hand of his acquaintance, and set out in the direction from which he had advanced, with the spirit of his former pace.

'There is something wrang with the lad,' muttered the Morrison to himself; 'but we will maybe see better into it the morn's morning.'

But long ere the morning dawned, the catastrophe of our tale had taken place. It was two hours after the affray had happened, and it was totally forgotten by almost every one, when Robin Oig returned to Heskett's inn. The place was filled at once by various sorts of men and with noises corresponding to their character. There were the grave low sounds of men engaged in busy traffic, with the laugh, the song, and the riotous jest of those who had nothing to do but to enjoy themselves. Among the last was Harry Wakefield, who, amidst a grinning group of smock-frocks, hobnailed shoes, and jolly English physiognomies, was trolling forth the old ditty,

> 'What though my name be Roger,
> Who drives the plough and cart—'

when he was interrupted by a well-known voice saying in a high and stern voice, marked by the sharp Highland accent, 'Harry Waakfelt, if you be a man, stand up!'

'What is the matter?—what is it?' the guests demanded of each other.

'It is only a d-d Scotsman,' said Fleecebumpkin, who was by this time very drunk, 'whom Harry Wakefield helped to his broth to-day, who is now come to have his cauld kail het again.'

'Harry Waakfelt,' repeated the same ominous summons, 'stand up, if you be a man!'

There is something in the tone of deep and concentrated passion which attracts attention and imposes awe, even by the very sound. The guests shrunk back on every side, and gazed at the Highlander as he stood in the middle of them, his brows bent, and his features rigid with resolution.

'I will stand up with all my heart, Robin, my boy, but it shall be to shake hands with you, and drink down all unkindness. It is not the fault of your heart, man, that you don't know how to clench your hands.'

By this time he stood opposite to his antagonist; his open and unsuspecting look strangely contrasted with the stern purpose which gleamed wild, dark, and vindictive in the eyes of the Highlander.

"T is not thy fault, man, that, not having the luck to be an Englishman, thou canst not fight more than a schoool-girl.'

'I *can* fight,' answered Robin Oig, sternly but calmly, 'and you shall know it. You, Harry Waakfelt, showed me to-day how the Saxon churls fight; I show you now how the Highland *dunniè-wassel* fights.'

He seconded the word with the action, and plunged the dagger, which he suddenly displayed, into the broad breast of the English yeoman, with such fatal certainty and force that the hilt made a hollow sound against the breast-bone, and the double-edged point split the very heart of his victim. Harry Wakefield fell and expired with a single groan. His assassin next seized the bailiff by the collar, and offered the bloody poniard to his throat, whilst dread and surprise rendered the man incapable of defence.

'It were very just to lay you beside him,' he said, 'but the blood of a base pickthank shall never mix on my father's dirk with that of a brave man.'

As he spoke, he cast the man from him with so much force that he fell on the floor, while Robin, with his other hand, threw the fatal weapon into the blazing turf-fire.

'There,' he said, 'take me who likes, and let fire cleanse blood if it can.'

The pause of astonishment still continuing, Robin Oig asked for a peace-officer, and a constable having stepped out, he surrendered himself to his custody.

'A bloody night's work you have made of it,' said the constable.

'Your own fault,' said the Highlander. 'Had you kept his hands off me two hours since, he would have been now as well and merry as he was twa minutes since.'

'It must be sorely answered,' said the peace-officer.

'Never you mind that. Death pays all debts; it will pay that too.'

The horror of the bystanders began now to give way to indignation; and the sight of a favourite companion murdered in the midst of them, the provocation being, in their opinion, so utterly inadequate to the excess of vengeance, might have induced them to kill the perpetrator of the deed even upon the very spot. The constable, however, did his duty on this occasion, and, with the assistance of some of the more reasonable persons present, procured horses to guard the prisoner to Carlisle, to abide his doom at the next assizes. While the escort was preparing, the prisoner neither expressed

the least interest nor attempted the slightest reply. Only, before he was carried from the fatal apartment, he desired to look at the dead body, which,
raised from the floor, had been deposited upon the large table (at the head of
which Harry Wakefield had presided but a few minutes before, full of life,
vigour, and animation), until the surgeons could examine the mortal wound.
The face of the corpse was decently covered with a napkin. To the surprise
and horror of the bystanders, which displayed itself in a general 'Ah!'
drawn through clenched teeth and half-shut lips, Robin Oig removed the
cloth, and gazed with a mournful but steady eye on the lifeless visage,
which had been so lately animated, that the smile of good-humoured confidence in his own strength, of conciliation at once and contempt towards his
enemy, still curled his lip. While those present expected that the wound,
which had so lately flooded the apartment with gore, would send forth fresh
streams at the touch of the homicide, Robin Oig replaced the covering with
the brief exclamation—'He was a pretty man!'

My story is nearly ended. The unfortunate Highlander stood his trial at
Carlisle. I was myself present, and as a young Scottish lawyer, or barrister
at least, and reputed a man of some quality, the politeness of the sheriff of
Cumberland offered me a place on the bench. The facts of the case were
proved in the manner I have related them; and whatever might be at first the
prejudice of the audience against a crime so un-English as that of asassina-
tion from revenge, yet when the rooted national prejudices of the prisoner
had been explained, which made him consider himself as stained with in-
delible dishonour when subjected to personal violence, when his previous
patience, moderation, and endurance were considered, the generosity of the
English audience was inclined to regard his crime as the wayward aberration
of a false idea of honour rather than as flowing from a heart naturally savage, or perverted by habitual vice. I shall never forget the charge of the
venerable judge to the jury, although not at that time liable to be much affected either by that which was eloquent or pathetic.
      'We have had,' he said, 'in the previous part of our duty (alluding to
some former trials), to discuss crimes which infer disgust and abhorrence,
while they call down the well-merited vengeance of the law. It is now our
still more melancholy task to apply its salutary though severe enactments to
a case of a very singular character, in which the crime, for a crime it is, and
a deep one, arose less out of the malevolence of the heart than the error of
the understanding—less from any idea of committing wrong than from an
unhappily perverted notion of that which is right. Here we have two men,
highly esteemed, it has been stated, in their rank of life, and attached, it
seems, to each other as friends, one of whose lives has been already sacrificed to a punctilio, and the other is about to prove the vengeance of the offended laws; and yet both may claim our commiseration at least, as men
acting in ignorance of each other's national prejudices, and unhappily mis-
guided rather than voluntarily erring from the path of right conduct.
      'In the original cause of the misunderstanding, we must in justice
give the right to the prisoner at the bar. He had acquired possession of the
enclosure, which was the object of competition, by a legal contract with the

proprietor, Mr. Ireby; and yet, when accosted with reproaches undeserved in themselves, and galling doubtless to a temper at least sufficiently susceptible of passion, he offered notwithstanding to yield up half his acquisition, for the sake of peace and good neighbourhood, and his amicable proposal was rejected with scorn. Then follows the scene at Mr. Heskett the publican's, and you will observe how the stranger was treated by the deceased, and, I am sorry to observe, by those around, who seem to have urged him in a manner which was aggravating in the highest degree. While he asked for peace and for composition, and offered submission to a magistrate, or to a mutual arbiter, the prisoner was insulted by a whole company, who seem on this occasion to have forgotten the national maxim of "fair play"; and while attempting to escape from the place in peace, he was intercepted, struck down, and beaten to the effusion of his blood.

'Gentlemen of the jury, it was with some impatience that I heard my learned brother, who opened the case for the crown, give an unfavourable turn to the prisoner's conduct on this occasion. He said the prisoner was afraid to encounter his antagonist in fair fight, or to submit to the laws of the ring; and that, therefore, like a cowardly Italian, he had recourse to his fatal stiletto, to murder the man whom he dared not meet in manly encounter. I observed the prisoner shrink from this part of the accusation with the abhorrence natural to a brave man; and as I would wish to make my words impressive when I point his real crime, I must secure his opinion of my impartiality by rebutting everything that seems to me a false accusation. There can be no doubt that the prisoner is a man of resolution—too much resolution. I wish to Heaven that he had less, or rather that he had had a better education to regulate it.

'Gentlemen, as to the laws my brother talks of, they may be known in the bull-ring, or the bear-garden, or the cockpit, but they are not known here. Or, if they should be so far admitted as furnishing a species of proof that no malice was intended in this sort of combat, from which fatal accidents do sometimes arise, it can only be so admitted when both parties are *in pari casu*, equally acquainted with, and equally willing to refer themselves to, that species of arbitrament. But will it be contended that a man of superior rank and education is to be subjected, or is obliged to subject himself, to this coarse and brutal strife, perhaps in opposition to a younger, stronger, or more skilful opponent? Certainly even the pugilistic code, if founded upon the fair play of Merry Old England, as my brother alleges it to be, can contain nothing so preposterous. And, gentlemen of the jury, if the laws would support an English gentleman, wearing, we will suppose, his sword, in defending himself by force against a violent personal aggression of the nature offered to this prisoner, they will not less protect a foreigner and a stranger, involved in the same unpleasing circumstances. If, therefore, gentlemen of the jury, when thus pressed by a *vis major*, the object of obloquy to a whole company, and of direct violence from one at least, and, as he might reasonably apprehend, from more, the panel had produced the weapon which his countrymen, as we are informed, generally carry about their persons, and the same unhappy circumstances had issued which you have heard detailed in evidence, I could not in my conscience have asked from you a verdict of murder. The prisoner's personal defence might indeed, even in that case, have gone more or less beyond the *moderamen in-culpatce tutelce* spoken of by lawyers, but the punishment incurred would have been that of manslaughter, not of murder. I beg leave to add, that I should have thought this milder species of charge was demanded in the case supposed, notwithstanding the statute of James I, cap, 8, which takes the case of slaughter by stabbing with a short weapon, even without malice prepense, out of the benefit of clergy. For this statute of stabbing, as it is termed, arose out of a temporary cause; and as the real guilt is the same, whether the slaughter be committed by the dagger or by sword or pistol, the benignity of the modern law places them all on the same, or nearly the same, footing.

'But, gentlemen of the jury, the pinch of the case lies in the interval of two hours interposed betwixt the reception of the injury and the fatal retaliation. In the heat of affray and *chaude melée*, law, compassionating the infirmities of humanity, makes allowance for the passions which rule such a stormy moment—for the sense of present pain, for the apprehension of further injury, for the difficulty of ascertaining with due accuracy the precise degree of violence which is necessary to protect the person of the individual, without annoying or injuring the assailant more than is absolutely necessary. But the time necessary to walk twelve miles, however speedily performed, was an interval sufficient for the prisoner to have recollected himself; and the violence with which he carried his purpose into effect, with so many circumstances of deliberate determination, could neither be induced by the passion of anger nor that of fear. It was the purpose and the act of predetermined revenge, for which law neither can, will, nor ought to have sympathy or allowance.

'It is true, we may repeat to ourselves, in alleviation of this poor man's unhappy action, that his case is a very peculiar one. The country which he inhabits was, in the days of many now alive, inaccessible to the laws not only of England, which have not even yet penetrated thither, but to those to which our neighbours of Scotland are subjected, and which must be supposed to be, and no doubt actually are, founded upon the general principles of justice and equity which pervade every civilized country. Amongst their mountains, as among the North American Indians, the various tribes were wont to make war upon each other, so that each man was obliged to go armed for his own protection. These men, from the ideas which they entertained for their own descent and of their own consequence, regarded themselves as so many cavaliers or men-at-arms, rather than as the peasantry of a peaceful country. Those laws of the ring, as my brother terms them, were unknown to the race of warlike mountaineers; that decision of quarrels by no other weapons than those which nature has given every man must to them have seemed as vulgar and as preposterous as to the *noblesse* of France. Revenge, on the other hand, must have been as familiar to their habits of society as to those of the Cherokees or Mohawks. It is indeed, as described by Bacon, at bottom a kind of wild untutored justice; for the fear of retaliation must withhold the hands of the oppressor where there is no regular law to check daring violence. But though all this may be granted, and though we may allow that, such having been the case of the Highlands in the days of the prisoner's fathers, many of the opinions and sentiments must still continue to influence the present generation, it cannot, and ought not, even in this most painful case, to alter the administration of the law, either in your hands, gentlemen of the jury, or in mine. The first object of civilisation is to place the general protection of the law, equally administered, in the room of that wild justice which every man cut and carved for himself, according to the length of his sword and the strength of his arm. The law says to the subjects, with a voice only inferior to that of the Deity, "Vengeance is mine." The instant that there is time for passion to cool and reason to interpose, an injured party must become aware that the law assumes the exclusive cognizance of the right and wrong betwixt the parties, and opposes her inviolable buckler to every attempt of the private party to right himself. I repeat, that this unhappy man ought personally to be the object rather of our pity than our abhorrence, for he failed in his ignorance and from mistaken notions of honour. But his crime is not the less that of murder, gentlemen, and, in your high and important office, it is your duty so to find. Englishmen have their angry passions as well as Scots; and should this man's action remain unpunished, you may unsheath, under various pretences, a thousand daggers betwixt the Land's End and the Orkneys.'

The venerable judge thus ended what, to judge by his apparent emotion, and by the tears which filled his eyes, was really a painful task. The jury, according to his instructions, brought in a verdict of Guilty; and Robin Oig M'Combich, alias M'Gregor, was sentenced to death, and left for execution, which took place accordingly. He met his fate with great firmness, and acknowledged the justice of his sentence. But he repelled indignantly the observations of those who accused him of attacking an unarmed man. 'I give a life for the life I took,' he said, 'and what can I do more?'

Too Dear!
Leo Tolstóy

(Adaptation of a story
by Guy de Maupassant)

Near the borders of France and Italy, on the shore of the Mediterranean Sea, lies a tiny little kingdom called Monaco. Many a small country town can boast more inhabitants than this kingdom, for there are only about seven thousand of them all told, and if all the land in the kingdom were divided there would not be an acre for each inhabitant. But in this toy kingdom there is a real kinglet; and he has a palace, and courtiers, and ministers, and a bishop, and generals, and an army.

It is not a large army, only sixty men in all, but still it is an army. There are also taxes in this kingdom, as elsewhere: a tax on tobacco, and on wine and spirits, and a poll-tax. But though the people there drink and smoke as people do in other countries, there are so few of them that the Prince would have been hard put to it to feed his courtiers and officials and to keep himself, if he had not found a new and special source of revenue. This special revenue comes from a gaming house, where people play roulette. People play, and whether they win or lose the keeper always gets a percentage of the turnover, and out of his profits he pays a large sum to the Prince. The reason he pays so much is that it is the only such gambling establishment left in Europe. Some of the little German sovereigns used to keep gaming houses of the same kind, but some years ago they were forbidden to do so. The reason they were stopped was because these gaming houses did so much harm. A man would come and try his luck, then he would risk all he had and lose it, then he would even risk money that did not belong to him and lose that, too, and then, in despair, he would drown or shoot himself. So the Germans forbade their rulers to make money in this way; but there was no one to stop the Prince of Monaco, and he remained with a monopoly of the business.

So now every one who wants to gamble goes to Monaco. Whether they win or lose, the Prince gains by it. 'You can't earn stone palaces by honest labour,' as the proverb says; and the Princelet of Monaco knows it is a dirty business, but what is he to do? He has to live; and to draw a revenue from drink and from tobacco is also not a nice thing. So he lives and reigns, and rakes in the money and holds his court with all the ceremony of a real king.

He has his coronation, his levees; he rewards, sentences, and pardons; and he also has his reviews, councils, laws and courts of justice: just like other kings, only all on a smaller scale.

Now it happened a few years ago that a murder was committed in this toy Prince's domains. The people of that kingdom are peaceable, and such a thing had not happened before. The judges assembled with much ceremony and tried the case in the most judicial manner. There were judges, and prosecutors, and jurymen and barristers. They argued and judged, and at last they condemned the criminal to have his head cut off as the law directs. So far so good. Next they submitted the sentence to the Prince. The Prince read the sentence and confirmed it. 'If the fellow must be executed, execute him.'

There was only one hitch in the matter; and that was that they had neither a guillotine for cutting heads off, nor the executioner. The Ministers considered the matter, and decided to address an inquiry to the French government, asking whether the French could not lend them a machine and an expert to cut off the criminal's head; and if so, would the French kindly inform them what it would cost. The letter was sent. A week later the reply came: a machine and an expert could be supplied, and the cost would be 16,000 francs. This was laid before the Prince. He thought it over. Sixteen thousand francs! 'The wretch is not worth the money,' said he. 'Can't it be done, somehow, cheaper? Why, 16,000 francs is more than two francs a head on the whole population. The people won't stand it, and it may cause a riot!'

So a Council was called to consider what could be done; and it was decided to send a similar inquiry to the Prince of Italy. The French government is republican, and has no proper respect for kings; but the Prince of Italy was a brother monarch, and might be induced to do the thing cheaper. So the letter was written, and a prompt reply was received.

The Italian government wrote that they would have pleasure in supplying both a machine and an expert; and the whole cost would be 12,000 francs, including travelling expenses. This was cheaper, but still it seemed too much. The rascal was really not worth the money. It would still mean nearly two francs more per head on the taxes. Another Council was called. They discussed and considered how it could be done with less expense. Could not one of the soldiers, perhaps, be got to do it in a rough and homely fashion? The General was called and was asked: 'Can't you find us a soldier who would cut the man's head off? In war they don't mind killing people. In fact, that is what they are trained for.' So the General talked it over with the soldiers to see whether one of them would not undertake the job. But none of the soldiers would do it. 'No,' they said, 'we don't know how to do it; it is not a thing we have been taught.'

What was to be done? Again Ministers considered and reconsidered. They assembled a Commission, and a Committee, and a Sub-Committee and at last they decided that the best thing would be to alter the death sentence to one of imprisonment for life. This would enable the Prince to show his mercy, and it would come cheaper.

The Prince agreed to this, and so the matter was arranged. The only hitch now was that there was no suitable prison for a man sentenced for life. There was a small lock-up where people were sometimes kept temporarily, but there was no strong prison fit for permanent use. However, they managed to find a place that would do, and they put the young fellow there and placed a guard over him. The guard had to watch the criminal, and had also to fetch his food from the palace kitchen.

The prisoner remained there month after month until a year had passed. But when a year had passed, the Princelet, looking over the account of his income and expenditure one day, noticed a new item of expenditure. This was for the keep of the criminal; nor was it a small item either. There was a special guard, and there was also the mans' food. It came to more than 600 francs a year. And the worst of it was that the fellow was still young and healthy, and might live for fifty years. When one came to reckon it up, the matter was serious. It would never do. So the Prince summoned his Ministers and said to them:

'You must find some cheaper way of dealing with this rascal. The present plan is too expensive.' And the Ministers met and considered and reconsidered, till one of them said, 'Gentlemen, in my opinion we must dismiss the guard.' 'But then,' rejoined another Minister, 'the fellow will run away.' 'Well,' said the first speaker, 'let him run away, and be hanged to him!' So they reported the result of their deliberations to the Princelet, and he agreed with them. The guard was dismissed, and they waited to see what would happen. All that happened was that at dinner-time the criminal came out, and, not finding his guard, he went to the Prince's kitchen to fetch his own dinner. He took what was given him, returned to the prison, shut the door on himself, and stayed inside. Next day the same thing occurred. He went for his food at the proper time; but as for running away, he did not show the least sign of it! What was to be done? They considered the matter again.

'We shall have to tell him straight out,' said they, 'that we do not want to keep him.' So the Minister of Justice had him brought before him.

'Why do you not run away?' said the Minister. 'There is no guard to keep you. You can go where you like, and the Prince will not mind.'

'I dare say the Prince would not mind,' replied the man, 'but I have nowhere to go. What can I do? You have ruined my character by your sentence, and people will turn their backs on me. Besides, I have got out of the way of working. You have treated me badly. It is not fair. In the first place, when once you sentenced me to death you ought to have executed me; but you did not do it. That's one thing. I did not complain about that. Then you sentenced me to imprisonment for life and put a guard to bring me my food; but after a time you took him away again and I had to fetch my own food. Again I did not complain. But now you actually want me to go away! I can't agree to that. You may do as you like, but I won't go away!'

What was to be done? Once more the Council was summoned. What course could they adopt? The man would not go. They reflected and considered. The only way to get rid of him was to offer him a pension. And so they reported to the Prince. 'There is nothing else for it,' said they; 'we must get rid of him somehow.' The sum fixed was 600 francs, and this was announced to the prisoner.

'Well,' said he, 'I don't mind, so long as you undertake to pay it regularly. On that condition I am willing to go.

So the matter was settled. He received one-third of his annuity in advance, and left the king's dominions. It was only a quarter of an hour by rail; and he emigrated, and settled just across the frontier, where he bought a bit of land, started market-gardening, and now lives comfortably. He always goes at the proper time to draw his pension. Having received it he goes to the gaming tables, stakes two or three francs, sometimes wins and sometimes loses, and the returns home. He lives peaceably and well.

It is a good thing that he did not commit his crime in a country where they do not grudge expense to cut a man's head off, or to keep him in prison for life.

10

Capital Punishment

If a punishment is unusually severe, if there is a strong probability that it is inflicted arbitrarily, if it is substantially rejected by contemporary society, and if there is no reason to believe that it serves any penal purpose more effectively than some less severe punishment, then the continued infliction of that punishment violates the command of the Clause that the State may not inflict inhuman and uncivilized punishments upon those convicted of crimes.

Justice Brennan
From *Furman v. Georgia*,
408 U.S. 238 (1972)

We have the abiding conviction that the death penalty, which "is unique in its severity and revocability," . . . is an excessive penalty for the rapist who, as such, does not take human life.

Justice White,
in an opinion joined by Justices
Stewart, Blackmun, and Stevens,
From *Coker v. Georgia*,
433 U.S. 584 (1977)

In the last section economics was introduced as a factor when considering punishment. Proponents of capital punishment are particularly vocal in this respect arguing that life terms for murderers serve no purpose except to burden the tax structure by billions of dollars annually. They also offer the following assertions to justify the death penalty: (1) the death penalty removes dangerous criminals from society and so protects the citizens; (2) retribution demands a life for a life; and (3) the death penalty serves as a necessary deterrent to others. Opponents, on the other hand, argue that (1) no studies have shown capital punishment to act as a deterrent to others; (2) society is protected by the incarceration of violent criminals; (3) reform, not retaliation, is the goal of punishment; and (4) capital punishment is cruel, barbaric, and inhumane.

First, what other arguments are there for and against capital punishment? Next, if our punishment structure is to include the death peanlty, who should be subjected to such a drastic sanction? Serial-killers? Repeat offenders who commit more than one act of murder? Those who evince a depraved indifference toward human life? Any killers regardless of justification or excuse? Those who commit an involuntary act caused by intoxication—whether by alcohol or drugs? What about an assisted suicide? Should the one giving assistance be executed? Should it matter whether the one committing suicide is terminally ill or depressed? Should we hang the person who attempts suicide but is unsuccessful? What about an attempted murder? Finally, should capital punishment be ordered for rapists, child abusers, or perpetrators of other heinous crimes?

If it is determined that capital punishment is appropriate in certain instances, then the method of capital punishment must be decided. Should hanging or the electric chair be reserved for the perpetrators of the most heinous crimes? Should the more humane lethal injection be given in all instances?

"In The Peanl Colony," by Franz Kafka, raises the following issues that concern the controversial practice of capital punishment:

• The condemned man doesn't appear to need reform—he is already like a "submissive dog." Does the punishment fit the crime?

• In this instance the prisoner is meant to learn of his sentence corporeally as it is engraved on his body. If the end result of the punishment is death, what is the point of learning what he has done wrong? We can only conclude that the real purpose of the machine is to exact retribution from the criminal rather than to reform him or to deter him from future crimes. Is not the real purpose of using the electric chair or hanging a man retribution? Wouldn't the goal of removing the offender from society be equally served by the use of a lethal injection?

• If we had a machine that could condition our lawmakers and our administrators of the law to "be just," would those legislators and judges feel that the death penalty serves the ends of justice?

• What is the point of delaying death once the sentence is imposed? In our legal system, the long interval between the crime and the death takes the form of a prison sentence in which the prisoner is allowed to explore all of the legal avenues of judicial appeal. Should these defendants be given free legal services for numerous years to delay what is often inevitable?

In writing "The Pit and the Pendulum," Edgar Allan Poe did not concern himself so much with the justice or the philosophy of capital punishment. Instead he provides an opportunity for the reader to live the terror experienced by a condemned man as he is subjected to torture and as he contemplates whether his death is months away or imminent.

In the Penal Colony
Franz Kafka

'It's a remarkable piece of apparatus,' said the officer to the explorer and surveyed with a certain air of admiration the apparatus which was after all quite familiar to him. The explorer seemed to have accepted merely out of politeness the Commandant's invitation to witness the execution of a soldier condemned to death for disobedience and insulting behaviour to a superior. Nor did the colony itself betray much interest in this execution. At least, in the small sandy valley, a deep hollow surrounded on all sides by naked crags, there was no one present save the officer, the explorer, the condemned man, who was a stupid-looking wide-mouthed creature with bewildered hair and face, and the soldier who held the heavy chain controlling the small chains locked on the prisoner's ankles, wrists, and neck, chains which were themselves attached to each other by communicating links. In any case, the condemned man looked so like a submissive dog that one might have thought he could be left to run free on the surrounding hills and would only need to be whistled for when the execution was due to begin.

The explorer did not much care about the apparatus and walked up and down behind the prisoner with almost visible indifference, while the officer made the last adjustments, now creeping beneath the structure, which was bedded deep in the earth, now climbing a ladder to inspect its upper parts. These were tasks that might well have been left to a mechanic, but the officer performed them with great zeal, whether because he was a devoted admirer of the apparatus or because for other reasons the work could be entrusted to no one else. 'Ready now!' he called at last and climbed down from the ladder. He looked uncommonly limp, breathed with his mouth wide open and had tucked two fine ladies' handkerchiefs under the collar of his uniform. 'These uniforms are too heavy for the tropics, surely,' said the explorer, instead of making some inquiry about the apparatus, as the officer had expected. 'Of course,' said the officer, washing his oily and greasy hands in a bucket of water that stood ready, 'but they mean home to us; we don't want to forget about home. Now just have a look at this machine,' he added at once, simultaneously drying his hands on a towel and indicating the apparatus. 'Up till now everything has to be set by hand, but from this moment it works all by itself.' The explorer nodded and followed him. The officer, anxious to secure himself against all contingencies, said: 'Things sometimes go wrong, of course; I hope that nothing goes wrong today, but we have to allow for the possibility. The machinery should go on working continuously for twelve hours. But if anything does go wrong it will only be some small matter, and can be set right at once.'

'Won't you take a seat?' he asked finally, drawing a cane chair out from among a heap of them and offering it to the explorer, who could not refuse it. He was now sitting at the edge of a grave, into which he glanced for a fleeting moment. It was not very deep. On one side of the grave the excavated soil had been piled up in a rampart, on the other side of it stood the apparatus.

'I don't know,' said the officer, 'if the Commandant has already explained this apparatus to you.' The explorer waved one hand vaguely; the officer asked for nothing better, since now he could explain the apparatus himself. 'This apparatus,' he said, taking hold of a crank-handle and leaning against it, 'was invented by our former Commandant. I assisted at the very earliest experiments and had a share in all the work until its completion. But the credit of inventing it belongs to him alone. Have you ever heard of our former Commandant? No? Well, it isn't saying too much if I tell you that the organization of the whole penal settlement is his work. We who were his friends knew even before he died that the organization of the colony was so perfect that his successor, even with a thousand new schemes in his head, would find it impossible to alter anything, at least for many years to come. And our prophecy has come true; the new Commandant has had to acknowledge its truth. A pity you never met the old Commandant! But,' the officer interrupted himself, 'I am rambling on, and here stands this apparatus before us. It consists, as you see of three parts. In the course of time each of these parts has acquired a kind of popular nickname. The lower one is called the "Bed," the upper one the "Designer," and this one here in the middle that moves up and down is called the "Harrow."'

'The Harrow?' asked the explorer. He had not been listening very attentively, the glare of the sun in the shadeless valley was altogether too strong, it was difficult to collect one's thoughts. All the more did he admire the officer, who in spite of his tight-fitting full-dress uniform coat, amply befogged and weighted down by epaulettes, was pursuing his subject with such enthusiasm and, besides talking, was still tightening a screw here and there with a spanner. As for the soldier, he seemed to be in much the same condition as the explorer. He had wound the prisoner's chain around both his wrists, propped himself on his rifle, let his head hang and was paying no attention to anything. That did not surprise the explorer, for the officer was speaking French, and certainly neither the soldier nor the prisoner understood a word of French. It was all the more remarkable, therefore, that the prisoner was none the less making an effort to follow the officer's explanations. With a kind of drowsy persistence he directed his gaze wherever the officer pointed a finger, and at the interruption of the explorer's question he, too, as well as the officer, looked around.

'Yes, the Harrow,' said the officer, 'a good name for it. The needles are set in like the teeth of a harrow and the whole thing works something like a harrow, although its action is limited to one place and contrived with much more artistic skill. Anyhow, you'll soon understand it. On the

Bed here the condemned man is laid—I'm going to describe the apparatus first before I set it in motion. Then you'll be able to follow the proceedings better. Besides, one of the cog-wheels in the Designer is badly worn; it creaks a lot when it's working; you can hardly hear yourself speak; spare parts, unfortunately, are difficult to get here. Well, here is the Bed, as I told you. It is completely covered with a layer of cotton-wool; you'll find out why later. On this cotton-wool the condemned man is laid, face down, quite naked, of course; here are straps for the hands, here for the feet, and here for the neck, to bind him fast. Here at the head of the Bed, where the man, as I said, first lays down his face, is this little gag of felt, which can be easily regulated to go straight into his mouth. It is meant to keep him from screaming and biting his tongue. Of course the man is forced to take the felt into his mouth, for otherwise his neck would be broken by the strap.' 'Is that cotton-wool?' asked the explorer, bending forward. 'Yes, certainly,' said the officer with a smile, 'feel it for yourself.' He took the explorer's hand and guided it over the Bed. 'It's specially prepared cotton-wool, that's why it looks so different; I'll tell you presently what it's for.' The explorer already felt a dawning interest in the apparatus; he sheltered his eyes from the sun with one hand and gazed up at the structure. It was a huge affair. The Bed and the Designer were of the same size and looked like two dark wooden chests. The Designer hung about two meters above the Bed; each of them was fastened at the corners by four rods of brass that almost flashed out rays in the sunlight. Beneath the chest shuttled the Harrow on a ribbon of steel.

The officer had scarcely noticed the explorer's previous indifference, but he was now well aware of his dawning interest; so he stopped explaining in order to leave a space of time for quiet observation. The condemned man imitated the explorer; since he could not use a hand to shelter his eyes he gazed upwards without shade.

'Well, the man lies down,' said the explorer, leaning back in his chair and crossing his legs.

'Yes,' said the officer, pushing his cap back a little and passing one hand over his heated face, 'now listen! Both the Bed and the Designer have an electric battery each; the Bed needs one for itself, the Designer one for the Harrow. As soon as the man is strapped down, the Bed is set in motion. It quivers in minute, very rapid vibrations, both from side to side and up and down. You will have seen similar apparatus in hospitals; but in our Bed the movements are all precisely calculated; you see, they have to correspond very exactly to the movements of the Harrow. And the Harrow is the instrument for the actual execution of the sentence.'

'And how does the sentence run?' asked the explorer.

'You don't know that either?' said the officer in amazement, and bit his lips. 'Forgive me if my explanations seem rather incoherent. I do beg your pardon. You see, the Commandant always used to do the explaining; but the new Commandant shirks this duty; yet that such an important visitor'—the explorer tried to deprecate the honour with both hands, the officer, however, insisted—'that such an important visitor should not even be told about the kind of sentence we pass is a new development, which' he was just on the point of using strong language but checked himself and said only: 'I was not informed, it is not my fault. In any case, I am certainly the best person to explain our procedure, since I have in here'—he patted his breast-pocket—'the relevant drawings made by our former Commandant.'

'The Commandant's own drawings?' asked the explorer. 'Did he combine everything in himself, then? Was he soldier, judge, mechanic, chemist, and draughtsman?'

'Indeed he was,' said the officer, nodding assent, with a remote, glassy look. Then he inspected his hands critically; they did not seem clean enough to him for touching the drawings; so he went over to the bucket and washed them again. Then he drew out a small leather brief-case and said: 'Our sentence does not sound severe. Whatever commandment the condemned man has disobeyed is written upon his body by the Harrow. This condemned man, for instance,'—the officer indicated the man—'will have written on his body: HONOUR THY SUPERIORS!'

The explorer glanced at the man; he stood, as the officer pointed him out, with bent head, apparently listening with all his ears in an effort to catch what was being said. Yet the movement of his blubber lips, closely pressed together, showed clearly that he could not understand a word. Many questions were troubling the explorer, but at the sight of the condemned man he asked only: 'Does he know his sentence?' 'No—' said the officer, eager to go on with his exposition, but the explorer interrupted him: 'He doesn't know the sentence that has been passed on him?' 'No—' said the officer again, pausing a moment as if to let the explorer elaborate his question, and then said: 'There would be no point in telling him. He'll learn it corporally, on his person.' The explorer intended to make no answer, but he felt the prisoner's gaze turned on him; it seemed to ask if he approved such goings on. So he bent forward again, having already leaned back in his chair, and put another question: 'But surely he knows that he has been sentenced?' 'Nor that either,' said the officer, smiling at the explorer, as if expecting him to make further surprising remarks. 'No,' said the explorer, wiping his forehead, 'then he cannot know either whether his defence was effective?' 'He has had no chance of putting up a defence,' said the officer, turning his eyes away, as if speaking to himself and so sparing the explorer the shame of hearing self-evident matters explained. 'But he must have had some chance of defending himself,' said the explorer, and rose from his seat.

The officer understood that he was in danger of having his exposition of the apparatus held up for a long time; so he went up to the explorer, took him by the arm, waved a hand towards the condemned man, who was standing very straight now that he had so obviously become the center of attention—the soldier had also given the chain a jerk—and said: 'This is how the matter stands. I have been appointed judge in this penal settlement; despite my youth; for I was the former Commandant's assistant in all penal matters and know more about the apparatus than anyone. My guiding principle is this: Guilt is never to be doubted. Other courts cannot follow that principle, for they consist of several opinions and have higher courts to scrutinize them. That is not the case here, or at least, it was not the case in the former Commandant's time. The new man has certainly shown some inclination to interfere with my judgements, but so far I have succeeded in fending him off and will go on succeeding. You will like to have the case explained; it is quite simple, like all of them. A captain reported to me this morning that this man, who had been assigned to him as a servant and slept before his door, had been asleep on duty. It is his duty, you see, to get up every time the hour strikes and salute the captain's door. Not an exacting duty, and very necessary, since he has to be a sentry as well as a servant, and must be alert in both functions. Last night the captain wanted to see if the man was doing his duty. He opened the door as the clock struck two and there was his man curled up asleep. He took a riding-whip and lashed him across the face. Instead of getting up and begging pardon the man caught hold of his master's legs, shook him and cried: "throw that whip away or I'll eat you alive." That's the evidence. The captain came to me an hour ago, I wrote down his statement and appended the sentence to it. Then I had the man put in chains. That was all quite simple. If I had first called the man before me and interrogated him, things would have got into a confused tangle. He would have told lies, and had I exposed these lies he would have backed them up with more lies, and so on and so forth. As it is, I've got him and I won't let him go. Is that quite clear now? But we're wasting time, the execution should be beginning and I haven't finished explaining the apparatus yet.' He pressed the explorer back into his chair, went up again to the apparatus and began: 'As you see, the shape of the Harrow corresponds to the human form; here is the harrow for the torso, here are the harrows for the legs. For the head there is only this one small spike. Is that quite clear?' He bent amiably forward towards the explorer, eager to provide the most comprehensive explanations.

The explorer considered the Harrow with a frown. Such a version of judicial procedure displeased him. He had to remind himself that this was in any case a penal settlement where extraordinary measures were needed and that military discipline must be enforced to the last. Yet he felt that some hope might be set on the new Commandant, who was apparently of a mind to bring in, although gradually, a new kind of procedure which the officer's narrow mind was incapable of understanding. This train of thought prompted his next question: 'Will the Commandant attend the execution?' 'It is not certain,' said the officer, wincing at the direct question, and his friendly expression darkened. 'That is just why we have to lose no time. Much as I dislike it, I shall have to cut my explanations short. But, of course, tomorrow, when the apparatus has been cleaned—its one drawback is that it gets so messy—I can recapitulate all the details. For the present, then, only the essentials.—When the man lies down on the Bed and it begins to vibrate, the Harrow is lowered on to his body. It regulates itself automatically so that the needles barely touch his skin; once contact is made the steel ribbon stiffens immediately into a rigid band. And then the performance begins. An ignorant onlooker would see no difference between one punishment and another. The Harrow appears to do its work with uniform regularity. As it quivers its points pierce the skin of the body which is itself quivering from the vibration of the Bed. So that the actual progress of the sentence can be watched, the Harrow is made of glass. Getting the needles fixed in the glass was a technical problem, but after many experiments we overcame the difficulty. No trouble was too great for us to take, you see. And now anyone can look through the glass and watch the inscription taking form on the body. Wouldn't you care to come a little nearer and have a look at the needles?'

The explorer got up slowly, walked across and bent over the Harrow. 'You see,' said the officer, 'there are two kinds of needles arranged in multiple patterns. Each long needle has a short one beside it. The long needle does the writing, and the short needle sprays a jet of water to wash away the blood and keep the inscription clear. Blood and water together are then conducted here through small runnels into this main runnel and down a waste-pipe into the grave.' With his finger the officer traced the exact course taken by the blood and water. To make the picture as vivid as possible he held both hands below the outlet of the waste-pipe as if to catch the outflow, and when he did this the explorer drew back his head and, feeling behind him with one hand, sought to return to his chair. To his horror he found that the condemned man too had obeyed the officer's invitation to examine the Harrow at close quarters and had followed him. He had pulled forward the sleepy soldier with the chain and was bending over the glass. One could see that his uncertain eyes were trying to perceive what the two gentlemen had been looking at, but, since he had not understood the explanation, he could not make head or tail of it. He was peering this way and that way. He kept running his eyes along the glass. The explorer wanted to drive him away, since what he was doing was probably culpable. But the officer firmly restrained the explorer with one hand and with the other took a clod of earth from the rampart and threw it at the soldier. He opened his eyes with a jerk, saw what the condemned man had dared to do, let his rifle fall, dug his heels into the ground, dragged his prisoner back so that he stumbled and fell immediately, and then stood looking down at him, watching him struggling and rattling in his chains. 'Set him on his feet!' yelled the officer, for he noticed that the explorer's attention was being too much distracted by the condemned man. In fact the explorer was even leaning right across the Harrow, without taking any notice of it, intent only in finding out what was happening to the condemned man. 'Be careful with him!' cried the officer again. He ran round the apparatus, himself caught the condemned man under the shoulders and with the soldier's help got him up on his feet, which kept slithering from under him.

'Now I know all about it,' said the explorer, as the officer came back to him. 'All except the most important thing,' the latter said, seizing the explorer's arm and pointing upwards: 'In the Designer are all the cogwheels that control the movements of the Harrow, and this machinery is regulated according to the inscription demanded by the sentence. I am still using the guiding plans drawn by the former Commandant. Here they are'—he extracted some sheets from the leather brief-case—'but I'm sorry I can't let you handle them, they are my most precious possession. Just take a seat and I'll hold them in front of you like this, then you'll be able to see everything quite well.' He spread out the first sheet of paper. The explorer would have liked to say something appreciative, but all he could see was a labyrinth of lines crossing and re-crossing each other, which covered the paper so thickly that it was difficult to discern the blank spaces between them. 'Read it,' said the officer. 'I can't,' said the explorer. 'Yet it's clear enough,' said the officer. 'It's very ingenious,' said the explorer evasively, 'but I can't make it out.' 'Yes,' said the officer with a laugh, putting the paper way again, 'it's no calligraphy for school children. It needs to be studied closely. I'm quite sure that in the end you would understand it too. Of course the script can't be a simple one; it's not supposed to kill a man straight off, but only after an interval of, on an average, twelve hours; the turning-point is reckoned to come at the sixth hour. So there have to be lots and lots of flourishes around the actual script; the script itself runs round the body only in a narrow girdle; the rest of the body is reserved for the embellishments. Can you appreciate now the work accomplished by the Harrow and the whole apparatus? Just watch it!' He ran up the ladder, turned a wheel, called down: 'Look out, keep to one side!' and everything started working. If the wheel had not creaked, it would have been marvelous. The officer, as if surprised by the noise of the wheel, shook his fist at it, then spread out his arms in excuse to the explorer and climbed down rapidly to peer at the working of the machine from below. Something perceptible to no one save himself was still not in order; he clambered up again, groped about with both hands in the interior of the Designer, then slid down one of the rods, instead of using the ladder, so as to get down quicker, and with the full force of his lungs, to make himself heard at all in the noise yelled in the explorer's ear: 'Can you follow it? The Harrow is beginning to write; when it finishes the first draft of the inscription on the back, the layer of cotton-wool begins to roll and slowly turns the body over, to give the Harrow fresh space for writing. Meanwhile the raw part that has been written on lies on the cotton-wool, which is specially prepared to staunch the bleeding and so makes all ready for a new deepening of the script. Then these teeth at the edge of the Harrow, as the body turns farther round, tear the cotton-wool away from the wounds, throw it into the grave and there is more work for the Harrow. So it keeps on writing deeper and deeper for the whole twelve hours. The first six hours the condemned man stays alive almost as before, he suffers only pain. After two hours the felt gag is taken away, for he has no longer strength to scream. Here, into this electrically heated basin at the head of the Bed, some warm rice-pap is poured, from which the man, if he feels like it, can take as much as the tongue can lap. Not one of them ever misses the chance. I can remember none, and my experience is extensive. Only about the sixth hour does the man lose all desire to eat. I usually kneel down here at the moment and observe this phenomenon. The man rarely swallows his last mouthful, he only rolls it round his mouth and spits it out into the grave. I have to duck just then or he would spit it in my face. But how quiet he grows at just about the sixth hour! Enlightenment comes to the most dull-witted. It begins around the eyes. From there it radiates. A moment that might tempt one to get under the Harrow with him. Nothing more happens after that, the man only begins to understand the inscription, he purses his mouth as if he were listening. You have seen how difficult it is to decipher the script with one's eyes; but our man deciphers it with his wounds. To be sure, that is a hard task; he needs six hours to accomplish it. By that time the Harrow has pierced him quite through and casts him in to the grave, were he pitches down upon the blood and water and the cotton-wool. Then the judgment has been fulfilled, and we, the soldier and I, bury him.'

The explorer had inclined his ear to the officer and, with his hands in his jacket pockets, watched the machine at work. The condemned man watched it too, but uncomprehendingly. He bent forward a little and was intent on the moving needles, when the soldier, at a sign from the officer, slashed through his shirt and trousers from behind with a knife, so that they fell off; he tried to catch at his falling clothes to cover his nakedness, but the soldier lifted him into the air and shook the last remnants from him. The officer stopped the machine, and in the sudden silence the condemned man was laid under the Harrow. The chains were loosened and the straps fastened on instead; in the first moment that seemed almost a relief to the condemned man. And now the Harrow was adjusted a little lower, since he was a thin man. When the needle-points touched him a shudder ran over his skin; while the soldier was busy strapping his right hand, he flung out his left hand blindly; but it happened to be in the direction towards where the explorer was standing. The officer kept watching the explorer sideways, as if seeking to read from his face the impression made on him by the execution, which had been at least cursorily explained to him.

The wrist-strap broke; probably the soldier had drawn it too tight. The officer had to intervene, the soldier held up the broken piece of the strap to show him. So the officer went over to him and said, his face still turned towards the explorer: 'This is a very complex machine, things are always breaking or giving way here and there; but one must not thereby allow oneself to be diverted in one's general judgment. In any case, this strap is easily made good; I shall simply use a chain; the delicacy of the vibrations for the right arm will, of course, be a little impaired.' And while he fastened the chain, he added: 'The resources for maintaining the machine are now very much reduced. Under the former Commandant I had free access to a sum of money set aside entirely for this purpose. There was a store, too, in which spare parts were kept for repairs of all kinds. I confess I have been almost prodigal with them, I mean in the past, not now as the new Commandant pretends, always looking for an excuse to attack our old way of doing things. Now he has taken charge of the machine money himself, and if I send for a new strap they ask for the broken old strap as evidence, and the new strap takes ten days to appear and then is of shoddy material and not much good. But how I am supposed to work the machine without a strap, that's something nobody bothers about.'

The explorer thought to himself: It's always a ticklish matter to intervene decisively in other people's affairs. He was neither a member of the penal colony nor a citizen of the state to which it belonged. Were he to denounce this execution or actually try to stop it, they could say to him: 'You are a stranger, mind your own business.' He could make no answer to that, unless he were to add that he was amazed at himself in this connexion, for he travelled only as an observer, with no intention at all of altering other people's methods of administering justice. Yet here he found himself strongly tempted. The injustice of the procedure and the inhumanity of the execution were undeniable. No one could suppose that he had any selfish interest in the matter, for the condemned man was a complete stranger, not a fellow countryman or even at all sympathetic to him. The explorer himself had recommendations from high quarters, had been received here with great courtesy, and the very fact that he had been invited to attend the execution seemed to suggest that his views would be welcome. And this was all the more likely since the Commandant, as he had heard only too plainly, was no upholder of the procedure and maintained an attitude almost of hostility to the officer.

At that moment the explorer heard the officer cry out in rage. He had just, with considerable difficulty, forced the felt gag into the condemned man's mouth when the man, in an irresistible access of nausea, shut his eyes and vomited. Hastily the officer snatched him away from the gag and tried to hold his head over the grave; but it was too late, the vomit was running all over the machine. 'It's all the fault of that Commandant!' cried the officer, senselessly shaking the brass rods in front, 'the machine is befouled like a pig-sty.' With trembling hands he indicated to the explorer what had happened. 'Have I not tried for hours at a time to get the Commandant to understand that the prisoner must fast for a whole day before the execution. But our new, mild doctrine thinks otherwise. The Commandant's ladies stuff the man's mouth with sugar-candy before he's led off. He has lived on stinking fish his whole life long and now he has to guzzle sugar-candy! But it could still be possible, I should have nothing to say against it, but why won't they get me a new felt gag, which I have been begging for the last three months. How should a man not feel sick when he takes a felt gag into his mouth which more than a hundred men have already slobbered and gnawed in their dying moments?'

The condemned man had laid his head down and looked peaceful, the soldier was busy trying to clean the machine with the condemned man's shirt. The officer advanced towards the explorer, who in some vague presentiment fell back a pace, but the officer seized him by the hand, and drew him to one side. 'I should like to exchange a few words with you in confidence,' he said. 'May I?' 'Of course,' said the explorer, and listened with downcast eyes.

'This procedure and method of execution, which you are now having the opportunity to admire, has at the moment no longer any open adherents in our colony. I am its sole advocate, and at the same time the sole advocate of the old Commandant's tradition. I can no longer reckon on any further extension of the method, it takes all my energy to maintain it as it is. During the old Commandant's lifetime the colony was full of his adherents; his strength of conviction I still have in some measure, but not an atom of his power; consequently the adherents have skulked out of sight, there are still many of them but not one of them will admit it. If you were to go into the tea-hose today, an execution day, and listen to what is being said, you would perhaps hear only ambiguous remarks. These would all be made by adherents, but under the present Commandant and his present doctrines they are of no use to me. And now I ask you: because of this Commandant and the women who influenced him, is such a piece of work, the work of a lifetime,'—he pointed to the machine—'to fall into disuse? Ought one to let that happen? Even if one has only come as a stranger to our island for a few days? And yet there's no time to lose, an attack of some kind is impending on my function as a judge; conferences are already being held in the Commandant's office from which I am excluded; even your coming here today seems to me a significant move; they are cowards and use you as a screen, you, a stranger. How different an execution was in the old days! A whole day before the ceremony the valley was packed with people; they all came only to look on; early in the morning the Commandant appeared with his ladies; fanfares roused the whole camp; I reported that everything was in readiness; the assembled company—no high official dared to absent himself—arranged itself round the machine; this pile of cane chairs is a miserable survival from that epoch. The machine was freshly cleaned and glittering, I got new spare parts for almost every execution. Before hundreds of spectators—all of them standing on tip-toe as far as the heights there—the condemned man was laid under the Harrow by the Commandant himself. What is left today for a common soldier to do was then my task, the task of the presiding judge, and was an honour for me. And then the execution began! No discordant noise spoilt the working of the machine. Many did not care to watch it but lay with closed eyes in the sand; they all knew; now Justice is being done. In the silence one heard nothing but the condemned man's sighs, half muffled by the felt gag. Nowadays the machine can no longer wring from anyone a sigh louder than the felt gag can stifle; but in those days the writing needles let drop an acid fluid which we're not permitted to use today. Well, and then came the sixth hour. It was impossible to grant all the requests to be allowed to watch it from near by. The Commandant in his wisdom ordained that the children should have the preference; I, of course, because of my office had the privilege of always being at hand; often enough I would be squatting there with a small child in either arm. How we all absorbed the look of transfiguration on the face of the sufferer, how we bathed our cheeks in the radiance of that justice, achieved at last and fading so quickly! What times these were, my comrade!' The officer had obviously forgotten whom he was addressing; he had embraced the explorer and laid his head on his shoulder. The explorer was deeply embarrassed, impatiently he stared over the officer's head. The soldier had finished his cleaning job and was now pouring rice-pap from a pot into the basin. As soon as the condemned man, who seemed to have recovered himself entirely, noticed this action he began to reach for the rice with his tongue. The soldier kept pushing him away, since the rice-pap was certainly meant for a later hour, yet it was just as unfitting that the soldier himself should thrust his dirty hands into the basin and eat out of it, before the other's avid face.

The officer quickly pulled himself together. 'I didn't want to upset you,' he said, 'I know it is impossible to make those days credible now. Anyhow, the machine is still working and it is still effective in itself. It is effective in itself even though it stands alone in this valley. And the corpse still falls at the last into the grave with an incomprehensively gentle wafting motion, even though there are no hundreds of people swarming round like flies as formerly. In those days we had to put a strong fence round the grave; it has long since been torn down.'

The explorer wanted to withdraw his face from the officer and looked round at him random. The officer thought he was surveying the valley's desolation; so he seized him by the hands, turned him round to meet his eyes, and asked: 'Do you observe the shame of it?'

But the explorer said nothing. The officer left him alone for a little; with legs apart, hands on hips, he stood very still, gazing at the ground. Then he smiled encouragingly at the explorer and said: 'I was quite near you yesterday when the Commandant gave you the invitation. I heard him giving it. It know the Commandant. I divined at once what he was after. Although he is powerful enough to take measures against me, he doesn't dare to do it yet, but he certainly means to use your verdict against me, the verdict of an illustrious foreigner. He has calculated it carefully: this is your second day on the island, you did not know the old Commandant and his ways, you are conditioned by European ways of thought, perhaps you object on principle to capital punishment in general and to such mechanical instruments of death in particular, beside you will see that the execution has no support from the public, a shabby ceremony—carried out with a machine already somewhat old and worn—now, taking all that into consideration, would it not be likely (so thinks the Commandant) that you might disapprove of my methods? And if you disapprove, you wouldn't conceal the fact (I'm still speaking from the Commandant's point of view), for you are a man to feel confidence in your own well-tried conclusions? True, you have seen and learned to appreciate the peculiarities of many people, and so you would not be likely to take a strong line against our proceedings, as you might do in your own country. But the Commandant has no need of that. A casual, even an unguarded remark will be enough. It doesn't even need to represent what you really think, so long as it can be used speciously to serve his purpose. He will try to prompt you with sly questions, of that I am certain. And his ladies will sit around you and prick up their ears; you might be saying something like this: "In our country we have a different way of carrying out justice," or "In our country the prisoner has a chance to defend himself before he is sentenced," or "We haven't used torture since the Middle Ages." All these statements are as true as they seem natural to you, harmless remarks that pass no judgements on my methods. But how would the Commandant react to them? I can see him, our good Commandant, pushing his chair away immediately and rushing on to the balcony, I can see his ladies streaming out after him, I can hear his voice—the ladies call it a voice of thunder—well, and this is what he says: "A famous Western investigator, sent out to study criminal procedure in all the countries of the world, has just said that our old tradition of administering justice is inhumane. Such a verdict from such a personality makes it impossible for me to countenance these methods any longer. Therefore from this very day I ordain," and so on. You may want to interpose that you never said any such thing, that you never called my methods inhumane, on the contrary, your profound experience leads you to believe they are most humane and most in consonance with human dignity, and you admire the machine greatly—but it will be too late; you won't even get on to the balcony, crowded as it will be with ladies; you may try to draw attention to yourself; you may want to scream out; but a lady's hand will close your lips—and I and the old Commandant will be done for.'

The explorer had to suppress a smile; so easy, then, was the task he had felt to be so difficult. He said evasively: 'You over-estimate my influence; the commandant has read my letters of recommendation, he knows that I am no expert in criminal procedure. If I were to give an opinion, it would be as a private individual, an opinion no more influential than that of any ordinary person, and in any case much less influential than that of the Commandant, who, I am given to understand, has very extensive powers in this penal settlement. If his attitude to your procedure is as definitely hostile as you believe, then I fear the end of your tradition is at hand, even without any humble assistance from me.'

Had it dawned on the officer at last? No, he still did not understand. He shook his head emphatically, glanced briefly round at the condemned man and the soldier, who both flinched away from the rice, came close up to the explorer and without looking at his face but fixing his eye on some spot on his coat said in a lower voice than before: 'You don't know the Commandant; you feel yourself—forgive the expression—a kind of outsider so far as all of us are concerned; yet, believe me, your influence cannot be rated too highly. I was simply delighted when I heard that you were to attend the execution all by yourself. The Commandant arranged it to aim a blow at me, but I shall turn it to my advantage. Without being distracted by lying whispers and contemptuous glances—which could not have been avoided had a crowd of people attended the execution—you have heard my explanations, seen the machine, and are now in the course of watching the execution. You have doubtless already formed your own judgement; if you still have some small uncertainties, the sight of the execution will resolve them. And now I make this request to you: Help me against the Commandant!' The explorer would not let him go on. 'How could I do that?' he cried, 'it's quite impossible. I can neither help nor hinder you.' 'Yes, you can ,' said the officer. With certain apprehension the explorer saw that the officer had clenched his fists. 'Yes, you can,' repeated the officer, still more insistently. 'I have a plan that is bound to succeed. You believe your influence is insufficient. I know that it is sufficient. But even granted that you are right, is it not necessary, for the sake of preserving this tradition, to try even what might prove insufficient? Listen to my plan, then. The first thing necessary for you to carry it out is to be as reticent as possible regarding your verdict on these proceedings. Unless you are asked a direct question you must say nothing at all; but what you do say must be brief and general; let it be remarked that you would prefer not to discuss the matter, that you are out of patience with it, that if you were to let yourself go you would use strong language. I don't ask you to tell any lies; by no means; you should give only curt answers, such as: "Yes, I saw the execution," or "Yes, I had it explained to me." Just that, nothing more. There are grounds enough for any impatience you betray, although not such as will occur to the Commandant. Of course, he will mistake your meaning and interpret it to please himself. That's what my plan depends on. Tomorrow in the Commandant's office there is to be a large conference of all the high administrative officials, the Commandant presiding. Of course the Commandant is the kind of man to have turned these conferences into public spectacles. He has had a gallery built that is always packed with spectators. I am compelled to take part in the conferences, but they make me sick with nausea. Now, whatever happens, you will certainly be invited to this conference; if you behave today as I suggest the invitation will become an urgent request. But if for some mysterious reason you're not invited, you'll have to ask for an invitation: there's no doubt of your getting it then. So tomorrow you're sitting in the Commandant's box with the ladies. He keeps looking up to make sure you're there. After various trivial and ridiculous matters, brought in merely to impress the audience—mostly harbour works, nothing but harbour works!—our judicial procedure comes up for discussion too. If the Commandant doesn't introduce it, or not soon enough, I'll see that it's mentioned. I'll stand up and report that today's execution has taken place. Quite briefly, only a statement. Such a statement is not usual, but I shall make it. The Commandant thanks me, as always, with an amiable smile, and then he can't restrain himself, he seizes the excellent opportunity. "It has just been reported," he will say, or words to that effect, "that an execution has taken place. I should like merely to add that this execution was witnessed by the famous investigator who has, as you all know, honoured our colony so exceptionally by his visit to us. His presence at today's session of our conference also contributes to the importance of this occasion. Should we not now ask the famous investigator to give us his verdict on our traditional mode of execution and the procedure that leads up to it?" Of course there is loud applause, general agreement, I am more insistent than anyone. This Commandant bows to you and says: "Then in the name of the assembled company, I put the question to you." And now you advance to the front of the box. Lay your hands where everyone can see them or the ladies will catch them and press your fingers. And then at last you can speak out. I don't know how I'm going to endure the tension of waiting for that moment. Don't put any restraint on yourself when you make your speech, publish the truth aloud, lean over the front of the box, shout, yes indeed, shout your verdict, your unshakable conviction, at the Commandant. Yet perhaps you wouldn't care to do that, it's not in keeping with your character, in your country perhaps people do these things differently, well, that's all right too, that will be quite as effective, don't even stand up, just say a few words, even in a whisper, so that only the officials beneath you will hear them, that will be quite enough, you don't even need to mention the lack of public support for the execution, the creaking wheel, the broken strap, the filthy stump of felt, no, I'll take all that upon me, and, believe me, if my indictment doesn't drive him out of the conference hall, it will force him to his knees to make the acknowledgement: "Old Commandant, I humble myself before you." That is my plan: will you help me to carry it out? But of course you are willing, what is more, you must.' And the officer seized the explorer by both arms and gazed, breathing heavily, into his face. He had shouted the last sentence so loudly that even the soldier and the condemned man were startled into attending; they had not understood a word but they stopped eating and looked over at the explorer, chewing their previous mouthfuls.

From the very beginning the explorer had no doubt about what answer he must give; in his lifetime he had experienced too much to have any uncertainty here; he was fundamentally honourable and unafraid. And yet now, facing the soldier and the condemned man, he did hesitate for as long as it took to draw one breath. At last, however, he said, as he had to: 'No.'

The officer blinked several times but did not turn his eyes away. 'Would you like me to explain?' asked the explorer. The officer nodded, mutely. 'I do not approve of your procedure,' said the explorer then, 'even before you took me into your confidence—of course I shall never in any circumstances betray your confidence—I was already wondering whether it would be my duty to intervene and whether my intervention would have the slightest chance of success. I realized to whom I ought to turn: to the Commandant, of course. You have made that fact even clearer, but without having strengthened my resolution, on the contrary, your sincere conviction has touched me, even though it cannot influence my judgement.'

The officer remained mute, turned to the machine, caught hold of a brass rod, and then, leaning back a little, gazed at the Designer as if to assure himself that all was in order. The soldier and the condemned man seemed to have come to some understanding; the condemned man was making signs to the soldier, difficult though his movements were because of the tight straps; the soldier was bending down to him; the condemned man whispered something and the soldier nodded.

The explorer followed the officer and said: 'You don't know yet what I mean to do. I shall tell the Commandant what I think of the procedure, certainly, but not at a public conference, only in private; nor shall I stay here long enough to attend any conference; I am going away early tomorrow morning, or at least embarking on my ship.'

It did not look as if the officer had been listening. 'So you did not find the procedure convincing,' he said to himself and smiled, as an old man smiles at childish nonsense and yet pursues his own meditations behind the smile.

'Then the time has come,' he said at last and suddenly looked at the explorer with bright eyes that held some challenge, some appeal for cooperation. 'The time for what?' asked the explorer uneasily, but got no answer.

'You are free,' said the officer to the condemned man in the native tongue. The man did not believe it at first. 'Yes, you are set free,' said the officer. For the first time the condemned man's face woke to real animation. Was it true? Was it only a caprice of the officer's, that might change again? Had the foreign explorer begged him off? What was it? One could read these questions on his face. But not for long. Whatever it might be, he wanted to be really free if he might, and he began to struggle so far as the Harrow permitted him.

'You'll burst my straps,' cried the officer, 'lie still! We'll soon loosen them.' And signing the soldier to help him, he set about doing so. The condemned man laughed wordlessly to himself, now he turned his face left toward the officer now right towards the soldier, nor did he forget the explorer.

'Draw him out,' ordered the officer. Because of the Harrow this had to be done with some care. The condemned man had already torn himself a little in the back through his impatience.

From now on, however, the officer paid hardly any attention to him. He went up to the explorer, pulled out the small leather brief-case again, turned over the papers in it, found the one he wanted and showed it to the explorer. 'Read it,' he said. 'I can't,' said the explorer, 'I told you before that I can't make out these scripts.' 'Try taking a close look at it,' said the officer and came quite near to the explorer so that they might read it together. But when even that proved useless, he outlined the script with his little finger, holding it high above the paper as if the surface dared not be sullied by touch, in order to help the explorer to follow the script in that way. The explorer did make an effort, meaning to please the officer in this respect at least, but he was quite unable to follow. Now the officer began to spell it, letter by letter, and then read out the words. '"BE JUST!" is what is written there,' he said, 'surely you can read it now.' The explorer went so close to the paper that the officer feared he might touch it and drew it farther away; the explorer made no remark, yet it was clear that he still could not decipher it. '"Be just!" is what is written there,' said the officer once more. 'Maybe,' said the explorer, 'I am prepared to believe you.' 'Well, then,' said the officer, at least partly satisfied, and climbed up the ladder with the paper; very carefully he laid it inside the Designer and seemed to be changing the disposition of all the cog-wheels; it was a troublesome piece of work and must have involved wheels that were extremely small, for sometimes the officer's head vanished altogether from sight inside the Designer, so precisely did he have to regulate the machinery.

The explorer, down below, watched the labor uninterruptedly, his neck grew stiff, and his eyes smarted from the glare of sunshine over the sky. The soldier and the condemned man were now busy together. The man's shirt and trousers which were already lying in the grave, were fished out by the point of the soldier's bayonet. The shirt was abominably dirty and its owner washed it in the bucket of water. When he put on the shirt and trousers both he and the soldier could not help guffawing, for the garments were of course slit up behind. Perhaps the condemned man felt it incumbent on him to amuse the soldier, he turned round and round in his slashed garments before the soldier, who squatted on the ground beating his knees with mirth. All the same, they presently controlled their mirth out of respect for the gentlemen.

When the officer had at length finished his task aloft, he surveyed the machinery in all its details once more with a smile, but this time shut the lid of the Designer, which had stayed open till now, climbed down, looked into the grave and then at the condemned man, noting with satisfaction that the clothing had been taken out, then went over to wash his hands in the water-bucket, perceived too late that it was disgustingly dirty, was unhappy because he could not wash his hands, in the end thrust them into the sand—this alternative did not please him, but he had to put up with it—then stood upright and began to unbutton his uniform jacket. As he did this, the two ladies' handkerchiefs he had tucked at the back of his collar fell into his hands. 'Here are your handkerchiefs,' he said, and threw them to the condemned man. And to the explorer he said in explanation: 'A gift from the ladies.'

In spite of the obvious haste with which he was discarding first his uniform jacket and then all his clothing he handled each garment with loving care, he even ran his fingers caressingly over the silver lace on the jacket and shook a tassel into place. This loving care was certainly out of keeping

with the fact that as soon as he had a garment off he flung it at once with a
kind of unwilling jerk into the grave. The last thing left to him was his
small-sword with the sword-belt. He drew it out of the scabbard, broke it,
then gathered all together, the bits of the sword, the scabbard and the belt,
and flung them so violently down that they clattered into the grave.

Now he stood naked there. The explorer bit his lips and said nothing. He knew very well what was going to happen, but he had no right to
obstruct the officer in anything. If the judicial procedure which the officer
cherished were really so near its end—possibly as a result of the explorer's
intervention, to which he felt himself pledged—then the officer was doing
the right thing; in his place the explorer would not have acted otherwise.

The soldier and the condemned man did not understand at first what
was happening, to begin with they were not even looking on. The condemned man was gleeful at having got the handkerchiefs back, but he was
not allowéd to enjoy them for long, since the soldier snatched them with a
sudden, unexpected grab. Now the condemned man in turn was trying to
twitch them from under the belt where the soldier had tucked them, but the
soldier was on his guard. So they were wrestling, half in jest. Only when
the officer stood quite naked was their attention caught. The condemned
man especially seemed struck with the notion that a great change of fortune
was impending. What had happened to him was now going to happen to
the officer. Perhaps even to the very end. Apparently the foreign explorer
had given the order for it. So this was revenge. Although he himself had
not suffered to the end, he was to be revenged to the end. A broad, silent
grin now appeared on his face and stayed there all the rest of the time.

The officer, however, had turned to the machine. It had been clear
enough previously that he understood the machine well, but now it was almost staggering to see how he managed it and how it obeyed him. His
hand had only to approach the Harrow for it to rise and sink several times
till it was adjusted to the right position for receiving him; he touched only
the edge of the Bed and already it was vibrating; the felt gag came to meet
his mouth, one could see that the officer was really reluctant to take it, but
he shrank from it only a moment, soon he submitted and received it. Everything was ready, only the straps hung down at the sides, yet they were obviously unnecessary, the officer did not need to be fastened down. Then
the condemned man noticed the loose straps, in his opinion the execution
was incomplete unless the straps were buckled, he gestured eagerly to the
soldier and they ran together to strap the officer down. The latter had already stretched out one foot to push the lever that started the Designer; he
saw the two men coming up, so he drew his foot back and let himself be
buckled in. But now he could not reach the lever; neither the soldier nor the
condemned man would be able to find it, and the explorer was determined
not to lift a finger. It was not necessary; as soon as the straps were fastened
the machine began to work; the Bed vibrated, the needles flickered above
the skin, the Harrow rose and fell. The explorer had been staring at it quite
a while before he remembered that a wheel in the Designer should have been
creaking; but everything was quiet, not even the slightest hum could be
heard.

Because it was working so silently the machine simply escaped one's attention. The explorer observed the soldier and the condemned man. The latter was the more animated of the two, everything in the machine interested him, now he was bending down and now stretching up on tip-toe, his forefinger was extended all the time pointing out details to the soldier. This annoyed the explorer. He was resolved to stay till the end, but he could not bear the sight of these two. 'Go back home,' he said. The soldier would have been willing enough, but the condemned man took the order as a punishment. With clasped hands he implored to be allowed to stay, and when the explorer shook his head and would not relent, he even went down on his knees. The explorer saw that it was no use merely giving orders, he was on the point of going over and driving them away. At that moment he heard a noise above him in the Designer. He looked up. Was the cog-wheel going to make trouble after all? But it was something quite different. Slowly the lid of the Designer rose up and then clicked wide open. The teeth of a cog-wheel showed themselves and rose higher, soon the whole wheel was visible, it was as if some enormous force were squeezing the Designer so that there was no longer room for the wheel, the wheel moved up till it came to the very edge of the Designer, fell down, rolled along the sand a little on its rim and then lay flat. But a second wheel was already rising after it, followed by many others, large and small and indistinguishably minute, the same thing happened to all of them, at every moment one imagined the Designer must now really be empty, but another complex of numerous wheels was already rising into sight, falling down, trundling along the sand and lying flat. This phenomenon made the condemned man completely forget the explorer's command, the cog-wheels fascinated him, he was always trying to catch one and at the same time urging the soldier to help, but always drew back his hand in alarm, for another wheel always came hopping along which, at least on its first advance, scared him off.

The explorer, on the other hand, felt greatly troubled; the machine was obviously going to pieces; its silent working was a delusion; he had a feeling that he must now stand by the officer since the officer was no longer able to look after himself. But while the tumbling cog-wheels absorbed his whole attention he had forgotten to keep an eye on the rest of the machine; now that the last cog-wheel had left the Designer, however, he bent over the Harrow and had a new and still more unpleasant surprise. The Harrow was not writing, it was only jabbing, and the Bed was not turning the body over but only bringing it up quivering against the needles. The explorer wanted to do something, if possible, to bring the whole machine to a standstill, for this was no exquisite torture such as the officer desired, this was plain murder. He stretched out his hands. But at that moment the Harrow rose with the body spitted on it and moved to the side, as it usually did only when the twelfth hour had come. Blood was flowing in a hundred streams, not mingled with water; the water-jets too had failed to function. And now the last action failed to fulfill itself, the body did not drop off the long needles, streaming with blood it went on hanging over the grave without falling into it. The Harrow tried to move back to its old position, but as if it had itself noticed that it had not yet got rid of its burden it stuck after all where it was, over the grave. 'Come and help!' cried the explorer to the other two, and himself seized the officer's feet. He wanted to push against the feet while the others seized the head from the opposite side so the officer might be slowly eased off the needles. But the other two could not make up their minds to come; the condemned man actually turned away; the explorer had to go over to them and force them into position at the officer's head. And here, almost against his will, he had to look at the face of the corpse. It was as it had been in life; no sign was visible of the promised redemption; what the others had found in the machine the officer had not found; the lips were firmly pressed together, the eyes were open, with the same expression as in life, their look was calm and convinced, through the forehead went the point of the great iron spike.

*

As the explorer with the soldier and the condemned man behind him, reached the first houses of the settlement, the soldier pointed to one of them and said: 'There is the tea-house.'

In the ground floor of the house was a deep, low, cavernous space, its walls and ceiling blackened with smoke. It was open to the road all along its length. Although this tea-house was very little different from the other houses of the settlement, which were all very dilapidated, even up to the Commandant's palatial headquarters, it made on the explorer the impression of a historic tradition of some kind, and he felt the power of past days. He went near to it, followed by his companions, right up between the empty tables which stood in the road before it, and breathed the cool heavy air that came from the interior. 'The old man's buried here,' said the soldier, 'the priest wouldn't let him lie in the churchyard. Nobody knew where to bury him for a while, but in the end they buried him here. The officer never told you about that, for sure, because of course that's what he was most ashamed of. He even tried several times to dig the old man up by night, but he was always chased away.' 'Where is the grave?' asked the explorer, who found it impossible to believe the soldier. At once both of them, the soldier and the condemned man, ran before him pointing with outstretched hands in the direction where the grave should be. They led the explorer right up to the back wall, where guests were sitting at a few tables. These were apparently dock labourers, strong men with short, glistening, full black beards. None had a jacket, their shirts were torn, they were poor, humble creatures. As the explorer drew near some of them got up, pressed close to the wall, and stared at him. 'It's a stranger,' ran the whisper around him, 'he wants to see the grave.' They pushed one of the tables aside, and under it there was really a grave-stone. It was a simple stone, low enough to be covered by a table. There was an inscription on it in very small letters, the explorer had to kneel down to read it. This was what it said: 'Here rests the old Commandant. His adherents, who now must be nameless, have dug this grave and set up this stone. There is a prophecy that after a certain number of years the Commandant will rise again and lead his adherents from this house to recover the colony. Have faith and wait!' When the explorer had read this and risen to his feet he saw all the by-standers around him smiling, as if they too had read the inscription, had found it ridiculous and were expecting him to agree with them. The explorer ignored this, distributed a few coins among them, waited till the table was pushed over the grave again, quitted the tea-house and made for the harbour.

The soldier and the condemned man had found some acquaintances in the tea-house, who detained them. But they must have soon shaken them off, for the explorer was only halfway down the long flight to steps leading to the boats when they came rushing after him. Probably they wanted to force him at the last minute to take them with him. While he was bargaining below with a ferryman to row him to the steamer, the two of them came headlong down the steps, in silence, for they did not dare to shout. But by the time they reached the foot of the steps the explorer was already in the boat, and the ferryman was just casting off from the shore. They could have jumped into the boat, but the explorer lifted a heavy knotted rope from the floor-boards, threatened them with it, and so kept them from attempting the leap.

The Pit and the Pendulum
Edgar Allan Poe

*Impia tortorum longos hic turba furores
Sanguinis innocui, non satiata, aluit.
Sospite nunc patriâ, fracto nunc funeris antro,
Mors ubi dira fuit vita salusque patent.*

[QUATRAIN COMPOSED FOR THE GATES OF A MARKET TO BE
ERECTED UPON THE SITE OF THE JACOBIN CLUB HOUSE AT
PARIS.]

I was sick—sick unto death with that long agony; and when they at length
unbound me, and I was permitted to sit, I felt that my senses were leaving
me. The sentence—the dread sentence of death—was the last of distinct ac-
centuation which reached my ears. After that, the sound of the inquisitorial
voices seemed merged in one dreamy indeterminate hum. It conveyed to
my soul the idea of *revolution*—perhaps from its association in fancy with
the burr of a millwheel. This only for a brief period; for presently I heard
no more. Yet, for a while, I saw; but with how terrible an exaggeration! I
saw the lips of the black-robed judges. They appeared to me white—whiter
than the sheet upon which I trace these words—and thin even to grotesqueness; thin with the intensity of their expression of firmness—of immoveable
resolution—of stern contempt of human torture. I saw that the decrees of
what to me was Fate, were still issuing from those lips. I saw them writhe
with a deadly locution. I saw them fashion the syllables of my name; and I
shuddered because no sound succeeded. I saw, too, for a few moments of
delirious horror, the soft and nearly imperceptible waving of the sable
draperies which enwrapped the walls of the apartment. And then my vision
fell upon the seven tall candles upon the table. At first they wore the aspect
of charity, and seemed white slender angels who would save me; but then,
all at once, there came a most deadly nausea over my spirit, and I felt every
fibre in my frame thrill as if I had touched the wire of a galvanic battery,
while the angel forms became meaningless spectres, with heads of flame,
and I saw that from them there would be no help. And then there stole into
my fancy, like a rich musical note, the thought of what sweet rest there must
be in the grave. The thought came gently and stealthily, and it seemed long
before it attained full appreciation; but just as my spirit came at length prop-

erly to feel and entertain it, the figures of the judges vanished, as if magically from before me; the tall candles sank into nothingness; their flames went out utterly; the blackness of darkness supervened; all sensations appeared swallowed up in a mad rushing descent as of the soul into Hades. Then silence, and stillness, and night were the universe.

I had swooned; but still will not say that all of consciousness was lost. What of it there remained I will not attempt to define, or even to describe; yet all was not lost. In the deepest slumber—no! In delirium—no! In a swoon—no! In death—no! Even in the grave all *is not* lost. Else there is no immortality for man. Arousing from the most profound of slumbers, we break the gossamer web of *some* dream. Yet in a second afterward, (so frail may that web have been,) we remember not that we have dreamed. In the return to life from the swoon there are two stages; first, that of the sense of mental or spiritual; secondly, that of the sense of physical, existence. It seems probable that if, upon reaching the second stage, we could recall the impressions of the first, we should find these impressions eloquent in memories of the gulf beyond. And that gulf is—what? How at least shall we distinguish its shadows from those of the tomb? But if the impressions of what I have termed the first stage, are not, at will, recalled, yet, after long interval, do they not come unbidden, while we marvel whence they come? He who has never swooned, is not he who finds strange palaces and wildly familiar faces in coals that glow; is not he who beholds floating in midair the sad visions that the many may not view; is not he who ponders over the perfume of some novel flower—is not he whose brain grows bewildered with the meaning of some musical cadence which has never before arrested his attention.

Amid frequent and thoughtful endeavors to remember; amid earnest struggles to regather some token of the state of seeming nothingness into which my soul had lapsed, there have been moments when I have dreamed of success; there have been brief, very brief periods when I have conjured up remembrances which the lucid reason of a later epoch assures me could have had reference only to that condition of seeming unconsciousness. These shadows of memory tell, indistinctly, of tall figures that lifted and bore me in silence down—down—still down—till a hideous dizziness oppressed me at the mere idea of the interminableness of the descent. They tell also of a vague horror at my heart, on account of that heart's unnatural stillness. Then comes a sense of sudden motionlessness throughout all things; as if those who bore me (a ghastly train!) had outrun, in their descent, the limits of the limitless, and paused from the wearisomeness of their toil. After this I call to mind flatness and dampness; and then all is *madness*—the madness of a memory which busies itself among forbidden things.

Very suddenly there came back to my soul motion and sound—the tumultuous motion of the heart, and, in my ears, the sound of its beating. Then a pause in which all is blank. Then again sound, and motion, and touch—a tingling sensation pervading my frame. Then the mere consciousness of existence, without thought—a condition which lasted long. Then, very suddenly, *thought*, and shuddering terror, and earnest endeavor to comprehend my true state. Then a strong desire to lapse into insensibility. Then a rushing revival of soul and a successful effort to move. And now a full memory of the trial, of the judges, of the sable draperies, of the sentence, of the sickness, of the swoon. Then entire forgetfulness of all that followed; of all that a later day and much earnestness of endeavor have enabled me vaguely to recall.

So far, I had not opened my eyes. I felt that I lay upon my back, unbound. I reached out my hand, and it fell heavily upon something damp and hard. There I suffered it to remain for many minutes, while I strove to imagine where and *what* I could be. I longed, yet dared not to employ my vision. I dreaded the first glance at objects around me. It was not that I feared to look upon things horrible, but that I grew aghast lest there should be *nothing* to see. At length, with a wild desperation at heart, I quickly unclosed my eyes. My worst thoughts, then, were confirmed. The blackness of eternal night encompassed me. I struggled for breath. The intensity of the darkness seemed to oppress and stifle me. The atmosphere was intolerably close. I still lay quietly, and made effort to exercise my reason. I brought to mind the inquisitorial proceedings, and attempted from that point to deduce my real condition. The sentence had passed; and it appeared to me that a very long interval of time had since elapsed. Yet not for a moment did I suppose myself actually dead. Such a supposition, notwithstanding what we read in fiction, is altogether inconsistent with real existence;—but where and in what state was I? The condemned to death, I knew, perished usually at the *autos-da-fé,* and one of these had been held on the very night of the day of my trial. Had I been remanded to my dungeon, to await the next sacrifice, which would not take place for many months? This I at once saw could not be. Victims had been in immediate demand. Moreover, my dungeon, as well as all the condemned cells at Toledo, had stone floors, and light was not altogether excluded.

A fearful idea now suddenly drove the blood in torrents upon my heart, and for a brief period, I once more relapsed into insensibility. Upon recovering, I at once started to my feet, trembling convulsively in every fibre. I thrust my arms wildly above and around me in all directions. I felt nothing; yet dreaded to move a step, lest I should be impeded by the walls of a tomb. Perspiration burst from every pore, and stood in cold big beads upon my forehead. The agony of suspense grew at length intolerable, and I cautiously moved forward, with my arms extended, and my eyes straining from their sockets, in the hope of catching some faint ray of light. I proceeded for many paces; but still all was blackness and vacancy. I breathed more freely. It seemed evident that mine was not, at least, the most hideous of fates.

And now, as I still continued to step cautiously onward, there came thronging upon my recollection a thousand vague rumors of the horrors of Toledo. Of the dungeons there had been strange things narrated—fables I had always deemed them—but yet strange, and too ghastly to repeat, save in a whisper. Was I left to perish of starvation in this subterranean world of darkness; or what fate, perhaps even more fearful, awaited me? That the result would be death, and a death of more than customary bitterness, I knew too well the character of my judge to doubt. The mode and the hour were all that occupied or distracted me.

My outstretched hands at length encountered some solid obstruction.

It was a wall, seemingly of stone masonry—very smooth, slimy, and cold. I followed it up; stepping with all the careful distrust with which certain antique narratives had inspired me. This process, however, afforded me no means of ascertaining the dimensions of my dungeon; as I might make its circuit, and return to the point whence I set out, without being aware of the fact; so perfectly uniform seemed the wall. I therefore sought the knife which had been in my pocket, when led into the inquisitorial chamber; but it was gone; my clothes had been exchanged for a wrapper of coarse serge. I had thought of forcing the blade in some minute crevice of the masonry, so as to identify my point of departure. The difficulty, nevertheless, was but trivial; although, in the disorder of my fancy, it seemed at first insuperable. I tore a part of the hem from the robe and placed the fragment at full length, and at right angles to the wall. In groping my way around the prison, I could not fail to encounter this rag upon completing the circuit. So, at least I thought: but I had not counted upon the extent of the dungeon, or upon my own weakness. The ground was moist and slippery. I staggered onward for some time, when I stumbled and fell. My excessive fatigue induced me to remain prostrate; and sleep soon overtook me as I lay.

Upon awakening, and stretching forth an arm, I found beside me a loaf and a pitcher with water. I was too much exhausted to reflect upon this circumstance, but ate and drank with avidity. Shortly afterward, I resumed my tour around the prison, and with much toil, came at last upon the fragment of the serge. Up to the period when I fell I had counted fifty-two paces, and upon resuming my walk, I had counted forty-eight more—when I arrived at the rag. There were in all, then, a hundred paces; and, admitting two paces to the yard, I presumed the dungeon to be fifty yards in circuit. I had met, however, with many angles in the wall, and thus I could form no guess at the shape of the vault; for vault I could not help supposing it to be.

I had little object—certainly no hope—in these researches; but a vague curiosity prompted me to continue them. Quitting the wall, I resolved to cross the area of the enclosure. At first I proceeded with extreme caution, for the floor, although seemingly of solid material, was treacherous with slime. At length, however, I took courage, and did not hesitate to step firmly—endeavoring to cross in as direct a line as possible. I had advanced some ten or twelve paces in this manner, when the remnant of the torn hem of my robe became entangled between my legs. I stepped on it, and fell violently on my face.

In the confusion attending my fall, I did not immediately apprehend a somewhat startling circumstance, which yet, in a few seconds afterward, and while I still lay prostrate, arrested my attention. It was this: my chin rested upon the floor of the prison, but my lips and the upper portion of my head, although seemingly at a less elevation than the chin, touched nothing. At the same time my forehead seemed bathed in a clammy vapor, and the peculiar smell of decayed fungus arose to my nostrils. I put forward my arm, and shuddered to find that I had fallen at the very brink of a circular pit, whose extent, of course, I had no means of ascertaining at the moment. Groping about the masonry just below the margin, I succeeded in dislodging a small fragment, and let it fall into the abyss. For many seconds I hearkened to its reverberations as it dashed against the sides of the chasm in its descent; at length there was a sudden plunge into water, succeeded by loud echoes. At the same moment there came a sound resembling the quick opening, and as rapid closing of a door overhead, while a faint gleam of light flashed suddenly through the gloom, and as suddenly faded away.

I saw clearly the doom which had been prepared for me, and congratulated myself upon the timely accident by which I had escaped. Another step before my fall, and the world had seen me no more. And the death just avoided, was of that very character which I had regarded as fabulous and frivolous in the tales respecting the Inquisition. To the victims of its tyranny, there was the choice of death with its direct physical agonies, or death with its most hideous moral horrors. I had been reserved for the latter. By long suffering my nerves had been unstrung, until I trembled at the sound of my own voice, and had become in every respect a fitting subject of the species of torture which awaited me.

Shaking in every limb, I groped my way back to the wall; resolving there to perish rather than risk the terrors of the wells, of which my imagination now pictured many in various positions about the dungeon. In other conditions of mind I might have had courage to end my misery at once by a plunge into one of these abysses; but now I was the veriest of cowards. Neither could I forget what I had read of these pits—that the *sudden* extinction of life formed no part of their most horrible plan.

Agitation of spirit kept me awake for many long hours; but at length I again slumbered. Upon arousing, I found by my side, as before, a loaf and a pitcher of water. A burning thirst consumed me, and I emptied the vessel at a draught. It must have been drugged; for scarcely had I drunk, before I became irresistibly drowsy. A deep sleep fell upon me—a sleep like that of death. How long it lasted of course, I know not; but when, once again, I unclosed my eyes, the objects around me were visible. By a wild sulphurous lustre, the origin of which I could not at first determine, I was enabled to see the extent and aspect of the prison.

In its size I had been greatly mistaken. The whole circuit of its walls did not exceed twenty-five yards. For some minutes this fact occasioned me a world of vain trouble; vain indeed—for what could be of less importance, under the terrible circumstances which environed me, than the mere dimensions of my dungeon? But my soul took a wild interest in trifles, and I busied myself in endeavors to account for the error I had committed in my measurement. The truth at length flashed upon me. In my first attempt at exploration I had counted fifty-two paces, up to the period when I fell: I must then have been within a pace or two of the fragment of serge; in fact, I had nearly performed the circuit of the vault. I then slept—and, upon awaking, I must have returned upon my steps—thus supposing the circuit nearly double what it actually was. My confusion of mind prevented me from observing that I began my tour with the wall to the left, and ended it with the wall to the right.

I had been deceived, too, in respect to the shape of the enclosure. In feeling my way I had found many angles, and thus deduced an idea of great irregularity; so potent is the effect of total darkness upon one arousing from lethargy or sleep! The angles were simply those of a few slight depressions, or niches, at odd intervals. The general shape of the prison was square. What I had taken for masonry seemed now to be iron, or some other metal, in huge plates, whose sutures or joints occasioned the depression. The entire surface of this metallic enclosure was rudely daubed in all the hideous and repulsive devices to which the charnel superstition of the monks has given rise. The figures of fiends in aspects of menace, with skeleton forms, and other more really fearful images, overspread and disfigured the walls. I observed that the outlines of these monstrosities were sufficiently distinct, but that the colors seemed faded and blurred, as if from the effects of a damp atmosphere. I now noticed the floor, too, which was of stone. In the centre yawned the circular pit from whose jaws I had escaped; but it was the only one in the dungeon.

All this I saw indistinctly and by much effort—for my personal condition had been greatly changed during slumber. I now lay upon my back, and at full length, on a species of low framework of wood. To this I was securely bound by a long strap resembling a surcingle. It passed in many convolutions about my limbs and body, leaving at liberty only my head, and my left arm to such extent, that I could by dint of much exertion, supply myself with food from an earthen dish which lay by my side on the floor. I saw, to my horror, that the pitcher had been removed. I say, to my horror—for I was consumed with intolerable thirst. This thirst it appeared to be the design of my persecutors to stimulate—for the food in the dish was meat pungently seasoned.

Looking upward, I surveyed the ceiling of my prison. It was some thirty or forty feet overhead, and constructed much as the side walls. In one of its panels a very singular figure riveted my whole attention. It was the painted picture of Time as he is commonly represented, save that, in lieu of a scythe, he held what, at a casual glance, I supposed to be the pictured image of a huge pendulum, such as we see on antique clocks. There was something, however, in the appearance of this machine which caused me to regard it more attentively. While I gazed directly upward at it, (for its position was immediately over my own,) I fancied that I saw it in motion. In an instant afterward the fancy was confirmed. Its sweep was brief, and of course slow. I watched it for some minutes, somewhat in fear, but more in wonder. Wearied at length with observing its dull movement, I turned my eyes upon the other objects in the cell.

A slight noise attracted my notice, and, looking to the floor, I saw several enormous rats traversing it. They had issued from the well, which lay just within view to my right. Even then, while I gazed, they came up in troops, hurriedly, with ravenous eyes, allured by the scent of the meat. From this it required much effort and attention to scare them away.

It might have been half an hour, perhaps even an hour, (for I could take but imperfect note of time,) before I again cast my eyes upward. What I then saw confounded and amazed me. The sweep of the pendulum had increased in extent by nearly a yard. As a natural consequence, its velocity was also much greater. But what mainly disturbed me was the idea that it had perceptibly *descended*. I now observed—with what horror it is needless to say—that its nether extremity was formed of a crescent of glittering steel, about a foot in length from horn to horn; the horns upward, and the under edge evidently as keen as that of a razor. Like a razor also, it seemed massy and heavy, tapering from the edge into a solid and broad structure above. It was appended to a weighty rod of brass, and the whole *hissed* as it swung through the air.

I could no longer doubt the doom prepared for me by monkish ingenuity in torture. My cognizance of the pit had become known to the inquisitorial agents—the *pit* whose horrors had been destined for so bold a recusant as myself—the *pit*, typical of hell, and regarded by rumor as the Ultima Thule of all their punishments. The plunge into this pit I had avoided by the merest of accidents, and I knew that surprise, or entrapment into torment, formed an important portion of all the grotesquerie of these dungeon deaths. Having failed to fall, it was no part of the demon plan to hurl me into the abyss; and thus (there being no alternative) a different and a milder destruction awaited me. Milder! I half smiled in my agony as I thought of such application of such a term.

What boots it to tell of the long, long hours of horror more than mortal, during which I counted the rushing vibrations of the steel! Inch by inch—line by line—with a descent only appreciable at intervals that seemed ages—down and still down it came! Days passed—it might have been that many days passed—ere it swept so closely over me as to fan me with its acrid breath. The odor of the sharp steel forced itself into my nostrils. I prayed—I wearied heaven with my prayer for its more speedy descent. I grew frantically mad, and struggled to force myself upward against the sweep of the fearful scimitar. And then I fell suddenly calm, and lay smiling at the glittering death, as a child at some rare bauble.

There was another interval of utter insensibility; it was brief; for, upon again lapsing into life there had been no perceptible descent in the pendulum. But it might have been long—for I knew there were demons who took note of my swoon, and who could have arrested the vibration at pleasure. Upon my recovery, too, I felt very—oh, inexpressibly—sick and weak, as if through long inanition. Even amid the agonies of that period, the human nature craved food. With painful effort I outstretched my left arm as far as my bonds permitted, and took possession of the small remnant which had been spared me by the rats. As I put a portion of it within my lips, there rushed to my mind a half formed thought of joy—of hope. Yet what business had *I* with hope? It was, as I say, a half formed thought— man has many such, which are never completed. I felt that it was of joy —of hope; but I felt also that it had perished in its formation. In vain I struggled to perfect—to regain it. Long suffering had nearly annihilated all my ordinary powers of mind. I was an imbecile—an idiot.

The vibration of the pendulum was at right angles to my length. I saw that the crescent was designed to cross the region of the heart. It would fray the serge of my robe—it would return and repeat its operations— again—and again. Notwithstanding its terrifically wide sweep, (some thirty feet or more,) and the hissing vigor of its descent, sufficient to sunder these very walls of iron, still the fraying of my robe would be all that, for several minutes, it would accomplish. And at this thought I paused. I dared not go farther than this reflection. I dwelt upon it with a pertinacity of attention— as if, in so dwelling, I could arrest *here* the descent of the steel. I forced myself to ponder upon the sound of the crescent as it should pass across the garment—upon the peculiar thrilling sensation which the friction of cloth produces on the nerves. I pondered upon all this frivolity until my teeth were on edge.

Down—steadily down it crept. I took a frenzied pleasure in contrasting its downward with its lateral velocity. To the right—to the left—far and wide—with the shriek of a damned spirit! To my heart, with the stealthy pace of the tiger! I alternately laughed and howled, as the one or the other idea grew predominant.

Down—certainly, relentlessly down! It vibrated within three inches of my bosom! I struggled violently—furiously—to free my left arm. This was free only from the elbow to the hand. I could reach the latter, from the platter beside me, to my mouth, with great effort, but no farther. Could I have broken the fastenings above the elbow, I would have seized and attempted to arrest the pendulum. I might as well have attempted to arrest an avalanche!

Down—still unceasingly—still inevitably down! I gasped and struggled at each vibration. I shrunk convulsively at its every sweep. My eyes followed its outward or upward whirls with the eagerness of the most unmeaning despair; they closed themselves spasmodically at the descent, although death would have been a relief, oh, how unspeakable! Still I quivered in every nerve to think how slight a sinking of the machinery would precipitate that keen, glistening axe upon my bosom. It was *hope* that prompted the nerve to quiver—the frame to shrink. It was *hope*—the hope that triumphs on the rack—that whispers to the death-condemned even in the dungeon of the Inquisition.

I saw that some ten or twelve vibrations would bring the steel in actual contact with my robe—and with this observation there suddenly came over my spirit all the keen, collected calmness of despair. For the first time during many hours—or perhaps days—I *thought*. It now occurred to me, that the bandage, or surcingle, which enveloped me, was *unique*. I was tied by no separate cord. The first stroke of the razor-like crescent athwart any portion of the band, would so detach it that it might be unwound from my person by means of my left hand. But how fearful, in that case, the proximity of the steel! The result of the slightest struggle, how deadly! Was it likely, moreover, that the minions of the torturer had not foreseen and provided for this possibility? Was it probable that the bandage crossed my bosom in the track of the pendulum? Dreading to find my faint, and, as it seemed, my last hope frustrated, I so far elevated my head as to obtain a distinct view of my breast. The surcingle enveloped my limbs and body close in all directions—*save in the path of the destroying crescent.*

Scarcely had I dropped my head back into its original position, when there flashed upon my mind what I cannot better describe than as the unformed half of that idea of deliverance to which I have previously alluded, and of which a moiety only floated indeterminately through my brain when I raised food to my burning lips. The whole thought was now present—feeble, scarcely sane, scarcely definite—but still entire. I proceeded at once, with the nervous energy of despair, to attempt its execution.

For many hours the immediate vicinity of the low framework upon which I lay, had been literally swarming with rats. They were wild, bold, ravenous—their red eyes glaring upon me as if they waited but for motion-lessness on my part to make me their prey. "To what food," I thought, "have they been accustomed in the well?"

They had devoured, in spite of all my efforts to prevent them, all but a small remnant of the contents of the dish. I had fallen into an habitual see-saw, or wave of the hand about the platter, and, at length, the unconscious uniformity of the movement deprived it of effect. In their voracity, the vermin frequently fastened their sharp fangs in my fingers. With the parti-cles of the oily and spicy viand which now remained, I thoroughly rubbed the bandage wherever I could reach it; then, raising my hand from the floor, I lay breathlessly still.

At first, the ravenous animals were startled and terrified at the change—at the cessation of movement. They shrank alarmedly back; many sought the well. But this was only for a moment. I had not counted in vain upon their voracity. Observing that I remained without motion, one or two of the boldest leaped upon the framework, and smelt at the surcingle. This seemed the signal for a general rush. Forth from the well they hurried in fresh troops. They clung to the wood—they overran it, and leaped in hun-dreds upon my person. The measured movement of the pendulum dis-turbed them not at all. Avoiding its strokes they busied themselves with the anointed bandage. They pressed—they swarmed upon me in ever accumu-lating heaps. They writhed upon my throat; their cold lips sought my own; I was half stifled by their thronging pressure; disgust, for which the world has no name, swelled my bosom, and chilled, with a heavy clamminess, my heart. Yet one minute, and I felt that the struggle would be over. Plainly I perceived the loosening of the bandage. I knew that in more than one place it must be already severed. With a more than human resolution I lay *still*.

Nor had I erred in my calculations—nor had I endured in vain. I at length felt that I was *free*. The surcingle hung in ribands from my body. But the stroke of the pendulum already pressed upon my bosom. It had di-vided the serge of the robe. It had cut through the linen beneath. Twice again it swung, and a sharp sense of pain shot through every nerve. But the moment of escape had arrived. At a wave of my hand my deliverers hurried tumultuously away. With a steady movement—cautious, sidelong, shrink-ing, and slow—I slid from the embrace of the bandage and beyond the reach of the scimitar. For the moment, at least, *I was free*.

Free!—and in the grasp of the Inquisition! I had scarcely stepped from my wooden bed of horror upon the stone floor of the prison, when the motion of the hellish machine ceased and I beheld it drawn up, by some in-visible force, through the ceiling. This was a lesson which I took desper-ately to heart. My every motion was undoubtedly watched. Free!—I had but escaped death in one form of agony, to be delivered unto worse than death in some other. With that thought I rolled my eyes nervously around on the barriers of iron that hemmed me in. Something unusual—some change which, at first, I could not appreciate distinctly—it was obvious, had taken place in the apartment. For many minutes of a dreamy and trembling abstraction, I busied myself in vain, unconnected conjecture. During this period, I became aware, for the first time, of the origin of the sulphurous light which illumined the cell. It proceeded from a fissure, about half an inch in width, extending entirely around the prison at the base of the walls, which thus appeared, and, were completely separated from the floor. I endeavored, but of course in vain, to look through the aperture.

As I arose from the attempt, the mystery of the alteration in the chamber broke at once upon my understanding. I had observed that, although the outlines of the figures upon the walls were sufficiently distinct, yet the colors seemed blurred and indefinite. These colors had now assumed, and were momentarily assuming, a startling and most intense brilliancy, that gave to the spectral and fiendish portraitures an aspect that might have thrilled even firmer nerves than my own. Demon eyes, of a wild and ghastly vivacity, glared upon me in a thousand directions, where none had been visible before, and gleamed with the lurid lustre of a fire that I could not force my imagination to regard as unreal.

Unreal!—Even while I breathed there came to my nostrils the breath of the vapour of heated iron! A suffocating odour pervaded the prison! A deeper glow settled each moment in the eyes that glared at my agonies! A richer tint of crimson diffused itself over the pictured horrors of blood. I panted! I gasped for breath! There could be no doubt of the design of my tormentors—oh! most unrelenting! oh! most demoniac of men! I shrank from the glowing metal to the centre of the cell. Amid the thought of the fiery destruction that impended, the idea of the coolness of the well came over my soul like balm. I rushed to its deadly brink. I threw my straining vision below. The glare from the enkindled roof illumined its inmost recesses. Yet, for a wild moment, did my spirit refuse to comprehend the meaning of what I saw. At length it forced—it wrestled its way into my soul—it burned itself in upon my shuddering reason. Oh! for a voice to speak!—oh! horror!—oh! any horror but this! With a shriek, I rushed from the margin, and buried my face in my hands—weeping bitterly.

The heat rapidly increased, and once again I looked up, shuddering as with a fit of the ague. There had been a second change in the cell—and now the change was obviously in the *form*. As before, it was in vain that I at first endeavored to appreciate or understand what was taking place. But not long was I left in doubt. The Inquisitorial vengeance had been hurried by my two-fold escape, and there was to be no more dallying with the King of Terrors. The room had been square. I saw that two of its iron angles were now acute—two, consequently, obtuse. The fearful difference quickly increased with a low rumbling or moaning sound. In an instant the apartment had shifted its form into that of a lozenge. But the alteration stopped not here—I neither hoped nor desired it to stop. I could have clasped the red walls to my bosom as a garment of eternal peace. "Death," I said, "any death but that of the pit!" Fool! might I have not known that *into the pit* it was the object of the burning iron to urge me? Could I resist its glow? Or, if even that, could I withstand its pressure? And now, flatter and flatter grew the lozenge, with a rapidity that left me no time for contemplation. Its centre, and of course, its greatest width, came just over the yawning gulf. I shrank back—but the closing walls pressed me resistlessly onward. At length for my seared and writhing body there was no longer an inch of foothold on the firm floor of the prison. I struggled no more, but the agony of my soul found vent in one loud, long, and final scream of despair. I felt that I tottered upon the brink—I averted my eyes—

There was a discordant hum of human voices! There was a loud blast as of many trumpets! There was a harsh grating as of a thousand thunders! The fiery walls rushed back! An outstretched arm caught my own as I fell, fainting, into the abyss. It was that of General Lasalle. The French army had entered Toledo. The Inquisition was in the hands of its enemies.

11

The Guilty Conscience

To sit alone with my conscience
Will be judgment enough for me.
Conscience and Future Judgment
Charles William Stubbs

Thus conscience does make cowards of us all.
Hamlet
William Shakespeare

Justice is a temporary thing that must at last come to an end;
but the conscience is eternal and will never die.
On Marriage
Martin Luther

In stating that our legal system needs to incorporate extensive means of punishment in order to maintain law and order, we are assuming that many individuals are inherently bad rather than inherently good. Yet, in spite of a court system that is overburdened with criminal defendants, the majority of the population travels through life with little more than a parking fine or a speeding ticket. What is it then that makes most people obedient to the law while others transgress the legal code without remorse?

In the section entitled "Criminality from a Sense of Guilt," from his work *Character and Culture*, Freud tells us that "in their narrations about their early years, particularly before puberty, people who have afterwards become very upright have told me of forbidden actions that they had formerly committed—such as thefts, frauds, and even arson." In studying those cases Freud came to the

surupising conclusion that such deeds are done precisely *because* they are forbidden, and because by carrying them out the doer enjoys a sense of mental relief. He suffered from an oppressive feeling of guilt, of which he did not know the origin, and after he had committed a misdeed the oppression was mitigated. The sense of guilt was at least in some way accounted for.

To Freud, humankind has an "obscure sense of guilt" that it cannot identify or understand but which "derives from the Oedipus-complex and is a reaction to the two great criminal intentions of killing the father and having sexual relations with the mother." Interestingly, the antithesis of Freud's theory concerning the character type who commits a criminal act to mitigate a preexisting feeling of guilt is the character type whose highly developed superego leads to control of criminal impulses. This theory finds its roots in Freud's theory of the development of the psyche, which is divided into three parts—id, ego, and superego. As one psychology professor described it: Picture if you will a big chocolate cake that is forbidden on your diet. Your id says "eat it all," your superego says "don't touch it," and your ego says "eat a small slice." The superego is responsible for what we know as the guilty conscience, the thinking that keeps most of us out of trouble with the law. Ironically, according to Freud, it is an overdeveloped superego that leads some people to carry out criminal or forbidden acts. To lend support to his own work, Freud mentions that in the section entitled "On the Pale Criminal," from Zarathustra, Nietzsche also recognized "the pre-existence of the guilty consciousness and the efficacy of the deed in rationalizing this feeling." Unfortunately for humankind, if Freud and Nietzsche are correct, then people's actions are predetermined by the early development of their psyche and by the resulting restraining or overdeveloped superego. Some people are led into a life of crime in order to relieve a preexisting sense of guilt, and yet others go through life as law-abiding citizens.

Edgar Allan Poe's short story "The Tell-Tale Heart" is a morbid and fascinating account of a guilty conscience in action. If everyone had such highly developed guilty consciences as the story's protagonist does, legal trials would be unnecessary for the purpose of determining guilt and innocence. Even if the superego failed to hold the reigns on a forbidden impulse, such a highly developed guilty conscience would lead the perpetrator to "admit the deed."

Interestingly Poe's fascination with guilt and innocence led him to a similar conclusion as that postulated by Freud and Nietzsche. Notice that the narrator mentions that there was no object of passion to this crime; that he does not know how the idea entered his brain, but that, "once conceived, it haunted [him] day and night." The narrator also informs the reader that his objective was not robbery. Could it be that this protagonist demonstrates the tendency of "One of the Pale Ones" who gives vent to his impulses in order to relieve a preexisting sense of guilt?

If Poe's protagonist represents "One of the Pale Ones," then the protagonist, Parson Hooper, in Nathaniel Hawthorne's tale "The Minister's Black Veil" represents one person whose highly developed superego has led not to the carrying out of criminal acts but to a restraint that hampers the reality testing of his ego. Not satisfied with merely doing penance for his own sins, Parson Hooper wears the black veil as a symbol of the collective guilt of all of humankind.

The Tell-Tale Heart
Edgar Allan Poe

True!—nervous—very, very dreadfully nervous I had been and am; but why *will* you say that I am mad? The disease had sharpened my senses—not destroyed—not dulled them. Above all was the sense of hearing acute. I heard all things in the heaven and in the earth. I heard many things in hell. How, then, am I mad? Hearken! and observe how healthily—how calmly I can tell you the whole story.

Now this is the point. You fancy me mad. Madmen know nothing. But you should have seen *me*. You should have seen how wisely I proceeded—with what caution—with what foresight—with what dissimulation I went to work! I was never kinder to the old man than during the whole week before I killed him. And every night, about midnight, I turned the latch of his door and opened it—oh, so gently! And then, when I had made an opening sufficient for my head, I put in a dark lantern, all closed, closed, so that no light shone out, and then I thrust in my head. Oh, you would have laughed to see how cunningly I thrust it in! I moved it slowly—very, very slowly, so that I might not disturb the old man's sleep. It took me an hour to place my whole head within the opening so far that I could see him as he lay upon his bed. Ha!—would a madman have been so wise as this? And then, when my head was well in the room, I undid the lantern cautiously—oh, so cautiously—cautiously (for the hinges creaked)—and I undid it just so much that a single thin ray fell upon the vulture eye. And this I did for seven long nights—every night just at midnight—but I found the eye always closed; and so it was impossible to do the work; for it was not the old man who vexed me, but his Evil Eye. And every morning, when the day broke, I went boldly into the chamber, and spoke courageously to him, calling him by name in a hearty tone, and inquiring how he had passed the night. So you see he would have been a very profound old man, indeed, to suspect that every night, just at twelve, I looked in upon him while he slept.

Upon the eighth night I was more than usually cautious in opening the door. A watch's minute-hand moves more quickly than did mine. Never before that night had I *felt* the extent of my own powers—of my sagacity. I could scarcely contain my feelings of triumph. To think that there I was, opening the door, little by little, and he not even to dream of my secret deeds or thoughts. I fairly chuckled at the idea; and perhaps he heard me; for he moved on the bed suddenly, as if startled. Now you may think that I drew back—but no. His room was as black as pitch with the thick darkness, (for the shutters were close fastened through fear of robbers,) and so I knew that he could not see the opening of the door, and I kept pushing it on steadily, steadily.

I had my head in, and was about to open the lantern, when my thumb slipped upon the tin fastening, and the old man sprang up in the bed, crying out—"Who's there?"

I kept quite still and said nothing. For a whole hour I did not move a muscle, and in the mean time I did not hear him lie down. He was still sitting up in the bed, listening: just as I have done, night after night, hearkening to the death-watches in the wall.

Presently I heard a slight groan, and I knew it was the groan of mortal terror. It was not a groan of pain or of grief—oh, no!—it was the low stifled sound that arises from the bottom of the soul when overcharged with awe. I knew the sound well. Many a night, just at midnight, when all the world slept, it has welled up from my own bosom, deepening, with its dreadful echo, the terrors that distracted me. I say I knew it well. I knew what the old man felt, and pitied him, although I chuckled at heart. I knew that he had been lying awake ever since the first slight noise, when he had turned in the bed. His fears had been ever since growing upon him. He had been trying to fancy them causeless, but could not. He had been saying to himself—"It is nothing but the wind in the chimney—it is only a mouse crossing the floor," or "it is merely a cricket which has made a single chirp." Yes, he had been trying to comfort himself with these suppositions; but he had found all in vain. *All in vain*; because Death, in approaching him, had stalked with his black shadow before him, and enveloped the victim. And it was the mournful influence of the unperceived shadow that caused him to feel—although he neither saw nor heard—to *feel* the presence of my head within the room.

When I had waited a long time, very patiently, without hearing him lie down, I resolved to open a little—a very, very little crevice in the lantern. So I opened it—you cannot imagine how stealthily, stealthily—until, at length, a single dim ray, like the thread of the spider, shot from out the crevice and fell upon the vulture eye.

It was open—wide, wide open—and I grew furious as I gazed upon it. I saw it with perfect distinctness—all a dull blue, with a hideous veil over it that chilled the very marrow in my bones; but I could see nothing else of the old man's face or person: for I had directed the ray as if by instinct, precisely upon the damned spot.

And now have I not told you that what you mistake for madness is but over acuteness of the senses?—now, I say, there came to my ears *a low, dull, quick sound, much such a sound as a watch makes when enveloped in cotton*. I knew *that* sound well, too. It was the beating of the old man's heart. It increased my fury, as the beating of a drum stimulates the soldier into courage.

But even yet I refrained and kept still. I scarcely breathed. I held that lantern motionless. I tried how steadily I could maintain the ray upon the eye. Meantime the hellish tattoo of the heart increased. It grew quicker and quicker, and louder and louder every instant. The old man's terror *must* have been extreme! It grew louder, I say, louder every moment!—do you mark me well? I have told you that I am nervous; so I am. And now at the dead hour of the night, amid the dreadful silence of that old house, so strange a noise as this excited me to uncontrollable terror. Yet, for some minutes longer I refrained and stood still. But the beating grew louder, louder! I thought the heart must burst. And now a new anxiety seized me—the sound would be heard by a neighbor! The old man's hour had come! With a loud yell, I threw open the lantern and leaped into the room. He shrieked once—once only. In an instant I dragged him to the floor, and pulled the heavy bed over him. I then smiled gayly, to find the deed so far done. But, for many minutes, the heart beat on with a muffled sound. This, however, did not vex me; it would not be heard through the wall. At length it ceased. The old man was dead. I removed the bed and examined the corpse. Yes, he was stone, stone dead. I placed my hand upon the heart and held it there many minutes. There was no pulsation. He was stone dead. His eye would trouble me no more.

If you still think me mad, you will think so no longer when I describe the wise precautions I took for the concealment of the body. The night waned, and I worked hastily, but in silence. First of all I dismembered the corpse. I cut off the head and the arms and the legs.

I then took up three planks from the flooring of the chamber, and deposited all between the scantlings. I then replaced the boards so cleverly, so cunningly, that no human eye—not even *his*,—could have detected anything wrong. There was nothing to wash out—no stain of any kind—no blood-spot whatever. I had been too wary for that. A tub had caught all—ha! ha!

When I had made an end of these labors, it was four o'clock—still dark as midnight. As the bell sounded the hour, there came a knocking at the street door. I went down to open it with a light heart,—for what had I *now* to fear? There entered three men, who introduced themselves, with perfect suavity, as officers of the police. A shriek had been heard by a neighbor during the night; suspicion of foul play had been aroused; information had been lodged at the police office, and they (the officers) had been deputed to search the premises.

I smiled,—for what had I to fear? I bade the gentlemen welcome. The shriek, I said, was my own in a dream. The old man, I mentioned, was absent in the country. I took my visitors all over the house. I bade them search—search *well*. I led them, at length, to *his* chamber. I showed them his treasures, secure, undisturbed. In the enthusiasm of my confidence, I brought chairs into the room, and desired them *here* to rest from their fatigues, while I myself, in the wild audacity of my perfect triumph, placed my own seat upon the very spot beneath which reposed the corpse of the victim.

The officers were satisfied. My manner had convinced them. I was singularly at ease. They sat, and while I answered cheerily, they chatted of familiar things. But, ere long, I felt myself getting pale and wished them gone. My head ached, and I fancied a ringing in my ears: but still they sat and still chatted. The ringing became more distinct: it continued and became more distinct: I talked more freely to get rid of the feeling: but it continued and gained definitiveness—until, at length, I found that the noise was *not* within my ears.

No doubt I now grew *very* pale; but I talked more fluently, and with a heightened voice. Yet the sound increased—and what could I do? It was *a low, dull, quick sound—much such a sound as a watch makes when enveloped in cotton.* I gasped for breath—and yet the officers heard it not. I talked more quickly—more vehemently; but the noise steadily increased. I arose and argued about trifles, in a high key, and with violent gesticulations; but the noise steadily increased. Why *would* they not be gone? I paced the floor to and fro with heavy strides, as if excited to fury by the observations of the men—but the noise steadily increased. Oh God! what *could* I do? I foamed—I raved—I swore! I swung the chair upon which I had been sitting, and grated it upon the boards, but the noise arose over all and continually increased. It grew louder—louder—*louder*! And still the men chatted pleasantly, and smiled. Was it possible they heard not? Almighty God!—no, no! They heard!—they suspected!—they *knew*!—they were making a mockery of my horror!—this I thought, and this I think. But anything was better than this agony! Anything was more tolerable than this derision! I could bear those hypocritical smiles no longer! I felt that I must scream or die!—and now—again!—hark! louder! louder! louder! *louder*!—

"Villains!" I shrieked, "dissemble no more! I admit the deed!—tear up the planks!—here, here!—it is the beating of his hideous heart!"

The Minister's Black Veil
Nathaniel Hawthorne

The sexton stood in the porch of Milford meeting-house, pulling busily at
the bell-rope. The old people of the village came stooping along the street.
Children, with bright faces, tripped merrily beside their parents, or mim-
icked a graver gait, in the conscious dignity of their Sunday clothes. Spruce
bachelors looked sidelong at the pretty maidens, and fancied that the Sabbath sunshine made them prettier than on week days. When the throng had
mostly streamed into the porch, the sexton began to toll the bell, keeping his
eye on the Reverend Mr. Hooper's door. The first glimpse of the clergyman's figure was the signal for the bell to cease its summons.

"But what has good Parson Hooper got upon his face?" cried the
sexton in astonishment.

All within hearing immediately turned about, and beheld the semblance of Mr. Hooper, pacing slowly his meditative way towards the
meeting-house. With one accord they started, expressing more wonder than
if some strange minister were coming to dust the cushions of Mr. Hooper's
pulpit.

"Are you sure it is our parson?" inquired Goodman Gray of the
sexton.

"Of a certainty it is good Mr. Hooper," replied the sexton. "He was
to have exchanged pulpits with Parson Shute, of Westbury; but Parson
Shute sent to excuse himself yesterday, being to preach a funeral sermon."

The cause of so much amazement may appear sufficiently slight.
Mr. Hooper, a gentlemanly person, of about thirty, though still a bachelor,
was dressed with due clerical neatness, as if a careful wife had starched his
band, and brushed the weekly dust from his Sunday's garb. There was but
one thing remarkable in his appearance. Swathed about his forehead, and
hanging down over his face, so low as to be shaken by his breath, Mr.
Hooper had on a black veil. On a nearer view it seemed to consist of two
folds of crape, which entirely concealed his features, except the mouth and
chin, but probably did not intercept his sight, further than to give a darkened
aspect to all living and inanimate things. With this gloomy shade before
him, good Mr. Hooper walked onward, at a slow and quiet pace, stooping
somewhat, and looking on the ground, as is customary with abstracted
men, yet nodding kindly to those of his parishioners who still waited on the

meeting-house steps. But so wonder-struck were they that his greeting hardly met with a return.

"I can't really feel as if good Mr. Hooper's face was behind that piece of crape," said the sexton.

"I don't like it," muttered an old woman, as she hobbled into the meeting-house. "He has changed himself into something awful, only by hiding his face."

"Our parson has gone mad!" cried Goodman Gray, following him across the threshold.

A rumor of some unaccountable phenomenon had preceded Mr. Hooper into the meeting-house, and set all the congregation astir. Few could refrain from twisting their heads towards the door; many stood upright, and turned directly about; while several little boys clambered upon the seats, and came down again with a terrible racket. There was a general bustle, a rustling of the women's gowns and shuffling of the men's feet, greatly at variance with that hushed repose which should attend the entrance of the minister. But Mr. Hooper appeared not to notice the perturbation of his people. He entered with an almost noiseless step, bent his head mildly to the pews on each side, and bowed as he passed his oldest parishioner, a white-haired great-grandsire, who occupied an arm-chair in the centre of the aisle. It was strange to observe how slowly this venerable man became conscious of something singular in the appearance of his pastor. He seemed not fully to partake of the prevailing wonder, till Mr. Hooper had ascended the stairs, and showed himself in the pulpit, face to face with his congregation, except for the black veil. That mysterious emblem was never once withdrawn. It shook with his measured breath, as he gave out the psalm; it threw its obscurity between him and the holy page, as he read the Scriptures; and while he prayed, the veil lay heavily on his uplifted countenance. Did he seek to hide it from the dread Being whom he was addressing?

Such was the effect of this simple piece of crape, that more than one woman of delicate nerves was forced to leave the meeting-house. Yet perhaps the pale-faced congregation was almost as fearful a sight to the minister, as his black veil was to them.

Mr. Hooper had the reputation of a good preacher, but not an energetic one: he strove to win his people heavenward by mild, persuasive influences, rather than to drive them thither by the thunders of the Word. The sermon which he now delivered was marked by the same characteristics of style and manner as the general series of his pulpit oratory. But there was something, either in the sentiment of the discourse itself, or in the imagination of the auditors, which made it greatly the most powerful effort that they had ever heard from their pastor's lips. It was tinged, rather more darkly than usual, with the gentle gloom of Mr. Hooper's temperament. The subject had reference to secret sin, and those sad mysteries which we hide from our nearest and dearest, and would fain conceal from our own consciousness, even forgetting that the Omniscient can detect them. A subtle power was breathed into his words. Each member of the congregation, the most innocent girl, and the man of hardened breast, felt as if the preacher had crept upon them, behind his awful veil, and discovered their hoarded iniquity of deed or thought. Many spread their clasped hands on their bosoms. There was nothing terrible in what Mr. Hooper said, at least, no violence; and yet, with every tremor of his melancholy voice, the hearers quaked. An unsought pathos came hand in hand with awe. So sensible were the audience of some unwonted attribute in their minister, that they longed for a breath of wind to blow aside the veil, almost believing that a stranger's visage would be discovered, though the form, gesture, and voice were those of Mr. Hooper.

At the close of the services, the people hurried out with indecorous confusion, eager to communicate their pent-up amazement, and conscious of lighter spirits the moment they lost sight of the black veil. Some gathered in little circles, huddled closely together, with their mouths all whispering in the centre; some went homeward alone, wrapt in silent meditation; some talked loudly, and profaned the Sabbath day with ostentatious laughter. A few shook their sagacious heads, intimating that they could penetrate the mystery; while one or two affirmed that there was no mystery at all, but only that Mr. Hooper's eyes were so weakened by the midnight lamp, as to require a shade. After a brief interval, forth came good Mr. Hooper also, in the rear of his flock. Turning his veiled face from one group to another, he paid due reverence to the hoary heads, saluted the middle aged with kind dignity as their friend and spiritual guide, greeted the young with mingled authority and love, and laid his hands on the little children's heads to bless them. Such was always his custom on the Sabbath day. Strange and bewildered looks repaid him for his courtesy. None, as on former occasions, aspired to the honor of walking by their pastor's side. Old Squire Saunders, doubtless by an accidental lapse of memory, neglected to invite Mr. Hooper to his table, where the good clergyman had been wont to bless the food, almost every Sunday since his settlement. He returned, therefore, to the parsonage, and, at the moment of closing the door, was observed to look back upon the people, all of whom had their eyes fixed upon the minister. A sad smile gleamed faintly from beneath the black veil, and flickered about his mouth, glimmering as he disappeared.

"How strange," said a lady, "that a simple black veil, such as any woman might wear on her bonnet, should become such a terrible thing on Mr. Hooper's face!"

"Something must surely be amiss with Mr. Hooper's intellects," observed her husband, the physician of the village. "But the strangest part of the affair is the effect of this vagary, even on a sober-minded man like myself. The black veil, though it covers only our pastor's face, throws its influence over his whole person, and makes him ghostlike from head to foot. Do you not feel it so?"

"Truly do I," replied the lady; "and I would not be alone with him for the world. I wonder he is not afraid to be alone with himself!"

"Men sometimes are so," said her husband.

The afternoon service was attended with similar circumstances. At its conclusion, the bell tolled for the funeral of a young lady. The relatives and friends were assembled in the house, and the more distant acquaintances stood about the door, speaking of the good qualities of the deceased, when their talk was interrupted by the appearance of Mr. Hooper, still cov-

ered with his black veil. It was now an appropriate emblem. The clergyman stepped into the room where the corpse was laid, and bent over the
coffin, to take a last farewell of his deceased parishioner. As he stooped,
the veil hung straight down from his forehead, so that, if her eyelids had not
been closed forever, the dead maiden might have seen his face. Could Mr.
Hooper be fearful of her glance, that he so hastily caught back the black
veil? A person who watched the interview between the dead and living,
scrupled not to affirm, that, at the instant when the clergyman's features
were disclosed, the corpse had slightly shuddered, rustling the shroud and
muslin cap, though the countenance retained the composure of death. A superstitious old woman was the only witness of this prodigy. From the coffin Mr. Hooper passed into the chamber of the mourners, and thence to the
head of the staircase, to make the funeral prayer. It was a tender and heart-
dissolving prayer, full of sorrow, yet so imbued with celestial hopes, that
the music of a heavenly harp, swept by the fingers of the dead, seemed
faintly to be heard among the saddest accents of the minister. The people
trembled, though they but darkly understood him when he prayed that they,
and himself, and all of mortal race, might be ready, as he trusted this young
maiden had been, for the dreadful hour that should snatch the veil from their
faces. The bearers went heavily forth, and the mourners followed, sadden-
ing all the street, with the dead before them, and Mr. Hooper in his black
veil behind.

"Why do you look back?" said one in the procession to his partner.

"I had a fancy," replied she, "that the minister and the maiden's
spirit were walking hand in hand."

"And so had I, at the same moment," said the other.

That night, the handsomest couple in Milford village were to be
joined in wedlock. Though reckoned a melancholy man, Mr. Hooper had a
placid cheerfulness for such occasions, which often excited a sympathetic
smile where livelier merriment would have been thrown away. There was
no quality of his disposition which made him more beloved than this. The
company at the wedding awaited his arrival with impatience, trusting that
the strange awe, which had gathered over him throughout the day, would
now be dispelled. But such was not the result. When Mr. Hooper came,
the first thing that their eyes rested on was the same horrible black veil,
which had added deeper gloom to the funeral, and could portend nothing
but evil to the wedding. Such was its immediate effect on the guests that a
cloud seemed to have rolled duskily from beneath the black crepe, and
dimmed the light of the candles. The bridal pair stood up before the minister. But the bride's cold fingers quivered in the tremulous hand of the
bridegroom, and her deathlike paleness caused a whisper that the maiden
who had been buried a few hours before was come from her grave to be
married. If ever another wedding were so dismal, it was that famous one
where they tolled the wedding knell. After performing the ceremony, Mr.
Hooper raised a glass of wine to his lips, wishing happiness to the new-
married couple in a strain of mild pleasantry that ought to have brightened
the features of the guests, like a cheerful gleam from the hearth. At that
moment, catching a glimpse of his figure in the looking-glass, the black veil
involved his own spirit in the horror with which it overwhelmed all others.

His frame shuddered, his lips grew white, he spilt the untasted wine upon the carpet, and rushed forth into the darkness. For the Earth, too, had on her Black Veil.

The next day, the whole village of Milford talked of little else than Parson Hooper's black veil. That, and the mystery concealed behind it, supplied a topic for discussion between acquaintances meeting in the street, and good women gossiping at their open windows. It was the first item of news that the tavern-keeper told to his guests. The children babbled of it on their way to school. One imitative little imp covered his face with an old black handkerchief, thereby so affrighting his playmates that the panic seized himself, and he well-nigh lost his wits by his own waggery.

It was remarkable that of all the busybodies and impertinent people in the parish, not one ventured to put the plain question to Mr. Hooper, wherefore he did this thing. Hitherto, whenever there appeared the slightest call for such interference, he had never lacked advisers, nor shown himself averse to be guided by their judgment. If he erred at all, it was by so painful a degree of self-distrust, that even the mildest censure would lead him to consider an indifferent action as a crime. Yet, though so well acquainted with this amiable weakness, no individual among his parishioners chose to make the black veil a subject of friendly remonstrance. There was a feeling of dread, neither plainly confessed nor carefully concealed, which caused each to shift the responsibility upon another, till at length it was found expedient to send a deputation of the church, in order to deal with Mr. Hooper about the mystery, before it should grow into a scandal. Never did an embassy so ill discharge its duties. The minister received them with friendly courtesy, but became silent, after they were seated, leaving to his visitors the whole burden of introducing their important business. The topic, it might be supposed, was obvious enough. There was the black veil swathed round Mr. Hooper's forehead, and concealing every feature above his placid mouth, on which, at times, they could perceive the glimmering of a melancholy smile. But that piece of crape, to their imagination, seemed to hang down before his heart, the symbol of a fearful secret between him and them. Were the veil but cast aside, they might speak freely of it, but not till then. Thus they sat a considerable time, speechless, confused, and shrinking uneasily from Mr. Hooper's eye, which they felt to be fixed upon them with an invisible glance. Finally, the deputies returned abashed to their constituents, pronouncing the matter too weighty to be handled, except by a council of the churches, if, indeed, it might not require a general synod.

But there was one person in the village unappalled by the awe with which the black veil had impressed all beside herself. When the deputies returned without an explanation, or even venturing to demand one, she, with the calm energy of her character, determined to chase away the strange cloud that appeared to be settling round Mr. Hooper, every moment more darkly than before. As his plighted wife, it should be her privilege to know what the black veil concealed. At the minister's first visit, therefore, she entered upon the subject with a direct simplicity, which made the task easier both for him and her. After he had seated himself, she fixed her eyes steadfastly upon the veil, but could discern nothing of the dreadful gloom that had so overawed the multitude: it was but a double fold of crape, hanging down from his forehead to his mouth, and slightly stirring with his breath.

"No," said she aloud, and smiling, "there is nothing terrible in this piece of crape, except that it hides a face which I am always glad to look upon. Come, good sir, let the sun shine from behind the cloud. First lay aside your black veil: then tell me why you put it on."

Mr. Hooper's smile glimmered faintly.

"There is an hour to come," said he, "when all of us shall cast aside our veils. Take it not amiss, beloved friend, if I wear this piece of crape till then."

"Your words are a mystery, too," returned the young lady. "Take away the veil from them, at least."

"Elizabeth, I will," said he, "so far as my vow may suffer me. Know, then, this veil is a type and a symbol, and I am bound to wear it ever, both in light and darkness, in solitude and before the gaze of multitudes, and as with strangers, so with my familiar friends. No mortal eye will see it withdrawn. This dismal shade must separate me from the world: even you, Elizabeth, can never come behind it!"

"What grievous affliction hath befallen you," she earnestly inquired, "that you should thus darken your eyes forever?"

"If it be a sign of mourning," replied Mr. Hooper, "I, perhaps, like most other mortals, have sorrows dark enough to be typified by a black veil."

"But what if the world will not believe that it is the type of an innocent sorrow?" urged Elizabeth. "Beloved and respected as you are, there may be whispers that you hide your face under the consciousness of secret sin. For the sake of your holy office, do away this scandal!"

The color rose into her cheeks as she intimated the nature of the rumors that were already abroad in the village. But Mr. Hooper's mildness did not forsake him. He even smiled again—that same sad smile, which always appeared like a faint glimmering of light, proceeding from the obscurity beneath the veil.

"If I hide my face for sorrow, there is cause enough," he merely replied; "and if I cover it for secret sin, what mortal might not do the same?"

And with this gentle, but unconquerable obstinacy did he resist all her entreaties. At length Elizabeth sat silent. For a few moments she appeared lost in thought, considering, probably, what new methods might be tried to withdraw her lover from so dark a fantasy, which, if it had no other meaning, was perhaps a symptom of mental disease. Though of a firmer character than his own, the tears rolled down her cheeks. But, in an instant, as it were, a new feeling took the place of sorrow: her eyes were fixed insensibly on the black veil, when, like a sudden twilight in the air, its terrors fell around her. She arose, and stood trembling before him.

"And do you feel it then, at last?" said he mournfully.

She made no reply, but covered her eyes with her hand, and turned to leave the room. He rushed forward and caught her arm.

"Have patience with me, Elizabeth!" cried he, passionately. "Do not desert me, though this veil must be between us here on earth. Be mine, and hereafter there shall be no veil over my face, no darkness between our souls! It is but a mortal veil—it is not for eternity! O! you know not how lonely I am, and how frightened, to be alone behind my black veil. Do not leave me in this miserable obscurity forever!"

"Lift the veil but once, and look me in the face," said she.

"Never! It cannot be!" replied Mr. Hooper.

"Then farewell!" said Elizabeth.

She withdrew her arm from his grasp, and slowly departed, pausing at the door, to give one long shuddering gaze, that seemed almost to penetrate the mystery of the black veil. But, even amid his grief, Mr. Hooper smiled to think that only a material emblem had separated him from happiness, though the horrors, which it shadowed forth, must be drawn darkly between the fondest of lovers.

From that time no attempts were made to remove Mr. Hooper's black veil, or, by a direct appeal, to discover the secret which it was supposed to hide. By persons who claimed a superiority to popular prejudice, it was reckoned merely an eccentric whim, such as often mingles with the sober actions of men otherwise rational, and tinges them all with its own semblance of insanity. But with the multitude, good Mr. Hooper was irreparably a bugbear. He could not walk the street with any peace of mind, so conscious was he that the gentle and timid would turn aside to avoid him, and that others would make it a point of hardihood to throw themselves in his way. The impertinence of the latter class compelled him to give up his customary walk at sunset to the burial ground; for when he leaned pensively over the gate, there would always be faces behind the gravestones, peeping at his black veil. A fable went the rounds that the stare of the dead people drove him thence. It grieved him, to the very depth of his kind heart, to observe how the children fled from his approach, breaking up their merriest sports, while his melancholy figure was yet afar off. Their instinctive dread caused him to feel more strongly than aught else, that a preternatural horror was interwoven with the threads of the black crape. In truth, his own antipathy to the veil was known to be so great, that he never willingly passed before a mirror, nor stooped to drink at a still fountain, lest, in its peaceful bosom, he should be affrighted by himself. This was what gave plausibility to the whispers, that Mr. Hooper's conscience tortured him for some great crime too horrible to be entirely concealed, or otherwise than so obscurely intimated. Thus, from beneath the black veil, there rolled a cloud into the sunshine, an ambiguity of sin or sorrow, which enveloped the poor minister, so that love or sympathy could never reach him. It was said that ghost and fiend consorted with him there. With self-shudderings and outward terrors, he walked continually in its shadow, groping darkly within his own soul, or gazing through a medium that saddened the whole world. Even the lawless wind, it was believed, respected his dreadful secret, and never blew aside the veil. But still good Mr. Hooper sadly smiled at the pale visages of the worldly throng as he passed by.

Among all its bad influences, the black veil had the one desirable effect, of making its wearer a very efficient clergyman. By the aid of his mysterious emblem—for there was no other apparent cause—he became a man of awful power over souls that were in agony for sin. His converts always regarded him with a dread peculiar to themselves, affirming, though but figuratively, that, before he brought them to celestial light, they had been with him behind the black veil. Its gloom, indeed, enabled him to sympathize with all dark affections. Dying sinners cried aloud for Mr. Hooper, and would not yield their breath till he appeared; though ever, as he stooped to whisper consolation, they shuddered at the veiled face so near their own. Such were the terrors of the black veil, even when Death had bared his visage! Strangers came long distances to attend service at his church, with the mere idle purpose of gazing at his figure, because it was forbidden them to behold his face. But many were made to quake ere they departed! Once, during Governor Belcher's administration, Mr. Hooper was appointed to preach the election sermon. Covered with his black veil, he stood before the chief magistrate, the council, and the representatives, and brought so deep an impression, that the legislative measures of that year were characterized by all the gloom and pity of our earliest ancestral sway.

In this manner Mr. Hooper spent a long life, irreproachable in outward act, yet shrouded in dismal suspicions; kind and loving, though unloved, and dimly feared; a man apart from men, shunned in their health and joy, but ever summoned to their aid in mortal anguish. As years wore on, shedding their snows above his sable veil, he acquired a name throughout the New England churches, and they called him Father Hooper. Nearly all his parishioners, who were of mature age when he was settled, had been borne away by many a funeral: he had one congregation in the church, and a more crowded one in the churchyard; and having wrought so late into the evening, and done his work so well, it was now good Father Hooper's turn to rest.

Several persons were visible by the shaded candlelight, in the death chamber of the old clergyman. Natural connections he had none. But there was the decorously grave, though unmoved physician, seeking only to mitigate the last pangs of the patient whom he could not save. There were the deacons, and other eminently pious members of his church. There, also, was the Reverend Mr. Clark, of Westbury, a young and zealous divine, who had ridden in haste to pray by the bedside of the expiring minister. There was the nurse, no hired handmaiden of death, but one whose calm affection had endured thus long in secrecy, in solitude, amid the chill of age, and would not perish, even at the dying hour. Who, but Elizabeth! And there lay the hoary head of good Father Hooper upon the death pillow, with the black veil still swathed about his brow, and reaching down over his face, so that each more difficult gasp of his faint breath caused it to stir. All through life that piece of crape had hung between him and the world: it had separated him from cheerful brotherhood and woman's love, and kept him in that saddest of all prisons, his own heart; and still it lay upon his face, as if to deepen the gloom of his darksome chamber, and shade him from the sunshine of eternity.

For some time previous, his mind had been confused, wavering doubtfully between the past and the present, and hovering forward, as it were, at intervals, into the indistinctness of the world to come. There had been feverish turns, which tossed him from side to side, and wore away what little strength he had. But in his most convulsive struggles, and in the wildest vagaries of his intellect, when no other thought retained its sober influence, he still showed an awful solicitude lest the black veil should slip aside. Even if his bewildered soul could have forgotten, there was a faithful woman at his pillow, who, with averted eyes, would have covered that aged face, which she had last beheld in the comeliness of manhood. At length the death-stricken old man lay quietly in the torpor of mental and bodily exhaustion, with an imperceptible pulse, and breath that grew fainter and fainter, except when a long, deep, and irregular inspiration seemed to prelude the flight of his spirit.

The minister of Westbury approached the bedside.

"Venerable Father Hooper," said he, "the moment of your release is at hand. Are you ready for the lifting of the veil that shuts in time from eternity?"

Father Hooper at first replied merely by a feeble motion of his head; then, apprehensive, perhaps, that his meaning might be doubtful, he exerted himself to speak.

"Yea," said he, in faint accents, "my soul hath a patient weariness until that veil be lifted."

"And is it fitting," resumed the Reverend Mr. Clark, "that a man so given to prayer, of such a blameless example, holy in deed and thought, so far as mortal judgment may pronounce; is it fitting that a father in the church should leave a shadow on his memory, that may seem to blacken a life so pure? I pray you, my venerable brother, let not this thing be! Suffer us to be gladdened by your triumphant aspect as you go to your reward. Before the veil of eternity be lifted, let me cast aside this black veil from your face!"

And thus speaking, the Reverend Mr. Clark bent forward to reveal the mystery of so many years. But, exerting a sudden energy, that made all the beholders stand aghast, Father Hooper snatched both his hands from beneath the bedclothes, and pressed them strongly on the black veil, resolute to struggle, if the minister of Westbury would contend with a dying man.

"Never!" cried the veiled clergyman. "On earth, never!"

"Dark old man!" exclaimed the affrighted minister, "with what horrible crime upon your soul are you now passing to the judgment?"

Father Hooper's breath heaved; it rattled in his throat; but, with a mighty effort, grasping forward with his hands, he caught hold of life, and held it back till he should speak. He even raised himself in bed; and there he sat, shivering with the arms of death around him, while the black veil hung down, awful, at that last moment, in the gathered terrors of a lifetime. And yet the faint, sad smile, so often there, now seemed to glimmer from its obscurity, and linger on Father Hooper's lips.

"Why do you tremble at me alone?" cried he, turning his veiled face round the circle of pale spectators. "Tremble also at each other! Have men avoided me, and women shown no pity, and children screamed and fled, only for my black veil? What, but the mystery which it obscurely typifies, has made this piece of crape so awful? When the friend shows his inmost heart to his friend; the lover to his best beloved; when man does not vainly shrink from the eye of his Creator, loathsomely treasuring up the secret of his sin; then deem me a monster, for the symbol beneath which I have lived, and die! I look around me, and, lo! on every visage a Black Veil!"

While his auditors shrank from one another, in mutual affright,

Father Hooper fell back upon his pillow, a veiled corpse, with a faint smile lingering on the lips. Still veiled, they laid him in his coffin, and a veiled corpse they bore him to the grave. The grass of many years has sprung up and withered on that grave, the burial stone is moss-grown, and good Mr. Hooper's face is dust; but awful is still the thought that it mouldered beneath the Black Veil!

12

Justice

Hogan's r-right whin he says: "Justice is blind."
Blind she is, an' deef an' dumb an' has a wooden leg.

> *Mr. Dooley's Opinions—*
> *Cross-Examinations*
> Mr. Dooley
> [Finley Peter Dunne]

Shall mortal man be more just than God?
shall a man be more pure than his maker?

> Job 4:17

Justice is truth in action.

> A speech made on February 11, 1851
> Benjamin Disraeli, Earl of Beaconsfield

Justice is an abstraction that is difficult to define, yet it is the topic of many controversies and debates. In Book V of his *Nicomachean Ethics*, Aristotle deals with two kinds of justice: Distributive Justice and Corrective Justice. Distributive Justice concerns the division of property and wealth among the citizens of the State. Corrective Justice, on the other hand, is similar to our notion of legal justice.

In his *A Treatise of Human Nature*, the philosopher David Hume grapples with the concept of Distributive Justice, concluding that humankind should continue to own such property and wealth as owned when the State came into existence. The role of justice is to allow people to protect, utilize, and contract regarding such property and wealth. At the heart of any discussion on Distributive Justice is the question of whether or not it is just to take from the rich and give to the poor, whether or not the State is justified in acting as Robin Hood.

If we were able to redistribute all of the property and wealth so that each person had exactly the same share, how long would the status quo last? To attempt to keep such even distribution would be to do away with all notions of laissez faire, private contract theory, democracy, and probably the work ethic. Would people be sufficiently motivated to put forth the necessary energy and effort in order to become educated and so hold responsible positions if they knew that their share of the wealth would remain the same even if they undertook a menial task? Or should the people performing the menial tasks be compensated more than those who had the privilege of the education and are so spared the menial labor?

Whereas Distributive Justice plays a major role in political theory, it is Corrective Justice that is at the heart of our judicial system. Consider the various issues that Corrective Justice raises in relation to each of the topics which have already been discussed.

Natural, Divine, and Positive Law. Is there some kind of "natural justice" that is inherent in human nature? If so, is this justice based on a notion of "fairness"? Should we all be able to agree on what is fair and, therefore, devise positive laws with this ideal standard in mind? Notice that our idea of fairness affects whether or not we believe that the God of the Old Testament is just.

Obedience to Positive Law. If one person believes that a law which exists is unjust, should he or she obey that law? What about if 10 people, 100 people, or 1,000 people believe that the same law is unjust? Should the majority decide whether a law is just or unjust?

Equality. The discussion concerning justice and equality centers not only around the concept of Distributive Justice, as discussed previously, but also around the notion of civil rights and the injustice of a legal system that does not administer legal or corrective justice evenhandedly among its citizens.

Standards and Presumptions. If all laws were just, would we need standards and presumptions? Do the standards and presumptions *make* the laws just?

Finding the Truth. Even if we were able to arrive at a consensus as to the meaning of justice—at least in relation to punishment—we cannot be sure that justice is served unless the truth is reached.

The Jury System. If the process of reaching a unanimous verdict requries one or more jurors to alter their concept of justice to that of the other jurors, do we know that justice has been done? Might it not be possible that the one dissenter had the right concept of justice?

Trial Lawyers in Action. Ironically, lawyers are said to be officers of the Court; yet, with the nature of our adversarial process, it is not their responsibility to worry about fairness or justice for all of the players—only for their own clients.

The Judicial Process. It is the impartial judge who is said to be the dispenser of justice and who has the ultimate responsibility for "fairness" in the legal system. Should judges be schooled in philosophy and educated as to how the legislators arrive at their rules so the judge can be certain that he or she understands and shares their notions of justice?

Theories of Punishment. Theoretically, to determine a society's notion of justice, we only need to look at its theories of punishment. How well do our theories of punishment reflect our society's notions of justice?

Capital Punishment. To confirm the idea that people are not in agreement as to the meaning of justice, we need only to listen to the debate concerning capital punishment.

The Guilty Conscience. Some philosophers distinguish political justice from moral justice. Is moral justice akin to natural justice—inherent within human nature? Is moral justice something we learn through a process of conditioning—taught by our guardians and, later, through our interaction with society.

The two short stories which follow, "Mateo Falcone," by Prosper Mérimée, and "Barn Burning," by William Faulkner, deal poignantly with the notion of justice. As much sympathy as Mateo's child evokes, and despite the ache we feel for Mateo's wife, we may also identify with Mateo's perverted sense of moral justice. Similarly, we feel the agony experienced by the protagonist of "Barn Burning" as he delivers justice to the father whom he loves in spite of the wrenching pain that such an act causes him.

Mateo Falcone
Prosper Mérimée

As you leave Porto Vecchio and journey north-west, towards the interior of
the island, you find that the ground rises rather rapidly; and after a three
hours' jaunt along winding paths, obstructed by huge boulders, and sometimes interrupted by ravines, you find yourself on the edge of a very extensive *maquis*. The *maquis* is the home of the Corsican shepherd and of all
those who are at odds with the law. You must know that the Corsican
farmer, to save himself the trouble of fertilising his land, sets fire to a certain amount of woodland. If the fire spreads farther than is necessary, so
much the worse; come what come may, he is quite sure of obtaining a good
harvest by planting the ground fertilised by the ashes of the trees it formerly
bore. When the ripe grain is gathered,—for they leave the straw, which it
would require some labour to collect,—the roots which are left unburned in
the ground put forth in the following spring very vigorous shoots, which
reach a height of seven or eight feet in a few years. It is this species of
dense underbrush which is called the *maquis*. It consists of trees and
bushes of different kinds, mingled together as God pleases. Only with
hatchet in hand can man open a path through it; and there are some *maquis*
so dense and thick that even the wild sheep cannot break through.

If you have killed a man, betake yourself to the *maquis* of Porto
Vecchio, and you can live there in safety with a good rifle, powder, and
shot. Do not forget a brown cloak provided with the hood, to serve as a
covering and as a mattress. The shepherds will give you milk, cheese, and
chestnuts, and you will have no reason to fear the law, or the dead man's
kindred, except when you are forced to go down in to the town to replenish
your stock of ammunition.

Mateo Falcone, when I was in Corsica, in 18—, had his home about
half a league from this *maquis*. He was a rather wealthy man for that country; living nobly—that is to say, without working—on the produce of his
flocks, which were driven to pasture here and there upon the mountains by
shepherds, a sort of nomadic people. When I saw him, two years subsequent to the episode I am about to relate, he seemed to me to be not more
than fifty years old at most. Imagine a small, but sturdily built man, with
curly hair as black as jet, aquiline nose, thin lips, large bright eyes, and a
complexion of the hue of a boot-flap. His skill in marksmanship was considered extraordinary, even in his country, where there are so many good

shots. For example, Mateo would never fire at a wild sheep with buckshot; but he would bring one down at a hundred and twenty yards with a bullet in the head or the shoulder, as he pleased. He used his weapons as readily at night as by day, and I was told of this instance of his skill, which will seem incredible perhaps to those who have not travelled in Corsica. A candle was placed at a distance of twenty-four yards, behind a piece of transparent paper as large as a plate. He took aim, then the candle was extinguished, and, a minute later, in the absolute darkness, he fired and hit the paper three times out of four.

With such transcendent talent, Mateo Falcone had won a great reputation. He was said to be as true a friend as he was a dangerous enemy; always ready to oblige, and generous to the poor, he lived at peace with all the world in the district of Porto Vecchio. But the story was told of him, that at Corte, where he married his wife, he had disposed very summarily of a rival who was reputed to be as redoubtable in war as in love; at all events, Mateo was given credit for a certain rifle shot which surprised the aforesaid rival as he was shaving in front of a little mirror that hung at his window. When the affair was forgotten, Mateo married. His wife, Giuseppa, gave him at first three daughters (which caused him to fret and fume), and finally a son, whom he named Fortunato; he was the hope of the family, the heir to the name. The daughters were well married; their father could at need rely upon the dagger and carbines of his sons-in-law. The son was only ten years old, but he already gave rich promise for the future.

On a certain day in autumn Mateo left the house early, with his wife, to inspect one of his flocks at a clearing in the *maquis*. Fortunato would have liked to go with them, but the clearing was too far; moreover, some one must stay behind to watch the house; so the father refused; we shall see whether he had reason to repent.

He had been absent several hours, and little Fortunato was lying placidly in the sun, watching the blue mountains, and thinking that, on the following Sunday, he was going to the town to dine with his uncle the *caporal*, when he was suddenly interrupted in his meditations by the report of a firearm. He rose and turned towards the plain from which the sound came. Other reports followed, at unequal intervals, coming constantly nearer. At last, on a path leading from the plain to Mateo's house, appeared a man wearing a pointed cap such as the mountaineers wear, with a long beard, clad in rags, and hardly able to drag himself along, using his rifle as a cane. He had received a bullet in the thigh.

That man was a bandit, who, having started under cover of the darkness to go to the town for powder, had fallen into an ambush of Corsican voltigeurs. After a stout defence he had succeeded in beating a retreat, hotly pursued, and firing from one rock after another. But he was only a little in advance of the soldiers, and his wound made it impossible to reach the *maquis* before he was overtaken.

He went up to Fortunato and said;

"You are Mateo Falcone's son?"

"Yes."

"I am Gianetto Sanpiero. I am pursued by the yellow collars. Hide me, for I can't go any farther."

"What will my father say if I hide you without his leave?"

"He will say that you did well."

"Who knows?"

"Hide me quick; they're coming."

"Wait till my father comes home."

"Wait? damnation! They will be here in five minutes. Come, hide me, or I'll kill you."

Fortunato replied with the utmost coolness:

"Your gun's empty, and there ain't any cartridges left in your *carchera*."

"I have my stiletto."

"But can you run as fast as I can?"

He gave a leap and placed himself out of danger.

"You are not Mateo Falcone's son! Will you let me be arrested in front of your house?"

The child seemed to be moved.

"What will you give me if I hide you?" he said, drawing nearer.

The bandit felt in a leather pocket that hung from his belt and took out a five-franc piece, which he had kept in reserve, no doubt, to buy powder. Fortunato smiled at sight of the silver; he seized it and said to Gianetto:

"Don't be afraid."

He instantly dug a great hole in a haystack that stood near the house. Gianetto crept into it, and the child covered him so as to let him have a little air to breath, but so that it was impossible to suspect that the hay concealed a man. He conceived also an ingeniously crafty idea, worthy of a savage. He took a cat and her kittens and placed them on the haystack, to make it appear that it had not been disturbed recently. Then, noticing marks of blood on the path near the house, he carefully covered them with dirt, and, when that was done, lay down again in the sun with the most perfect tranquillity.

A few minutes later, six men in brown uniform with yellow facings commanded by an adjutant halted in front of Mateo's door. This adjutant was distantly related to the Falcones. (It is well known that in Corsica degrees of kinship are followed out much farther than elsewhere.) His name was Tiodoro Gamba; he was an active officer, greatly feared by the bandits, several of whom he had already run to earth.

"Good-day, my young cousin," he said to Fortunato, walking to where he lay; "how you've grown! Did you see a man pass by just now?"

"Oh! I ain't as tall as you yet, cousin," replied the child, with a stupid expression.

"That will come. But tell me, didn't you see a man pass?"

"Didn't I see a man pass?"

"Yes, a man with a black velvet pointed cap and a red and yellow embroidered jacket?"

"A man in a pointed cap and a red and yellow embroidered jacket?"

"Yes; answer at once, and don't repeat my questions."

"Monsieur le curé passed our door this morning, on his horse Piero. He asked me how papa was and I told him—"

"Ah, you little scamp, you are playing sly! Tell me quick which

way Gianetto went; for he's the man we're looking for, and I am certain he
took this path."

"Who knows?"

"Who knows? I know that you saw him."

"Does a fellow see people pass when he's asleep?"

"You weren't asleep, good-for-nothing; the shots woke you."

"Do you think, cousin, that your guns make such a great noise? My
father's carbine makes a lot more."

"May the devil take you, you infernal rascal! I am perfectly sure
you saw Gianetto. Perhaps you have hidden him even. Come, boys; go
into the house, and see if our man isn't there. He was only going on one
foot, and he knows too much, the villain, to try to get to the *maquis* at that
gait. Besides, the marks of blood stopped here."

"What will papa say?" queried Fortunato, with a mocking laugh.
"What will he say when he knows that you went into his house when he
was away?"

"You good-for-nothing!" said Adjutant Gamba, taking him by the
ear, "do you know that it rests with me to make you change your tune?
Perhaps, if I give you twenty blows or so with the flat of my sabre, you
will conclude to speak."

But Fortunato continued to laugh sneeringly.

"My father is Mateo Falcone!" he said with emphasis.

"Do you know, you little scamp, that I can take you to Corte or to
Bastia? I'll make you sleep in a dungeon on straw, with irons on your feet,
and I'll have you guillotined, if you don't tell me where Gianetto Sanpiero
is."

The child laughed heartily at this absurd threat.

"My father's Mateo Falcone," he repeated.

"Adjutant," said one of the voltigeurs in an undertone, "let us not get
into a row with Mateo."

Gamba was evidently perplexed. He talked in a low tone with his
soldiers, who had already searched the whole house. It was not a very long
operation, for a Corsican's cabin consists of a single square room. The
furniture consists of a table, benches, chests, and household and hunting
implements. Meanwhile little Fortunato patted his cat and seemed to derive
a wicked enjoyment from the embarrassment of the voltigeurs and his
cousin.

A soldier approached the haystack. He saw the cat and thrust his
bayonet carelessly into the hay, shrugging his shoulders, as if he realised
that it was an absurd precaution. Nothing stirred; and the child's face did
not betray the slightest excitement.

The adjutant and his squad were at their wit's end; they were already
glancing meaningly toward the plain as if proposing to return whence they
came, when their leader, convinced that threats would have no effect on
Falcone's son, determined to make one last effort, and to try the power of
caresses and gifts.

"You seem to be a very wide-awake youngster, cousin," said he.
"You will go far. But you are playing a low game with me; and if I wasn't
afraid of distressing my cousin Mateo, deuce take me if I wouldn't carry

you off with me!"

"Bah!"

"But, when my cousin returns I'll tell him the story, and he'll give you the lash till the blood comes, to punish you for lying."

"And then?"

"You will see. But, I say, be a good boy, and I'll give you something."

"And I'll give you a piece of advice, cousin; if you stay here any longer, Gianetto will be in the *maquis*, and then it will take more than one fox like you to catch him."

The adjutant took a silver watch from his pocket, worth perhaps thirty francs; and observing that little Fortunato's eyes sparkled as he looked at it, he said, holding it up at the end of its steel chain:

"Rascal! you'd like to have a watch like this hanging round your neck, and you'd stroll through the streets of Porto Vecchio, as proud as a peacock; and people would ask you: 'What time is it?' and you'd say: 'Look at my watch!'"

"When I'm big, my uncle the *caporal* will give me a watch."

"Yes; but your uncle's son has got one now—not such a fine one as this, to be sure. Still, he's younger than you."

The child sighed.

"Well! would you like this watch, my little cousin?"

Fortunato, with his eye fixed on the watch, resembled a cat to which a whole chicken is presented. As the beast feels sure that he is being made a fool of, he dare not touch it with his claws, and he turns his eyes away from time to time to avoid the risk of yielding to temptation; but he licks his chops every instant, and seems to say to his master: "What a cruel joke this is!"

But Adjutant Gamba seemed to be in earnest in his offer of the watch. Fortunato did not put out his hand; but he said with a bitter smile:

"Why do you make sport of me?"

"By God! I am not joking. Just tell me where Gianetto is, and this watch is yours."

Fortunato smiled an incredulous smile and, fastening his black eyes on the adjutant's, he strove to read therein how far he should put faith in his words.

"May I lose my epaulets," cried the adjutant, "if I don't give you the watch on that condition! My comrades are witnesses; and I can't go back on my word."

As he spoke, he held the watch nearer and nearer, so that it almost touched the child's pale cheek. His face betrayed the battle that was taking place in his mind between covetousness and respect for the duties of hospitality. His bare breast rose and fell violently, and he seemed on the point of suffocation. Meanwhile the watch swung to and fro; turned, and sometimes touched the end of his nose. At last, by slow degrees, his right hand rose toward the watch; the ends of his fingers touched it; and he felt the full weight of it on his hand, but still the adjutant did not let go the end of the chain. The face was sky-blue, the case newly polished—in the sun it shone like fire. The temptation was too great.

Fortunato raised his left hand, too, and pointed with his thumb, over his left shoulder, to the haystack against which he was leaning. The adjutant understood him instantly. He let go the end of the chain; Fortunato realised that he was the sole possessor of the watch. He sprang up with the agility of a stag, and ran some yards away from the haystack, which the voltigeurs began at once to demolish.

They soon saw the hay begin to move; and a man covered with blood came forth, dagger in hand; but when he tried to raise himself, his stiffened wound prevented him from standing erect. He fell. The adjutant threw himself upon him and tore his stiletto from his hand. In a trice he was securely bound, despite his resistance.

Gianetto, lying on the ground and corded like a bundle of sticks, turned his head toward Fortunato, who had drawn near.

"Son of—!" he said, with more scorn than anger.

The child tossed him the piece of silver which he had received from him, feeling that he no longer deserved it; but the outlaw seemed to pay no heed to that movement. He said to the adjutant, as coolly as possible:

"I can't walk, my dear Gamba; you will have to carry me to the town."

"You ran faster than a kid just now," retorted the cruel victor; "but never fear; I am so pleased to have caught you, that I would carry you on my back a whole league without getting tired. However, my boy, we'll make a litter for you with some branches and your cloak; and we shall find horses at Crespoli's farm."

"Good," said the prisoner; "just put a little straw on your litter, too, so that I can be more comfortable."

While the voltigeurs busied themselves, some in making a sort of litter with chestnut branches, others in dressing Gianetto's wound, Mateo Falcone and his wife suddenly appeared at a bend in the path leading to the *maquis*. The woman was stooping painfully beneath the weight of an enormous bag of chestnuts, while her husband sauntered along, carrying nothing save one rifle in his hand and another slung over his shoulder; for it is unworthy of a man to carry any other burden than his weapons.

At sight of the soldiers, Mateo's first thought was that they had come to arrest him. But why that thought? Had Mateo any difficulties to adjust with the authorities? No. He enjoyed an excellent reputation. He was, as they say, a person of good fame; but he was a Corsican and a mountaineer; and there are few Corsican mountaineers who, by carefully searching their memory, cannot find some trifling peccadillo—such as a rifle shot, a dagger thrust, or other bagatelle. Mateo's conscience was clearer than most, for he had not aimed his rifle at a man for more than ten years; but he was prudent none the less, and he placed himself in a position to make a stout defence, if need be.

"Wife," he said to Giuseppa, "put down your bag and be ready."

She instantly obeyed. He gave her the gun that he carried slung over his shoulder, which might be in his way. He cocked the one he had in his hand, and walked slowly toward his house, skirting the trees that lined the path, and ready, at the slightest hostile demonstration, to jump behind the largest trunk, where he could fire without exposing himself. His wife followed at his heels, holding his spare gun and his cartridge-box. A good housewife's work, in case of a fight, is to load her husband's weapons.

The adjutant, on the other hand, was greatly disturbed to see Mateo advance thus with measured steps, with rifle raised and finger on trigger.

"If by any chance," he thought, "Mateo proves to be related to Gianetto, or if he is his friend and should take it into his head to defend him, the charges of his two rifles would reach two of us, as sure as a letter reaches its address; and suppose he should draw a bead on me, notwithstanding our relationship!"

In his perplexity he adopted an extremely courageous course—he went forward alone toward Mateo, to tell him what had happened, accosting him as an old acquaintance; but the short distance that separated them seemed to him terribly long.

"Hello! my old comrade," he cried; "how goes it, old fellow? It's me, Gamba, your cousin."

Mateo, without a word in reply, halted, and as the other spoke he raised the barrel of his gun slowly, so that it was pointed at the sky when the adjutant met him.

"Good-day, brother," said the adjutant, "it's a long while since I saw you."

"Good-day, brother."

"I looked in to say good-day to you and Cousin Pepa as I passed. We have had a long jaunt to-day; but we ought not to complain of fatigue, as we have made a famous capture. We have caught Gianetto Sanpiero."

"God be praised!" cried Giuseppa. "He stole a milch goat from us last week."

Those words made Gamba's heart glad.

"Poor devil!" said Mateo, "he was hungry."

"The rascal defended himself like a lion," continued the adjutant, slightly mortified; "he killed one of my men, and, not content with that, he broke Corporal Chardon's arm; but there's no great harm done; he was only a Frenchman. After that, he hid himself so completely that the devil himself couldn't have found him. If it hadn't been for my little cousin, Fortunato, I could never have unearthed him."

"Fortunato!" cried Mateo.

"Fortunato!" echoed Giuseppa.

"Yes, Gianetto was hidden under the haystack yonder; but my little cousin showed me the trick. And I'll tell his uncle the *caporal*, so that he'll send him a handsome present for his trouble. And his name and yours will be in the report I shall send the advocate-general."

"Malediction!" muttered Mateo.

They had joined the squad. Gianetto was already lying on the litter, ready to start. When he saw Mateo with Gamba, he smiled a strange smile; then, turning towards the door of the house, he spat on the threshold, saying:

"House of a traitor!"

Only a man who had made up his mind to die would have dared to utter the word traitor as applying to Falcone. A quick thrust of the stiletto, which would not have needed to be repeated, would have paid for the insult instantly. But Mateo made no other movement than to put his hand to his forehead, like a man utterly crushed.

Fortunato had gone into the house when he saw his father coming. He soon reappeared with a mug of milk, which he handed to Gianetto with downcast eyes.

"Away from me!" shouted the outlaw in a voice of thunder. Then, turning to one of the voltigeurs, "Comrade," he said, "give me a drink."

The soldier placed his gourd in his hands, and the outlaw drank the water given him by a man with whom he had recently exchanged rifle shots. Then he asked that his hands might be bound so that they would be folded on his breast, instead of behind his back.

"I like to lie comfortably," he said.

They readily gratified him; the adjutant gave the signal for departure, bade adieu to Mateo, who made no reply, and marched down at a rapid pace towards the plain.

Nearly ten minutes passed before Mateo opened his mouth. The child glanced uneasily, now at his mother and now at his father, who, leaning upon his gun, gazed at him with an expression of intense wrath.

"You begin well!" said Mateo at last, in a voice which, although calm, was terrifying to one who knew the man.

"Father!" cried the child stepping forward, with tears in his eyes, as if to throw himself at his feet.

But Mateo cried:

"Away from me!"

And the child stopped and stood still, sobbing, a few steps from his father.

Giuseppa approached. She had spied the watch chain, one end of which protruded from Fortunato's shirt.

"Who gave you that watch?" she asked in a harsh tone.

"My cousin the adjutant."

Falcone seized the watch, and hurled it against a stone, breaking it into a thousand pieces.

"Woman," he said, "is this child mine?"

Giuseppa's brown cheeks turned a brick red.

"What do you say, Mateo? Do you know who you're talking to?"

"Well, this child is the first of his race that ever did an act of treachery."

Fortunato's sobs and hiccoughs redoubled in force, and Falcone still kept his lynx-eyes fastened on him. At last he struck the butt of his gun on the ground, then threw it over his shoulder again and started back toward the *maquis*, calling to Fortunato to follow him. The child obeyed.

Giuseppa ran after Mateo and grasped his arm.

"He is your son," she said in a trembling voice, fixing her black eyes on her husband's, as if to read what was taking place in his mind.

"Let me alone," replied Mateo, "I am his father."

Giuseppa embraced her son and entered her cabin, weeping. She fell on her knees before an image of the virgin and prayed fervently. Meanwhile Falcone walked some two hundred yards along the path, and did not stop until they reached a narrow ravine into which he descended. He sounded the earth with the butt of his rifle, and found it soft and easy to dig.

It seemed to him a suitable spot for his design.

"Fortunato, go and stand by that big stone."

The child did what he ordered, then knelt.

"Say your prayers."

"Father, father, don't kill me!"

"Say your prayers!" Mateo repeated, in a terrible voice.

The child, stammering and sobbing, repeated the *Pater* and the *Credo*. The father, in a loud voice, said *Amen*! at the end of each prayer.

"Are those all the prayers you know?"

"I know the *Ave Maria*, too, father, and the litany my aunt taught me."

"That's very long, but no matter."

The child finished the litany in a feeble voice.

"Have you finished?"

"Oh, father! mercy! forgive me! I won't do it again! I will pray so hard to my uncle the *caporal* that he'll forgive Gianetto!"

He continued to speak; Mateo had cocked his gun, and he took aim at him, saying:

"May God forgive you!"

The child made a desperate effort to rise and grasp his father's knees; but he had not time. Mateo fired, and Fortunato fell stark dead.

Without glancing at the body, Mateo returned to his house to fetch a spade, in order to bury his son. He had taken only a few steps, when he met Giuseppa, who was running after them, terrified by the report.

"What have you done?" she cried.

"Justice."

"Where is he?"

"In the ravine. I am going to bury him. He died the death of a Christian; I will have a mass sung for him. Send word to my son-in-law Tiodoro Bianchi to come and live with us."

Barn Burning
William Faulkner

The store in which the Justice of the Peace's court was sitting smelled of cheese. The boy, crouched on his nail keg at the back of the crowded room, knew he smelled cheese, and more: from where he sat he could see the ranked shelves close-packed with the solid, squat, dynamic shapes of tin cans whose labels his stomach read, not from the lettering which meant nothing to his mind but from the scarlet devils and the silver curve of fish—this, the cheese which he knew he smelled and the hermetic meat which his intestines believed he smelled coming in intermittent gusts momentary and brief between the other constant one, the smell and sense just a little of fear because mostly of despair and grief, the old fierce pull of blood. He could not see the table where the Justice sat and before which his father and his father's enemy (*our enemy* he thought in that despair; *ourn! mine and hisn both! He's my father!*) stood, but he could hear them, the two of them that is, because his father had said no word yet:

"But what proof have you, Mr. Harris?"

"I told you. The hog got into my corn. I caught it up and sent it back to him. He had no fence that would hold it. I told him so, warned him. The next time I put the hog in my pen. When he came to get it I gave him enough wire to patch up his pen. The next time I put the hog up and kept it. I rode down to his house and saw the wire I gave him still rolled on to the spool in his yard. I told him he could have the hog when he paid me a dollar pound fee. That evening a nigger came with the dollar and got the hog. He was a strange nigger. He said, 'He say to tell you wood and hay kin burn.' I said, 'What?' 'That whut he say to tell you,' the nigger said, 'Wood and hay kin burn.' That night my barn burned. I got the stock out but I lost the barn."

"Where is the nigger? Have you got him?"

"He was a strange nigger, I tell you. I don't know what became of him."

"But that's not proof. Don't you see that's not proof?"

"Get that boy up here. He knows." For a moment the boy thought too that the man meant his older brother until Harris said, "Not him. The little one. The boy," and, crouching, small for his age, small and wiry like his father, in patched and faded jeans even too small for him, with straight, uncombed, brown hair and eyes gray and wild as storm scud, he saw the men between himself and the table part and become a lane of grim faces, at the end of which he saw the Justice, a shabby, collarless, graying man in spectacles, beckoning him. He felt no floor under his bare feet; he seemed to walk beneath the palpable weight of the grim turning faces. His father, stiff in his black Sunday coat donned not for the trial but for the moving, did not even look at him. *He aims for me to lie*, he thought, again with that frantic grief and despair. *And I will have to do hit.*

"What's your name, boy?" the Justice said.

"Colonel Sartoris Snopes," the boy whispered.

"Hey?" the Justice said. "Talk louder. Colonel Sartoris? I reckon anybody named for Colonel Sartoris in this country can't help but tell the truth, can they?" The boy said nothing. *Enemy! Enemy!* he thought; for a moment he could not even see, could not see that the Justice's face was kindly nor discern that his voice was troubled when he spoke to the man named Harris: "Do you want me to question this boy?" But he could hear, and during those subsequent long seconds while there was absolutely no sound in the crowded little room save that of quiet and intent breathing it was as if he had swung outward at the end of a grape vine, over a ravine, and at the top of the swing had been caught in a prolonged instant of mesmerized gravity, weightless in time.

"No!" Harris said violently, explosively. "Damnation! Send him out of here!" Now time, the fluid world, rushed beneath him again, the voices coming to him again through the smell of cheese and sealed meat, the fear and despair and the old grief of blood:

"This case is closed. I can't find against you, Snopes, but I can give you advice. Leave this country and don't come back to it."

His father spoke for the first time, his voice cold and harsh, level, without emphasis: "I aim to. I don't figure to stay in a country among people who . . ." he said something unprintable and vile, addressed to no one.

"That'll do," the Justice said. "Take your wagon and get out of this country before dark. Case dismissed."

His father turned, and he followed the stiff black coat, the wiry figure walking a little stiffly from where a Confederate provost's man's musket ball had taken him in the heel on a stolen horse thirty years ago, followed the two backs now, since his older brother had appeared from somewhere in the crowd, no taller than the father but thicker, chewing tobacco steadily, between the two lines of grim-faced men and out of the store and across the worn gallery and down the sagging steps and among the dogs and half-grown boys in the mild May dust, where as he passed a voice hissed:

"Barn burner!"

Again he could not see, whirling; there was a face in a red haze, moonlike, bigger than the full moon, the owner of it half again his size, he leaping in the red haze toward the face, feeling no blow, feeling no shock when his head struck the earth, scrabbling up and leaping again, feeling no blow this time either and tasting no blood, scrabbling up to see the other boy in full flight and himself already leaping into pursuit as his father's hand jerked him back, the harsh, cold voice speaking above him: "Go get in the wagon."

It stood in a grove of locusts and mulberries across the road. His two hulking sisters in their Sunday dresses and his mother and his sister in calico and sunbonnets were already in it, sitting on and among the sorry residue of the dozen and more movings which even the boy could remember—the battered stove, the broken beds and chairs, the clock inlaid with mother-of-pearl, which would not run, stopped at some fourteen minutes past two o'clock of a dead and forgotten day and time, which had been his mother's dowry. She was crying, though when she saw him she drew her sleeve across her face and began to descend from the wagon. "Get back," the father said.

"He's hurt. I got to get some water and wash his . . ."

"Get back in the wagon," his father said. He got in too, over the tail-gate. His father mounted to the seat where the older brother already sat and struck the gaunt mules two savage blows with the peeled willow, but without heat. It was not even sadistic; it was exactly that same quality which in later years would cause his descendants to over-run the engine before putting a motor car into motion, striking and reining back in the same movement. The wagon went on, the store with its quiet crowd of grimly watching men dropped behind; a curve in the road hid it. *Forever* he thought. *Maybe he's done satisfied now, now that he has . . .* stopping himself, not to say it aloud even to himself. His mother's hand touched his shoulder.

"Does hit hurt?" she said.

"Naw," he said. "Hit don't hurt. Lemme be."

"Can't you wipe some of the blood off before hit dries?"

"I'll wash tonight," he said. "Lemme be, I tell you."

The wagon went on. He did not know where they were going. None of them ever did or ever asked, because it was always somewhere, always a house of sorts waiting for them a day or two days or even three days away. Likely his father had already arranged to make a crop on another farm before he . . . Again he had to stop himself. He (the father) always did. There was something about his wolflike independence and even courage when the advantage was at least neutral which impressed strangers, as if they got from his latent ravening ferocity not so much a sense of dependability as a feeling that his ferocious conviction in the rightness of his own actions would be of advantage to all whose interest lay with his.

That night they camped, in a grove of oaks and beeches where a spring ran. The nights were still cool and they had a fire against it, of a rail lifted from a nearby fence and cut into lengths—a small fire, neat, niggard almost, a shrewd fire; such fires were his father's habit and custom always, even in freezing weather. Older, the boy might have remarked this and wondered why not a big one; why should not a man who had not only seen the waste and extravagance of war, but who had in his blood an inherent voracious prodigality with material not his own, have burned everything in sight? Then he might have gone a step farther and thought that that was the reason: that niggard blaze was the living fruit of nights passed during those four years in the woods hiding from all men, blue or gray, with his strings of horses (captured horses, he called them). And older still, he might have divined the true reason: that the element of fire spoke to some deep mainspring of his father's being, as the element of steel or of powder spoke to other men, as the one weapon for the preservation of integrity, else breath were not worth the breathing, and hence to be regarded with respect and used with discretion.

But he did not think this now and he had seen those same niggard blazes all his life. He merely ate his supper beside it and was already half asleep over his iron plate when his father called him, and once more he followed the stiff back, the stiff and ruthless limp, up the slope and on to the starlit road where, turning, he could see his father against the stars but without face or depth—a shape black, flat, and bloodless as though cut from tin in the iron folds of the frockcoat which had not been made for him, the voice harsh like tin and without heat like tin:

"You were fixing to tell them. You would have told him." He didn't answer. His father struck him with the flat of his hand on the side of the head, hard but without heat, exactly as he had struck the two mules at the store, exactly as he would strike either of them with any stick in order to kill a horse fly, his voice still without heat or anger: "You're getting to be a man. You got to learn. You got to learn to stick to your own blood or you ain't going to have any blood to stick to you. Do you think either of them, any man there this morning, would? Don't you know all they wanted was a chance to get at me because they knew I had them beat? Eh?" Later, twenty years later, he was to tell himself, "If I had said they wanted only truth, justice, he would have hit me again." But now he said nothing. He was not crying. He just stood there. "Answer me," his father said.

"Yes," he whispered. His father turned.

"Get on to bed. We'll be there tomorrow."

Tomorrow they were there. In the early afternoon the wagon stopped before a paintless two-room house identical almost with the dozen others it had stopped before even in the boy's ten years, and again, as on the other dozen occasions, his mother and aunt got down and began to unload the wagon, although his two sisters and his father and brother had not moved.

"Likely hit ain't fitten for hawgs," one of the sisters said.

"Nevertheless, fit it will and you'll hog it and like it," his father said. "Get out of them chairs and help your Ma unload."

The two sisters got down, big, bovine, in a flutter of cheap ribbons; one of them drew from the jumbled wagon bed a battered lantern, the other a worn broom. His father handed the reins to the older son and began to climb stiffly over the wheel. "When they get unloaded, take the team to the barn and feed them." Then he said, and at first the boy thought he was still speaking to his brother: "Come with me."

"Me?" he said.

"Yes," his father said. "You."

"Abner," his mother said. His father paused and looked back—the harsh level stare beneath the shaggy, graying, irascible brows.

"I reckon I'll have a word with the man that aims to begin tomorrow owning me body and soul for the next eight months."

They went up the road. A week ago—or before last night, that is— he would have asked where they were going, but not now. His father had struck him before last night but never before had he paused afterward to explain why; it was as if the blow and the following calm, outrageous voice still rang, repercussed, divulging nothing to him save the terrible handicap of being young, the light weight of his few years, just heavy enough to prevent his soaring free of the world as it seemed to be ordered but not heavy enough to keep him footed solid in it, to resist it and try to change the course of its events.

Presently he could see the grove of oaks and cedars and the other flowering trees and shrubs where the house would be, though not the house yet. They walked beside a fence massed with honeysuckle and Cherokee roses and came to a gate swinging open between two brick pillars, and now, beyond a sweep of drive, he saw the house for the first time and at that instant he forgot his father and the terror and despair both, and even when he remembered his father again (who had not stopped) the terror and despair did not return. Because, for all the twelve movings, they had sojourned until now in a poor country, a land of small farms and fields and houses, and he had never seen a house like this before. *Hit's big as a courthouse* he thought quietly, with a surge of peace and joy whose reason he could not have thought into words, being too young for that: They are safe from him. *People whose lives are a part of this peace and dignity are beyond his touch, he no more to them than a buzzing wasp capable of stinging for a little moment but that's all; the spell of this peace and dignity rendering even the barns and stable and cribs which belong to it impervious to the puny flames he might contrive* . . . this, the peace and joy, ebbing for an instant as he looked again at the stiff black back, the stiff and implacable limp of the figure which was not dwarfed by the house, for the reason that it had never looked big anywhere and which now, against the serene columned backdrop, had more than ever that impervious quality of something cut ruthlessly from tin, depthless, as though, sidewise to the sun, it would cast no shadow. Watching him, the boy remarked the absolutely undeviating course which his father held and saw the stiff foot come squarely down in a pile of fresh droppings where a horse had stood in the drive and which his father could have avoided by a simple change of stride. But it ebbed only for a moment, though he could not have thought this into words either, walking on in the spell of the house, which he could even want but without envy, without sorrow, certainly never with that ravening and jealous rage which unknown to him walked in the ironlike black coat before him: Maybe he will feel it too. *Maybe it will even change him now from what maybe he couldn't help but be.*

They crossed the portico. Now he could hear his father's stiff foot as it came down on the boards with clocklike finality, a sound out of all proportion to the displacement of the body it bore and which was not dwarfed either by the white door before it, as though it had attained to a sort of vicious ravening minimum not to be dwarfed by anything—the flat, wide, black hat, the formal coat of broadcloth which had once been black but which had now that friction-glazed greenish cast of the bodies of old house flies, the lifted sleeve which was too large, the lifted hand like a curled claw. The door opened so promptly that the boy knew the Negro must have been watching them all the time, an old man with neat grizzled hair, in a linen jacket, who stood barring the door with his body, saying, "Wipe yo foots, white man, fo you come in here. Major ain't home no-how."

"Get out of my way, nigger," his father said, without heat too, flinging the door back and the Negro also and entering, his hat still on his head. And now the boy saw the prints of the stiff foot on the doorsill and saw them appear on the pale rug behind the machinelike deliberation of the foot which seemed to bear (or transmit) twice the weight which the body compassed. The Negro was shouting "Miss Lula! Miss Lula!" somewhere behind them, then the boy, deluged as though by a warm wave by a suave turn of carpeted stair and a pendant glitter of chandeliers and a mute gleam of gold frames, heard the swift feet and saw her too, a lady—perhaps he had never seen her like before either—in a gray, smooth gown with lace at the throat and an apron tied at the waist and the sleeves turned back, wiping cake or biscuit dough from her hands with a towel as she came up the hall, looking not at his father at all but at the tracks on the blond rug with an expression of incredulous amazement.

"I tried," the Negro cried. "I tole him to . . ."

"Will you please go away?" she said in a shaking voice. "Major de Spain is not at home. Will you please go away?"

His father had not spoken again. He did not speak again. He did not even look at her. He just stood stiff in the center of the rug, in his hat, the shaggy iron-gray brows twitching slightly above the pebble-colored eyes as he appeared to examine the house with brief deliberation. Then with the same deliberation he turned; the boy watched him pivot on the good leg and saw the stiff foot drag round the arc of the turning, leaving a final long and fading smear. His father never looked at it, he never once looked down at the rug. The Negro held the door. It closed behind them, upon the hysteric and indistinguishable woman-wail. His father stopped at the top of the steps and scraped his boot clean on the edge of it. At the gate he stopped again. He stood for a moment, planted stiffly on the stiff foot, looking back at the house. "Pretty and white, ain't it?" he said. "That's sweat. Nigger sweat. Maybe it ain't white enough yet to suit him. Maybe he wants to mix some white sweat with it."

Two hours later the boy was chopping wood behind the house within which his mother and aunt and the two sisters (the mother and aunt, not the two girls, he knew that; even at this distance and muffled by walls the flat loud voices of the two girls emanated an incorrigible idle inertia) were setting up the stove to prepare a meal, when he heard the hooves and saw the linen-clad man on a fine sorrel mare, whom he recognized even before he saw the rolled rug in front of the Negro youth following on a fat bay carriage horse—a suffused, angry face vanishing, still at full gallop, beyond the corner of the house where his father and brother were sitting in the two tilted chairs; and a moment later, almost before he could have put the axe down, he heard the hooves again and watched the sorrel mare go back out of the yard, already galloping again. Then his father began to shout one of the sisters' names, who presently emerged backward from the kitchen door dragging the rolled rug along the ground by one end while the other sister walked behind it.

"If you ain't going to tote, go on and set up the wash pot," the first said.

"You, Sarty!" the second shouted. "Set up the wash pot!" His father appeared at the door, framed against that shabbiness, as he had been against that other bland perfection, impervious to either, the mother's anxious face at his shoulder.

"Go on," the father said. "Pick it up." The two sisters stooped, broad, lethargic; stooping, they presented an incredible expanse of pale cloth and a flutter of tawdry ribbons.

"If I thought enough of a rug to have to git hit all the way from France I wouldn't keep hit where folks coming in would have to tromp on hit," the first said. They raised the rug.

"Abner," the mother said. "Let me do it."

"You go back and get dinner," his father said. "I'll tend to this."

From the woodpile through the rest of the afternoon the boy watched them, the rug spread flat in the dust beside the bubbling wash pot, the two sisters stooping over it with that profound and lethargic reluctance, while the father stood over them in turn, implacable and grim, driving them though never raising his voice again. He could smell the harsh homemade lye they were using; he saw his mother come to the door once and look toward them with an expression not anxious now but very like despair; he saw his father turn, and he fell to with the axe and saw from the corner of his eye his father raise from the ground a flattish fragment of field stone and examine it and return to the pot, and this time his mother actually spoke: "Abner. Abner. Please don't. Please, Abner."

Then he was done too. It was dusk; the whippoorwills had already begun. He could smell coffee from the room where they would presently eat the cold food remaining from the mid-afternoon meal, though when he entered the house he realized they were having coffee again probably because there was a fire on the hearth, before which the rug now lay spread over the backs of the two chairs. The tracks of his father's foot were gone. Where they had been were now long, water-cloudy scoriations resembling the sporadic course of a Lilliputian mowing machine.

It still hung there while they ate the cold food and then went to bed, scattered without order or claim up and down the two rooms, his mother in one bed, where his father would later lie, the older brother in the other, himself, the aunt, and the two sisters on pallets on the floor. But his father was not in bed yet. The last thing the boy remembered was the depthless, harsh silhouette of the hat and coat bending over the rug and it seemed to him that he had not even closed his eyes when the silhouette was standing over him, the fire almost dead behind it, the stiff foot prodding him awake. "Catch up the mule," his father said.

When he returned with the mule his father was standing in the black door, the rolled rug over his shoulder. "Ain't you going to ride?" he said.

"No. Give me your foot."

He bent his knee into his father's hand, the wiry, surprising power flowed smoothly, rising, he rising with it, on to the mule's bare back (they had owned a saddle once; the boy could remember it though not when or where) and with the same effortlessness his father swung the rug up in front of him. Now in the starlight they retraced the afternoon's path, up the dusty road rife with honeysuckle, through the gate and up the black tunnel of the drive to the lightless house, where he sat on the mule and felt the rough warp of the rug drag across his thighs and vanish.

"Don't you want me to help?" he whispered. His father did not answer and now he heard again that stiff foot striking the hollow portico with that wooden and clocklike deliberation, that outrageous overstatement of the weight it carried. The rug, hunched, not flung (the boy could tell that even in the darkness) from his father's shoulder, struck the angle of wall and floor with a sound unbelievably loud, thunderous, then the foot again, unhurried and enormous; a light came on in the house and the boy sat, tense, breathing steadily and quietly and just a little fast, though the foot itself did not increase its beat at all, descending the steps now; now the boy could see him.

"Don't you want to ride now?" he whispered. "We kin both ride now," the light within the house altering now, flaring up and sinking. *He's coming down the stairs now*, he thought. He had already ridden the mule up beside the horse block; presently his father was up behind him and he doubled the reins over and slashed the mule across the neck, but before the animal could begin to trot the hard, thin arm came round him, the hard, knotted hand jerking the mule back to a walk.

In the first red rays of the sun they were in the lot, putting plow gear on the mules. This time the sorrel mare was in the lot before he heard it at all, the rider collarless and even bareheaded, trembling, speaking in a shaking voice as the woman in the house had done, his father merely looking up once before stooping again to the hame he was buckling, so that the man on the mare spoke to his stooping back:

"You must realize you have ruined that rug. Wasn't there anybody here, any of your women . . ." He ceased, shaking, the boy watching him, the older brother leaning now in the stable door, chewing, blinking slowly and steadily at nothing apparently. "It cost a hundred dollars. But you never had a hundred dollars. You never will. So I'm going to charge you twenty bushels of corn against your crop. I'll add it in your contract and when you come to the commissary you can sign it. That won't keep Mrs. de Spain quiet but maybe it will teach you to wipe your feet off before you enter her house again."

Then he was gone. The boy looked at his father, who still had not spoken or even looked up again, who was now adjusting the logger-head in the hame.

"Pap," he said. His father looked at him—the inscrutable face, the shaggy brows beneath which the gray eyes glinted coldly. Suddenly the boy went toward him, fast, stopping as suddenly. "You done the best you could!" he cried. "If he wanted hit done different why didn't he wait and tell you how? He won't git no twenty bushels! He won't git none! We'll get hit and hide hit! I kin watch . . ."

"Did you put the cutter back in that straight stock like I told you?"

"No, sir," he said.

"Then go do it."

That was Wednesday. During the rest of that week he worked

steadily, at what was within his scope and some which was beyond it, with an industry that did not need to be driven nor even commanded twice; he had this from his mother, with the difference that some at least of what he did he liked to do, such as splitting wood with the half-size axe which his mother and aunt had earned, or saved money somehow, to present him with at Christmas. In company with the two older women (and on one afternoon, even one of the sisters), he built pens for the shoat and the cow which were a part of his father's contract with the landlord, and one afternoon, his father being absent, gone somewhere on one of the mules, he went to the field.

They were running a middle buster now, his brother holding the plow straight while he handled the reins, and walking beside the straining mule, the rich black soil shearing cool and damp against his bare ankles, he thought *Maybe this is the end of it. Maybe even that twenty bushels that seems hard to have to pay for just a rug will be a cheap price for him to stop forever and always from being what he used to be*; thinking, dreaming now, so that his brother had to speak sharply to him to mind the mule: *Maybe he even won't collect the twenty bushels. Maybe it will all add up and balance and vanish—corn, rug, fire; the terror and grief, the being pulled two ways like between two teams of horses—gone, done with for ever and ever.*

Then it was Saturday; he looked up from beneath the mule he was harnessing and saw his father in the black coat and hat. "Not that," his father said. "The wagon gear." And then, two hours later, sitting in the wagon bed behind his father and brother on the seat, the wagon accomplished a final curve, and he saw the weathered paintless store with its tattered tobacco—and patent-medicine posters and the tethered wagons and saddle animals below the gallery. He mounted the gnawed steps behind his father and brother, and there again was the lane of quiet, watching faces for the three of them to walk through. He saw the man in spectacles sitting at the plank table and he did not need to be told this was a Justice of the Peace; he sent one glare of fierce, exultant, partisan defiance at the man in collar and cravat now, whom he had seen but twice before in his life, and that on a galloping horse, who now wore on his face an expression not of rage but of amazed unbelief which the boy could not have known was at the incredible circumstance of being sued by one of his own tenants, and came and stood against his father and cried at the Justice: "He ain't done it! He ain't burnt . . ."

"Go back to the wagon," his father said.

"Burnt?" the Justice said. "Do I understand this rug was burned too?"

"Does anybody here claim it was?" his father said. "Go back to the wagon." But he did not, he merely retreated to the rear of the room, crowded as that other had been, but not to sit down this time, instead, to stand pressing among the motionless bodies, listening to the voices:

"And you claim twenty bushels of corn is too high for the damage you did to the rug?"

"He brought the rug to me and said he wanted the tracks washed out of it. I washed the tracks out and took the rug back to him."

"But you didn't carry the rug back to him in the same condition it was in before you made the tracks on it."

His father did not answer, and now for perhaps half a minute there was no sound at all save that of breathing, the faint, steady suspiration of complete and intent listening.

"You decline to answer that, Mr. Snopes?" Again his father did not answer. "I'm going to find against you, Mr. Snopes. I'm going to find that you were responsible for the injury to Major de Spain's rug and hold you liable for it. But twenty bushels of corn seems a little high for a man in your circumstances to have to pay. Major de Spain claims it cost a hundred dollars. October corn will be worth about fifty cents. I figure that if Major de Spain can stand a ninety-five-dollar loss on something he paid cash for, you can stand a five-dollar loss you haven't earned yet. I hold you in damages to Major de Spain to the amount of ten bushels of corn over and above your contract with him, to be paid to him out of your crop at gathering time. Court adjourned."

It had taken no time hardly, the morning was but half begun. He thought they would return home and perhaps back to the field, since they were late, far behind all other farmers. But instead his father passed on behind the wagon, merely indicating with his hand for the older brother to follow with it, and crossed the road toward the blacksmith shop opposite, pressing on after his father, overtaking him, speaking, whispering up at the harsh, calm face beneath the weathered hat: "He won't git no ten bushels neither. He won't git one. We'll . . ." until his father glanced for an instant down at him, the face absolutely calm, the grizzled eyebrows tangled above the cold eyes, the voice almost pleasant, almost gentle:

"You think so? Well, we'll wait till October anyway."

The matter of the wagon—the setting of a spoke or two and the tightening of the tires—did not take long either, the business of the tires accomplished by driving the wagon into the spring branch behind the shop and letting it stand there, the mules nuzzling into the water from time to time, and the boy on the seat with the idle reins, looking up the slope and through the sooty tunnel of the shed where the slow hammer rang and where his father sat on an upended cypress bolt, easily, either talking or listening, still sitting there when the boy brought the dripping wagon up out of the branch and halted it before the door.

"Take them on to the shade and hitch," his father said. He did so and returned. His father and the smith and a third man squatting on his heels inside the door were talking, about crops and animals; the boy, squatting too in the amoniac dust and hoof-parings and scales of rust, heard his father tell a long and unhurried story out of the time before the birth of the older brother even when he had been a professional horsetrader. And then his father came up beside him where he stood before a tattered last year's circus poster on the other side of the store, gazing rapt and quiet at the scarlet horses, the incredible poisings and convolution of tulle and tights and the painted leers of comedians, and said, "It's time to eat."

But not at home. Squatting beside his brother against the front wall, he watched his father emerge from the store and produce from a paper sack a segment of cheese and divide it carefully and deliberately into three with his pocket knife and produce crackers from the same sack. They all three squatted on the gallery and ate, slowly, without talking; then in the store again, they drank from a tin dipper tepid water smelling of the cedar bucket and of living beech trees. And still they did not go home. It was a horse lot this time, a tall rail fence upon and along which men stood and sat and out of which one by one horses were led, to be walked and trotted and then cantered back and forth along the road while the slow swapping and buying went on and the sun began to slant westward, they—the three of them—watching and listening, the older brother with his muddy eyes and his steady, inevitable tobacco, the father commenting now and then on certain of the animals, to no one in particular.

It was after sundown when they reached home. They ate supper by lamplight, then, sitting on the doorstep, the boy watched the night fully accomplish, listening to the whippoorwills and the frogs, when he heard his mother's voice: "Abner! No! No! Oh, God. Oh, God. Abner!" and he rose, whirled, and saw the altered light through the door where a candle stub now burned in a bottle neck on the table and his father, still in the hat and coat, at once formal and burlesque as though dressed carefully for some shabby and ceremonial violence, emptying the reservoir of the lamp back into the five-gallon kerosene can from which it had been filled, while the mother tugged at his arm until he shifted the lamp to the other hand and flung her back, not savagely or viciously, just hard, into the wall, her hands flung out against the wall for balance, her mouth open and in her face the same quality of hopeless despair as had been in her voice. Then his father saw him standing in the door.

"Go to the barn and get that can of oil we were oiling the wagon with," he said. The boy did not move. Then he could speak.

"What . . ." he cried. "What are you . . ."

"Go get that oil," his father said. "Go."

Then he was moving, running, outside the house, toward the stable: this the old habit, the old blood which he had not been permitted to choose for himself, which had been bequeathed him willy nilly and which had run for so long (and who knew where, battening on what of outrage and savagery and lust) before it came to him. *I could keep on,* he thought. *I could run on and on and never look back, never need to see his face again. Only I can't. I can't,* the rusted can in his hand now, the liquid sploshing in it as he ran back to the house and into it, into the sound of his mother's weeping in the next room, and handed the can to his father.

"Ain't you going to even send a nigger?" he cried. "At least you sent a nigger before!"

This time his father didn't strike him. The hand came even faster than the blow had, the same hand which had set the can on the table with almost excruciating care flashing from the can toward him too quick for him to follow it, gripping him by the back of his shirt and on to tiptoe before he had seen it quit the can, the face stooping at him in breathless and frozen ferocity, the cold, dead voice speaking over him to the older brother who leaned against the table, chewing with that steady, curious, sidewise motion of cows:

"Empty the can into the big one and go on. I'll catch up with you."

"Better tie him up to the bedpost," the brother said.

"Do like I told you," the father said. Then the boy was moving, his bunched shirt and the hard, bony hand between his shoulder-blades, his toes just touching the floor, across the room and into the other one, past the sisters sitting with spread heavy thighs in the two chairs over the cold hearth, and to where his mother and aunt sat side by side on the bed, the aunt's arms about his mother's shoulders.

"Hold him," the father said. The aunt made a startled movement. "Not you," the father said. "Lennie. Take hold of him. I want to see you do it." His mother took him by the wrist. "You'll hold him better than that. If he gets loose don't you know what he is going to do? He will go up yonder." He jerked his head toward the road. "Maybe I'd better tie him."

"I'll hold him," his mother whispered.

"See you do then." Then his father was gone, the still foot heavy and measured upon the boards, ceasing at last.

Then he began to struggle. His mother caught him in both arms, he jerking and wrenching at them. He would be stronger in the end, he knew that. But he had no time to wait for it. "Lemme go!" he cried. "I don't want to have to hit you!"

"Let him go!" the aunt said. "If he don't go, before God, I am going up there myself!"

"Don't you see I can't?" his mother cried. "Sarty! Sarty! No! No! Help me, Lizzie!"

Then he was free. His aunt grasped at him but it was too late. He whirled, running, his mother stumbled forward on to her knees behind him, crying to the nearer sister: "Catch him, Net! Catch him!" But that was too late too, the sister (the sisters were twins, born at the same time, yet either of them now gave the impression of being, encompassing as much living meat and volume and weight as any other two of the family) not yet having begun to rise form the chair, her head, face, alone merely turned, presenting to him in the flying instant an astonishing expanse of young female features untroubled by any surprise even, wearing only an expression of bovine interest. Then he was out of the room, out of the house, in the mild dust of the starlit road and the heavy rifeness of honeysuckle, the pale ribbon unspooling with terrific slowness under his running feet, reaching the gate at last and turning in, running, his heart and lungs drumming, on up the drive toward the lighted house, the lighted door. He did not knock, he burst in, sobbing for breath, incapable for the moment of speech; he saw the astonished face of the Negro in the linen jacket without knowing when the Negro had appeared.

"De Spain!" he cried, panted. "Where's . . ." then he saw the white man too emerging from a white door down the hall. "Barn!" he cried. "Barn!"

"What?" the white man said. "Barn?"

"Yes!" the boy cried. "Barn!"

"Catch him!" the white man shouted.

But it was too late this time too. The Negro grasped his shirt, but the entire sleeve, rotten with washing, carried away, and he was out that door too and in the drive again, and had actually never ceased to run even while he was screaming into the white man's face.

Behind him the white man was shouting, "My horse! Fetch my horse!" and he thought for an instant of cutting across the park and climbing the fence into the road, but he did not know the park nor how high the vine-massed fence might be and he dared not risk it. So he ran on down the drive, blood and breath roaring; presently he was in the road again though he could not see it. He could not hear either: the galloping mare was almost upon him before he heard her, and even then he held his course, as if the very urgency of his wild grief and need must in a moment more find him wings, waiting until the ultimate instant to hurl himself aside and into the weed-choked roadside ditch as the horse thundered past and on, for an instant in furious silhouette against the stars, the tranquil early summer night sky which, even before the shape of the horse and rider vanished, strained abruptly and violently upward: a long, swirling roar incredible and soundless, blotting the stars, and he springing up and into the road again, running again, knowing it was too late yet still running even after he heard the shot and, an instant later, two shots, pausing now without knowing he had ceased to run, crying "Pap! Pap!," running again before he knew he had begun to run, stumbling, tripping over something and scrabbling up again without ceasing to run, looking backward over his shoulder at the glare as he got up, running on among the invisible trees, panting, sobbing, "Father! Father!"

At midnight he was sitting on the crest of a hill. He did not know it was midnight and he did not know how far he had come. But there was no glare behind him now and he sat now, his back toward what he had called home for four days anyhow, his face toward the dark woods which he would enter when breath was strong again, small, shaking steadily in the chill darkness, hugging himself into the remainder of his thin, rotten shirt, the grief and despair now no longer terror and fear but just grief and despair. *Father. My father*, he thought. "He was brave!" he cried suddenly, aloud but not loud, no more than a whisper: "He was! He was in the war! He was in Colonel Sartoris' cav'ry!" not knowing that his father had gone to that war a private in the fine old European sense, wearing no uniform, admitting the authority of and giving fidelity to no man or army or flag, going to war as Malbrouck himself did: for booty—it meant nothing and less than nothing to him if it were enemy booty or his own.

The slow constellations wheeled on. It would be dawn and then sun-up after a while and he would be hungry. But that would be tomorrow and now he was only cold, and walking would cure that. His breathing was easier now and he decided to get up and go on, and then he found that he had been asleep because he knew it was almost dawn, the night almost over. He could tell that from the whippoorwills. They were everywhere now among the dark trees below him, constant and inflectioned and ceaseless, so that, as the instant for giving over to the day birds drew nearer and nearer, there was no interval at all between them. He got up. He was a little stiff, but walking would cure that too as it would the cold, and soon there would be the sun. He went on down the hill, toward the dark woods within which the liquid silver voices of the birds called unceasing—the rapid and urgent beating of the urgent and quiring heart of the late spring night. He did not look back.

Part Four
Criminal Matters

13

Juvenile Delinquency

"Your name," said the judge, as he eyed her,
With kindly look, yet keen,
"Is—"
"Mary Maguire, if you please, sir."
"And your age?"
"I am turned fifteen."
"Well, Mary,"—and then from a paper
He slowly and gravely read—
"You are charged here—I am sorry to say it—
With stealing three loaves of bread."

"Guilty or Not Guilty"
Author Unknown

Our earth is degenerate . . . Children no longer obey their
parents.

A carving on a stone
by an Egyptian priest
of 4,000 B.C.

Sigmund Freud and Erik Erikson are two theorists who have significantly
shaped our thoughts about human development. Freud constructed a system which links the oral, anal, phallic, latent, and genital stages. Erikson
postulated on the Eight Ages of Man—eight conflict stages—infancy (with
two stages of conflict), early childhood, middle and late childhood, adolescence, young adulthood, middle adulthood, and late adulthood. The stages
that concern us as they relate to juvenile delinquency are Freud's genital
stage and Erikson's stage of Adolescence, a stage marked by the conflict of
"Identity vs. Role Confusion."
     According to Freud, sometime between the ages of 13 and 19, each
individual enters the genital stage during which he or she experiences a
strong urge to engage in sexual activity because of the enormous physiolog-
ical changes that occur in puberty. Under Freud's theory, as the adolescent
now finds a love partner of his or her own, he or she comes to identify with
the same-sexed parent incorporating the attitudes and behavior of that parent
and so allowing him or her to complete the resolution of the Oedipus or

Electra complex that occurred earlier and during which the child had wished
to sexually possess the parent of the opposite sex.

Erikson accepted Freud's basic developmental stages but created a
whole life-span anthropological approach stressing the importance and influence of culture and society on the resulting personality. Unlike Freud,
who believed that the adolescent's formation of a stable personality depended on identification with the same-sexed parent and a resolution of sexual conflicts, Erikson stressed the importance of the adolescent conflict
which he called "Identity vs. Role Confusion." During this conflict, a successful resolution depends on the ability of the individual to select a vocation and direction in life from which he or she receives confidence and purpose. According to Freud, problems in personality development occur
when the individual becomes fixated at a stage or regresses to an earlier
stage; similarly Erikson postulates that problems develop if the individual is
unable to confront successfully and deal with the conflict of any given
stage.

Although Freud and Erikson help to begin our understanding of
personality development and lead us to see that conflicts during the stage
of adolescence can result in disturbed individuals who may become
juvenile delinquents, neither theory adequately allows for the tremendous
pressure experienced by the teenagers of today as they face schoolyards
and streets in which alcohol and drugs are as commonplace as hotdogs
and soda machines. Consider the following list of drugs which is studied
as part of the health class: heroin, morphine, methaqualone, cocaine,
marijuana, barbiturates, amphetamines, LSD, PCP, opium, codeine,
methadone, and hashish. In the same class, teenagers learn that the wrong
choice of a sexual partner can lead to AIDS and death. Many of the
teenagers in those health classes have the added burden of coming from
fragmented families in which there is no same-sexed parent with whom to
identify. Is it any wonder that many of our teenagers are depressed or
suicidal? Or that juvenile delinquency is a major problem in our troubled
society?

In "Barn Burning" we saw Colonel Sartoris Snopes "being pulled
two ways," between doing what was right and just and following his
father's unlawful path. Ironically, and fortunately for Sartoris, the identification with his father begins but is not completed. Instead Sartoris breaks
the unhealthy bonds with his family and does "not look back." Why is it
that some children raised in an environment in which many would predict
juvenile delinquency manage to break from their unhealthy and destructive
families while others do not?

"Hard to Be Good" by Bill Barich shows Shane dealing with the
problems faced by many of today's teenagers:

• A 'bust" in which the police are rough in the handling of the
teenagers and after which the police lie about the events.

• A father who deserted him and his mother.

• Shuttling backward and forward between his mother, grandparents, and a string of stepfathers (one of whom has punched both Shane and his mother).

- He is always blamed for his "attitude."

- The ever-present "other"—in schools, in neighborhoods, on planes—who have tales to tell about drugs, who impose on others to get them out of trouble, or who entice others into trouble with them.

- A mother who is about to start a new family on whom she is likely to devote more attention than on the older child from a prior marriage whose father has long since left.

- It's hard to be good.

Shane demonstrates both Freud's and Erikson's theories at work. Although he doesn't have his own father with whom to identify, Shane finds that Bentley—a past user of marijuana and an old hippie—is someone with whom he identifies. At the same time he finds himself falling in love with a female other than his mother, so working through the resolution of his Oedipus complex: He is embarrassed by his mother's naked body, and he tells her to cover up. As he works on the conflict of Identity vs. Role Diffusion, he learns that he can do a day's work for a day's pay for which he is respected. Bentley even gives him the coveted car as a reward. He needs to hear someone say, as Bentley does, "You ain't such a bad apple, after all."

Unlike Sartoris and Shane, Paul from "Paul's Case" by Willa Cather, finds no successful solution to the conflicts of adolescence. Like Shane, he is raised in a one-parent family, but he is exposed to the stern upbringing of his father rather than the liberal ways of a mother such as Shane's. Like Sartoris, Paul wishes to escape the oppression of his environment, but, unlike Sartoris, Paul self-destructs in the process. Like many teenagers, Paul seizes the day—the literary term is carpe diem; he basks in luxury, wraps himself in music and warm company, but like his symbolic red carnation, he finds that his day in the sun is transitory and fleeting.

Hard to Be Good
Bill Barich

Shane got arrested just before his sixteenth birthday. It was a dumb bust, out on a suburban street corner in Anaheim, California, on a warm spring night. A couple of cops were cruising through the haze and saw some kids passing around a joint, and they pulled over and did some unwarranted pushing and shoving, which resulted in a minor-league riot. Shane did not hit either of the cops, although they testified to the contrary in court, but he did break the antenna off their patrol car, so the judge was not entirely wrong to give him a suspended sentence and six months' probation. The whole affair was no big deal to Shane, since he didn't feel guilty about what he'd done—the cops had been *asking* for trouble—but it upset his grandparents, with whom he'd been living for some time.

His grandfather, Charlie Harris, drove him home after the court appearance. Harris was a retired phone-company executive, stocky and white-haired, who had great respect for the institutions of the world. "I hope you know how lucky are to get off easy," he said. "The judge could have thrown the book at you."

Shane was slumped in his seat, studying his fingernails. "It was a farce," he said.

"You take that kind of attitude and you'll wind up in the penitentiary."

"I'm not going to wind up in any penitentiary. Anyhow, the cops didn't tell the truth."

"Then they must have had a reason," Harris said.

After this, Harris made several secretive phone calls to his daughter Susan, who was Shane's mother. She lived in the redwood country north of San Francisco with her third husband, Roy Bentley. Bentley was some kind of wealthy manufacturer. Shane heard only bits of the conversations, but he was still able to guess what they were about. His grandparents were fed up with him. They'd been on his case ever since his school grades had started to drop, and it did no good anymore for him to explain that his math teacher failed everybody who wasn't a jock, or that his chemistry teacher was notoriously unfair—to the Harrises, teachers were in the same unimpeachable category as judges, cops, and ministers.

So Shane was not surprised when his grandfather broke the bad news. This happened one night when they were watching the stockcar races out in Riverside. They both loved speed and machinery. After the next-to-last race, Harris put his arm around Shane and told him that Susan wanted him to spend a couple of months with her during the summer. He used a casual tone of voice, but Shane understood that something irreversible had been set in motion.

"It's because of the bust, isn't it?" he asked. "I said it wasn't my fault."

"Nobody's blaming you. Your mother just wants to see you. Things are going well for her now."

"You really think Susan wants to see me?"

"Of course I do," said Harris, giving Shane a squeeze. "Listen, this Bentley guy's loaded. He owns a whole ranch. Your mom says you can have a separate cabin all to yourself. You'll have a wonderful visit."

"Not when all my friends are here," Shane said. "What's there to do in Mendocino?"

"Same stuff you do here. Don't be a baby, Shane. Where's your spirit of adventure?"

"It dissolved."

Harris moved his arm. "If you're going to take that attitude," he said, "we won't discuss it any further."

"It's always *my* attitude, isn't it? Never anybody else's."

"Shane," said Harris, as calmly as he could, "You just simmer down. You're not always going to get your own way in life. That's the simple truth of the matter." He paused for a moment. "The important thing for you to remember is that we love you."

"Oh sure," said Shane. "Sure you do."

Right after school let out in June, Shane got a check in the mail from his mother. She sent enough for him to buy a first-class plane ticket, but he bought a regular ticket instead and spent the difference on some Quaaludes and a bunch of new tapes for his cassette player. The drive to the airport seemed endless. At the last minute, his grandmother had decided to come along, too, so he was forced to sit in the back seat, like a little kid. The space was too small for his body; he thought he might explode through the metal and glass, the way the Incredible Hulk exploded through clothes. He watched the passing landscape with its giant neon figures, its many exaggerated hamburgers and hot dogs. It appeared to him now as a register of all the experiences he would be denied. He would have a summer without surf and beer, without friends, and possibly without sunshine.

The scene at the airport was as difficult as he feared it might be. His grandmother started sniffling, and then his grandfather went through a big hugging routine, and then Shane himself had to repress a terrible urge to cry. He was glad when the car pulled away, taking two white heads with it. In the coffee shop, he drank a Coke and swallowed a couple of 'ludes to calm his nerves. As the pills took hold, he began to be impressed by the interior of the terminal. It seemed very slick and shiny, hard-surfaced, with light bouncing around everywhere. The heels of people's shoes caused a lot of noise.

Susan had enclosed a snapshot with her check, and Shane removed it from his wallet to study it again. It showed his mother and Roy Bentley posed on the deck of their house. Bentley was skinny, sparsely bearded, with rotten teeth. He looked more like a dope dealer than a manufacturer. Shane figured that he probably farmed marijuana in Mendocino, where sinsemilla grew with such astounding energy that it made millionaires out of extremely improbable types. He hoped that Bentley would at least be easy to get along with; in the past, he'd suffered at the hands of Susan's men. She tended to fall for losers. Shane's father had deserted her when Shane was ten months old, vanishing into Canada to avoid both his new family and the demands of his draft board. Her second husband, a frustrated drummer for a rock band, had a violent temper. He'd punched Susan, and he'd punched Shane. Their flat in the Haight-Ashbury came to resemble a combat zone. It was the drummer's random attacks that had prompted Susan to send Shane to stay with her parents. He was supposed to be there for only a few months, but the arrangements continued for more than three years. Shane still hated the drummer. He had fantasies about meeting him someday and smashing his fingers one by one with a ball peen hammer.

When Shane's flight was announced, he drifted down a polished corridor and gave his boarding pass to a stewardess whom he was sure he'd seen in an advertisement for shampoo. He had requested a seat over a wing, so he could watch the pilot work the flaps, and he had to slip by another young man to reach it. The young man smiled a sort of monkey smile at him. He was slightly older than Shane, maybe seventeen or eighteen, and dressed in a cheap department-store suit of Glen plaid.

Once the plane had taken off, Shane finagled a miniature bourbon from the shampoo lady and drank it in a gulp. The alcohol shot to his head. He felt exhilarated and drowsy, all at the same time. He glanced over at the young man next to him, who gave off a powerful aura of cleanliness, as though he'd been scoured with buckets and brushes, and said, without thinking much about it, "Hey, I'm really ripped."

The young man smiled his pleasant monkey smile. "It's O.K.," he said reassuringly. "Jesus loves you anyhow."

Shane thought the young man had missed the point. "I'm not talking bourbon," he whispered. "I'm talking drugs."

"I guess I must have done every drug there is," the young man said. He tugged on his right ear, which, like his left, was big. "I can understand the attraction."

The young man truned out to be Darren Grady. His parents were citrus growers. He was travelling to a seminary outside San Francisco.

"You're going to be a priest?" Shane asked.

Grady shook his head. "Its more in the nature of a brotherhood. Maybe you've seen those ads in magazines asking for new brothers?" Shane had not seen the ads. "I never noticed them, either," Grady went on, chewing a handful of peanuts, "until I got the call. You want to know how I got it? I was tripping on acid at Zuma Beach, and I saw this ball of fire over the ocean. Then I heard the ball speak. 'Judgment is near,' it said. I'm not kidding you. This really happened. At first, I thought I was hallucinating, but it wouldn't go away, even after I came down."

"So what'd you do?"

"Went and saw a doctor at the free clinic. He told me to lay off the dope. So I did. But I couldn't get rid of the ball."

"That's what made you want to be a priest?"

Grady frowned. "I can never tell it right," he said, picking through the peanut dust at the bottom of his little blue-and-silver bag.

Shane was moved by Grady's story. He'd had similar baffling trips, during which his mind had disgorged images of grievous importance, but he'd never ascribed a religious meaning to any of them. He felt foolish for bragging about taking pills. In order to set the record straight, he explained to Grady that he'd been exposed to drugs very early in life, because his mother had been a hippie; she'd named him after her favorite movie.

"It's not as bad as some names," Grady said. "I had a guy named Sunbeam in my class last year. Anyhow, you can go into court and get it changed."

Shane didn't want to see another judge, ever. "It doesn't bother me much now," he said, looking out at the sky. "When we lived in the Haight, Susan's husband, he was this drummer—he'd let me pass around joints during parties. Sometimes he'd let me have a hit. Susan knew, but I don't think she cared. I was so small, probably not much of it got into me. I don't know, though. I hate it when I see little kids smoking dope around school. You ought to be at least thirteen before you start.

"Maybe you should never start," Grady said.

"I wouldn't go that far. It helps to calm you."

"Grady tapped his breastbone. "The calm should come from inside," he said.

It seemed to Shane that Grady was truly wise for his age, so he confided all his troubles. Grady listened patiently until he was done. "I don't want to downplay it, Shane," he said, "but I'm sure it'll be over soon. that's how it is with troubles. They float from one person to the next. It's bound to come clear for you real soon."

Shane's high had worn off by the time the plane landed. He and Grady took a bus into the city, and at the Greyhound station, off Market Street, they exchanged addresses and phone numbers. The light outside the station was intense, bathing bums and commuters in gold. Shane was feeling relaxed, but he got anxious again when Grady left for the seminary. He was nervous about seeing Susan; their last visit, down in Anaheim at Christmas, had been marked by stupid quarrels. He tried talking to a soldier who was also waiting around, but it didn't work. The soldier was chewing about four sticks of gum. Shane asked him to buy a bottle of apple wine, so they could split it, and when the soldier did Shane drank most of it, washing down two more pills in the process. He was semiconscious on the bus ride up the coast. The town of Mendocino, arranged on a cliff overlooking the Pacific, struck him as a misinterpretation of New England. "It's cute," he said, to nobody in particular.

From the lobby of an inn on the main drag, he phoned his mother, and then he fell asleep in a chair. Later, he heard somebody (he thought it was Susan) say, "Aw, Roy, he's wrecked," so he said a few words in return and walked wobbly-legged to a station wagon. The next thing he knew, somebody was handing him a sandwich. He took it apart, laying the various components—cheese, tomatoes, alfalfa sprouts, two slices of bread—on the table. It occurred to him that he wasn't hungry. He said something to that effect, and somebody said something back—Bentley, the guy from the photo. He followed Bentley into a black night. Moisture from redwood branches dripped onto his head. The air seemed to be eating into his skin. Bentley unlocked the door of a cabin that smelled of pitch and camphor, and said something about extra blankets. Then Shane was alone. The whirlies hit him, and he stumbled to a small, unstable bed. After he was under the covers, the whirlies subsided, and he was able to assess his surroundings. He thought they were pretty nice. The only thing that concerned him was that there seemed to be animals in the cabin—they didn't scratch or howl, but he was aware of them anyway, lurking just beyond his line of vision.

The animals were ducks, two of them, with bulbs inside glowing like hearts. Shane saw them when he woke in the morning. Gradually, he remembered where he was, alone with the details of his arrival, and he felt disgusted and ashamed and yanked the covers over his head.

For some reason, he started thinking about Darren Grady. He was certain that Grady had never pulled such a dumb stunt. He wondered if Grady had made it to the seminary and if the other priests had shaved off his hair; he wondered, too, if Grady would recall their meeting or if all such mundane occurrences would automatically vanish from his mind, to be replaced by a steady image of God. Fifteen minutes or so passed in this fashion, helping to temper Shane's guilt and instill in him a new commitment to righteous behavior. He didn't pretend that he could ever be as wise and good as Grady, but he considered it within his power to improve. He got out of bed, examined the ducks more closely—they were lamps—and then, outside the cabin, he dumped his remaining pills on the ground and crushed them to dust. The act was like drawing breath.

Bentley's place was indeed like a ranch, fenced in and isolated from any neighbors. There were a few outbuildings, including a chicken coop and a beat-up barn missing boards from its siding. Inside the barn, Shane found birds' nests, rusty tools, and a broken-down old Chrysler with fish fins. Parts from the Chrysler's carburetor were scattered on a shelf, leaking oil.

Shane expected to be jumped on as soon as he opened the door to the main house, but nobody seemed to be around. He had no memory of its interior, except as a series of difficult-to-negotiate planes and angles. In the kitchen, he poured himself a glass of orange juice and sat down to read the sports page of a day-old paper. He heard his mother call to him from upstairs. "Is that you, Shane?" she asked. "Come up here right now. I want to talk to you."

He poured more juice and went up. "Where are you, Susan?"

"In here. I'm taking a bath."

The bathroom door was ajar; steam escaped from within. Shane peeked and saw his mother in the tub, under a layer of froth and bubbles. Her hair was pinned up; it was thick, still mostly black, with a few gray strands. Shane thought she was immensely beautiful. He couldn't remember how old she was—maybe forty. The number was an ancient one, but he believed that it didn't really apply.

"Don't just stand there," she said. "It's drafty. Come in and shut the door." When he was inside, she said, "you look a little better today."

"Feel a little better," Shane said.

"How about a kiss for the old lady?"

He bent down, intending to kiss her on the cheek, but she lifted her arms from the water and embraced him. The sudden movement lifted her out of the soapsuds, so that her breasts were briefly visible. Shane had seen her naked before, countless times—in bathtubs and at nude beaches—but the quality of her flesh seemed different now, echoing as it did the flesh in the girlie magazines that he hid in his room in Anaheim.

"Oh, Shane," she said, pushing him away, "you were such a mess last night. What happened to you?"

Shane put his hands in his pockets. "Me and this friend of mine, Grady, we bought a bottle of apple wine and drank it at the bus station." He was quiet for a second or two. "I'm sorry I did it," he added.

"Well, you *should* be sorry. You gave us a real scare. When you behave like that, it makes me think you want me to feel guilty. I know I shouldn't have left you with Grandma and Grandpa for so long. You're my responsibility and I've done a poor job of raising you."

Shane recognized this as therapist talk; Susan was always seeing one kind of counsellor or another. Left to her own devices, she would have sputtered and thrown something at him. Once, she'd almost beaned him with a ladle; another time, an entire needlepoint kit had whistled by his ear. "You can't *raise* me, Susan," he said. "I'm not spinach."

She laughed and looked directly at him. "No, you're not spinach. But you'd better be telling me the truth about last night. It better not be pills again."

"It's not pills."

"It better not be, because if you get caught fooling with them you could go to jail, you know. It's a violation of your probation. I don't understand how you got arrested in the first place. Who were those kids you were hanging around with?"

"There's nothing wrong with the kids," Shane said heatedly. "The cops started it. Anyway, Susan since when are you so much against drugs? You used to smoke a joint every morning."

"I haven't smoked marijuana in years."

"Sure, Susan."

"Don't you dare talk to me like that, Shane," she said. "I'm your mother."

"I know."

"I'm not trying to be moralistic or anything. I just want you to keep out of trouble." She stood up in the tub; water dripped down her breasts, all down her body. "Give me that towel, will you honey?"

He grabbed a towel from the rack and threw it at her, much too hard.

She pressed the towel against her chest. "*Now* what is it?"

"What do you *think* it is? Christ, Susan, don't you have any modesty?"

"I'm sorry," she said, embarrassed. "I forgot how old you are." She wrapped herself tightly in a terry-cloth robe. "Go downstairs and I'll make us some breakfast."

The eggs she fried were brown and fertile, with brilliant orange yolks. She served them on red ceramic plates from Mexico. The colors made Shane's head swim, but he still ate with appetite. He was glad the confrontation with Susan was over. Their future together no longer seemed littered with obstacles. As she moved about the kitchen, banging pots and pans in the careless way she had, he felt a deep and abiding fondness for her, even though he knew that she had presented him with a complicated life by refusing to simplify her own. Charlie Harris called her a "nonconformist," and Shane supposed that he was right—if you ordered Susan to do one thing, she'd be certain to do the opposite. He respected her independent streak, because he had a similar streak in him; they were joined in a bond forged of trial and error.

After Susan cleared the table, she gave him some towels to put in the cabin and told him that she was going into town. He wanted to go with her, but she wouldn't let him.

"I don't mind errands," he said. He wanted to see what Mendocino looked like when it wasn't scrambled. "I could help you carry bags and stuff."

"We'll go tomorrow," Susan said firmly. "I'll have more time then. Today I've got my yoga class and a doctor's appointment." She came up behind him and hugged him. He could smell her sweet, fresh hair. Her breasts pressed against his backbone. "I love you very, very much," she said. "Now go get yourself clean."

Shane went dutifully out of the house, but he was worried a little. The word "doctor" had an awful connotation, like "teacher" or "cop." He had a terrible feeling that Susan might be sick. So a new thing began to haunt him—he ought to have been a better son. He remembered how in March his grandmother had reminded him to mail a birthday card to Susan, and how he had gone to the pharmacy and bought himself a candy bar instead. What possible use would candy be when Susan was in her grave? "You're so selfish," he said to himself, kicking at a pinecone. Every problem in the world, he saw, had its roots in some falling away from goodness.

That afternoon, around lunch time, Shane was in the old barn, sitting behind the wheel of the Chrysler and staring at the bird-peopled rafters, when Bentley wandered in and interrupted his daydream, which had to do with driving at great speeds over the surface of the moon. In person, Bentley looked even more disreputable than he had in the photograph. He could have been a bowlegged prospector who'd spent the last thirty or forty years eating nothing but desert grit. His rotten teeth were like bits of sandstone hammered into his gums. "How's the boy?" he asked in a twangy, agreeable voice, leaning his elbows on the car door.

"The boys' fine," Shane said. "He's just fine."

"Well, I'm happy about that. I'd like to have the boy step from behind the steering wheel of the car so that I can have a chat with him."

Reluctantly, Shane got out of the car. His hands were balled into fists. Down in Anaheim, he'd decided that if Bentley was a puncher, he'd punch first.

"Take it easy," Bentley said. "I'm not going to hit you."

"Wouldn't put it past you to try," Shane muttered.

Bentley lifted an expensive lizard-skin cowboy boot and ground out the cigarette he'd been smoking against the sole. "I lost my taste for violence a long time ago," he said. "Course, if I needed to, I could still fold you up and put you in my pocket with the Marlboros."

"I'm warning you," Shane said, backing off.

"The trouble is, Shane," said Bentley, following him, "your mother and I got a good thing going, and I don't want some wise-ass punk from surfer land to come around and spoil it. You pull the kind of crap you pulled last night one more time, and I'll stick you into a Jiffy bag and mail you home to the old folks."

"You can't boss me around."

At this, Bentley chuckled a bit, revealing the stumps in his mouth. "Sure I can," he said. "So long as you're on my property, and living off my kindness, I am most assuredly your boss. And here's some more news, my friend—I'm putting you to work." When Shane protested, Bentley cut him short by jabbing him in the sternum. "I'm giving you two choices. Either you can work by yourself at the ranch, and do some painting and cleaning, or your can work with me at the factory."

"What's your business?"

"I'm a manufacturer."

"Yeah, but what do you manufacture?"

"What I manufacture," said Bentley, "is ducks."

They went to visit the factory in Bentley's station wagon, which smelled of stale tobacco and leather. "See that rise?" Bentley asked Shane, as they passed a sloping hillside off to the right. "If you were to walk to the top of it and then down into the gully, you'd come to another twenty-acre parcel I own."

"Do you have another house there?"

Bentley gave him a peculiar look. "No house, no nothing," he said. "It just sits. It's appreciating in value. We'll have a picnic there someday."

"My grandfather," said Shane, "he loves to barbecue."

"We don't barbecue," Bentley said. "What we do is eat that organic food that Susan cooks. The woman has a fear of meat." He turned on the radio; a country singer was singing about beer and divorce. "Listen here, boy," Bentley continued, "I want you to have a good time this summer. I'm not naive about dope. I've done my share of it. But you have to learn yourself some moderation. Moderation is the key. You keep on abusing yourself the way you're going, you'll wind up in a pine box."

"My grandfather said I'd wind up in the penitentiary."

"That, too," Bentley said.

The factory was situated at the edge of town, in a concrete building that might once have been a machine shop. Inside, ten or twelve young longhairs, both men and women, formed an assembly line at long wooden tables. As Bentley had said, they were making ducks—or duck lamps—by gluing two pieces of heavy-duty celluloid around a metal stand that had a socket at the top for a bulb. Once the duck halves were glued together, they were secured with rubber bands and left to dry for a day or two. The excess glue was later wiped from the ducks with solvent, and they were put in cardboard boxes and cradled in excelsior. The wholesale price was twelve dollars a duck, but they were sold in trendy stores for as much as forty apiece. The materials came from Hong Kong.

Shane was shocked. His mind boggled at the notion that somebody could earn a fortune on celluloid ducks. The arithmetic didn't seem right. Forty dollars? Who'd pay forty dollars? A movie star? Were there enough duck-loving movie stars to provide Bentley with the capital to own a ranch and forty-odd acres? Apparently so. But Shane remained suspicious—the scam was too good to be true. He wished that Harris, who was always harping on the importance of hard work, could be there to watch Bentley as he lounged around the shop, smoking cigarettes and joking with his crew. Harris would go right through the roof; he'd say the whole shebang was un-American. Shane liked the atmosphere, though. Nobody treated the craft of duck-making very seriously. Besides, a tall blond girl with ironed hair kept glancing at him from across the room; he fell into an immediate fantasy about her. He told Bentley he'd prefer to work at the factory instead of at the ranch.

"I'll start you in the morning," Bentley said. "You'll be a duck packer. You'll pack so many damn ducks, you'll be quacking in your sleep."

They locked up after everybody had quit for the day. On the ride home, Shane's thoughts drifted back to Susan, and he asked Bentley if anything was wrong with her.

"No way," Bentley said. "She's a fine, fine lady. Absolutely perfect."

"I mean, is she sick or anything?"

"Sick? No, she's not sick. She's just got some female trouble. When you get older, you'll learn that every woman has it sooner or later. They can't avoid it, and you can't help 'em with it. It's just something they have to go through on their own," Bentley said with a sigh. "We'll talk about it more when we get to the ranch."

But Shane didn't bring up the subject again (he was afraid of what he might hear), and Bentley volunteered no further information. Instead, they returned to the barn and played with the Chrysler until they were both covered with oil. They cleaned the points and plugs and reinstalled the carburetor. Bentley showed Shane how the engine had been modified to make it operate at maximum efficiency. "Let's fire up the sumbitch," he said wiping his face on a polka-dotted bandanna. He let Shane sit in the driver's seat and try the ignition, but the engine wouldn't turn over. "Pump the pedal," he said. Shane pumped it and tried the ignition again. The engine roared. It sounded big in the barn, scattering robins and swallows into the dusk. Shane floored the pedal briefly and felt himself transported; energy ran through him as though he were a sieve.

After Shane had been at the factory for three weeks, he sent a postcard to his Anaheim pal Burt, the kid who'd actually hit a cop during the bust. He described his cabin, the redwoods, and the facory. "If you want to come up here," he wrote, "I can squeeze in another bed easy. And don't worry about me doing any you-know-what. I'm off that stuff for good."

Twice his grandparents called to see how he was getting along. He still felt estranged from them, and this was compounded when they told him they'd bought a camper and were going to Joshua Tree National Monument until mid-August unless Shane planned to come back before then.

"Me?" he asked, sounding wounded. "Since when do *I* have plans?"

For the next twenty-four hours, he was sullen and depressed, but he had to work at it, because he was having so much fun on the job. Every morning at eight, he and Bentley headed off together into a coastal fogbank that was always just beginning to disperse. They drank coffee from Styrofoam cups and told each other duck jokes while they watched the sky separate into a confetti mist under which the town of Mendocino stood exposed, back from wherever it went at night. Shane packed boxes with a ponytailed guy who was known as Eager on account of his last name, Beaver. Eager was anything but—he had a meticulous nature, and he took pains to be sure that each duck was nestled as comfortably as possible in its excelsior. He could have been packing eggs or glassware. "C'mon, Eager," Shane said to him one afternoon. "They're not alive, you know."

The tall blond girl was Emma King. She was nineteen, a college student. Shane followed her around like a dog. When the weather was hot, Emma came to the factory in white shorts and a red halter top, and Shane would monitor her every movement from his packing station, waiting for her to reach down for a tube of glue or bend low for the X-Acto knife she kept dropping on the floor. She had a boyfriend she saw on weekends, but she told Shane that she'd go to the movies with him before he returned to Anaheim. "I'm in love with this heavy girl, she's *nineteen!!!*" he wrote on another postcard to Burt. "We go drinking together after work." This was almost true, or at least at the outer fringe of validity. One Friday, Eager *had* invited him to go to a tavern in the woods where anybody could get served, but he'd decided against it to avoid trouble. Later, he heard that Emma had been there, so in his mind they were linked.

He asked her for a photo, but she didn't have any, so he borrowed Susan's camera and snapped her in different poses, while she pretended to complain. The cutest shot was one of Emma kissing a duck on its beak. Shane taped it to the dashboard of the Chrysler. He thought of it as his car now. Bentley had promised it to him in lieu of wages if he could pass his driver's test. Already, he was practicing. He did Y-turns and parallel parking. Some evenings, he and Bentley took a ride to the ocean, steaming down dirt roads that were dotted with Scotch broom and beach poppies. Once, Bentley let him go by himself, without any adult supervision, and he handled the Chrysler with such authority and skill that he developed a stitch in his side from excitement. It was a mystery to him how things kept changing.

Another mystery was his mother. He'd never seen her so happy.

He could not reconcile so much happiness, in fact, with scraggly, bow-legged, rotten-toothed Bentley. Here was a man who could walk around for days with egg in his beard and never even notice. The scent of nicotine was embedded in his clothes and maybe in his skin. Could it be that love had nothing to do with beauty? If Bentley could provoke love, then so could a stone or a twig. So could a garbage can.

But there was no denying Susan's contentment. She thrived on Bentley's generosity. She seemd to float around the house, gliding barefoot an inch or two above the floor, dressed in blouses and peasant skirts that showed off her bosomy fullness. She baked bread, hummed romantic tunes, and filled all her vases with flowers. She was constantly hugging her egg-stained lover, patting him on his flat little prospector's ass. The affection spilled over to Shane. Susan's arms were always grasping for him, making up for lost time. She drew him to her for purposes of both measurement and embrace. The very size of him seemed to thrill her—he'd grown from almost nothing! "Oh, Shane," she'd say in a husky voice, holding a hunk of his cheek between her thumb and index finger. "You're such a dear boy."

If Shane hadn't known better he would have sworn that she was stoned all the time, but he'd never seen any dope in the house. As far as he could tell, the Bentleys had adopted a much more civilized vice. They drank wine—a bottle or two every evening, with Bentley leading the way. The wine burnished their faces. It made them talkative, sentimental, occasionally teary-eyed. After dinner, if the fog wasn't too thick, they'd put on sweaters and sit on the deck and speak in conspiratorial tones about the day's events, while bats sailed about overhead, like punctuation. When there was nothing on TV, Shane sat with them, shivering no matter how many layers of clothing he wore.

"Thin blood," Bentley would say, teasing him. "Goddam thin Southern California surfer's blood."

"My blood's fine."

"It's *thin*, Shane. It takes six months for blood to adapt to a new climate."

Blood was yet another mystery. Sometimes Shane thought that he understood Susan better than Bentley did, simply because they were related by blood instead of marriage. Although he and Susan had often lived apart, had quarrelled and made mistakes, she was still his mother, and he was able, in a curious way, to anticipate her moods and know when something was bothering her. One night, as they sat outside, he saw that she was unusually quiet, removed from the conversation, and when Bentley went into the house he asked her if she'd got bad news at the doctor's office—she'd had another in her ongoing series of appointments that afternoon. The question made him tremble. Suppose she confessed something awful to him? Ignorance was a kind of protection. But she only smiled wistfully and patted his hand and said no, nothing very serious was wrong. It was just that the doctor had told her that she might need an operation—minor corrective surgery. She started to explain the problem to him in clinical terms, but it sounded indecent somehow to hear her describe her body as though it were an engine in need of repair, so he interrupted. "I know," he said, mimicking Bentley's sad resignation. "Female trouble." He put an arm around her, wanting to say more, but by then Bentley was back with full wineglasses and a word about the rising moon.

Shane's driving test was scheduled for a Thursday afternoon. Bentley gave him permission to come home early from work to practice. He backed the Chrysler into the barn several times without scratching it, and then he walked over to the house, hoping that Susan would make him a snack, but she'd gone to town for her yoga class. The phone rang while he was eating a boiled hot dog. Darren Grady was on the line, calling from Elk, a town south of Mendocino. Grady was upset, distressed, talking a mile a minute. He'd run away from the seminary. He was stranded, broke. Shane couldn't believe it. Where had Grady's wisdom gone? "Take it easy, Darren," he said. "Everything's going to be all right."

But Grady was blubbering. "I was trying to hitch to your place," he said, "But his highway patrol, he kicked me off the road. I cooled it in the bushes for a while and tried again, but here comes old highway patrol with his flasher on. I gave him the finger and split for town. I'm like a hunted cirminal, Shane. You got to help me."

Shane glanced at the kitchen clock. He figured that he could get to Elk and back before he and Bentley were scheduled to meet the state examiner, so he told Grady to sit tight. The drive over there took about twenty minutes and gave him a severe case of paranoia. Every car that approached him seemed from a distance to be black and ominous and full of cops.

Grady was where he said he'd be, in front of a restaurant. He was sitting on the curb and eating a hamburger—some ketchup was on his chin—and drinking a can of beer. When he saw Shane, he waved wildly and let loose his monkey smile. Shane was surprised that Grady still had hair—there was no bald spot or anything. The only truly abused part of him was his Glen plaid suit. All its department-store slickness had been rubbed away; there were holes in the knees of his trousers, as if he'd been on a long pilgrimage over concrete. Also, he'd lost his socks. The confidence he'd had on the plane was gone; now he was nothing but fidget. "I'll never forget you for this, Shane," he said, getting to his feet. "Is this yours?" he asked in wonderment, touching the Chrysler's fins. "It's a mean machine."

Shane eyed the half-demolished burger. "I thought you were broke," he said.

"I am, but I talked up the waitress in there"—Grady jerked his streaked face in the direction of the restaurant—"and traded her my Bible."

"She gave you beer for a Bible?"

"Just the hamburger. The beer I found."

This sounded fishy to Shane. "Where'd you find it?" he asked.

"Some guy left it on the seat of his car." Grady climbed into the Chrysler. For a moment, he seemed collected, drawn virtuously into himself, but then he fell apart and started bawling. "You're the only damn friend I've got," he said, blowing his nose in the hamburger wrapper.

Grady told Shane that he'd been on the road for three days. The first night, after he'd snuck out of the seminary, he hitched to San Francisco

and slept in the Greyhound station, thinking he would catch a bus to Anaheim in the morning, but when he woke he realized that he'd have to
confront his parents with the sorry evidence of his failure, so, instead of
phoning them, he walked over to Powell Street and ate a breakfast of crab
and shrimp at a place that was shaped like the prow of a ship, and then
spent twenty-two bucks playing video games at an arcade. This left him
with just one dollar to his name—his emergency dollar, which he kept
folded in sixteenths and hidden in the secret compartment of his wallet.
When he pulled it out, the slip of paper on which Shane had written Susan's
address and phone number fell to the floor.

"You get it?" Grady asked, turning towards Shane, who was paying
only a little attention, since he had to watch for cops. "It was a *sign!*"

"What about the ball?" Shane asked. His forehead was wrinkled in
concentration.

"Ball? What ball?"

"The ball from Zuma Beach. Did it come back while you were with
the priests?"

"It never did."

"Then why'd you leave?"

Grady shrugged. His fidgety fingers picked at his knees through
the holes in his pants. "It's hard to be good," he said. From the pockets of
his suit coat he took two fresh cans of beer and—before Shane could
protest—popped the tops. Shane accepted a can and tucked it between his
thighs. He hit a bump and got doused.

On the second day, Grady said, he'd reached the town of Healds-
burg. He said it was the hottest place he'd ever been to—hotter than Hell,
frankly. In the evening, when it got too dark to hitch anymore, he wandered to the town square, where there were palm trees and flowers and
benches, and he took off his shoes and socks and dunked his feet in a
fountain. The water felt soothing as it swirled between his toes, but a
bunch of Mexicans who were hanging around the square kept watching
him, and he thought they might knife him or otherwise do him harm. He
knew this was an irrational fear, but it was fear nonetheless, so he gathered
himself together in a hurry, slipped his wet feet into his shoes, and walked
briskly down a side street that led him to a vineyard, where he curled upon
the warm ground and slept the night away under cover of grape leaves. A
flaming sun woke him at dawn. He couldn't find his socks. Their absence
seemed to hurt him more than anything else. "Everybody knows you're
running away from something if you don't have socks on," he said, biting
his lower lip. "Who's going to stop for a person with bare ankles?" With
this, he finished his beer in a gulp and threw the empty can out the window.
The can rattled over the macadam, bounced two or three times, and rolled
past the nose of a highway-patrol car that was parked in the bushes, waiting
for speeders.

"Aw, Grady," Shane said.

Grady swivelled around to look back. "That's the guy I gave the
finger to," he said.

Shane felt as though his body had been stripped of a dimension and
then spliced into a deadly, predictable horror movie. He tried to imagine

that the cop hadn't seen the can—or, better, that the cop had decided to overlook it—but this didn't work, since the cop had left his hiding place and was approaching the Chrysler at a steady clip. Shane gave Grady the half-full beer he had between his thighs, and Grady dropped down in the seat and drank it off, then shoved the empty into the glove compartment. The cop came closer. Grady looked again, and, panicked, said, "He's going to bust us. Shane. I know by his face."

"You don't know for sure."

The cops' flasher went on.

Grady sank lower in the seat. "I'm holding, Shane," he said morosely.

Shane didn't want to take his eyes from the road. "You're *what*?"

"I'm holding some speed. I bought it at that arcade." He showed Shane four pills. "Should I throw them out the window?"

The pills got swallowed—Shane couldn't think of any other way to dispose of them. He and Grady ate two apiece, which lent a hallucinatory edge to subsequent events. The cop was wearing reflector sunglasses, for instance, so that Shane was able to watch himself react to the words that bubbled from between the cop's lips when the cop pulled them over. The cop spoke of littering, of underage drinking, of operating a motor vehicle without a license and without what he called a vehicular-registration slip. Eyeless, he led Shane and Grady to his car and locked them in the back seat behind a mesh screen. The pills really took hold on the ride to the police station, and Shane was possessed by a powerful sense of urgency and a concomitant inability to stop talking. He believed that he had an important message to deliver about the nature of goodness, and he delivered it ceaselessly—to the cop, to the officer who booked him, to the ink of the fingerprint pad, and to the cold iron bars of his cell.

Roy Bentley bailed out the boys. He came to the station with his attorney, a fashionably dressed man whose hair was all gray curls. The attorney seemed to know everybody around, and after a brief back-room conversation he reported to Bentley that the charges—except for littering—had been dropped. Bentley paid a stiff fine, then put the boys in his wagon and drove them to the ranch. They were amazed to be let go so quickly. "You must be important, Mr. Bentley," Grady said.

"You two are just lucky I've got some clout," Bentley told them. "A successful businessman is not a nobody up here. I'm a Democrat and I belong to the Rotary. But don't think it's over yet. You still got Shane's mother to face."

Susan exploded. There was no therapist talk this time. When Shane came through the door, slinking like an animal, she yelled and threw a potholder at him, and then, so as not to be discriminatory, she threw one at Grady, too. She grabbed Shane by the hair and held him in place while she lectured him. She said he was an ungrateful little bastard, spoiled indifferent, snotty, rotten to the core. He refused to argue, but in the morning, when she was almost rational again, he explained to her exactly why he had done what he'd done, so that she would understand that he hadn't been frivolous or irresponsible. "It was circumstances, see?" he said, sitting forward in his chair and kneading his hands. "I couldn't just leave him in Elk, could I? How would you feel if you called some friend of yours for help and the friend said no?"

"What about Roy, Shane?" she asked. "You could have phoned him at the factory, and he would have gone for Darren."

"But it was an emergency, Susan."

"The only emergency was that you didn't think."

The next day she was more forgiving, taking into account his unblemished record, and also the fact that he had been (at least to some extent) victimized. She also agreed that Grady could stay in the cabin for a few days, provided that he let his parents know where he was. This Grady did. "Hello, Dad?" he said to his father, while Shane listened in. "It's me, Darren, your son. Remember about the seminary? Well you were right. It didn't work out."

In the cabin, Shane and Grady lay on their beds in the dark and had long philosophical discussions. Grady said that when he got home he was going to forget about religion and enroll in a junior college to study biology, so he'd have a grasp of how the universe was put together. "Science today," he said, "it has the answer to mysteries that puzzled the ancients." Shane confessed that he was dreading his senior year in high school; he would be an entirely different person when he returned to that bleak, airless building, yet nobody would acknowledge it. "The system hates what's real," he said. Grady agreed.

On more than one occasion, they talked about how strange it is that sometimes when you do everything right, everything comes out wrong. Grady had examples. "I gave my sister this kitten for her birthday," he said, "and she was allergic to it." Or "Once when I was small, I washed my mom's car to surprise her, but I used steel wool and scratched up the paint."

Shane had other questions. "If it was me stranded in Elk," he asked, "would you have come and got me?"

"You know it," Grady said, with emotion crowding his throat.

Both of them took a solemn vow never to touch dope again, ever, in any form, no matter how tempted they might be.

Grady ended up staying for better than two weeks. Several important things happened while he was around.

First, Shane passed his rescheduled driver's test and celebrated by pinstriping the Chrysler and painting flames on both its doors. Then he asked Emma King to go the drive-in with him. They went to a kung-fu double feature on a Friday night. She sat so far away from him that it seemed a deliberate attempt to deny his existence. He thought that maybe older women expected men to be bold, so after a while he walked his fingers across the seat and brushed them against Emma's thigh. She sneezed. He withdrew. Later, on the steps of her house, much to his surprise, she kissed him full on the lips and told him he was sweet. He knew it was the only kiss he'd ever get from her, so, driving home, he made a mental inventory of the moment and its various tactile sensations.

Next, on a Saturday afternoon, he and Grady took the Chrysler to the main town beach, but it was crowded with hippies throwing Frisbees to their dogs, and Shane suggested that they go instead to this great isolated spot even he had never been to before—Bentley's twenty undeveloped acres. They had to slide under a barbed-wire fence that had No Trespassing and Private Property signs plastered all over it. The trail down into the gully was steep and overgrown; the gully, in fact, was more like a canyon with a stream trickling through it, and vegetation spouting from the soil. The vegetation was so thick and matted that it was almost impossible for them to distinguish individual plants, but one of the plants they *could* distinguish was marijuana. A few stalky specimens were growing wild, like weeds. All Shane's suspicions were confirmed—Bentley was a grower.

"That's why he had the attorney," he whispered to Grady.

"Are you going to say anything?"

"Uh-uh. No way."

But Shane's conscience bothered him. In the eyes of the law, Bentley was a criminal. Did this put Susan in jeopardy, too? Would she be considered an accessory to the crime? So Shane spilled the beans to Bentley. He told him about the find and waited for Bentley to react.

Bentley tugged at the strands of his beard. "Well, you got me, all right," he said sheepishly. "I did grow me a few crops of Colombian down there a while back, before I met your mother, but the whole experience rubbed me wrong. I had a couple of brushes with John Law, and they made me real nervous. That's why I took my profits and went into ducks. Ducks are as legal as it gets."

"What about the plants we saw?"

"Must be volunteers. That happens sometimes. Stuff grows from old seeds, leftover seeds. We'll go pull 'em up."

They pulled up all the marijuana plants in the gully, arranged them in a pyre, and burned them. "It's sad," said Bentley. "But it has to be."

Next, Susan went in to the hospital for her operation. The surgery was performed in the afternoon, and Shane was allowed to visit that evening. He was scared. Susan was in a private room. She was still groggy from her anesthesia, and she had an I.V. tube in her arm. He thought she was asleep, but she called to him in a funny, childlike voice and asked him to sit in a chair by the bed. "I'm in the clouds," she said, rubbing his hand.

"But are you O.K.?"

"I'm fine," she said. "The doctor fixed everything. He says I can probably have a baby now."

"A *baby*?"

"You think I'm too old, don't you?"

"I don't know," Shane said. "How am I supposed to know about babies?"

"Lots of women have babies at my age," Susan said, rubbing and rubbing. "Roy and I want to try. Oh, Shane honey, I made things so tough on you, I want another chance. Don't I deserve another chance?"

"Sure," said Shane. "Of course you do."

But the potential baby confused him, and also depressed him a bit. In his mind, it was rotten-toothed, bearded, and smelling of tobacco. He wondered why Susan would want to introduce such a creature into the world. "I'm never going to understand anything," he complained to Grady that night. "Not anything."

"What's there to understand?" Grady asked.

"Maybe you are wise, Grady," said Shane.

Grady left at the end of the week. Shane dropped him at the Greyhound stop in Mendocino. They shook hands in a special way they'd devised, with plenty of interlocked fingers and thumbs.

"I never had a friend like you before," Grady said. "I'll never forget what you did for me.

"I'd do it again," said Shane. "Any time."

In late August, there was an unseasonal thunderstorm. It rattled windowpanes and made chickens flap in their coops. When it was over, the morning sky was clear and absolutely free of fog. Shane got up early and changed the oil in the Chrysler. He filled the trunk with his belongings and put a pair of ducks for the Harrises on the back seat. Susan was not entirely recovered from her surgery, so he had to say goodbye to her in her bedroom, where she was propped up against pillows. She asked him again if he didn't want to transfer to a school in Mendocino and stay on with them, but he told her that he missed his grandparents and his friends. "I might come back next summer," he said, kissing her on the cheek. "You'll probably have the baby by then." Bentley stuck fifty dollars in the pocket of his jeans. "You ain't such a bad apple, after all," said Bentley with a smile. Shane drove off quickly, without looking back. The highway was still slick and wet from the rain, and the scent of eucalyptus was in the air.

Paul's Case
Willa Cather

It was Paul's afternoon to appear before the faculty of the Pittsburgh High
School to account for his various misdemeanors. He had been suspended a
week ago, and his father had called at the Principal's office and confessed
his perplexity about his son. Paul entered the faculty room suave and smiling. His clothes were a trifle outgrown, and the tan velvet on the collar of
his open overcoat was frayed and worn; but for all that there was something
of the dandy about him, and he wore an opal pin in his neatly knotted black
four-in-hand, and a red carnation in his buttonhole. This latter adornment
the faculty somehow felt was not properly significant of the contrite spirit
befitting a boy under the ban of suspension.

Paul was tall for his age and very thin, with high, cramped shoulders and a narrow chest. His eyes were remarkable for a certain hysterical
brilliancy, and he continually used them in a conscious, theatrical sort of
way, peculiarly offensive in a boy. The pupils were abnormally large, as
though he were addicted to belladonna, but there was a glassy glitter about
them which that drug does not produce.

When questioned by the Principal as to why he was there, Paul
stated, politely enough, that he wanted to come back to school. This was a
lie, but Paul was quite accustomed to lying; found it, indeed, indispensable
for overcoming friction. His teachers were asked to state their respective
charges against him, which they did with such a rancour and aggrievedness
as evinced that this was not a usual case. Disorder and impertinence were
among the offences named, yet each of his instructors felt that it was
scarcely possible to put into words the real cause of the trouble, which lay
in a sort of hysterically defiant manner of the boy's; in the contempt which
they all knew he felt for them, and which he seemingly made not the least
effort to conceal. Once, when he had been making a synopsis of a para-
graph at the blackboard, his English teacher had stepped to his side and attempted to guide his hand. Paul had started back with a shudder and thrust
his hands violently behind him. The astonished woman could scarcely have
been more hurt and embarrassed had he struck at her. The insult was so involuntary and definitely personal as to be unforgettable. In one way and
another, he had made all his teachers, men and women alike, conscious of
the same feeling of physical aversion. In one class he habitually sat with his
hand shading his eyes; in another he always looked out of the window dur-

ing the recitation; in another he made a running commentary on the lecture, with humorous intention.

His teachers felt this afternoon that his whole attitude was symbolized by his shrug and his flippantly red carnation flower, and they fell upon him without mercy, his English teacher leading the pack. He stood through it smiling, his pale lips parted over his white teeth. (His lips were continually twitching, and he had a habit of raising his eyebrows that was contemptuous and irritating to the last degree.) Older boys than Paul had broken down and shed tears under that baptism of fire, but his set smile did not once desert him, and his only sign of discomfort was the nervous trembling of the fingers that toyed with the buttons of his overcoat, and an occasional jerking of the other hand that held his hat. Paul was always smiling, always glancing about him, seeming to feel that people might be watching him and trying to detect something. This conscious expression, since it was as far as possible from boyish mirthfulness, was usually attributed to insolence or "smartness."

As the inquisition proceeded, one of his instructors repeated an impertinent remark of the boy's, and the Principal asked him whether he thought that a courteous speech to have made to a woman. Paul shrugged his shoulders slightly and his eyebrows twitched.

"I don't know," he replied. "I didn't mean to be polite or impolite, either. I guess it's a sort of way I have of saying things regardless."

The Principal, who was a sympathetic man, asked him whether he didn't think that a way it would be well to get rid of. Paul grinned and said he guessed so. When he was told that he could go, he bowed gracefully and went out. His bow was but a repetition of the scandalous red carnation.

His teachers were in despair, and his drawing master voiced the feeling of them all when he declared there was something about the boy which none of them understood. He added: "I don't really believe that smile of his comes altogether from insolence; there's something sort of haunted about it. The boy is not strong, for one thing. I happen to know that he was born in Colorado, only a few months before his mother died out there of a long illness. There is something wrong about the fellow."

The drawing master had come to realize that, in looking at Paul, one saw only his white teeth and the forced animation of his eyes. One warm afternoon the boy had gone to sleep at his drawing-board, and his master had noted with amazement what a white, blue-veined face it was; drawn and wrinkled like an old man's about the eyes, the lips twitching even in his sleep, and stiff with a nervous tension that drew them back from his teeth.

His teachers left the building dissatisfied and unhappy; humiliated to have felt so vindictive toward a mere boy, to have uttered this feeling in cutting terms, and to have set each other on, as it were, in the gruesome game of intemperate reproach. Some of them remembered having seen a miserable street cat set at bay by a ring of tormentors.

As for Paul, he ran down the hill whistling the Soldiers' Chorus from *Faust* looking wildly behind him now and then to see whether some of his teachers were not there to writhe under his light-heartedness. As it was now late in the afternoon and Paul was on duty that evening as usher at Carnegie Hall, he decided that he would not go home to supper. When he reached the concert hall the doors were not yet open, and as it was chilly outside, he decided to go up into the picture gallery—always deserted at this hour—where there were some of Raffelli's gay studies of Paris streets and an airy blue Venetian scene or two that always exhilarated him. He was delighted to find no one in the gallery but the old guard, who sat in one corner, a newspaper on his knee, a black patch over one eye and the other closed. Paul possessed himself of the place and walked confidently up and down, whistling under his breath. After a while he sat down before a blue Rico and lost himself. When he bethought him to look at his watch, it was after seven o'clock, and he rose with a start and ran downstairs, making a face at Augustus, peering out from the cast-room, and an evil gesture at the Venus of Milo as he passed her on the stairway.

When Paul reached the ushers' dressing-room half-a-dozen boys were there already, and he began excitedly to tumble into his uniform. It was one of the few that at all approached fitting, and Paul thought it very becoming—though he knew the tight, straight coat accentuated his narrow chest, about which he was exceedingly sensitive. He was always considerably excited while he dressed, twangling all over to the tuning of the strings and the preliminary flourishes of the horns in the music-room; but tonight he seemed quite beside himself, and he teased and plagued the boys until, telling him that he was crazy, they put him down on the floor and sat on him.

Somewhat calmed by his suppression, Paul dashed out to the front of the house to seat the early comers. He was a model usher: gracious and smiling he ran up and down the aisles; nothing was too much trouble for him; he carried messages and brought programmes as though it were his greatest pleasure in life, and all the people in his section thought him a charming boy, feeling that he remembered and admired them. As the house filled, he grew more and more vivacious and animated, and the colour came to his cheeks and lips. It was very much as though this were a great reception and Paul were the host. Just as the musicians came out to take their places, his English teacher arrived with checks for the seats which a prominent manufacturer had taken for the season. She betrayed some embarrassment when she handed Paul the tickets, and a *hauteur* which subsequently made her feel very foolish. Paul was startled for a moment, and had the feeling of wanting to put her out; what business had she here among all these fine people and gay colours? He looked her over and decided that she was not appropriately dressed and must be a fool to sit downstairs in such togs. The tickets had probably been sent her out of kindness, he reflected as he put down a seat for her, and she had about as much right to sit there as he had.

When the symphony began Paul sank into one of the rear seats with a long sigh of relief, and lost himself as he had done before the Rico. It was not that symphonies, as such, meant anything in particular to Paul, but the first sigh of the instruments seemed to fire some hilarious and potent spirit within him; something that struggled there like the Genius in the bottle found by the Arab fisherman. He felt a sudden zest of life; the lights danced before his eyes and the concert hall blazed into unimaginable splendor. When the soprano soloist came on, Paul forgot even the nastiness of his teacher's being there, and gave himself up to the peculiar stimulus such personages always had for him. The soloist chanced to be a German woman, by no means in her first youth, and the mother of many children; but she wore an elaborate gown and a tiara, and above all she had that indefinable air of achievement, that world-shine upon her, which, in Paul's eyes, made her a veritable queen of Romance.

After a concert was over Paul was always irritable and wretched until he got to sleep, and tonight he was even more than usually restless. He had the feeling of not being able to let down, of its being impossible to give up this delicious excitement which was the only thing that could be called living at all. During the last number he withdrew and, after hastily changing his clothes in the dressing-room, slipped out to the side door where the soprano's carriage stood. Here he began pacing rapidly up and down the walk, waiting to see her come out.

Over yonder the Schenley, in its vacant stretch, loomed big and square through the fine rain, the windows of its twelve stories glowing like those of a lighted card-board house under a Christmas tree. All the actors and singers of the better class stayed there when they were in the city, and a number of the big manufacturers of the place lived there in the winter. Paul had often hung about the hotel, watching the people go in and out, longing to enter and leave schoolmasters and dull care behind him forever.

At last the singer came out, accompanied by the conductor, who helped her into her carriage and closed the door with a cordial *auf wiedersehen*—which set Paul to wondering whether she were not an old sweetheart of his. Paul followed the carriage over to the hotel, walking so rapidly as not to be far from the entrance when the singer alighted and disappeared behind the swinging glass doors that were opened by a Negro in a tall hat and a long coat. In the moment that the door was ajar, it seemed to Paul that he, too, entered. He seemed to feel himself go after her up the steps, into the warm, lighted building, into an exotic, a tropical world of shiny, glistening surfaces and basking ease. He reflected upon the mysterious dishes that were brought into the dining-room, the green bottles in buckets of ice, as he had seen them in the supper party pictures of the *Sunday World* supplement. A quick gust of wind brought the rain down with sudden vehemence, and Paul was startled to find that he was still outside in the slush of the gravel driveway; that his boots were letting in the water and his scanty overcoat was clinging wet about him; that the lights in front of the concert hall were out, and that the rain was driving in sheets between him and the orange glow of the windows above him. There it was, what he wanted—tangibly before him, like the fairy world of a Christmas pantomime, but mocking spirits stood guard at the doors, and, as the rain beat in his face, Paul wondered whether he were destined always to shiver in the black night outside, looking up at it.

He turned and walked reluctantly toward the car tracks. The end had to come some time; his father in his night-clothes at the top of the stairs, explanations that did not explain, hastily improvised fictions that were forever tripping him up, his upstairs room and its horrible yellow wall-paper, the creaking bureau with the greasy plush collar-box, and over his painted wooden bed the pictures of George Washington and John Calvin, and the framed motto, "Feed my Lambs," which had been worked in red worsted by his mother.

Half an hour later, Paul alighted from his car and went slowly down one of the side streets off the main thoroughfare. It was a highly respectable street, where all the houses were exactly alike, and where business men of moderate means begot and reared large families of children, all of whom went to Sabbath-school and learned the shorter catechism, and were interested in arithmetic; all of whom were as exactly alike as their homes, and of a piece with the monotony in which they lived. Paul never went up Cordelia Street without a shudder of loathing. His home was next to the house of the Cumberland minister. He approached it tonight with the nerveless sense of defeat, the hopeless feeling of sinking back forever into ugliness and commonness that he had always had when he came home. The moment he turned into Cordelia Street he felt the waters close above his head. After each of these orgies of living, he experienced all the physical depression which follows a debauch; the loathing of respectable beds, of common food, of a house penetrated by kitchen odours; a shuddering repulsion for the flavorless, colorless mass of everyday existence; a morbid desire for cool things and soft lights and fresh flowers.

The nearer he approached the house, the more absolutely unequal Paul felt to the sight of it all; his ugly sleeping chamber; the cold bathroom with the grimy zinc tub, the cracked mirror, the dripping spigots; his father, at the top of the stairs, his hairy legs sticking out from his nightshirt, his feet thrust into carpet slippers. He was so much later than usual that there would certainly be inquiries and reproaches. Paul stopped short before the door. He felt that he could not be accosted by his father tonight; that he could not toss again on that miserable bed. He would not go in. He would tell his father that he had no carfare, and it was raining so hard he had gone home with one of the boys and stayed all night.

Meanwhile, he was wet and cold. He went around to the back of the house and tried one of the basement windows, found it open, raised it cautiously, and scrambled down the cellar wall to the floor. There he stood, holding his breath, terrified by the noise he had made, but the floor above him was silent, and there was no creak on the stairs. He found a soap-box, and carried it over to the soft ring of light that streamed from the furnace door, and sat down. He was horribly afraid of rats, so he did not try to sleep, but sat looking distrustfully at the dark, still terrified lest he might have awakened his father. In such reactions, after one of the experiences which made days and nights out of the dreary blanks of the calendar, when his senses were deadened, Paul's head was always singularly clear. Suppose his father had come down, pistol in hand, and he had cried out in time to save himself, and his father had been horrified to think how nearly he had killed him? Then, again, suppose a day should come when his father would remember that night, and wish there had been no warning cry to stay his hand? With this last supposition Paul entertained himself until daybreak.

The following Sunday was fine; the sodden November chill was broken by the last flash of autumnal summer. In the morning Paul had to go to church and Sabbath-school, as always. On seasonable Sunday afternoons the burghers of Cordelia Street always sat out on their front "stoops,"

and talked to their neighbours on the next stoop, or called to those across
the street in neighbourly fashion. The men sat placidly on gay cushions
placed upon the steps that led down to the sidewalk, while the women, in
their Sunday "waists," sat in rockers on the cramped porches, pretending to
be greatly at their ease. The children played in the streets; there were so
many of them that the place resembled the recreation grounds of a kinder-
garten. The men on the steps—all in their shirt sleeves, their vests unbuttoned—sat with their legs well apart, their stomachs comfortably protrud-
ing, and talked of the prices of things, or told anecdotes of the sagacity of
their various chiefs and overlords. They occasionally looked over the multitude of squabbling children, listened affectionately to their high-pitched,
nasal voices, smiling to see their own proclivities reproduced in their offspring, and interspersed their legends of the iron kings with remarks about
their sons' progress at school, their grades in arithmetic, and the amounts
they had saved in their toy banks.

On this last Sunday of November, Paul sat all the afternoon on the
lowest step of his "stoop," staring into the street, while his sisters, in their
rockers, were talking to the minister's daughters next door about how many
shirtwaists they had made in the last week, and how many waffles someone
had eaten at the last church supper. When the weather was warm, and his
father was in a particularly jovial frame of mind, the girls made lemonade,
which was always brought out in a red-glass pitcher, ornamented with for-
get-me-nots in blue enamel. This the girls thought very fine, and the neighbours always joked about the suspicious color of the pitcher.

Today Paul's father sat on the top step, talking to a young man who
shifted a restless baby from knee to knee. He happened to be the young
man who was daily held up to Paul as a model, and after whom it was his
father's dearest hope that he would pattern. This young man was of a
ruddy complexion, with a compressed, red mouth, and faded near-sighted
eyes, over which he wore thick spectacles, with gold bows that curved
about his ears. He was clerk to one of the magnates of a great steel corporation, and was looked upon in Cordelia Street as a young man with a future. There was a story that, some five years ago—he was not barely
twenty-six—he had been a trifle dissipated but in order to curb his appetites
and save the loss of time and strength that a sowing of wild oats might have
entailed, he had taken his chief's advice, oft reiterated to his employees, and
at twenty-one had married the first woman whom he could persuade to
share his fortunes. She happened to be an angular school-mistress, much
older than he, who also wore thick glasses, and who had now borne him
four children, all near-sighted, like herself.

The young man was relating how his chief, now cruising in the
Mediterranean, kept in touch with all the details of the business, arranging
his office hours on his yacht just as though he were at home, and "knocking
off work enough to keep two stenographers busy." His father told, in turn,
the plan his corporation was considering, of putting in an electric railway
plant at Cairo. Paul snapped his teeth; he had an awful apprehension that
they might spoil it all before he got there. Yet he rather liked to hear these
legends of the iron kings, that were told and retold on Sundays and holidays; these stories of palaces in Venice, yachts on the Mediterranean, and

high play at Monte Carlo appealed to his fancy, and he was interested in the triumphs of these cash boys who had become famous, though he had no mind for the cash-boy stage.

After supper was over, and he had helped to dry the dishes, Paul nervously asked his father whether he could go to George's to get some help in his geometry, and still more nervously asked for car fare. This latter request he had to repeat, as his father, on principle, did not like to hear requests for money, whether much or little. He asked Paul whether he could not go to some boy who lived nearer, and told him that he ought not to leave his school work until Sunday; but he gave him the dime. He was not a poor man, but he had a worthy ambition to come up in the world. His only reason for allowing Paul to usher was that he thought a boy ought to be earning a little.

Paul bounded upstairs, scrubbed the greasy odor of the dishwater from his hands with the ill-smelling soap he hated, and then shook over his fingers a few drops of violet water from the bottle he kept hidden in his drawer. He left the house with his geometry conspicuously under his arm, and the moment he got out of Cordelia Street and boarded a downtown car, he shook off the lethargy of two deadening days, and began to live again.

The leading juvenile of the permanent stock company which played at one of the downtown theaters was an acquaintance of Paul's, and the boy had been invited to drop in at the Sunday night rehearsals whenever he could. For more than a year Paul had spent every available moment loitering about Charley Edwards's dressing-room. He had won a place among Edwards's following not only because the young actor, who could not afford to employ a dresser, often found him useful, but because he recognized in Paul something akin to what churchmen termed "vocation."

It was at the theater and at Carnegie Hall that Paul really lived; the rest was but a sleep and a forgetting. This was Paul's fairy tale, and it had for him all the allurement of a secret love. The moment he inhaled the gassy, painty, dusty odor behind the scenes, he breathed like a prisoner set free, and felt within him the possibility of doing or saying splendid, brilliant, poetic things. The moment the cracked orchestra beat out the overture from *Martha*, or jerked at the serenade from *Rigoletto*, all stupid and ugly things slid from him, and his senses were deliciously, yet delicately fired.

Perhaps it was because, in Paul's world, the natural nearly always wore the guise of ugliness, that a certain element of artificiality seemed to him necessary in beauty. Perhaps it was because his experience of life elsewhere was so full of Sabbath-school picnics, petty economies, wholesome advice as to how to succeed in life, and the unescapable odors of cooking, that he found that existence so alluring, these smartly-clad men and women so attractive, that he was so moved by these starry apple orchards that bloomed perennially under the limelight.

It would be difficult to put it strongly enough how convincingly the stage entrance of that theater was for Paul the actual portal of Romance. Certainly none of the company ever suspected it, least of all Charley Edwards. It was very like the old stories that used to float about London of fabulously rich Jews, who had subterranean halls, with palms, and fountains, and soft lamps and richly apparelled women who never saw the disenchanting light of London day. So, in the midst of that smoke-palled city, enamored of figures and grimy toil, Paul had his secret temple, his wishing-carpet, his bit of blue-and-white Mediterranean shore bathed in perpetual sunshine.

Several of Paul's teachers had a theory that his imagination had been perverted by garish fiction; but the truth was, he scarcely ever read at all. The books at home were not such as would either tempt or corrupt a youthful mind, and as for reading the novels that some of his friends urged upon him—well, he got what he wanted much more quickly from music; any sort of music, from an orchestra to a barrel organ. He needed only the spark, the indescribable thrill that made his imagination master of his senses, and he could make plots and pictures enough of his own. It was equally true that he was not stage-struck—not, at any rate, in the usual acceptation of that expression. He had no desire to become an actor, any more than he had to become a musician. He felt no necessity to do any of these things; what he wanted was to see, to be in the atmosphere, float on the wave of it, to be carried out, blue league after blue league, away from everything.

After a night behind the scenes, Paul found the school-room more than ever repulsive; the bare floors and naked walls; the prosy men who never wore frock coats, or violets in their buttonholes; the women with the dull gowns, shrill voices, and pitiful seriousness about prepositions that govern the dative. He could not bear to have the other pupils think, for a moment, that he took these people seriously; he must convey to them that he considered it all trivial, and was there only by way of a jest, anyway. He had autograph pictures of all the members of the stock company which he showed his classmates, telling them the most incredible stories of his familiarity with these people, of his acquaintance with the soloist who came to Carnegie Hall, his supper with them and the flowers he sent them. When these stories lost their effect, and his audience grew listless, he became desperate and would bid all the boys good-by, announcing that he was going to travel for a while; going to Naples, to Venice, to Egypt. Then, next Monday, he would slip back, conscious and nervously smiling, his sister was ill, and he would have to defer his voyage until spring.

Matters went steadily worse with Paul at school. In the itch to let his instructors know how heartily he despised them and their homilies, and how thoroughly he was appreciated elsewhere, he mentioned once or twice that he had no time to fool with theorems; adding—with a twitch of the eyebrows and a touch of that nervous bravado which so perplexed them—that he was helping the people down at the stock company; they were old friends of his.

The upshot of the matter was, that the Principal went to Paul's father, and Paul was taken out of school and put to work. The manager at Carnegie Hall was told to get another usher in his stead; the door-keeper at the theater was warned not to admit him to the house; and Charley Edwards remorsefully promised the boy's father not to see him again.

The members of the stock company were vastly amused when some of Paul's stories reached them—especially the women. They were hard-working women, most of them supporting indigent husbands or brothers, and they laughed rather bitterly at having stirred the boy to such fervid and florid inventions. They agreed with the faculty and with his father that Paul's was a bad case.

The east-bound train was plowing through a January snow-storm; the dull dawn was beginning to show gray when the engine whistled a mile out of Newark. Paul started up from the seat where he had lain curled in uneasy slumber, rubbed the breath-misted window glass with his hand, and peered out. The snow was whirling in curling eddies above the white bottom lands, and the drifts lay already deep in the fields and along the fences, while here and there the long dead grass and dried weed stalks protruded black above it. Lights shone from the scattered houses, and a gang of laborers who stood beside the track waved their lanterns.

Paul had slept very little, and he felt grimy and uncomfortable. He had made the all-night journey in a day coach, partly because he was ashamed, dressed as he was, to go into a Pullman, and partly because he was afraid of being seen there by some Pittsburgh business man, who might have noticed him in Denny & Carson's office. When the whistle awoke him, he clutched quickly at his breastpocket, glancing about him with an uncertain smile. But the little, clay-bespattered Italians were still sleeping, the slatternly women across the aisle were in open-mouthed oblivion, and even the crumby, crying babies were for the nonce stilled. Paul settled back to struggle with his impatience as best he could.

When he arrived at the Jersey City station, he hurried through his breakfast, manifestly ill at ease and keeping a sharp eye about him. After he reached the Twenty-third Street station, he consulted a cabman, and had himself driven to a men's furnishing establishment that was just opening for the day. He spent upward of two hours there, buying with endless reconsidering and great care. His new street suit he put on in the fitting-room; the frock coat and dress clothes he had bundled into the cab with his linen. Then he drove to a hatter's and a shoe house. His next errand was at Tiffany's, where he selected his silver and a new scarf-pin. He would not wait to have his silver marked, he said. Lastly, he stopped at a trunk shop on Broadway, and had his purchases packed into various traveling bags.

It was a little after one o'clock when he drove up to the Waldorf, and after settling with the cabman, went into the office. He registered from Washington; said his mother and father had been abroad, and that he had come down to await the arrival of their steamer. He told his story plausibly and had no trouble, since he volunteered to pay for them in advance, in engaging his rooms; a sleeping-room, sitting-room and bath.

Not once, but a hundred times Paul had planned this entry into New York. He had gone over every detail of it with Charley Edwards, and in his scrap book at home there were pages of description about New York hotels, cut from the Sunday papers. When he was shown to his sitting-room on the eighth floor, he saw at a glance that everything was as it should be; there was but one detail in his mental picture that the place did not realize, so he rang for the bell boy and sent him down for flowers. He moved about nervously until the boy returned, putting away his new linen and fingering it delightedly as he did so. When the flowers came, he put them hastily into

water, and then tumbled into a hot bath. Presently he came out of his white
bath-room, resplendent in his new silk underwear, and playing with the tas-
sels of his red robe. The snow was whirling so fiercely outside his windows that he could scarcely see across the street, but within, the air was deliciously soft and fragrant. He put the violets and jonquils on the tabouret
beside the couch, and threw himself down with a long sigh, covering himself with a Roman blanket. He was thoroughly tired; he had been in such
haste, he had stood up to such a strain, covered so much ground in the last
twenty-four hours, that he wanted to think how it had all come about.
Lulled by the sound of the wind, the warm air, and the cool fragrance of the
flowers, he sank into deep, drowsy retrospection.

It had been wonderfully simple; when they had shut him out of the
theater and concert hall, when they had taken away his bone, the whole
thing was virtually determined. The rest was a mere matter of opportunity.
The only thing that at all surprised him was his own courage—for he realized well enough that he had always been tormented by fear, a sort of apprehensive dread that, of late years, as the meshes of the lies he had told
closed about him, had been pulling the muscles of his body tighter and
tighter. Until now, he could not remember the time when he had not been
dreading something. Even when he was a little boy, it was always there—
behind him, or before, or on either side. There had always been the shadowed corner, the dark place into which he dared not look, but from which
something seemed always to be watching him—and Paul had done things
that were not pretty to watch, he knew.

But now he had a curious sense of relief, as though he had at last
thrown down the gauntlet to the thing in the corner.

Yet it was but a day since he had been sulking in the traces; but yesterday afternoon he had been sent to the bank with Denny & Carson's
deposit, as usual—but this time he was instructed to leave the book to be
balanced. There was above two thousand dollars in checks, and nearly a
thousand in the bank notes which he had taken from the book and quietly
transferred to his pocket. At the bank he had made out a new deposit slip.
His nerves had been steady enough to permit of his returning to the office,
where he had finished his work and asked for a full day's holiday tomorrow, Saturday, giving a perfectly reasonable pretext. The bank book, he
knew, would not be returned before Monday or Tuesday, and his father
would be out of town for the next week. From the time he slipped the bank
notes into his pocket until he boarded the night train for New York, he had
not known a moment's hesitation. It was not the first time Paul had steered
through treacherous waters.

How astonishingly easy it had all been; here he was, the thing done;
and this time there would be no awakening, no figure at the top of the stairs.
He watched snowflakes whirling by his window until he fell asleep.

When he awoke, it was three o'clock in the afternoon. He bounded
up with a start; half of one of his precious days gone already! He spent
more than an hour in dressing, watching every stage of his toilet carefully in
the mirror. Everything was quite perfect; he was exactly the kind of boy he
had always wanted to be.

When he went downstairs, Paul took a carriage and drove up Fifth

Avenue toward the Park. The snow had somewhat abated; carriages and tradesmen's wagons were hurrying soundlessly to and fro in the winter twilight; boys in woolen mufflers were shoveling off the doorsteps; the avenue stages made fine spots of colour against the white street. Here and there on the corners were stands, with whole flower gardens blooming under glass cases, against the sides of which the snowflakes stuck and melted; violets, roses, carnations, lilies of the valley—somehow vastly more lovely and alluring that they blossomed thus unnaturally in the snow. The Park itself was a wonderful stage winter-piece.

When he returned, the pause of the twilight had ceased, and the tune of the streets had changed. The snow was falling faster, lights streamed from the hotels that reared their dozen stories fearlessly up into the storm, defying the raging Atlantic winds. A long, black stream of carriages poured down the avenue, intersected here and there by other streams, tending horizontally. There were a score of cabs about the entrance of his hotel, and his driver had to wait. Boys in livery were running in and out of the awning stretched across the sidewalk, up and down the red velvet carpet laid from the door to the street. Above, about, within it all was the rumble and roar, the hurry and toss of thousands of human beings as hot for pleasure as himself, and on every side of him towered the glaring affirmation of the omnipotence of wealth.

The boy set his teeth and drew his shoulders together in a spasm of realization; the plot of all dramas, the text of all romances, the nerve-stuff of all sensations was whirling about him like the snowflakes. He burnt like a faggot in a tempest.

When Paul went down to dinner, the music of the orchestra came floating up the elevator shaft to greet him. His head whirled as he stepped into the thronged corridor, he sank back into one of the chairs against the wall to get his breath. The lights, the chatter, the perfumes, the bewildering medley of colour—he had, for a moment, the feeling of not being able to stand it. But only for a moment; these were his own people, he told himself. He went slowly about the corridors, through the writing-rooms, smoking-rooms, reception-rooms, as though he were exploring the chambers of an enchanted palace, built and peopled for him alone.

When he reached the dining-room he sat down at a table near a window. The flowers, the white linen, the many-colored wine glasses, the gay toilettes of the women, the low popping of corks, the undulating repetitions of the *Blue Danube* from the orchestra, all flooded Paul's dream with bewildering radiance. When the roseate tinge of his champagne was added—that cold, precious, bubbling stuff that creamed and foamed in his glass—Paul wondered that there were honest men in the world at all. This was what all the world was fighting for, he reflected; this was what all the struggle was about. He doubted the reality of his past. Had he ever known a place called Cordelia Street, a place where fagged-looking business men got on the early car? Mere rivets in a machine they seemed to Paul,—sickening men, with combings of children's hair always hanging to their coats, and the smell of cooking in their clothes. Cordelia Street—Ah! that belonged to another time and country; had he not always been thus, had he not sat here night after night, from as far back as he could remember, looking pensively over just such shimmering textures, and slowly twirling the stem of a glass like this one between his thumb and middle finger? He rather thought he had.

He was not in the least abashed or lonely. He had no especial desire to meet or to know any of these people; all he demanded was the right to look on and conjecture, to watch the pageant. The mere stage properties were all he contended for. Nor was he lonely later in the evening, in his lodge at the Opera. He was now entirely rid of his nervous misgivings, of his forced aggressiveness, of the imperative desire to show himself different from his surroundings. He felt now that his surroundings explained him. Nobody questioned the purple; he had only to wear it passively. He had only to glance down at his attire to reassure himself that here it would be impossible for anyone to humiliate him.

He found it hard to leave his beautiful sitting room to go to bed that night, and sat long watching the raging storm from his turret window. When he went to sleep it was with the lights turned on in his bedroom; partly because of his old timidity, and partly so that, if he should wake in the night, there would be no wretched moment of doubt, no horrible suspicion of yellow-wallpaper, or of Washington and Calvin above his bed.

Sunday morning the city was practically snow-bound. Paul breakfasted late, and in the afternoon he fell in with a wild San Francisco boy, a freshman at Yale, who said he had run down for a "little flyer" over Sunday. The young man offered to show Paul the night side of the town, and the two boys went off together after dinner, not returning to the hotel until seven o'clock the next morning. They had started out in the confiding warmth of a champagne friendship, but their parting in the elevator was singularly cool. The freshman pulled himself together to make his train, and Paul went to bed. He awoke at two o'clock in the afternoon, very thirsty and dizzy, and rang for ice water, coffee and the Pittsburgh papers.

On the part of the hotel management, Paul excited no suspicion. There was this to be said for him, that he wore his spoils with dignity and in no way made himself conspicuous. Even under the glow of his wine he was never boisterous, though he found the stuff like a magician's wand for wonder-building. His chief greediness lay in his ears and eyes, and his excesses were not offensive ones. His dearest pleasures were the gray winter twilights in his sitting room; his quiet enjoyment of his flowers, his clothes, his wide divan, his cigarette and his sense of power. He could not remember a time when he had felt so at peace with himself. The mere release from the necessity of petty lying, lying every day and every day, restored his self-respect. He had never lied for pleasure, even at school; but to be noticed and admired, to assert his difference from other Cordelia Street boys; and he felt a good deal more manly, more honest, even, now that he had no need for boastful pretensions, now that he could, as his actor friends used to say, "dress the part." It was characteristic that remorse did not occur to him. His golden days went by without a shadow, and he made each as perfect as he could.

On the eighth day after his arrival in New York, he found the whole affair exploited in the Pittsburgh papers, exploited with a wealth of detail which indicated that local news of a sensational nature was at a low ebb.

The firm of Denny & Carson announced that the boy's father had refunded the full amount of the theft, and that they had no intention of prosecuting. The Cumberland minister had been interviewed, and expressed his hope of yet reclaiming the motherless lad, and his Sabbath-school teacher declared that she would spare no effort to that end. The rumor had reached Pittsburgh that the boy had been seen in a New York hotel, and his father had gone East to find him and bring him home.

Paul had just come in to dress for dinner; he sank into a chair, weak to the knees, and clasped his head in his hands. It was to be worse than jail, even; the tepid waters of Cordelia Street were to close over him finally and forever. The gray monotony stretched before him in hopeless, unrelieved years; Sabbath-school, Young People's Meeting, the yellow-papered room, the damp dish-towels; it all rushed back upon him with sickening vividness. He had the old feeling that the orchestra had suddenly stopped, the sinking sensation that the play was over. The sweat broke out on his face, and he sprang to his feet, looked about him with his white, conscious smile, and winked to himself in the mirror. With something of the old childish belief in miracles with which he had so often gone to class, all his lessons unlearned, Paul dressed and dashed whistling down the corridor to the elevator.

He had no sooner entered the dining room and caught the measure of the music, than his remembrance was lightened by his old elastic power of claiming the moment, mounting with it, and finding it all sufficient. The glare and glitter about him, the mere scenic accessories had again, and for the last time, their old potency. He would show himself that he was game, he would finish the thing splendidly. He doubted, more than ever, the existence of Cordelia Street, and for the first time he drank his wine recklessly. Was he not, after all, one of those fortunate beings born to the purple, was he not still himself, and in his own place? He drummed a nervous accompaniment to the Pagliacci music and looked about him, telling himself over and over that it had paid.

He reflected drowsily, to the swell of the music and the chill sweetness of his wine, that he might have done it more wisely. He might have caught an outbound steamer and been well out of their clutches before now. But the other side of the world had seemed too far away and too uncertain then; he could not have waited for it; his need had been too sharp. If he had to choose over again, he would do the same thing tomorrow. He looked affectionately about the dining room, now gilded with a soft mist. Ah, it had paid indeed!

Paul was awakened next morning by a painful throbbing in his head and feet. He had thrown himself across the bed without undressing, and had slept with his shoes on. His limbs and hands were lead heavy, and his tongue and throat were parched and burnt. There came upon him one of those fateful attacks of clear-headedness that never occurred except when he was physically exhausted and his nerves hung loose. He lay still and closed his eyes and let the tide of things wash over him.

His father was in New York; "stopping at some joint or other," he told himself. The memory of successive summers on the front stoop fell upon him like a weight of black water. He had not a hundred dollars left;

and he knew now, more than ever, that money was everything, the wall that stood between all he loathed and all he wanted. The thing was winding itself up; he had thought of that on his first glorious day in New York, and had even provided a way to snap the thread. It lay on his dressing-table now; he had got it out last night when he came blindly up from dinner, but the shiny metal hurt his eyes, and he disliked the looks of it, anyway.

He rose and moved about with a painful effort, succumbing now and again to attacks of nausea. It was the old depression exaggerated; all the world had become Cordelia Street. Yet somehow he was not afraid of anything, was absolutely calm; perhaps because he had looked into the dark corner at last, and knew. It was bad enough, what he saw there, but somehow not so bad as his long fear of it had been. He saw everything clearly now. He had a feeling that he had made the best of it, that he had lived the sort of life he was meant to live, and for half an hour he sat staring at the revolver. But he told himself that was not the way, so he went downstairs and took a cab to the ferry.

When Paul arrived at Newark, he got off the train and took another cab, directing the driver to follow the Pennsylvania tracks out of the town. The snow lay heavy on the roadways and had drifted deep in the open fields. Only here and there the dead grass or dried weed stalks projected, singularly black, above it. Once well into the country, Paul dismissed the carriage and walked, floundering along the tracks, his mind a medley of irrelevant things. He seemed to hold in his brain an actual picture of everything he had seen that morning. He remembered every feature of both his drivers, the toothless old woman from whom he had got his ticket, and all of his fellow-passengers on the ferry. His mind, unable to cope with vital matters near at hand, worked feverishly and deftly at sorting and grouping these images. They made for him a part of the ugliness of the world, of the ache in his head, and the bitter burning on his tongue. He stooped and put a handful of snow into his mouth as he walked, but that, too, seemed hot. When he reached a little hillside, where the tracks ran through a cut some twenty feet below him, he stopped and sat down.

The carnations in his coat were drooping with the cold, he noticed; their red glory all over. It occurred to him that all the flowers he had seen in the glass cases that first night must have gone the same way, long before this. It was only one splendid breath they had, in spite of their brave mockery at the winter outside the glass; and it was a losing game in the end, it seemed, this revolt against the homilies by which the world is run. Paul took one of the blossoms carefully from his coat and scooped a little hole in the snow, where he covered it up. Then he dozed a while, from his weak condition, seeming insensible to the cold.

The sound of an approaching train woke him, and he started to his feet, remembering only his resolution, and afraid lest he should be too late. He stood watching the approaching locomotive, his teeth chattering, his lips drawn away from them in a frightened smile; once or twice he glanced nervously sidewise, as though he were being watched. When the right moment came, he jumped. As he fell, the folly of his haste occurred to him with merciless clearness, the vastness of what he had left undone. There flashed through his brain, clearer than ever before, the blue of Adriatic water, the yellow of Algerian sands.

He felt something strike his chest, his body was being thrown swiftly through the air, on and on, immeasurably far and fast, while his limbs were gently relaxed. Then, because the picture-making mechanism was crushed, the disturbing visions flashed into black, and Paul dropped back into the immense design of things.

14

Murderers

That moment she was mine, mine, fair,
    Perfectly pure and good: I found
A thing to do, and all her hair
    In one long yellow string I wound
    Three times her little throat around,
And strangled her. No pain felt she;
    I am quite sure she felt no pain.
                                    "Porphyria's Lover"
                                    Robert Browning

If once a man indulges himself in murder, very soon he
comes to think little of robbing; and from robbing he comes
next to drinking and Sabbath-breaking, and from that to in-
civility and procrastination.
                        Murder Considered as One of the Fine Arts
                                    Thomas de Quincey

In a previous section, we considered juvenile delinquency and saw how one
youth broke away from the destructive behavior patterns of his overbearing
lawbreaking father. Unlike Sartoris, however, many juvenile delinquents
never break the pattern of inadequate parenting and face a future filled with
crime—from petty larceny to murder—spending much of their adult lives
behind prison bars. An extreme example is that of Charles Manson. Born
"no-name Maddox," an illegitimate son of a "loose" mother who was sentenced to five years for armed robbery, raised alternately by his mother and
his extremely religious aunt and uncle, Charles Manson found himself, at
the age of twelve, in the Gibault School for Boys, from which he ran away
after a few months. He then turned to burglary and armed robbery by the
age of thirteen. His life was punctuated with crime and incarceration until
finally—at the end of a trial which was said to be the longest ever in California, commencing on July 24, 1970, and ending on January 26, 1971—
he was convicted along with members of his "family" of first-degree murder
in the Tate-LaBianca murders. The jury's recommendation was the gas
chamber, but California changed the law and banned capital punishment in

time to change Manson's sentence to life in prison.

The mind of Charles Manson is explored in *The Family*, by Ed Sanders; *Manson in His Own Words*, by Nuel Emmons; and *Helter Skelter*, by District Attorney Vincent Bugliosi with Curt Gentry. Interest in Manson and in other murderers centers around mental capacity—are they psychotic, antisocial, or psychiatrically "normal"? The 1987 *Diagnostic and Statistical Manual of the American Psychiatric Association* (DSM III-R) defines psychotic and antisocial as follows:

Psychotic: Gross impairment in reality testing and the creation of a new reality. . . . When a person is psychotic, he or she incorrectly evaluates the accuracy of his or her perceptions and thoughts and makes incorrect inferences about external reality, even in the face of contrary evidence.

Antisocial Personality: The essential feature of this disorder is a pattern of irresponsible and antisocial behavior beginning in childhood or early adolescence and continuing into adulthood. . . . Lying, stealing, truancy, vandalism, initiating fights, running away from home, and physical cruelty are typical childhood signs. In adulthood . . . these people fail to conform to social norms and repeatedly perform antisocial acts that are grounds for arrest, such as destroying property, harassing others, stealing, and having an illegal occupation. . . . Finally, they generally have no remorse.

Consider Charles Manson with the above definitions in mind. Is he psychotic, antisocial—a term synonymous with "psychopathic" or "sociopathic"—or psychiatrically "normal"? What about the following murderers?

• A husband who kills his estranged wife in order to "teach her a lesson" for leaving him.

• A teenage robber who kills the cashier during the perpetration of the crime, not because she puts up resistance, but because he wishes "to see her squirm."

• The serial killer who sexually attacks then mutilates his victims believing God has told him to rid the world of whores.

• The participant in organized crime who kills his rivals for territory, power, and money.

• A mother who kills several of her babies for the attention each baby's death brings her.

• The young adult who murders his parent in order to hasten his inheritance.

Just as the psychiatric profession struggles with definitions of mental disorders, so the legal profession attempts to determine which types of criminal behavior should be excused on the basis of insanity. The test established in M'Naghten's Case, House of Lords (1843) is as follows: "At the time of the committing of the act, the accused party was labouring under such a defect of reason, from disease of mind, as not to know the nature and quality of the act he was doing; or, if he did know it, that he did not know he was doing what was wrong." Other legal tests of insanity include the Irresistible Impulse Test, the Durham Test, and the American Law Institute or Model Penal Code Test. Many of those formulations exclude antisocial behavior from their definitions.

If we were able to fit each murderer into the categories of psychotic, antisocial, or psychiatrically "normal," what are the implications for the legal system and its theories of punishment? Should we inflict capital punishment on the murderers who exhibit a psychotic tendency because there appears little in the way of treatment available to change their personalities? Should we attempt to rehabilitate murderers who exhibit antisocial personalities, or is such an attempt inappropriate since many have exhibited by their repeated criminal behavior that they do not change their behavior despite punishment? Should we try to reform the psychiatrically "normal" criminals on the basis that they have no underlying mental disorder? Or should we inflict capital punishment on the murderers with no mental disorders *because* they have no excuse for their behavior? Should we institutionalize murderers with mental disorders for the protection of society and for the protection of themselves? Finally, can a murderer be sane? Remember that many tend to think people are "normal" only if they follow the behavioral patterns of the majority.

It is difficult to speak of any killing without speaking of intention and defenses—both topics are addressed later. The following two stories of men accused of murder also deal with those notions. "Sicilian Honor," by Luigi Pirandello, is a story about the murder of Rosaria Femminella by her husband Tarara who admits splitting her head open with a hatchet but who defends and justifies his actions based on his provocation because of her unfaithfulness. Although provocation is a defense to murder, that provocation has to be such that a reasonable man under the same circumstances would be equally provoked. Would a reasonable man in Tarara's shoes have killed his wife?

Rather than dealing with a defense to murder, "Han's Crime," by Shiga Naoya, deals with the *intention* to commit such a crime. Keep this story in mind as we move to the next section entitled "The Mens Rea."

Sicilian Honor
Luigi Pirandello

As soon as prisoner Saru Argentu—known to his friends as Tarara—was brought into the caged dock of the squalid Court of Assizes he pulled out of his pocket an immense red cotton handkerchief heavily over-printed with yellow flowers and spread it with great care on the bench so as not to dirty the sky-blue colored suit which he had bought specially for his trial. A brand-new suit and a brand-new handkerchief they were.

Then—sitting on the bench—he quietly turned his smiling face to the peasants packing the part of the court left open to the public. His flat, fierce-looking face, freshly shaven but wrinkled and angular, with two heavy golden pendants dangling from his ears, gave him the peculiar appearance of a monkey which could not help being comic even in the sad atmosphere of a Sicilian Court.

A thick, horrid stench, a mixture of stable and perspiration, a stink of goats, a fustiness of filthy animals, was filling the room.

Some of the women, shading their eyes with black mantillas, could not help crying at the sight of the prisoner, but Tarara himself, craning his neck right and left, went on smiling from his cage, now lifting one of his heavy rough hands as a salute, now nodding at them as if he were pleased to see again so many familiar faces of friends and work companions.

It was, in fact, almost a joy for him to be at last able to appear at his trial after so many months of preventive prison. He was so poor that he had not even been able to pay for a counsel of his own choice, and he had to accept legal aid of the State; but, as far as his own person was concerned, he had at least been able to come to the trial in a new suit, well groomed and freshly shaven as on a Sunday.

After the first formalities, the jury sworn in, the President ordered the prisoner to stand.

"Your name?"

"Tarara."

"This is a nickname. What's your real name?"

"Well, yes. . . . Argentu, Saru Argentu, Your Honor, but they all know me as 'Tarara.'"

"Very well. How old are you?"

"I don't know, Your Honor."

"What, you don't know your own age?"

Tarara shrugged his shoulders, meaning that the question of age was a mere worldly vanity to which no one need attach too much importance.

"I live in the country, Your Honor. Who bothers about age, there?"

A burst of laughter filled the court, and the President, bending his head, began to consult the papers in front of him.

"You were born in 1873: you are therefore thirty-nine."

Tarara opened both arms as if bending to the inevitable.

"Your Honor knows best."

To prevent fresh laughter, the President avoided putting more formal questions by giving himself the answer: "It is so. . . . It is so. . . ." At last he said:

"Sit down. The Clerk will now read you the charge for which you are being tried."

The Clerk started reading the charge, but he had soon to stop, for the foreman of the jury, overpowered by the stench of the Court, was on the point of fainting. Orders were given for all windows and doors to be left open.

It was then that the prisoner's superiority over those who were going to be his judges appeared as clear and as unquestionable as daylight.

. . . . .

Sitting on his huge scarlet handkerchief, Tarara was entirely indifferent to that nasty stench with which he was so familiar. He could in fact still smile, hardly feeling the heat in his heavy sky-blue Sunday suit. Even the flies—which were upsetting the members of the jury, the public prosecutor, the clerk, the lawyers, the ushers and even the jailers—were not giving him the slightest trouble.

They were resting on this hands, buzzing around his face, sticking to his forehead or even to the corners of his mouth and eyes, but he was not feeling them, nor was he even trying to chase them away. Unconcerned with all this, he was all smiles for his friends. He was sure of his acquittal. He had murdered to defend his honor.

The young barrister briefed by the State for his defense had reassured him that although he was guilty of having murdered his wife, there could be no verdict of guilty, the murder indisputably having been committed on the discovery of her unfaithfulness.

In the blessed unawareness of the beasts, Tarara could therefore ignore even the remotest shadow of remorse. All that was puzzling him was the fact that he had been brought to answer for something which, after all, was no concern of anyone else but himself. All this staging of justice appeared to him as something inevitable, like Fate. Justice was for him like a bad year on land, nothing more. And justice, with all its solemn setting of high benches, bells, robes and uniforms was for Tarara something as mysterious as the great new steam mill of his village which had been opened with great pomp the previous year. One could bring his own grist to that mill, but who could guarantee that the flour one received back was from the same grist? It was a question of accepting with blind eyes and with resignation the flour which it pleased the miller to give.

Comparing the mysterious machinery of the steam mill (which had aroused in him so much diffidence) with the equally complicated and mysterious wheels of justice, Tarara could not help thinking that his case was like the grist brought to the mill: one had to accept the result which would come out of the trial as one had to accept the flour which came out of the mill.

He knew, of course, that he had split open his wife's head with a hatchet because, returning home on a Saturday night soaking with rain and covered with mud, he had found the whole lane astir over a horrible scandal which had broken out in his home. A few hours previously his wife had been discovered in his bedroom with the young Count Agatino Fiorica, the wealthy landowner. It was Fiorica's wife who had informed the police and who had caused the two lovers to be arrested according to the law. It had become impossible for the neighbors to hide the event from Tarara, for his wife had been kept at the police station all night with her lover and next morning, when Tarara saw her creeping back to his door, he had leapt on her holding the hatchet in his hand and splitting her head before anybody had time to stop him.

All this he knew, of course, but how different it seemed from that long story which the Clerk was reading. . . .

When the Clerk finished, the President asked the prisoner to stand again?

"Prisoner at the bar, you have now heard the crime with which you are charged."

Tarara made a slight gesture and with his usual smile he answered:

"To tell you the truth, Your Honor, I did not pay any attention."

The President looked at him sternly:

"You are accused of having willfully murdered with a hatchet your wife, Rosaria Femminella, on the morning of the 10th of December, 1911. What have you to say in your defense? Turn to the jury and speak to them clearly and with the respect due to justice."

Tarara laid a hand on his chest to convey his respect due to justice, but feeling that another burst of laughter might follow his words, he stood silent for a long time unable to find his words, uncertain and shy.

"Well," insisted the President, "what have you to say? Tell the jury all you know. . . ."

Tarara shrugged his shoulders and said:

"Your Honor and you, too, gentlemen, you are learned people who understood all that is written in those papers, but I live in the country. If the writing in those papers says that I have killed my wife, then it is true and let us talk no more about it."

Even the President this time had to join in the general laughter.

"Let us talk no more about it? I am afraid you will soon see that there will be a lot to talk about, on the contrary."

"I mean, Your Honor," explained Tarara, again laying his hand on his chest, "I mean to say that I did it. Yes, I did it, that's all. I did it because I couldn't help it."

"Order, order," shouted the President at the fresh outburst of laughter, furiously ringing his bell. "This is a Court of Justice, where a man is being tried for murder. I shall order to clear the Court if there is more laughter and I must warn the jury on the seriousness of their task."

Then turning sternly to the dock:

"What do you mean by saying you could not help it?"

"I mean, Your Honor, that it wasn't my fault."

"Not your fault? Whose fault then?"

"Allow me to interrupt, Your Honor." The young State counsel jumped up, getting alarmed at the aggressive tone of the President. "It is quite obvious that if we carry on like this we shall be entangling this poor man altogether. I think he is right in saying that the fault was not his but that of his wife, who was betraying him with Count Fiorica. It's as clear as daylight."

"Let the prisoner answer for himself," rebuked the President. Then, turning to Tarara: "Is this what you intended saying?"

Tarara first shook his head, then added:

"No, Your Honor. It wasn't that poor woman's fault either. It was all the fault of that lady, Count Fiorica's wife, who stirred matters up. What business had she, I am asking Your Honor, that woman to raise such a terrible scandal at my doorstep that even the stones of the street had to blush for shame? What business had she to follow that perfect gentleman Count Fiorica to the slum of a dirty peasant? God alone knows, Your Honor, what we poor people have to do to earn a crust of bread."

. . . . .

There were tears in his eyes, while he was clasping both hands on his chest, but all round the Court people were bending in convulsions of laughter. The President alone—and Tarara's counsel—had seen the importance of a statement which seemed to rob the defense of its principal argument: intense provocation.

"You confess, then?" said the President, "that you were aware of your wife's relations with Count Fiorica. Is it so?"

"Your Honor," interrupted the young counsel, jumping to his feet, "I protest. This question should have never been put. I formally object to it being put to my client."

"But I am following your client's own confession . . ." retorted the President.

"My client has never confessed. All he said is that the cause of his action was Signora Fiorica raising such a scandal on his doorstep. . . ."

"Quite right, but you cannot stop me asking the prisoner whether he knew before the day of the crime of the immoral relations of his wife with the Count."

The whole Court was getting restless. From every corner violent signs were made to Tarara that he should deny any knowledge of his wife's unfaithfulness, but Tarara remained shy, uncertain and frightened. He could find no words to answer, turning at times to his counsel and at times to the audience where dozens of hands were making frantic signs of denial.

"Must I. . . . Must I . . . say no?" he muttered to the audience.

"Old turnip," yelled somebody from the bottom of the court.

"You must tell the truth," admonished the President. "In your own interest."

"Well, Your Honor, I am telling the truth," said Tarara, trembling and crossing both hands on his chest. "I am. And the truth is this: I knew it and yet it was as if I didn't know it. The thing, Your Honor, was on the quiet and nobody could have dared to face me and tell me that I knew it. I am a peasant, gentlemen, and what can a peasant know when he toils like a beast in the fields from Monday morning till Saturday night? What does a peasant know of his troubles at home? Of course, if somebody had come to me and told me: 'Tarara, your wife and Count Fiorica are too friendly,' I would have rushed home and split my wife's head with my hatchet. But nobody had ever came to tell me, Your Honor, and in order not to raise trouble I even sent someone to give warning when I had to return home earlier than the end of the week. This shows, Your Honor, how careful I have been to avoid doing any harm to anybody. Men are what they are and women too. Of course men should know that women have it in their blood to be untrue even if their husband is never away, but women too should know that men cannot so lightly stand the scorn of their friends. . . . There are certain insults which slash your face like a knife. . . . No man can stand them. Now, gentlemen of the jury, you will understand me when I say that my poor wife would have never allowed me to be insulted, and in fact I have never even had a cross word with her, as all my neighbors can witness. But what fault have I, gentlemen of the jury, if that blessed lady, without any warning. . . . Yes, Your Honor, you should get her here, that lady, to face me and I would tell her: If your husband had had a similar affair with a spinster you might have pleased yourself as there was no husband to consider, but by what right have you come to upset me, who have always led a quiet life, who had nothing to do with the matter, who had always refused to see or hear anything, toiling from Monday morning to Saturday night in the fields to earn a living? Do you think you can allow yourself such fun? This scandal may be merely a joke for you: you are sure to take your husband back after a couple of days. But did it ever occur to you that your joke might affect the whole life of another man and that this man could not allow his face to be slashed by the ridicule you aroused and that he would have to act as a man must act? Why didn't you come to me first? I would have told you: Leave them alone. All men are alike. Man is a hunter. Can you really be jealous of a dirty peasant woman? Can you blame your husband if he fancies a bit of brown bread every now and then instead of the white one of every day? This, Your Honor, I would have told the lady and most likely nothing would have happened of what has happened through her fault, as I told you before, through her fault alone. . . ."

Hilarity mixed with loud comments followed the prisoner's long speech. With resounding ringings of the bell the President tried to restore order. Then he said:

"Prisoner at the bar. Is this your defense?"

"No, Your Honor, it is not my defense . . . it is the truth, merely the truth."

But as truth—even so candidly confessed—is not always easy to be accepted, the jury found Tarara guilty of murder with only mild provocation and a sentence of thirteen years' imprisonment followed.

Han's Crime
Shiga Naoya

Much to everyone's astonishment, the young Chinese juggler, Han, severed
his wife's carotid artery with one of his heavy knives in the course of a performance. The young woman died on the spot. Han was immediately arrested.

At the scene of the event were the director of the theater, Han's Chinese assistant, the announcer, and more than three hundred spectators.
There was also a policeman who had been stationed behind the audience.
Despite the presence of all these witnesses, it was a complete mystery
whether the killing had been intentional or accidental.

Han's act was as follows: his wife would stand in front of a wooden
board about the size of a door, and from a distance of approximately four
yards, he would throw his large knives at her so that they stuck in the board
about two inches apart, forming a contour around her body. As each knife
left his hand, he would let out a staccato exclamation as if to punctuate his
performance.

The examining judge first questioned the director of the theater.

"Would you say that this was a very difficult act?"

"No, Your Honor, it's not as difficult as all that for an experienced
performer. But to do it properly, you need steady nerves and complete concentration."

"I see. Then assuming that what happened was an accident, it was
an extremely unlikely type of accident?"

"Yes indeed, Your Honor. If accidents were not so very unlikely, I
should never have allowed the act in my theater."

"Well then, do you consider that this was done on purpose?"

"No, Your Honor, I do not. And for this reason: an act of this kind
performed at a distance of twelve feet requires not only skill but at the same
time a certain—well, intuitive sense. It is true that we all thought a mistake
virtually out of the question, but after what has happened, I think we must
admit that there was always the possibility of a mistake."

"Well then, which do you think it was—a mistake or on purpose?"

"That I simply cannot say, Your Honor."

The judge felt puzzled. Here was a clear case of homicide, but

whether it was manslaughter or pre-meditated murder it was impossible to
tell. If a murder, it was indeed a clever one, thought the judge.

Next the judge decided to question the Chinese assistant, who had
worked with Han for many years past.

"What was Han's normal behavior?" he asked.

"He was always very correct, Your Honor; he didn't gamble or
drink or run after women. Besides, last year he took up Christianity. He
studied English and in his free time always seemed to be reading collections
of sermons—the Bible and that sort of thing."

"And what about his wife's behavior?"

"Also very correct, Your Honor. Strolling players aren't always the
most moral people, as you know. Mrs. Han was a pretty little woman and
quite a few men used to make propositions to her, but she never paid the
slightest attention to that kind of thing."

"And what sort of temperaments did they have?"

"Always very kind and gentle, sir. They were extremely good to all
their friends and acquaintances and never quarreled with anyone. But . . ."
He broke off and reflected a moment before continuing. "Your Honor, I'm
afraid that if I tell you this, it may go badly for Han. But to be quite truthful, these two people, who were so gentle and unselfish to others, were
amazingly cruel in their relations to each other."

"Why was that?"

"I don't know, Your Honor."

"Was that the case ever since you first knew them?"

"No, Your Honor. About two years ago Mrs. Han was pregnant.
The child was born prematurely and died after about three days. That
marked a change in their relations. They began having terrible rows over
the most trivial things, and Han's face used to turn white as a sheet. He always ended by suddenly growing silent. He never once raised his hand
against her or anything like that—I suppose it would have gone against his
principles. But when you looked at him, Your Honor, you could see the
terrible anger in his eyes! It was quite frightening at times.

"One day I asked Han why he didn't separate from his wife, seeing
that things were so bad between them. Well, he told me that he had no real
grounds for divorce, even though his love for her had died. Of course, she
felt this and gradually stopped loving him too. He told me all this himself.
I think the reason he began reading the Bible and all those sermons was to
calm the violence in his heart and stop himself from hating his wife, whom
he had no real cause to hate. Mrs. Han was really a pathetic woman. She
had been with Han nearly three years and had traveled all over the country
with him as a strolling player. If she'd ever left Han and gone back home, I
don't think she'd have found it easy to get married. How many men would
trust a woman who'd spent all that time traveling about? I suppose that's
why she stayed with Han, even though they got on so badly."

"And what do you really think about this killing?"

"You mean, Your Honor, do I think it was an accident or done on
purpose?"

"That's right."

"Well, sir, I've been thinking about it from every angle since the day it happened. The more I think, the less I know what to make of it. I've talked about it with the announcer, and he also says he can't understand what happened."

"Very well. But tell me this: at the actual moment it did happen, did it occur to you to wonder whether it was accidental or on purpose?"

"Yes, sir, it did. I thought . . . I thought, 'He's gone and killed her.'"

"On purpose, you mean?"

"Yes, sir. However the announcer says that he thought, 'His hand's slipped.'"

"Yes, but he didn't know about their everyday relations as you did."

"That may be, Your Honor. But afterwards I wondered if it wasn't just because I did know about those relations that I thought, 'He's killed her.'"

"What were Han's reactions at the moment?"

"He cried out, 'Ha.' As soon as I heard that, I looked up and saw blood gushing from his wife's throat. For a few seconds she kept standing there, then her knees seemed to fold up under her and her body swayed forward. When the knife fell out, she collapsed on the floor, all crumpled in a heap. Of course there was nothing any of us could do—we just sat there petrified, staring at her. . . . As to Han, I really can't describe his reactions, for I wasn't looking at him. It was only when the thought struck me, 'He's finally gone and killed her,' that I glanced at him. His face was dead white and his eyes closed. The stage manager lowered the curtain. When they picked up Mrs. Han's body she was already dead. Han dropped to his knees then, and for a long time he went on praying in silence."

"Did he appear very upset?"

"Yes, sir, he was quite upset."

"Very well. If I have anything further to ask you, I shall call for you again."

The judge dismissed the Chinese assistant and now summoned Han himself to the stand. The juggler's intelligent face was drawn and pale; one could tell right away that he was in a state of nervous exhaustion.

"I have already questioned the director of the theater and your assistant," said the judge when Han had taken his place in the witness box. "I now propose to examine you."

Han bowed his head.

"Tell me," said the judge, "did you at any time love your wife?"

"From the day of our marriage until the child was born I loved her with all my heart."

"And why did the birth of the child change things?"

"Because I know it was not mine."

"Did you know who the other man was?"

"I had a good idea. I think it was my wife's cousin."

"Did you know him personally?"

"He was a close friend. It was he who first suggested that we get married. It was he who urged me to marry her."

"I presume that his relations with her occurred prior to your marriage."

"Yes, sir. The child was born eight months after we were married."

"According to your assistant, it was a premature birth."

"That is what I told everyone."

"The child died very soon after birth, did it not? What was the cause of death?"

"He was smothered by his mother's breasts."

"Did your wife do that on purpose?"

"She said it was an accident."

The judge was silent and looked fixedly at Han's face. Han raised his head but kept his eyes lowered as he awaited the next question. The judge continued.

"Did your wife confess these relations to you?"

"She did not confess, nor did I ever ask her about them. The child's death seemed like retribution for everything and I decided that I should be as magnanimous as possible, but . . ."

"But in the end you were unable to be magnanimous?"

"That's right. I could not help thinking that the death of the child was insufficient retribution. When apart from my wife, I was able to reason calmly, but as soon as I saw her, something happened inside me. When I saw her body, my temper would begin to rise."

"Didn't divorce occur to you?"

"I often thought that I should like to have a divorce, but I never mentioned it to my wife. My wife used to say that if I left her she could no longer exist."

"Did she love you?"

"She did not love me."

"Then why did she say such things?"

"I think she was referring to the material means of existence. Her home had been ruined by her elder brother, and she knew that no serious man would want to marry a woman who had been the wife of a strolling player. Also her feet were too small for her to do any ordinary work."

"What were your physical relations?"

"I imagine about the same as with most couples."

"Did your wife have any real liking for you?"

"I do not think she really liked me. In fact, I think it must have been very painful for her to live with me as my wife. Still, she endured it. She endured it with a degree of patience almost unthinkable for a man. She used to observe me with a cold, cruel look in her eyes as my life gradually went to pieces. She never showed a flicker of sympathy as she saw me struggling in agony to escape into a better, truer sort of existence."

"Why could you not take some decisive action—have it out with her, or even leave her if necessary?"

"Because my mind was full of all sorts of ideals."

"What ideals?"

"I wanted to behave towards my wife in such a way that there would be no wrong on my side. . . . But in the end it didn't work."

"Did you never think of killing your wife?"

Han did not answer and the judge repeated his question. After a long pause, Han replied, "Before the idea of killing her occurred to me, I often used to think it would be a good thing if she died."

"Well, in that case, if it had not been against the law, don't you think you might have killed her?"

"I wasn't thinking in terms of the law, sir. That's not what stopped me. It was just that I was weak. At the same time I had this overmastering desire to enter into a truer sort of life."

"Nevertheless you did think of killing your wife, did you not—later on, I mean?"

"I never made up my mind to do it. But, yes, it is correct to say that I did think about it once."

"How long was that before the event?"

"The previous night. . . . Or perhaps even the same morning."

"Had you been quarreling?"

"Yes, sir."

"What about?"

"About something so petty that it's hardly worth mentioning."

"Try telling me about it."

"It was a question of food. I get rather short-tempered when I haven't eaten for some time. Well, that evening my wife had been dawdling and our supper wasn't ready when it should have been. I got very angry."

"Were you more violent than usual?"

"No, but afterwards I still felt worked up, which was unusual. I suppose it was because I'd been worrying so much during those past weeks about making a better existence for myself, and realizing there was nothing I could do about it. I went to bed but couldn't sleep. All sorts of upsetting thoughts went through my mind. I began to feel that whatever I did, I should never be able to achieve the things I really wanted—that however hard I tried, I should never be able to escape from all the hateful aspects of my present life. This sad, hopeless state of affairs all seemed connected with my marriage. I desperately wanted to find a chink of light to lead me out of my darkness, but even this desire was gradually being extinguished. The hope of escape still flickered and sputtered within me, and I knew that if ever it should go out I would to all intents and purposes be a dead person.

"And then the ugly thought began flitting through my mind, 'If only she would die! If only she would die! Why should I not kill her?' The practical consequence of such a crime meant nothing to me any longer. No doubt I would go to prison, but life in prison could not be worse—could only be better—than this present existence. And yet somehow I had the feeling that killing my wife would solve nothing. It would have been a shirking of the issue, in the same way as suicide. I must go through each day's suffering as it came, I told myself; there was no way to circumvent that. That had become my true life: to suffer.

"As my mind raced along these tracks, I almost forgot that the cause of my suffering lay beside me. Utterly exhausted, I lay there unable to sleep. I fell into a blank state of stupefaction, and as my tortured mind turned numb, the idea of killing my wife gradually faded. Then I was overcome by the sad empty feeling that follows a nightmare. I thought of all my fine resolutions for a better life, and realized that I was too weakhearted to attain it. When dawn finally broke I saw that my wife also, had not been sleeping. . . ."

"When you got up, did you behave normally towards each other?"

"We did not say a single word to each other."

"But why didn't you think of leaving her, when things had come to this?"

"Do you mean, Your Honor, that that would have been a solution of my problem? No, no, that too would have been a shirking of the issue! As I told you, I was determined to behave towards my wife so that there would be no wrong on my side."

Han gazed earnestly at the judge, who nodded his head as a sign for him to continue.

"Next day I was physically exhausted and of course my nerves were ragged. It was agony for me to remain still, and as soon as I had got dressed I left the house and wandered aimlessly about the deserted parts of town. Constantly the thought kept returning that I must do something to solve my life, but the idea of killing no longer occurred to me. The truth is that there was a chasm between my thoughts of murder the night before and any actual decision to commit a crime! Indeed, I never even thought about that evening's performance. If I had, I certainly would have decided to leave out the knife-throwing act. There were dozens of others acts that could have been substituted.

"Well, the evening came and finally it was our turn to appear on the stage. I did not have the slightest premonition that anything out of the ordinary was to happen. As usual, I demonstrated to the audience the sharpness of my knives by slicing pieces of paper and throwing some of the knives at the floor boards. Presently my wife appeared, heavily made up and wearing an elaborate Chinese costume; after greeting the audience with her charming smile, she took up her position in front of the board. I picked up one of the knives and placed myself at the distance from her.

"That's when our eyes met for the first time since the previous evening. At once I understood the risk of having chosen this particular act for that night's performance! Obviously I would have to master my nerves, yet the exhaustion which had penetrated to the very marrow of my bones prevented me. I sensed that I could no longer trust my own arm. To calm myself I closed my eyes for a moment, and I sensed that my whole body was trembling.

"Now the time had come! I aimed my first knife above her head; it struck just one inch higher than usual. My wife raised her arms and I prepared to throw my next two knives under each of her arms. As the first one left the ends of my fingers, I felt as if something were holding it back; I no longer had the sense of being able to determine the exact destination of my knives. It was now really a matter of luck if the knife struck at the point intended; each of my movements had become deliberate and self-conscious.

"I threw one knife to the left of my wife's neck and was about to throw another to the right when I saw a strange expression in her eyes. She seemed to be seized by a paroxysm of fear! Did she have a presentiment that this knife, that in a matter of seconds would come hurtling towards her, was going to lodge in her throat? I felt dizzy, as if about to faint. Forcing the knife deliberately out of my hand, I as good as aimed it into space. . . ."

The judge was silent, peering intently at Han.

"All at once the thought came to me, 'I've killed her,'" said Han abruptly.

"On purpose, you mean?"

"Yes. Suddenly I felt that I had done it on purpose."

"After that I understand you knelt down beside your wife's body and prayed in silence."

"Yes sir. That was a rather cunning device that occurred to me on the spur of the moment. I realized that everyone knew me as a believer in Christianity. But while I was making a pretense of praying, I was in fact carefully calculating what attitude to adopt."

"So you were absolutely convinced that what you had done was on purpose?"

"I was. But I realized at once that I should be able to pretend it had been an accident."

"And why did you think it had been on purpose?"

"I had lost all sense of judgment."

"Did you think you'd succeeded in giving the impression it was an accident?"

"Yes, though when I thought about it afterwards it made my flesh creep. I pretended as convincingly as I could to be grief-stricken, but if there'd been just one really sharp-witted person about, he'd have realized right away that I was only acting. Well, that evening I decided that there was no good reason why I should not be acquitted; I told myself very calmly that there wasn't a shred of material evidence against me. To be sure, everyone knew how badly I got on with my wife, but if I persisted in saying that it was an accident, no one could prove the contrary. Going over in my mind everything that had happened, I saw that my wife's death could be explained very plausibly as an accident.

"And then a strange question came to my mind: why did I myself believe that it had *not* been an accident? The previous night I had thought about killing her, but might it not be that very fact which now caused me to think of my act as deliberate? Gradually I came to the point that I myself did not know what actually had happened! At that I became very happy— almost unbearably happy. I wanted to shout at the top of my lungs."

"Because you had come to consider it an accident?"

"No, that I can't say: because I no longer had the slightest idea as to whether it had been intentional or not. So I decided that my best way of being acquitted would be to make a clean breast of everything. Rather than deceive myself and everyone else by saying it was an accident, why not be completely honest and say I did not know what happened? I cannot declare it was a mistake; on the other hand I can't admit it was intentional. In fact, I can plead neither 'guilty' nor 'not guilty.'"

Han was silent. The judge, too, remained silent for a long moment before saying softly, reflectively, "I believe that what you have told me is true. Just one more question: do you not feel the slightest sorrow for your wife's death?"

"None at all! Even when I hated my wife most bitterly in the past, I never could have imagined I would feel such happiness in talking about her death."

"Very well, said the judge. "You may stand down."

Han silently lowered his head and left the room. Feeling strangely moved, the judge reached for his pen. On the document which lay on the table before him he wrote down the words, "Not guilty."

15

The Mens Rea

Actus non facit reum, nisi mens sit rea—"An unwarrantable act without a vicious will is no crime at all."

Translation
by Blackstone

When a man of sound memory and of the age of discretion unlawfully kills any reasonable creature in being, and under the King's peace, with malice aforethought, either express or implied by the law [he is guilty of murder].

Definition of murder
by Coke
in the seventeenth century

Any statutory offense that carries an element of the mental state that must accompany the criminal act if the defendant is to be found guilty of such an offense is said to require a mens rea. Offenses that carry no mens rea are called strict liability offenses—the mere carrying out of the act regardless of the mental state of the actor results in liability. The mens rea is usually identified within statutory language by words such as "purposely," "knowingly," or "recklessly," all of which imply that the crime was committed with a sense of awareness or intention.

It is common practice to refer to murder as an unlawful killing with "malice aforethought"—the requisite mental state for a conviction of murder—while referring to manslaughter as an unlawful killing without "malice aforethought"; but it should be pointed out that the absence of "malice aforethought" does not necessarily negate the implication of intention. For instance, manslaughter may be voluntary or involuntary, suggesting that one carries intention while the other does not, the latter perhaps carrying the element of negligence instead. In other words, "malice aforethought"—the mental state that common law required in order to distinguish a killing as murder rather than manslaughter—is now seen as the depraved indifference to human life associated with a particularly heinous crime, causing it to be classified as murder.

Yet, in spite of statutory and common law definitions, determining whether or not the accused has the requisite mental state for conviction of the crime of which he or she is charged is no simple task. In the previous section we saw how difficult it was for the judge—in spite of a defendant who appeared to be scrupulously honest in his testimony—to determine whether or not Han intended to murder is wife. Early in the story, the judge decided that this was "a clear case of homicide, but whether it was manslaughter or premeditated murder it was impossible to tell." The defendant admitted that he had thought about killing his wife on the night before or maybe on the very morning of her death. Han tells the judge that for a while he even believed himself that he had done the act on purpose, but later he was unable to determine whether or not he had intended to kill his wife when he threw the lethal knife. If Han himself did not see the truth clearly, how could the judge do so? Or is it possible that Han presented his version of the event to the judge in order to attempt to convince the judge of his innocence while knowing all the time that he intended to kill his wife?

James Thurber's "The Catbird Seat" raises another issue in relation to the mens rea. Clearly Mr. Martin *intends* to "rub out" Mrs. Ulgine Barrows when he goes to her house. He even looks for a weapon with which to carry out his diabolical plot, but then he very quickly realizes it is "all too grossly improbable." Can Mr. Martin be accused of *any* crime even though he abandons his original plan? It is often said that you cannot punish a man for his thoughts, but can you?

Criminal attempt is incorporated into many statutes and most of those statutes require some variation of the following elements: (1) the intention to commit the act; (2) performance of some component of the act—sometimes a substantial step toward the crime is required; and (3) failure to complete the crime. Applying this test to Mr. Martin's behavior, there is the intention, but what step or steps does he take? He keeps his gloves on in Mrs. Barrow's house; he buys and smokes cigarettes although he has never smoked before; he asks for a scotch and soda although he does not normally drink; and he looks for a murder weapon. Is this enough to convict him of attempted murder? In this case, Mr. Martin is unable to commit the crime. What does he mean when he says it was impossible? Was it because a suitable weapon was not available? Or was it because he recognized that he did not have the killer instinct? If he did not have the killer instinct, could he have had the requisite intention in the first place? Should the *reason* for his inability to complete the crime even be considered? Would it make a difference to our feelings about Mr. Martin's culpability if he had abandoned his plan to kill Mrs. Barrows because an unexpected visitor arrived at Mrs. Barrows' door?

Although we have been discussing murderers and the requisite mens rea for a conviction of the crime of murder, the mens rea is not limited to such cases. Melville Davisson Post's short story "The Animus Furandi" deals with, no less, the animus furandi—the intention to steal. As we are told: "If it be not present there can be no robbery, no matter how great the force, violence, or putting in fear, or how grave, serious, or irreparable the resulting injury." Law school students often donate law school textbooks to local prisons for the edification of the prisoner's and we usually think of those prisoners reading such law books in order to prepare an appeal on their own behalf. However, as "The Animus Furandi" so aptly illustrates, knowledge of the law can make robbers out of petty thieves—or should we say petty thieves out of robbers?

The Catbird Seat
James Thurber

Mr. Martin bought the pack of Camels on Monday night in the most crowded cigar store on Broadway. It was theater time and seven or eight men were buying cigarettes. The clerk didn't even glance at Mr. Martin, who put the pack in his overcoat pocket and went out. If any of the staff at F & S had seen him buy the cigarettes, they would have been astonished, for it was generally known that Mr. Martin did not smoke, and never had. No one saw him.

It was just a week to the day since Mr. Martin had decided to rub out Mrs. Ulgine Barrows. The term "rub out" pleased him because it suggested nothing more than the correction of an error—in this case an error of Mr. Fitweiler. Mr. Martin had spent each night of the past week working out his plan and examining it. As he walked home now he went over it again. For the hundreth time he resented the element of imprecision, the margin of guesswork that entered into the business. The project as he had worked it out was casual and bold, the risks were considerable. Something might go wrong anywhere along the line. And therein lay the cunning of his scheme. No one would ever see in it the cautious, painstaking hand of Erwin Martin, head of the filing department at F & S, of whom Mr. Fitweiler had once said, "Man is fallible but Martin isn't." No one would see his hand, that is, unless it were caught in the act.

Sitting in his apartment, drinking a glass of milk, Mr. Martin reviewed his case against Mrs. Ulgine Barrows, as he had every night for seven nights. He began at the beginning. Her quacking voice and braying laugh had first profaned the halls of F & S on March 7, 1941 (Mr. Martin had a head for dates). Old Roberts, the personnel chief, had introduced her as the newly appointed special adviser to the president of the firm, Mr. Fitweiler. The woman had appalled Mr. Martin instantly, but he hadn't shown it. He had given her his dry hand, a look of studious concentration, and a faint smile. "Well," she had said, looking at the papers on his desk, "are you lifting the oxcart out of the ditch?" As Mr. Martin recalled that moment, over his milk, he squirmed slightly. He must keep his mind on her crimes as a special adviser, not on her peccadillos as a personality. This he found difficult to do, in spite of entering an objection and sustaining it. The faults of the woman as a woman kept chattering on in his mind like an unruly witness. She had, for almost two years now, baited him. In the halls, in the elevator, even in his own office into which she romped now and then like a circus horse, she was constantly shouting these silly questions at him. "Are you lifting the oxcart out of the ditch? Are you tearing up the pea patch? Are you hollering down the rain barrel? Are you scraping around the bottom of the pickle barrel? Are you sitting in the catbird seat?"

It was Joey Hart, one of Mr. Martin's two assistants, who had explained what the gibberish meant. "She must be a Dodger fan," he had said. "Red Barber announces the Dodger games over the radio and he uses those expressions—picked 'em up down South." Joe had gone on to explain one or two. "Tearing up the pea patch" meant going on a rampage; "sitting in the catbird seat" meant sitting pretty, like a batter with three balls and no strikes on him. Mr. Martin dismissed all this with an effort. It had been annoying, it had driven him near to distraction, but he was too solid a man to be moved to murder by anything so childish. It was fortunate, he reflected as he passed on to the important charges against Mrs. Barrows, that he had stood up under it so well. He had maintained always an outward appearance of polite tolerance. "Why, I even believe you like the woman," Miss Paird, his other assistant, had once said to him. He had simply smiled.

A gavel rapped in Mr. Martin's mind and the case proper was resumed. Mrs. Ulgine Barrows stood charged with willful, blatant, and persistent attempts to destroy the efficiency and system of F & S. It was competent, material, and relevant to review her advent and rise to power. Mr. Martin had got the story from Miss Paird, who seemed always able to find things out. According to her, Mrs. Barrows had met Mr. Fitweiler at a party, where she had rescued him from the embraces of a powerfully built drunken man who had mistaken the president of F & S for a famous retired Middle Western football coach. She had led him to a sofa and somehow worked upon him a monstrous magic. The aging gentleman had jumped to the conclusion there and then that this was a woman of singular attainments, equipped to bring out the best in him and in the firm. A week later he had introduced her into F & S as his special adviser. On that day confusion got its foot in the door. After Miss Tyson, Mr. Brundage, and Mrs. Bartlett had been fired and Mr. Munson had taken his hat and stalked out, mailing in his resignation later, old Roberts had been emboldened to speak to Mr. Fitweiler. He mentioned that Mr. Munson's department had been "a little disrupted" and hadn't they perhaps better resume the old system there? Mr. Fitweiler had said certainly not. He had the greatest faith in Mrs. Barrow's ideas. "They require a little seasoning, a little seasoning, is all," he had added. Mr. Roberts had given it up. Mr. Martin reviewed in detail all the changes wrought by Mrs. Barrows. She had begun chipping at the cornices of the firm's edifice and now she was swinging at the foundation stones with a pickaxe.

Mr. Martin came now, in his summing up, to the afternoon of Monday, November 2, 1942—just one week ago. On that day, at 3 p.m., Mrs. Barrows had bounced into his office. "Boo!" she had yelled. "Are you scraping around the bottom of the pickle barrel?" Mr. Martin had looked at her form under his green eyeshade, saying nothing. She had begun to wander about the office, taking it in with her great, popping eyes. "Do you really need *all* these filing cabinets?" she had demanded suddenly. Mr. Martin's heart had jumped. "Each of these files," he had said, keeping his voice even, "plays an indispensable part in the system of F & S." She had brayed at him, "Well, don't tear up the pea patch!" and gone to the door. From there she had bawled, "But you sure have got a lot of fine scrap in here!" Mr. Martin could no longer doubt that the finger was on his beloved department. Her pickaxe was on the upswing, poised for the first blow. It had not come yet; he had received no blue memo from the enchanted Mr. Fitweiler bearing nonsensical instructions deriving from the obscene woman. But there was no doubt in Mr. Martin's mind that one would be forthcoming. He must act quickly. Already a precious week had gone by. Mr. Martin stood up in his living room, still holding his milk glass. "Gentlemen of the jury," he said to himself, "I demand the death penalty for this horrible person."

The next day Mr. Martin followed his routine, as usual. He polished his glasses more often and once sharpened an already sharp pencil, but not even Miss Paird noticed. Only once did he catch sight of his victim; she swept past him in the hall with a patronizing "Hi!" At five-thirty he walked home, as usual, and had a glass of milk, as usual. He had never drunk anything stronger in his life—unless you could count ginger ale. The late Sam Schlosser, the S of F & S, had praised Mr. Martin at a staff meeting several years before for his temperate habits. "Our most efficient worker neither drinks nor smokes," he had said. "The results speak for themselves." Mr. Fitweiler had sat by, nodding approval.

Mr. Martin was still thinking about that red-letter day as he walked over to the Schrafft's on Fifth Avenue near Forty-sixth Street. He got there, as he always did, at eight o'clock. He finished his dinner and the financial page of the *Sun* at a quarter to nine, as he always did. It was his custom after dinner to take a walk. This time he walked down Fifth Avenue at a casual pace. His gloved hands felt moist and warm, his forehead cold. He transferred the camels from his overcoat to a jacket pocket. He wondered, as he did so, if they did not represent an unnecessary note of strain. Mrs. Barrows smoked only Luckies. It was his idea to puff a few puffs on a Camel (after the rubbing-out), snuff it out in the ashtray holding her lipstick-stained Luckies, and thus drag a small red herring across the trail. Perhaps it was not a good idea. It would take time. He might even choke, too loudly.

Mr. Martin had never seen the house on West Twelfth Street where Mrs. Barrows lived, but he had a clear enough picture of it. Fortunately, she had bragged to everybody about her ducky first-floor apartment in the perfectly darling three-story red-brick. There would be no doorman or other attendants; just the tenants of the second and third floor. As he walked along, Mr. Martin realized that he would get there before nine-thirty. He had considered walking north on Fifth Avenue from Schrafft's to a point from which it would take him until ten o'clock to reach the house. At that hour people were less likely to be coming in or going out. But the procedure would have made an awkward loop in the straight thread of his casualness, and he had abandoned it. It was impossible to figure when people would be entering or leaving the house, anyway. There was a great risk at any hour. If he ran into anybody, he would simply have to place the rubbing-out of Ulgine Barrows in the inactive file forever. The same thing would hold true if there were someone in her apartment. In that case he would just say that he had been passing by, recognized her charming house and thought to drop in.

It was eighteen minutes after nine when Mr. Martin turned into Twelfth Street. A man passed him, and a man and a woman talking. There was no one within fifty paces when he came to the house, halfway down the block. He was up the steps and in the small vestibule in no time, pressing the bell under the card that said "Mrs. Ulgine Barrows." When the clicking in the lock started, he jumped forward against the door. He got inside fast, closing the door behind him. A bulb in a lantern hung from the hall ceiling on a chain seemed to give a monstrously bright light. There was nobody on the stair, which went up ahead of him along the left wall. A door opened down the hall in the wall on the right. He went toward it swiftly, on tiptoe.

"Well, for God's sake, look who's here!" bawled Mrs. Barrows, and her braying laugh rang out like the report of a shotgun. He rushed past her like a football tackle, bumping her. "Hey, quit shoving!" she said, closing the door behind them. They were in her living room, which seemed to Mr. Martin to be lighted by a hundred lamps. "What's after you?" she said. "You're as jumpy as a goat." He found he was unable to speak. His heart was wheezing in his throat. "I—yes," he finally brought out. She was jabbering and laughing as she started to help him off with his coat. "No, no," he said. "I'll put it here." He took it off and put it on a chair near the door. "Your hat and gloves, too," she said. "You're in a lady's house." He put his hat on top of the coat. Mrs. Barrows seemed larger than he had thought. He kept his gloves on. "I was passing by," he said. "I recognized—is there anyone here?" She laughed louder than ever. "No," she said, "we're all alone. You're as white as a sheet, you funny man. Whatever *has* come over you? I'll mix you a toddy." She started toward a door across the room. "Scotch-and-soda be all right? But say, you don't drink, do you?" She turned and gave him her amused look. Mr. Martin pulled himself together. "Scotch-and-soda will be all right," he heard himself say. He could hear her laughing in the kitchen.

Mr. Martin looked quickly around the living room for the weapon. He had counted on finding one there. There were andirons and a poker and something in a corner that looked like an Indian club. None of them would do. It couldn't be that way. He began to pace around. He came to a desk. On it lay a metal paper knife with an ornate handle. Would it be sharp enough? He reached for it and knocked over a small brass jar. Stamps spilled out of it and it fell to the floor with a clatter. "Hey," Mrs. Barrows yelled from the kitchen, "are you tearing up the pea patch?" Mr. Martin gave a strange laugh. Picking up the knife, he tried its point against his left wrist. It was blunt. It wouldn't do.

When Mrs. Barrows reappeared, carrying two highballs, Mr. Martin, standing there with his gloves on, became acutely conscious of the fantasy

he had wrought. Cigarettes in his pocket, a drink prepared for him—it was
all too grossly improbable. It was more than that; it was impossible.
Somewhere in the back of his mind a vague idea stirred, sprouted. "For
heavens' sake, take off those gloves," said Mrs. Barrows. "I always wear
them in the house," said Mr. Martin. The idea began to bloom, strange and
wonderful. She put the glasses on a coffee table in front of a sofa and sat
on the sofa. "Come over here, you odd little man," she said. Mr. Martin
went over and sat beside her. It was difficult getting a cigarette out of the
pack of Camels, but he managed it. She held a match for him, laughing.
"Well," she said, handing him his drink, "This is perfectly marvelous. You
with a drink and cigarette."

Mr. Martin puffed, not too awkwardly, and took a gulp of the high-
ball. "I drink and smoke all the time," he siad. He clinked his glass against
hers. "Here's nuts to that old windbag, Fitweiler," he said, and gulped
again. The stuff tasted awful, but he made no grimace. "Really, Mr. Martin," she said, her voice and posture changing, "you are insulting our employer." Mrs. Barrows was now all special adviser to the president. "I am
preparing a bomb," said Mr. Martin, "which will blow the old goat higher
than hell." He had only had a little of the drink, which was not strong. It
couldn't be that. "Do you take dope or something?" Mrs. Barrows asked
coldly. "Heroin," said Mr. Martin. "I'll be coked to the gills when I bump
that old buzzard off." "Mr. Martin!" she shouted, getting to her feet. "That
will be all of that. You must go at once." Mr. Martin took another swallow
of his drink. He tapped his cigarette out in the ashtray and put the pack of
Camels on the coffee table. Then he got up. She stood glaring at him. He
walked over and put on his hat and coat. "Not a word about this," he said,
and laid an index finger against his lips. All Mrs. Barrows could bring out
was "Really!" Mr. Martin put his hand on the doorknob. "I'm sitting in the
catbird seat," he said. He stuck his tongue out at her and left. Nobody saw
him go.

Mr. Martin got to his apartment, walking, well before eleven. No one saw
him go in. He had two glasses of milk after brushing his teeth, and he felt
elated. It wasn't tipsiness, because he hadn't been tipsy. Anyway, the
walk had worn off all effects of the whisky. He got in bed and read a magazine for a while. He was asleep before midnight.

Mr. Martin got to the office at eight-thirty the next morning, as
usual. At a quarter to nine, Ulgine Barrows, who had never before arrived
at work before ten, swept into his office. "I'm reporting to Mr. Fitweiler
now!" she shouted. "If he turns you over to the police, it's no more than
you deserve!" Mr. Martin gave her a look of shocked surprise. "I beg your
pardon?" he said. Mrs. Barrows snorted and bounced out of the room,
leaving Miss Paird and Joey Hart staring after her. "What's the matter with
the old devil now?" asked Miss Paid. "I have no idea," said Mr. Martin, resuming his work. The other two looked at him and then at each other.
Miss Paird got up and went out. She walked slowly past the closed door of
Mr. Fitweiler's office. Mrs. Barrows was yelling inside, but she was not
braying. Miss Paird could not hear what the woman was saying. She went
back to her desk.

Forty-five minutes later, Mrs. Barrows left the president's office and went into her own, shutting the door. It wasn't until half an hour later that Mr. Fitweiler sent for Mr. Martin. The head of the filing department, neat, quiet, attentive, stood in front of the old man's desk. Mr. Fitweiler was pale and nervous. He took his glasses off and twiddled them. He made a small, bruffing sound in this throat. "Martin," he said, "you have been with us more than twenty years." "Twenty-two, sir," said Mr. Martin. "In that time," pursued the president, "your work and your—uh—manner have been exemplary." "I trust so, sir," said Mr. Martin. "I have understood, Martin," said Mr. Fitweiler, "that you have never taken a drink or smoked." "That is correct, sir," said Mr. Martin. "Ah, yes." Mr. Fitweiler polished his glasses. "You may describe what you did after leaving the office yesterday, Martin," he said. Mr. Martin allowed less than a second for his bewildered pause. "Certainly, sir," he said. "I walked home. Then I went to Schrafft's for dinner. Afterward I walked home again. I went to bed early, sir, and read a magazine for a while. I was asleep before eleven." "Ah, yes," said Mr. Fitweiler again. He was silent for a moment, searching for the proper words to say to the head of the filing department. "Mrs. Barrows," he said finally, "Mrs. Barrows has worked hard, Martin, very hard. It grieves me to report that she has suffered a severe breakdown. It has taken the form of a persecution complex accompanied by distressing hallucinations." "I am very sorry, sir," said Mr. Martin. "Mrs. Barrows is under the delusion," continued Mr. Fitweiler, "that you visited her last evening and behaved yourself in an—uh—unseemly manner." He raised his hand to silence Mr. Martin's little pained outcry. "It is the nature of these psychological diseases," Mr. Fitweiler said, "to fix upon the least likely and most innocent party as the—uh—source of persecution. These matters are not for the lay mind to grasp, Martin. I've just had my psychiatrist, Dr. Fitch, on the phone. He would not, of course, commit himself, but he made enough generalizations to substantiate my suspicions. I suggested to Mrs. Barrows when she had completed her—uh—story to me this morning, that she visit Dr. Fitch, for I suspected a condition at once. She flew, I regret to say, into a rage, and demanded—uh—requested that I call you on the carpet. You may not know, Martin, but Mrs. Barrows had planned a reorganization of your department—subject to my approval, of course, subject to my approval. This brought you, rather than anyone else, to her mind—but again that is a phenomenon for Dr. Fitch and not for us. So, Martin, I am afraid Mrs. Barrows' usefulness here is at an end." "I am dreadfully sorry, sir," said Mr. Martin.

It was at this point that the door to the office blew open with the suddenness of a gas-main explosion and Mrs. Barrows catapulted through it. "Is the little rat denying it?" she screamed. "He can't get away with that!" Mr. Martin got up and moved discreetly to a point beside Mr. Fitweiler's chair. "You drank and smoked at my apartment," she bawled at Mr. Martin, "and you know it! You called Mr. Fitweiler an old windbag and said you were going to blow him up when you got coked to the gills on your heroin!" She stopped yelling to catch her breath and a new glint came into her popping eyes. "If you weren't such a drab, ordinary little man," she said "I'd think you'd planned it all. Sticking your tongue out, saying

you were sitting in the catbird seat, because you thought no one would believe me when I told it! My God, it's really too perfect!" She glared at Mr.
Fitweiler. "Can't you see how he has tricked us, you old fool? Can't you
see his little game?" But Mr. Fitweiler had been surreptitiously pressing all
the buttons under the top of his desk and employees of F & S began pouring into the room. "Stockton," said Mr. Fitweiler, "you and Fishbein will
take Mrs. Barrows to her home. Mrs. Powell, you will go with them."
Stockton, who had played a little football in high school, blocked Mrs. Barrows as she made for Mr. Martin. It took him and Fishbein together to
force her out of the door into the hall, crowded with stenographers and office boys. She was still screaming imprecations at Mr. Martin, tangled and
contradictory imprecations. The hubbub finally died out down the corridor.

   "I regret that this has happened," said Mr. Fitweiler. "I shall ask
you to dismiss it from your mind, Martin." "Yes, sir," said Mr. Martin,
anticipating his chief's "That will be all" by moving to the door. "I will
dismiss it." He went out and shut the door, and his step was light and
quick in the hall. When he entered his department he had slowed down to
his customary gait, and he walked quietly across the room to the W_{20} file,
wearing a look of studious concentration.

The Animus Furandi
Melville Davisson Post

I.

"I am tired of your devilish hints, why can't you come out with it, man?" The speaker was half angry.

Parks leaned forward on the table, his face was narrow and full of cunning. "Mystery is your long suit, Hogarth, I compliment you."

"You tire me," said the man; "if you have any reason for bringing me here at this hour of the night I want to know it."

"Would I be here in the office at two o'clock in the morning, with a detective and without a reason? Listen, I will be plain with you. I must get Mr. Mason out of New York; he is going rapidly, and unless he gets a sea-voyage and a change of country he will be in the mad-house. He is terribly thin and scarcely sleeps any more at all. No human being can imagine what a monster he is to manage, or in what an infinitely difficult position I have been placed. When we came here from Paris, after the unfortunate collapse of the canal syndicate, the situation that confronted me was of the most desperate character. Mr. Mason was practically a bankrupt. He had spent his entire fortune in a mighty effort to right the syndicate, and would have succeeded if it had not been for the treachery of some of the French officials. He had been absent so long from New York that his law practice was now entirely lost, and, worst of all, this mysterious tilt of his mind would render it utterly impossible for him ever to regain his clientage. For a time I was in despair. Mr. Mason was, of course, utterly oblivious to the situation, and there was no one with whom I could advise, even if I dared attempt it. When everything failed in Paris, Mr. Mason collapsed, physically. He was in the hospital for months; when he came out, his whole nature was wrenched into this strange groove, although his mind was apparently as keen and powerful as ever and his wonderful faculties unimpaired. He seemed now possessed by this one idea, that all the difficulties of men were problems and that he could solve them.

"A few days after we landed in New York, I wandered into the court-house; a great criminal had been apprehended and was being tried for a desperate crime. I sat down and listened. As the case developed, it occurred to me that the man had botched his work fearfully, and that if he could have had Mr. Mason plan his crime for him he need never have been punished. Then the inspiration came. Why not turn this idea of Mr. Mason to account?

"I knew that the city was filled with shrewd, desperate men, who feared nothing under high heaven but the law, and were willing to take desperate chances with it. I went to some of them and pointed out the mighty aid that I could give; they hooted at the idea, and said that crime was crime and the old ways were the best ways."

Parks paused and looked up at the detective. "They have since changed their minds," he added.

"What did Mr. Mason think of your method of securing clients?" said Hogarth.

"That was my greatest difficulty," continued Parks. "I resorted to every known trick in order to prevent him from learning how the men happened to come to him, and so far I have been successful. He has never suspected me, and has steadily believed that those who came to him with difficulties were attracted by his great reputation. By this means, Mr. Mason has made vast sums of money, but what he has done with it is a mystery. I have attempted to save what I could, but I have not enough for this extended trip to the south of France. Now, do you understand me?"

"Yes," answered the detective, "you want to find where his money is hidden."

"No," said Parks, with a queer smile, "I am not seeking impossible ventures. What Randolph Mason chooses to make a mystery will remain so to the end of time, all the detectives on the earth to the contrary."

"What do you want, then?" asked Hogarth, doggedly.

Parks drew his chair nearer to the man and lowered his voice. "My friend," he said, "this recent change in the administration of the city has thrown you out on your uppers. Your chief is gone for good, and with him all your hopes in New York. It was a rout, my friend, and they have all saved themselves but you. What is to become of you?"

"God knows!" said the detective. "Of course I am still a member of the agency, but there is scarcely bread in that."

"This world is a fighting station," continued parks. "The one intention of the entire business world is robbery. The man on the street has no sense of pity; he grows rich because he conceives some shrewd scheme by which he is enabled to seize and enjoy the labor of others. His only object is to avoid the law; he commits the same wrong and causes the same resulting injury as the pirate. The word 'crime,' Hogarth, was invented by the strong with which to frighten the weak; it means nothing. Now listen, since the thing is a cutthroat game, why not have our share of the spoil?"

Hogarth's face was a study; Parks was shrewdly forcing the right door.

"My friend," the little man went on, "we can make a fortune by a twist of the wrist, and go scot-free with the double eagles clinking in our pockets. We can make it in a day, and thereafter wag our heads at fortune and snap our fingers at the law."

"How?" asked the detective. The door had broken and swung in.

"I will tell you," said Parks, placing his hand confidentially on the man's shoulder. "Mr. Mason has a plan. I know it, because yesterday he was walking up Broadway, apparently oblivious to everything. Suddenly his face cleared up, and he stopped and snapped his fingers. "'Good!' he said, 'a detective could do it, and it would be child play, child play.'"

Hogarth's countenance fell. "Is that all?" he said.

"All!" echoed Parks, bringing his hand down on the table. "Isn't that enough, man? You don't know Randolph Mason. If he has a plan by which a detective can make a haul, it is good, do you hear, and it goes."

"What does this mean, Parks?" said a voice.

The little clerk sprang up and whirled round. In his vehemence he had not noticed the door-way. Randolph Mason stood in the shadow. He was thin and haggard, his face was shrunken and unshaven, and he looked worn and exhausted.

"Oh, sir," said Parks, gathering himself quickly, "this is my friend Braxton Hogarth, and he is in great trouble. He came here to ask me for help; we have been talking over the matter for many hours, and I don't see any way out for him."

"Where has the trap caught him?" said Mason, coming into the room.

"It is an awful strange thing, sir," answered the clerk. "Mr. Hogarth's only son is the teller of the Bay State Bank in New Jersey. This morning they found that twenty thousand dollars was missing from the vault. No one had access to the vault yesterday but young Hogarth. The cashier was in this city, the combination was not known to any others. There is no evidence of robbery. The circumstances are so overwhelming against young Hogarth that the directors went to him and said plainly that if the money was in its place by Saturday night he would not be prosecuted, and the matter would be hushed up. He protested his innocence, but they simply laughed and would not listen to him. The boy is prostrated, and we know that he is innocent, but there is no way on earth to save him unless Mr. Hogarth can raise the money, which is a hopeless impossibility."

Parks paused, and glanced at Hogarth, the kind of glance that obtains among criminals when they mean, "back up the lie."

The detective buried his face in his hands.

"The discretion of Fate is superb," said Mason. "She strikes always the vulnerable spot. She gives wealth if one does not need it; fame, if one does not care for it; and drives in the harpoon where the heart is."

"The strange thing about it all, sir," continued parks, "is that Mr. Hogarth has been a detective all his life and now is a member of the Atlantic Agency. It looks like the trailed thing turning on him."

"A detective!" said Mr. Mason, sharply. "Ah, there is the open place, and there we will force through."

The whole appearance of the man changed in an instant. He straightened up, and his face lighted with interest. He drew up a chair and sat down at the table, and there, in the chill dark of that November morning, he unfolded the daring details of his cross-plot, and the men beside him stared in wonder.

II.

About one o'clock on Thursday afternoon, William Walson, manager of the great Oceanic Coal Company, stepped out of the Fairmont Banking House in the Monongahela mining regions of West Virginia. It was pay-day at his mine, and he carried a black leather satchel in his hand containing twenty thousand dollars in bills. At this time the gigantic plant of this company was doing an enormous business. The labor unions of the vast Pennsylvania coal regions were out on the bitterest and most protracted strike of all history. The West Virginia operators were moving the heavens in order to supply the market; every man who could hold a pick was at work under the earth day and night.

The excitement was something undreamed of. The region was overrun with straggling workmen, tramps, "hobos," and the scum criminals of the cities, and was transformed as if by magic into a hunting-ground where the keen human ferret stalked the crook and the killer with that high degree of care and patience which obtains only with the man-hunter.

William Walson was tall, with short red beard and red hair, black eyes, and rather a sharp face; his jaw was square, bespeaking energy, but his expression was rather that of a man who won by the milder measures of conciliation and diplomacy. For almost a month he had been taxing his physical strength to the uttermost, and on this afternoon he looked worn and tired out utterly. He walked hurriedly from the bank door to the buckboard, untied the horse, raised the seat, and put the satchel down in the box under the cushion, then climbed in and drove away.

The great plant of the Oceanic Coal Company was on a branch of the railroad, some considerable distance from the main line by rail, but only a few miles over the hills from the Fairmont Junction. William Walson struck out across the country road. The sun shone warm. He had lost so much sleep that presently he began to feel drowsy, and as the horse jogged along he nodded in his seat.

About a mile from the town, at the foot of a little hill in the woods, a man stepped suddenly out from the fence and caught the horse by the bridle. Walson started and looked up. As he did so the stranger covered him with a revolver and bade him put up his hands and get out of the buck-board. The coal dealer saw in a moment that the highwayman meant what he said, and that resistance would be folly. He concluded also that he was confronted by one of the many toughs at large in the neighborhood, and that the fellow's intention was simply to rob him of his personal effects and such money as he might have in his pockets; it was more than probable that the man before him had no knowledge of the money hidden under the seat and would never discover it.

"Tie your horse, sir," said the highwayman.

Walson loosed the hitch strap and fastened the horse to a small tree by the roadside.

"Turn your back to me," said the robber, "and put out your hands behind you." The coal dealer obeyed, thinking that the fellow was now going through his pockets. To his surprise and astonishment the man came up close behind him and snapped a pair of handcuffs on his wrists.

"What do you mean by this? cried Walson, whirling round on his heels.

The big man with the revolver grinned. "You will find out soon enough," he said. "Move along, the walking is good."

William Walson was utterly at sea. He could not understand why this man should kidnap him, and start back with him to the town. What could the highwayman possibly mean by this queer move? At any rate it was evident that he had no knowledge of the money, and Walson reasoned shrewdly that, if he remained quiet and submissive, the vast sum in the buck-board would escape the notice of this erratic thief.

The two men walked along in silence for some time; the highway-man was big, with keen gray eyes and a shrewd face; he seemed curiously elated. When the two came finally to the brow of the hill overlooking the town, Walson stopped and turned to his strange captor; he was now convinced that the fellow was a lunatic.

"Sir," he said, "what in Heaven's name are you trying to do?"

"Introduce you to your fellows in Sing Sing, my friend," answered the highwayman. "The gang will be glad to welcome Red Lead Jim."

It all came to the coal dealer in a moment. "Oh, you miserable ass!" he cried, "what an infernal mistake! My name is William Walson, I am the manager of the Oceanic Coal Company, there is twenty thousand dollars in that buck-board. I must go back to it or it will be lost. Here take off these damned handcuffs, and be quick about it." And he literally danced up and down in the road with rage.

His companion leaned against the fence and roared with laughter. "You are a smooth one, Red, but the job and your twenty thousand will keep."

Walson's face changed. "Come," he said, "let us get this fool business over," and he began to run down the hill to the town, his captor following close beside him.

Men came out into the street in astonishment when they saw the strange pair. Walson was dusty and cursing like a pirate. He called upon the crowd that was quickly gathering, to identify him and arrest his idiotic kidnapper. The people explained that Mr. Walson was all right, that he was a prominent citizen, that it was all some horrible mistake. But the fellow hung on to his arm until he got him to the jail. There the sheriff freed Walson and demanded an explanation. The mob crowded around to hear what it all meant. The stranger seemed utterly astonished at the way the people acted. He said that his name was Braxton Hogarth, that he was a New York detective, an employee of the Atlantic Agency; that he was trailing one Red Lead Jim, a famous bank cracker who was wanted in New York for robbery and murder; that he had tracked him to West Virginia, and that coming suddenly upon William Walson in the road he had believed him to be the man, had arrested him, and brought him at once to the town in order to have him extradited. He said that if Walson was not the man it was the most remarkable case of mistaken identity on record. He then produced a photograph, to which was attached a printed description. The photograph was an excellent likeness of Walson, and the description fitted him perfectly. The coal dealer was dumbfounded and joined with the crowd in admitting the excusableness of the detective's mistake under the very peculiar circumstances, but he said that the story might not be true, and asked the sheriff to hold the detective in custody until he was fully convinced that everything was as Hogarth said. The detective declared himself perfectly satisfied with this arrangement, and William Walson secured a horse and hurried back to his buck-board.

The perilous vocation of Hogarth had inured him to tragic positions. He was thoroughly master of his hand and was playing it with quiet and accurate precision. He asked the sheriff to telegraph the agency and inform it of the situation and said that it would immediately establish the truth of his statement.

That night the mining town of Fairmont was in an uproar. The streets were filled with excited men loudly discussing the great misfortune that had so strangely befallen the manager of the Oceanic Coal Company. It had happened that when William Walson returned to his buck-board, after his release by the sheriff, he found the horse lying dead by the roadside, and the buck-board a heap of ashes and broken irons. The charred remains of the satchel were found under the heap of rubbish, but it was impossible to determine whether the money had been carried away or destroyed by the fire. A jug that had lately contained liquor was found near by. All the circumstances indicated that the atrocious act was the malicious work of some one of the roving bands of drunken cut-throats. But the wonder of it all was the coincidence of the detective and the glaring boldness of the fiend "hobos."

The Atlantic Agency of New York answered the sheriff's telegram immediately, confirming Hogarth's statement, and referring to the District Attorney of New York and the Chief of Police. These answered that the agency was all right and that its statement should be accepted as correct. Finally, as a last precaution, the sheriff and the president of the Oceanic Coal Company talked with the New York Police Chief by long-distance telephone. When they were at length assured that the detective's story was true, he was released and asked to go with the president before the board of directors. Here he went fully over the whole matter, explaining that the man, Red Lead Jim, was a desperate character, and for that reason he had been so severe and careful, not daring to risk the drive back to town in the buck-board. When asked his theory of the robbery, he said that the first impression of the people was undoubtedly correct, that the country was full of wandering gangs of desperate blacklegs, that the money being in paper was perhaps destroyed by the fire and not discovered at all by the thugs in their malicious and drunken deviltry.

The board of directors were not inclined to censure Hogarth, suggesting that after all he had perhaps saved the life of William Walson, as it was evident that the drunken "hobos" would have murdered him if he had been present when they chanced upon the horse and buck-board. Nevertheless, the detective seemed utterly prostrated over the great loss that had resulted from his unfortunate mistake, and left for New York on the first train.

III.

The following night two men stepped from the train at Jersey City and turned down towards the ferry. For a time they walked along in silence; suddenly the big one turned to his companion.

"Parks," he said, "you are a lightning operator, my boy, you should play the mob in a Roman drama."

"I fixed the 'hobo' evidence all right, Hogarth," answered the other, "and I have not forgotten the trust fund," whereupon he winked at his big companion and tapped on the breast of his coat significantly.

The detective's face lighted up and then grew anxious. "Well," he said, lowering his voice, "are we going to try the other end of it?"

"Why not?" answered the little clerk. "Don't we need the trust fund doubled?"

IV.

The great gambling house of Morehead, Opstein, & Company was beginning to be deserted by the crowd that had tempted the fickle goddess all night long to their great hurt. It was now four o'clock in the morning, and only one or two of the more desperate losers hung on to play. Snakey the Parson, a thin delicate knave, with a long innocent, melancholy face, was dealing faro for the house. "Snakey" was a "special" in the parlance of the guild; his luck was known to come in "blizzards"; if he won, to use the manager's language, he won out through the ceiling, and if he lost, he lost down to his health. For this reason Snakey the Parson was not a safe man as a "regular," but he was a golden bonanza when the cards went his way, and to-night they were going his way.

The stragglers drifted out one by one and the dealer was preparing to quit the table when the door opened and two men entered: one was a little old man with a white beard and a lean, hungry face; the other was a big, half-drunken cattle drover. The two came up to the table and stood for a moment looking at the lay-out. A faint smile passed over the face of Snakey the Parson, he knew the types well, they were western cattle-shippers with money.

"How high do ye go, mister?" asked the little man.

"Against the sky," answered the dealer, sadly.

"Then I'll jist double me pile," said the little old man, reaching down into his pocket and fishing up a roll of bills wrapped in a dirty old newspaper. He counted the money and placed it upon the table.

The dealer looked up in astonishment. "Ten thousand!" he said.

"Yep, " answered the old man, "an I want ter bet hit on the jack er spades."

The dealer pushed a stack of yellow chips across the table.

"No, sires," said the player, "you don't give me no buttons. I'll put my pile on this side and you put your pile on t'other side, and the winner takes 'em."

Snakey the Parson wavered a moment. It was against the rules, but here was too good a thing to lose. He turned, counted out the money, and placed it on his right, and began to deal from the box. The cards fell rapidly. For a time the blacks ran on the side of the house. Suddenly they changed and the queen and the ten of spades fell on the left. The dealer saw the card under his thumb and paused. The keen eyes of the old man were fixed on him. He determined to take the long chance, knowing that the loss was only temporary; and the jack of spades came up and fell on the side of the stranger.

With a whoop of joy the old man clutched the money. "I am going to try her agin!" he cried.

"Hold on," said the big cattle-drover, pushing up to the table; "my wad is as good as yourn; it is my turn now."

The dealer grinned. "You can both play, gentlemen," he said, speaking with a low, sweet accent.

"No, we can't," muttered the drover, with the childish obstinacy of a half-drunken man. "I want the whole shootin match to myself; he can have the next whirl at her."

Thereupon the drover dragged a big red pocket book from somewhere inside his coat, took out a thick, straight package of bills, and laid it down on the table.

"How much?" said the dealer, running his finger over the end of the package.

"Same as Abe's," said the drover.

"Here," said the little old man, peevishly, "if you won't let me play, bet my roll with yourn," and he pushed the ten thousand of his own money to his companion, and placed the money, which he had won from the bank, in his pocket. The drover took the money and piled it up on the ace of spades.

The dealer's face grew pensive and sweet; it was all right this time; he was going to round off the night with a golden *coup d'état*. He opened the safe behind him, counted out twenty thousand in big bills, and piled it up on one side of the bank. Then he opened the box and began. The old man wandered around the room; the big, half-drunken cattle-shipper hung over the table. Snakey the Parson scarcely saw either; he was intent on manipulating the box, and his hand darted in and out like a white snake. Suddenly the ace of spades flew out, and fell on the side of the house. The quick dealer clapped his left hand over the box and put out his right for the player's money. As he did so, the big drover bent forward and thrust a revolver into his face.

"No, you don't," he growled, "this is my money and I will not leave it, thank you."

Snakey the parson glanced at the man and knew that he had been fooled, but he was composed and clear-headed. Under the box on the right were weapons and the electric button; he began to take his right hand slowly from the table.

"Stop!" said the drover, sharply, "that game won't work!"

The dealer looked up into the player's face, and dropped his hands; he was a brave man, and desperate, as gamblers go, but he knew death when he saw it; his face turned yellow and became ghastly, but he did not move.

The drover took up his money from the lay-out and handed it to the old man. He used his left hand only, and did not take his eyes from the gambler's face. The old man thrust the bundle of bills in his pocket, and hurried from the room. The gambler sat rigid as a wax figure. The drover waited until his companion had sufficient time to get thoroughly away from the house; then he began to move slowly backward to the door, keeping the gambler covered with the weapon. The faro dealer watched every move of the drover, like a hawk, but he did not attempt to take his hand from the table; the muzzle of the revolver was too rigid; it was simply moving backward from his face in a dead straight line. At the door the drover stopped, drew himself together, then sprang suddenly through and bounded down the stairs.

Snakey the Parson touched the electric button, and as the drover rushed into the street, two policemen caught him by the shoulder.

V.

"Well," said the Police Chief, "I am tired of making an ass of myself; Mr. Mason says this cattle drover has committed no crime except a petty assault, and if he is right, I want to know it. That man beats the very devil. Every time I have sent up a case against his protest the judges have pitched me out on my neck, and the thing has got to be cursedly monotonous."

The District Attorney smiled grimly, and turned around in his chair. "Have you given me all the details?" he said.

"Yes," answered the official, "just exactly as they occurred."

The District Attorney arose, thrust his hands into his pockets, and looked down at the great manhunter; there was a queer set to his mouth, and the merest shadow of a twinkle in his eyes.

"Well, my friend," he said, "you are pitched out on your neck again."

The official drew a deep breath, and his face fell. "Then it is not robbery?" he said.

"No," answered the attorney.

"Well," mused the Police Chief, "this law business is too high for me. I have spent my life dealing with crimes, and I thought I knew one when I saw it; but I give it up, I don't know the first principles. Why, here is a fellow who voluntarily goes into a gambling house, plays and loses, then draws a revolver and forcibly takes away the money which, by the rules of the play, belongs to the house; robs the dealer by threatening to kill him; steals the bank's money, and fights his way out. It cannot matter that the man robbed was a lawbreaker himself, or that the crime occurred in a gambling house. It is the law of New York that has been violated; the place and parties are of no importance. Here is certainly the force and the putting in fear that constitute the vital element of robbery; and yet you say it is not robbery. You have me lost all right."

"My dear sir," put in the District Attorney, "the vital element of robbery is not the force and terror but is what is called in the books the *animus furandi*, meaning the intention to steal. The presence of this felonious intent determines whether or not the wrong is a crime. If it be not present there can be no robbery, no matter how great the force, violence, or putting in fear, or how grave, serious, or irreparable the resulting injury.

"It is true indeed that the force and terror are elements, but the vital one is the intent. If by force and violence one takes his own property from the possession of another, it is no robbery; nor is it robbery for one to take the property of another by violence under the belief that it is his own, or that he has some right to it, or by mistake or misunderstanding, although vast loss be caused thereby and great wrong and hurt result."

"I have no hope of ever understanding it," said the Police Chief; "I am only a common man with a short life time."

"Why, sir," continued the attorney, "it is as plain as sunlight. Robbery is compounded of larceny and force. It is larceny from the person by violence, but in order to constitute it the property must be taken from the peaceable possession of the party and it must be taken *animo furandi*. Neither of these happened in the case you state, because the faro dealer, by means of an unlawful game, could not secure any color of right or title to the money which he should win by it. Therefore the money taken was not his property, and could not have been taken from his peaceable possession.

"In the second place, this vital element of robbery, the *animus furandi*, is totally wanting, for the reason that the player, in forcibly seizing the money which he had lost, was actuated by no intention to steal, but, on the contrary, was simply taking possession of his own property, property to which he had a full legal right and title."

"But," put in the officer, "there was the other ten thousand which the old man won, they got away with that; if the game was unlawful they had no right to that."

"True," said the lawyer. "The old man had no title to the ten thousand which he had won, but he did not steal it; the dealer gave it to him of his own free will, and the old man had it in his possession by the full voluntary consent of the dealer some time before the resort to violence. There was clearly no crime in this."

"Damn it all," said the Police Chief, warily, "is there no way to get at him, can't we railroad him before a jury?"

The District Attorney looked at the baffled officer and grinned ominously. "My friend," he said, "there is no power in Venice can alter a decree established. The courts have time and again passed upon cases exactly similar to this, and have held that there was no crime, except, perhaps, a petty misdemeanor. We could not weather a proceeding on *habeas corpus* ten minutes; we could never get to a jury. When the judge came to examine the decisions on this question we would go out, as you expressed it, on our necks."

"Well," muttered the Police Chief, as he pulled on his coat, "it is just as Randolph Mason said, out he goes."

The attorney laughed and turned to his desk. The officer crossed to the door, jerked it open, then stopped and faced round. "Mr. District Attorney," he said, "won't there be hell to pay when the crooks learn the law?" Then he stalked through and banged the door after him.

The District Attorney looked out of the window and across the street at the dirty row of ugly buildings. "Humph!" he said, "there is something in that last remark of the Chief."

VI.

Braxton Hogarth, detective, member of the Atlantic Agency, in good standing, now, by right of law and by virtue of his craft, restored to his freedom and identity, stepped back and was swallowed up by the crowd.

The great ocean liner steamed out from the port of New York on its pathless journey to the sunny south of France. Randolph Mason sat in an invalid chair close up to the rail of the deck; he was grim, emaciated, and rigidly ugly. His body was exhausted, worn out utterly long ago, but the fierce mysterious spirit of the man was tireless and wrought on unceasingly.

For a time he was silent, his eyes wide, and his jaw set like a wolf trap. Suddenly he clutched the rail and staggered to his feet.

"Parks," he muttered,—"Parks, this ship is worth a million dollars. Come with me to the cabin and I will show you how it may be wrested from the owners and no crime committed; do you understand me, Parks? no crime!"

16

Defenses of Necessity and Passion

But, children, you should never let
Such angry passions rise;
Your little hands were never made
To tear each other's eyes.
From *Divine Songs, Against
Quarreling and Fighting*
Isaac Watts

Necessitas inducit privilegium quoad jura privata—Necessity
carrieth a privilege in itself.
. . . .
So spake the Fiend, and with necessity,
The tyrant's plea, excused his devilish deeds.
From *Regina v. Dudley and Stephens*
Queen's Bench Division
14 Q.B.D. 238 (1884)

In the previous section we considered mens rea—the term used to refer to the requisite mental state for the conviction of certain crimes. This notion is important in any discussion of defenses which might be raised to attempt to excuse the defendant's actions. A successful argument might be based on the allegation that the act of which the defendant is accused occurred for one of the following reasons: (1) the act was an accident or a mistake; (2) the act was involuntary and was caused by either intoxication or drug use or both; (3) the defendant suffered from insanity or diminished mental capacity. Notice that these arguments attempt to negate the element of the mens rea in order to excuse the behavior and so exculpate the defendant. But if the element of the mens rea is met, then the defendant can turn to defenses which might be used to *justify* rather than *excuse* his actions—duress, coercion, self-defense, defense of property, or provocation. The defendant admits the intention to carry out the crime but claims he is exculpated because the crime was justified. The two short stories that follow deal with the justification defenses of necessity and provocation in murder cases—both of the defendants confess to the killing and acknowledge their intention to commit the crimes of which they are accused.

Necessity was at the heart of the defense raised in the British case *Regina v. Dudley and Stephens* argued in 1884. The case concerned three English seamen and one teenage boy who found themselves caught in a storm on the high seas. With no vessel in sight and without food or water, Dudley and Stephens decided to kill the boy by putting a knife in his throat. When the deed was done, all three seamen fed upon the boy's body and blood for four days. Does killing under these circumstances constitute murder? Could this action be justified as an act of necessity? There are, Lord Bacon said, three kinds of necessity, the first of which is "necessity of conservation of life." This court asks whether conservation of one's own life justifies the taking of the life of this "unoffending and unresisting boy? . . .Was it more necessary to kill him than one of the grown men? The answer must be 'no'. . . . It is not suggested that in this particular case the deeds were 'devilish,' but it is quite plain that such a principle once admitted might be made the legal cloak for unbridled passion and atrocious crime." The sentence of death was passed on the prisoners.

As you read the short story "Rosalie Prudent," by Guy de Maupassant, keep *Regina v. Dudley and Stephens* in mind, and consider the following points: First, the judge comes to an early conclusion that Rosalie Prudent committed the act in a moment of despair and insanity. Does this judge believe that all murderers are insane or is he seeking to excuse her actions rather than to see her subjected to capital punishment? Should the judge's sympathy for the defendant affect his judgment of the case? Next, what defense is Rosalie Prudent raising? Is it the defense of passion or the defense of necessity? We usually think of a crime of passion as one done by an irate lover on discovering infidelity, but notice the passion with which Rosalie Prudent carried out the deed. If the defense is one of necessity, for whom was it necessary? This is analogous to the position in which many women who undergo in vitro fertilization find themselves. In order to enhance the chances of a live birth, some physicians routinely implant eight, nine, or ten pre-embryos. If the implant is successful and the resulting number is in excess of that which the mother desires to deliver or that which she can safely carry to term, then the physician reduces the pregnancy to the desired or safe number by selectively aborting some of the developing embryos—the argument is one of necessity. Is not the choice for the mother as agonizing as that made by Rosalie Prudent?

The second story in this section, also by Guy de Maupassant, is "The Assassin." Here, the defense that is raised is one of anger or passion. First, can the lawyer who represents all men from princes to tramps, who is more sympathetic to the client by the size of the crime, who sees corruption and infamy each day, remain honorable himself? Second, how persuaded are you by the lawyer's rhetoric? Do you believe that a young lawyer would be so smooth and convincing? Third, dying declarations are usually inadmissible except that the dying declaration of the victim of a homicide may be used if the declaration was made at a time when the victim believed his death was impending and if he did subsequently die from the event to which his testimony relates. Should it matter to whom the alleged statements are made? What if they are made to a policeman? What if they are allegedly made to the deceased's lover who happens to be the accused Accusgo's wife? In this story, the victim and the accused are alone in the room at the time the act was committed. Do we have to assume that someone else entered before the victim died? What is the problem of using a dead man's testimony? Finally, should this defendant be acquitted of the crime of murder on the defense of passion? If so, should he be found guilty of some lesser crime?

Rosalie Prudent
Guy de Maupassant

There was a mystery in that affair about Rosalie Prudent, which neither the jury, nor the judge, nor the prosecuting attorney of the republic himself could understand.

The girl Rosalie was a servant at the house of the Varambot family, of Mantes. She became *enceinte*, and, unknown to her employers, had given birth to a child in the garret, during the night, and had then killed the child and buried it in the garden.

It was the ordinary story of most of the infanticides committed by servants. But one act remained inexplicable. The examination of the girl's room had resulted in the discovery of a complete *layette* for an infant, made by Rosalie herself, who had passed her nights during three months in cutting out the garments and sewing them. The grocer where she had bought her candles (paid for out of her wages), in order to perform this long task, came forward and testified to the fact of their purchase. In addition it was learned that the midwife of the town, informed by Rosalie of her condition, had given her all the advice and information necessary in case the child should be born at a time when aid was impossible to obtain. She had found a place also, at Poissy, for Rosalie Prudent, who foresaw her loss of situation, as the Varambots were severe on the subject of morality.

They appeared in court, the man and his wife, small provincials of moderate means, exasperated against the vulgar creature who had besmirched the immaculateness of their house. They would have liked to see her guillotined at once, without trial, and they overwhelmed her with insults which in their mouths became accusations.

The guilty one, a tall, handsome girl of lower Normandy, fairly well educated for her station, wept without ceasing, and made no reply to them or to anyone. The Court came to the conclusion that she had accomplished that act of barbarity in a moment of despair and insanity, since everything indicated that she had hoped to keep her infant and bring it up.

The judge tried once more to make her speak, to get her to acknowledge her crime, and having asked her with great kindness to do so, he made her understand at last that the jury sitting there to judge her did not wish her death, but were ready to pity her.

The girl appeared to be making up her mind to speak at last.

"Tell us now at first who is the father of that child," said the judge.

Until that moment she had refused obstinately to divulge this fact. Now she replied suddenly, looking straight at her employers, who had come there in a rage to calumniate her.

"It is Monsieur Joseph, the nephew of Monsieur Varambot!"

Varambot and his wife started, and both cried at the same time:

"It is false! She lies! It is infamous!"

The judge bade them be silent, and said:

"Continue, I beg of you, and tell us how it happened."

Then the girl began to speak hurriedly, seeming to find some comfort for her poor, solitary, bruised heart in giving vent to her sorrow before these severe-looking men, whom she had taken until then for enemies and inflexible judges.

"Yes it was Monsieur Joseph Varambot—it happened when he came for his vacation last summer."

"What is the occupation of this monsieur Joseph Varambot?"

"He is underofficer in the artillery, Monsieur. He was two months at the house—two months of the summer. I wasn't thinking of anything when he began to look at me, and then to say things to me, and finally to make love to me the whole day long. I was easy, Monsieur! He told me I was a handsome girl, that I pleased him, that I was to his taste. For myself, he pleased me, to be sure. What would you have? Anyone listens to those things, when one is alone—as I am. I am alone on the earth, Monsieur. There is no one to whom I can talk—no one to whom I can tell my troubles. I have neither father, nor mother, nor brother, nor sister—no one! He seemed like a brother who had come to me when he began to talk to me. And then he asked me to go down to the river one evening, so that we might talk without making so much noise. And I went down there. Could I have known what would happen? He put his arms around my waist—of course I didn't want to,—no, no! I couldn't help it. I wanted to cry, the air was so soft and warm—it was clear moonlight—I couldn't help it! No, I swear it to you, I couldn't help it—he did what he pleased. That lasted three weeks, as long as he remained. I would have followed him to the end of the world. But he went away, and I didn't know that I was *enceinte*—I didn't! I didn't know it until the month afterward."

She began to weep so violently that they were obliged to give her time to compose herself. Then the judge spoke, in the tone of a father confessor: "Go on, my girl, go on."

She continued: "When I knew that I was *enceinte*, I told Madame Boudin, the midwife, to whom one can tell these things; and I asked her what to do in case that happened without her. And then I made the clothes, night after night, until one o'clock in the morning; and then I looked for another place, for I knew very well I should be discharged: but I wished to remain in that house until the end, in order to economize the pennies, seeing that I had no money and that I would need it for the little one."

"Then you did not wish to kill him?"

"Oh, surely not, Monsieur."

"Why did you kill him, then?"

"Here's how it happened. It came sooner than I thought it would. It took me in the kitchen as I was washing my dishes. Monsieur and

Madame Varambot had retired already, so I went upstairs, without trouble,
holding to the banisters. I lay down on the floor in my room, so as not to
soil the bed. That lasted perhaps one hour—but it may have been two or
three—I can't tell, so much pain did I have,—and then—and then it was
over, and I took up my baby!

"Oh, yes! I was happy, for sure! I did everything that Madame
Boudin told me, everything! Then I laid him on the bed,—and then another
pain began, and it was a pain to kill anyone. If you knew what that was,
you others, you wouldn't do as much I'm sure! I fell on my knees, and
then on my back on the floor, and then it began all over again, and that, too,
lasted one hour, or perhaps two and there I was all alone. Finally there
came another little one, yes, another, two of them, like that! I took it up as I
took the first one, and I put it on the bed by the side of the other. One—
two! Can it be possible, I said! Two babies! And I, who earn twenty
francs a month! Say—was it possible for me to take care of them? To care
for one—yes, I might do that by depriving myself, but not two!

"The thought of that turned my head. What do I know about it, I?
Could I choose, say! Do I know? I saw myself come to my last day! I
couldn't keep two, so I put the pillow on them without knowing what I was
doing—and I threw myself on the bed and upon them, too. And I stayed
there, rolling and crying, until daylight, which I saw through the window.
I looked at them—they were both dead under the pillow, quite dead. Then I
took them under my arm, I went down the stairs, and out in the garden; I
took the gardener's spade and I buried them in the ground, as deep as I
could, one here and the other there, not together, so that they could not talk
of their mother, if they do talk, the little dead children. Do I know?

"And then I went back to my bed, and I was so sick that I could not
get up. They made the doctor come, and he understood everything. That is
the truth, Monsieur the judge. Do what you want to me. I am ready."

During her speech half of the jury-men had been wiping their eyes
over and over again, trying to hide their emotion. All the women in the
court room were sobbing.

"At what spot in the garden did you bury the other infant?" asked the
judge.

"Which one did you find?" Rosalie inquired.

"The one that was under the artichokes."

"Ah! the other is buried under the strawberries beside the well!"
The poor girl began again to sob so loud that it was enough to break one's
heart to hear her. The jury acquitted her.

The Assassin
Guy de Maupassant

The guilty man was defended by a very young lawyer, a beginner, who spoke thus:

"The facts are undeniable, gentlemen of the jury. My client, an honest man, an irreproachable employee, gentle and timid, assassinated his employer in a moment of anger which seems to me incomprehensible. If you will allow me, I would like to look into the psychology of the crime, so to speak, without wasting any time or attempting to excuse anything. We shall then be able to judge better.

"John Nicholas Lougère is the son of very honorable people, who made of him a simple, respectful man.

"That is his crime: respect! It is a sentiment, gentlemen, which we of today no longer know, of which the name alone seems to exist while its power has disappeared. It is necessary to enter certain old, modest families to find this severe tradition, this religion of a thing or of a man, this sentiment where belief takes on a sacred character, this faith which doubts not, nor smiles, nor entertains a suspicion.

"One cannot be an honest man, a truly honest man in the full force of the term, and be respectful. The man who respects has his eyes closed. He believes. We others, whose eyes are wide open upon the world, who live here in this hall of justice, this purger of society, where all infamy runs aground, we others who are the confidants of shame, the devoted defenders of all human meanness, the support, not to say the supporters, of male and female sharpers, from a prince to a tramp, we who welcome with indulgence, with complacence, with a smiling benevolence all the guilty and defend them before you, we who, if we truly love our profession, measure our legal sympathy by the size of the crime, we could never have a respectful soul. We see too much of this river of corruption, which catches the chiefs of power as well as the lowest scamp; we know too much of how it gives and takes and sells itself. Places, offices, honors brutally exchanged for a little money, or skillfully exchanged for title and interests in industrial enterprises, or sometimes, simply for the kiss of a woman.

"Our duty and our profession force us to be ignorant of nothing, to suspect everybody, because everybody is doubtful; and we are taken by surprise when we find ourselves face to face with a man, like the assassin seated before you, who possesses the religion of respect to such a degree that he will become a martyr for it.

"We others, gentlemen, have a sense of honor, a certain need of propriety, from a disgust of baseness, from a sentiment of personal dignity and pride; but we do not carry at the bottom of our hearts the blind, inborn, brutal faith of this man.

"Let me tell you the story of his life:

"He was brought up, like many another child, to separate all human acts into two parts: the good and the bad. He was shown the good with an irresistible authority which made him only distinguish the bad, as we distinguish day and night. His father did not belong to the superior race of minds who, looking from a height, see the sources of belief and recognize the social necessities born of these distinctions.

"He grew up, religious and confident, enthusiastic and limited. At twenty-two he married. His wife was a cousin brought up as he was, simple and pure as he was. He had the inestimable privilege of having for a companion an honest woman with a true heart, the rarest and most respectable thing in the world. He had for his mother that veneration which surrounds mothers in patriarchal families, that profound respect which is reserved for divinities. This religion he reflected somewhat upon his wife, and it became scarcely less as conjugal familiarity increased. He lived in absolute ignorance of double dealing, in a state of constant uprightness and tranquil happiness which made him a being apart from the world. Deceiving no one he had never a suspicion that any one would deceive him.

"Some time before his marriage, he had become cashier in the office of Mr. Langlais, the man who was lately assassinated by him.

"We know, gentlemen of the jury, by the testimony of Mrs. Langlais and of her brother, Mr. Perthuis, a partner of her husband, of all the family and of all the higher employees of the bank, that Lougère was a model employee, upright, submissive, gentle, prompt, and deferential toward his superiors. They treated him with the consideration due to his exemplary conduct. He was accustomed to this homage and to a kind respect shown to Mrs. Lougère, whose worthiness was upon all lips.

"But she died of typhoid fever in a few days' time. He assuredly felt a profound grief, but the cold, calm grief of a methodical heart. Only from his pallor and from a change in his looks was one able to judge how deeply he had been wounded.

"Then, gentlemen, the most natural thing in the world happened.

"This man had been married ten years. For ten years he had been accustomed to feel the presence of a woman near him always. He was habituated to her care, her familiar voice upon his return, the goodnight at evening, the cheerful greeting of the morning, the gentle rustle of the dress so dear to the feminine heart, to that caress, at once lover-like and maternal, which renders life pleasant, to that loved presence that made the hours move less slowly. He was also accustomed to being spoiled at table, perhaps, and to all those attentions which become, little by little, so indispensable.

"He could no longer live alone. Then, to pass the interminable evenings, he got into the habit of spending an hour or two in a neighboring wine shop. He would drink a glass and sit there motionless, following, with heedless eye, the billiard balls running after one another under the smoke of the pipes, listening to, without hearing, the discussion of the players, the disputes of his neighbors over politics, and the sound of laughter that sometimes went up from the other end of the room, from some unusual joke. He often ended by going to sleep, from sheer lassitude and weariness. But, at the bottom of his heart and of his flesh, there was the irresistible need of a woman's heart and flesh; and, without thinking, he approached each evening a little nearer to the desk where the cashier, a pretty blonde, sat, attracted to her unconquerably, because she was a woman.

"At first they chatted and he got into the habit, so pleasant for him, of passing the evening by her side. She was gracious and kind, as one learns in this occupation to smile, and she amused herself by making him renew his order as often as possible, which makes business good.

"But each day Lougère was becoming more and more attached to this woman whom he did not know, whose whole existence he was ignorant of, and whom he loved only because he was in the way of seeing nobody else.

"The little creature was crafty, and soon perceived that she could reap some benefit from this guileless man; she then sought out the best means of exploiting him. The most effective, surely, was to marry him.

"This she accomplished without difficulty.

"Need I tell you, gentlemen of the jury, that the conduct of this girl had been most irregular and that marriage, far from putting a check to her flight, seemed on the contrary to render it more shameless?

"From the natural sport of feminine astuteness, she seemed to take pleasure in deceiving this honest man with all the employees of his office. I said with all. We have letters, gentlemen. There was soon a public scandal, of which the husband alone, as usual, was the only one ignorant.

"Finally, this wretch, with an interest easy to understand, seduced the son of the proprietor, a young man nineteen years old, upon whose mind and judgment she had a deplorable influence. Mr. Langlais, whose eyes had been closed up to that time, through friendship for his employee, resented having his son in the hands, I should say in the arms of this dangerous woman, and was legitimately angry.

"He made the mistake of calling Lougère to him on the spot and of speaking to him of his paternal indignation.

"There remains nothing more for me to say, gentlemen, except to read to you the recital of the crime, made by the lips of the dying man, and submitted as evidence. It says:

"'I learned that my son had given to this woman, that same night, ten thousand francs, and my anger was stronger on that account. Certainly, I never suspected the honorableness of Lougère, but to certain kind a blindness is more dangerous than positive faults. And so I had him come to me and told him that I should be obliged to deprive myself of his service.

"'He remained standing before me terrified, and not comprehending. He ended by demanding, rather excitedly, some explanation. I refused to give him any, affirming that my reasons were wholly personal. He believed then that I suspected him of indelicacy and, very pale, besought, implored me to explain. Held by this idea, he was strong and began to talk loud. As I kept silent, he abused and insulted me, until he arrived at such a degree of exasperation that I was fearful of results.

"'Then, suddenly, upon a wounding word that stuck upon a full heart, I threw the whole truth in his face.

"'He stood still some seconds, looking at me with haggard eyes. Then I saw him take from my desk the long shears, which I use for making margins to certain registers, I saw him fall upon me with uplifted arm, and I felt something enter my throat just above the breast, without noticing any pain.'

"This, gentlemen of the jury, is the simple recital of this murder. What more can be said for his defense? He respected his second wife with blindness because he respected his first with reason."

After a short deliberation, the prisoner was acquitted.

Part Five
Civil Matters

17

Property Concepts

The first man who, having fenced in a piece of land, said,
"This is mine," and found people naïve enough to believe
him, that man was the true founder of civil society.

Discours sur l'Origine et le Fondement
de l'Inégalité parmi les Hommes
Jean Jacques Rousseau

Every man holds his property subject to the general right of
the community to regulate its use to whatever degree the
public welfare may require it.

From a speech,
Osawatomie, August 31, 1910
Theodore Roosevelt

In considering defenses to criminal charges, we must discuss the right to
defend one's own property. *People v. Cebbalos*, 12 Cal. 3d 470 (1974)
concerns one citizen who took that right seriously. After some tools were
stolen from his garage in March 1970, and upon discovering in May that his
garage doors had been bent and that someone had tried to pry them open,
Don Ceballos loaded and mounted a .22 caliber pistol in the garage. A few
days later two teenage boys—the ones who had previously robbed the
garage—returned to the Ceballos' property, removed the locks on the
garage doors with a crowbar, and as the doors were pulled outward, one of
the boys was hit in the face with a bullet which emitted from the loaded
pistol. Asked why he set up the gun, the defendant replied: "Because
somebody was trying to steal my property . . . and I don't want to come
home some night and have the thief in there." He told the police that he
didn't have much and he wanted to protect what he did have. The Court affirmed the lower court verdict in which the jury found Ceballos guilty of assault with a deadly weapon. Stating that deadly force could not be used
solely for the protection of property, the court cited *Commonwealth v. Emmons*, 157 Pa. Super. 495 thus: "The preservation of human life and limb
from grievous harm is more important to society than the protection of
property."

Many people believe they have the legal right to shoot and kill a trespasser on his or her property even if the life of the property owner or the life of someone else who is present is not at stake. The Constitution does offer the property owner some protection for the right to peaceful enjoyment of, and the right not to be duly deprived of, his or her property, but that protection is from the states and not from robbers. Those rights are found in the amendments to the Constitution that follow: **Amendment IV:** "The right of the people to be secure in their persons, houses, papers, and effects, against unreasonable searches and seizures shall not be violated"; **Amendment V:** ". . . nor deprived of life, liberty, or property, without due process of law; nor shall private property be taken for public uses, without just compensation."

In which of the following instances is the State justified in "taking" the property owner's land by eminent domain?

• The state wishes to tear down all of the houses along both sides of a highway that needs to be widened to accommodate eight rather than six lanes of traffic.

• The state wishes to build an airport and needs to take down sixty-four houses constructed in the last two years, each valued at half a million dollars.

• The state wishes to build State offices to house the department that handles the lottery and the offtrack betting.

• The state wishes to build low-cost housing on a twelve-acre farm that has been in the farmer's family for over two hundred years.

Should the consideration of "taking" by "eminent domain" be as to whether or not the use is intended for public welfare? If so, how do you define "public welfare"—the greatest good for the greatest number? It is likely that the state will win its argument on utilitarian principles in most instances. How should the compensation for the taking be measured? Market value? Replacement value? Sentimental value? Lost profits over a year or over a lifetime?

If it disturbs you to realize that the land you own may not be yours one day because of the whim of the state, ask yourself if there is any other way which you could lose your real property involuntarily other than by an act of God. One way is by adverse possession—a common law concept that allows the adverse possessor to gain title to land by satisfying the following elements:

• **Open and Notorious:** Used as the true owner would use the land.

• **Continuous:** Used in the same continuity as the true owner would use the land; that is, summers only for a summer camp.

• **Claim of Right:** Tells the world he or she owns the land by his or her actions and/or words.

• **Hostile:** Does not have the true owner's permission to use the land.

• **Statutory Period:** In New York, the period of time during which each element must be present is ten years.

The two short stories that follow deal with the plights of two men as they strive to acquire property—one from a sense of greed, the other out of necessity. Notice the irony in Leo Tolstóy's "How Much Land Does a Man Need?" with the answer, "Six feet from his head to his heels was all he needed." Hamlin Garland's "Under the Lion's Paw" invokes sympathy for Mr. Haskins, yet Mr. Butler has the right to choose the asking price for his farm and reject any counter-offer made by Haskins. Is Mr. Butler a heartless owner of tenant farms or an astute businessman who strikes a hard bargain?

How Much Land Does a Man Need?
Leo Tolstóy

I

An elder sister came to visit her younger sister in the country. The elder
was married to a tradesman in town, the younger to a peasant in the village.
As the sisters sat over their tea talking, the elder began to boast of the
advantages of town life: saying how comfortably they lived there, how well
they dressed, what fine clothes her children wore, what good things they ate
and drank, and how she went to the theatre, promenades, and entertain-
ments.

The younger sister was piqued, and in turn disparaged the life of a
tradesman, and stood up for that of a peasant.

'I would not change my way of life for yours,' said she. 'We may
live roughly, but at least we are free from anxiety. You live in better style
than we do, but though you often earn more than you need, you are very
likely to lose all you have. You know the proverb, "Loss and gain are
brothers twain." It often happens that people who are wealthy one day are
begging their bread the next. Our way is safer. Though a peasant's life is
not a fat one, it is a long one. We shall never grow rich, but we shall always have enough to eat.'

The elder sister said sneeringly:

'Enough? Yes, if you like to share with the pigs and the calves!
What do you know of elegance or manners! However much your goodman
may slave, you will die as you are living—on a dung heap—and your children the same.'

'Well, what of that?' replied the younger. 'Of course our work is
rough and coarse. But on the other hand, it is sure, and we need not bow to
anyone. But you, in your towns, are surrounded by temptations; to-day all
may be right, but to-morrow the Evil One may tempt your husband with
cards, wine, or women, and all will go to ruin. Don't such things happen
often enough?'

Pahóm, the master of the house, was lying on the top of the stove
and he listened to the women's chatter.

'It is perfectly true,' thought he. 'Busy as we are from childhood
tilling mother earth, we peasants have no time to let any nonsense settle in
our heads. Our only trouble is that we haven't land enough. If I had plenty

of land, I shouldn't fear the devil himself!'

The women finished their tea, chatted a while about dress, and then cleared away the tea-things and lay down to sleep.

But the Devil had been sitting behind the stove and had heard all that was said. He was pleased that the peasant's wife had led her husband into boasting, and that he had said that if he had plenty of land he would not fear the Devil himself.

'All right,' thought the Devil. 'We will have a tussle. I'll give you land enough; and by means of that land I will get you into my power.'

II

Close to the village there lived a lady, a small land-owner who had an estate of about three hundred acres. She had always lived on good terms with the peasants until she engaged as her steward an old soldier, who took to burdening the people with fines. However careful Pahóm tried to be, it happened again and again that now a horse of his got among the lady's oats, now a cow strayed into her garden, now his calves found their way into her meadows—and he always had to pay a fine.

Pahóm paid up, but grumbled, and going home in a temper, was rough with his family. All through that summer, Pahóm had much trouble because of this steward, and he was even glad when winter came and the cattle had to be stabled. Though he grudged the fodder when they could no longer graze on the pasture-land, at least he was free from anxiety about them.

In the winter the news got about that the lady was going to sell her land and that the keeper of the inn on the high road was bargaining for it. When the peasants heard this they were very much alarmed.

'Well,' thought they, 'if the innkeeper gets the land, he will worry us with fines worse than the lady's steward. We all depend on that estate.'

So the peasants went on behalf of their Commune, and asked the lady not to sell the land to the innkeeper, offering her a better price for it themselves. The lady agreed to let them have it. Then the peasants tried to arrange for the Commune to buy the whole estate, so that it might be held by them all in common. They met twice to discuss it, but could not settle the matter; the Evil One sowed discord among them and they could not agree. So they decided to buy the land individually, each according to his means; and the lady agreed to this plan as she had to the other.

Presently Pahóm heard that a neighbour of his was buying fifty acres, and that the lady had consented to accept one half in cash and to wait a year for the other half. Pahóm felt envious.

'Look at that,' thought he, 'the land is all being sold, and I shall get none of it.' So he spoke to his wife.

'Other people are buying,' said he, 'and we must also buy twenty acres or so. Life is becoming impossible. That steward is simply crushing us with his fines.'

So they put their heads together and considered how they could manage to buy it. They had one hundred rúbles laid by. They sold a colt and one half of their bees, hired out one of their sons as a labourer and took his wages in advance; borrowed the rest from a brother-in-law, and so scraped together half the purchase money.

Having done this, Pahóm chose out a farm of forty acres, some of it wooded, and went to the lady to bargain for it. They came to an agreement, and he shook hands with her upon it and paid her a deposit in advance. Then they went to town and signed the deeds; he paying half the price down, and undertaking to pay the remainder within two years.

So now Pahóm had land of his own. He borrowed seed, and sowed it on the land he had bought. The harvest was a good one, and within a year he had managed to pay off his debts both to the lady and to his brother-in-law. So he became a landowner, ploughing and sowing his own land, making hay on his own land, cutting his own trees, and feeding his cattle on his own pasture. When he went out to plough his fields, or to look at his growing corn, or at his grass-meadows, his heart would fill with joy. The grass that grew and the flowers that bloomed there seemed to him unlike any that grew elsewhere. Formerly, when he had passed by that land, it had appeared the same as any other land, but now it seemed quite different.

III

So Pahóm was well-contented, and everything would have been right if the neighbouring peasants would only not have trespassed on his corn-fields and meadows. He appealed to them most civilly, but they still went on: now the Communal herdsmen would let the village cows stray into his meadows, then horses from the night pasture would get among his corn. Pahóm turned them out again and again, and forgave their owners, and for a long time he forbore to prosecute any one. But at last he lost patience and complained to the District Court. He knew it was the peasants' want of land, and no evil intent on their part, that caused the trouble, but he thought: 'I cannot go on overlooking it or they will destroy all I have. They must be taught a lesson.'

So he had them up, gave them one lesson, and then another, and two or three of the peasants were fined. After a time Pahóm's neighbours began to bear him a grudge for this, and would now and then let their cattle on to his land on purpose. One peasant even got into Pahóm's wood at night and cut down five young lime trees for their bark. Pahóm passing through the wood one day noticed something white. He came nearer and saw the stripped trunks lying on the ground, and close by stood the stumps where the trees had been. Pahóm was furious.

'If he had only cut one here and there it would have been bad enough,' thought Pahóm, 'but the rascal has actually cut down a whole clump. If I could only find out who did this, I would pay him out.'

He racked his brains as to who it could be. Finally he decided: 'It must be Simon—no one else could have done it.' So he went to Simon's homestead to have a look round, but he found nothing, and only had an angry scene. However, he now felt more certain than ever that Simon had done it, and he lodged a complaint. Simon was summoned. The case was tried, and retried, and at the end of it all Simon was acquitted, there being no evidence against him. Pahóm felt still more aggrieved, and let his anger loose upon the Elder and the Judges.

'You let thieves grease your palms,' said he. 'If you were honest folk yourselves you would not let a thief go free.'

So Pahóm quarrelled with the Judges and with his neighbours. Threats to burn his building began to be uttered. So though Pahóm had more land, his place in the Commune was much worse than before.

About this time a rumour got about that many people were moving to new parts.

'There's no need for me to leave my land,' thought Pahóm. 'But some of the others might leave our village and then there would be more room for us. I would take over their land myself and make my estate a bit bigger. I could then live more at ease. As it is, I am still too cramped to be comfortable.'

One day Pahóm was sitting at home when a peasant, passing through the village, happened to call in. He was allowed to stay the night, and supper was given him. Pahóm had a talk with this peasant and asked him where he came from. The stranger answered that he came from beyond the Vólga, where he had been working. One word led to another, and the man went on to say that many people were settling in those parts. He told how some people from his village had settled there. They had joined the Commune, and had had twenty-five acres per man granted them. The land was so good, he said, that the rye sown on it grew as high as a horse, and so thick that five cuts of a sickle made a sheaf. One peasant, he said, had brought nothing with him but his bare hands, and now he had six horses and two cows of his own.

Pahóm's heart kindled with desire. He thought:

'Why should I suffer in this narrow hole, if one can live so well elsewhere? I will sell my land and my homestead here, and with the money I will start afresh over there and get everything new. In this crowded place one is always having trouble. But I must first go and find out all about it myself.'

Towards summer he got ready and started. He went down the Vólga on a steamer to Samára, then walked another three hundred miles on foot, and at last reached the place. It was just as the stranger had said. The peasants had plenty of land: every man had twenty-five acres of communal land given him for his use and any one who had money could buy, besides, at two shillings an acre as much good freehold land as he wanted.

Having found out all he wished to know, Pahóm returned home as autumn came out, and began selling off his belongings. He sold his land at a profit, sold his homestead and all his cattle and withdrew from membership of the Commune. He only waited till the spring, and then started with his family for the new settlement.

IV

As soon as Pahóm and his family reached their new abode, he applied for admission into the Commune of a large village. He stood treat to the Elders and obtained the necessary documents. Five shares of Communal land were given him for his own and his sons' use: that is to say—125 acres (not all together, but in different fields) besides the use of the Communal pasture. Pahóm put up the buildings he needed, and bought cattle. Of the Communal land alone he had three times as much as at his former home, and the land was good cornland. He was ten times better off than he had been. He had plenty of arable land and pasturage, and could keep as many head of cattle as he liked.

At first, in the bustle of building and settling down, Pahóm was pleased with it all, but when he got used to it he began to think that even here he had not enough land. The first year, he sowed wheat on his share of the Communal land and had a good crop. He wanted to go on sowing wheat, but had not enough Communal land for the purpose, and what he had already used was not available; for in those parts wheat is only sown on virgin soil or on fallow land. It is sown for one or two years, and then the land lies fallow till it is again overgrown with prairie grass. There were many who wanted such land and there was not enough for all; so that people quarrelled about it. Those who were better off wanted it for growing wheat, and those who were poor wanted it to let to dealers, so that they might raise money to pay their taxes. Pahóm wanted to sow more wheat, so he rented land from a dealer for a year. He sowed much wheat and had a fine crop, but the land was too far from the village—the wheat had to be carted more than ten miles. After a time Pahóm noticed that some peasant-dealers were living on separate farms and were growing wealthy; and he thought:

'If I were to buy some freehold land and have a homestead on it, it would be a different thing altogether. Then it would all be nice and compact.'

The question of buying freehold land recurred to him again and again.

He went on in the same way for three years, renting land and sowing wheat. The seasons turned out well and the crops were good, so that he began to lay money by. He might have gone on living contentedly, but he grew tired of having to rent other people's land every year, and having to scramble for it. Wherever there was good land to be had, the peasants would rush for it and it was taken up at once, so that unless you were sharp about it you got none. It happened in the third year that he and a dealer together rented a piece of pasture land from some peasants; and they had already ploughed it up, when there was some dispute and the peasants went to law about it, and things fell out so that the labour was all lost.

'If it were my own land,' thought Pahóm, 'I should be independent, and there would not be all this unpleasantness.'

So Pahóm began looking out for land which he could buy; and he came across a peasant who had bought thirteen hundred acres, but having got into difficulties was willing to sell again cheap. Pahóm bargained and haggled with him, and at last they settled the price at 1,500 rúbles, part in cash and part to be paid later. They had all but clinched the matter when a passing dealer happened to stop at Pahóm's one day to get a feed for his horses. He drank tea with Pahóm and they had a talk. The dealer said that he was just returning from the land of the Bashkírs, far away, where he had bought thirteen thousand acres of land, all for 1,000 rúbles. Pahóm questioned him further, and the tradesman said:

'All one need do is to make friends with the chiefs. I gave away about one hundred rúbles worth of silk robes and carpets, besides a case of tea, and I gave wine to those who would drink it; and I got the land for less than a penny an acre.' And he showed Pahóm the title-deeds, saying:

'The land lies near a river, and the whole prairie is virgin soil.'

Pahóm plied him with questions, and the tradesman said:

'There is more land there than you could cover if you walked a year, and it all belongs to the Bashkírs. They are as simple as sheep, and land can be got almost for nothing.'

'There now,' thought Pahóm, 'with my one thousand rúbles, why should I get only thirteen hundred acres, and saddle myself with a debt besides? If I take it out there, I can get more than ten times as much for the money.'

V

Pahóm inquired how to get to the place, and as soon as the tradesman had left him, he prepared to go there himself. He left his wife to look after the homestead, and started on his journey taking his man with him. They stopped at a town on their way and bought a case of tea, some wine, and other presents, as the tradesman had advised. On and on they went until they had gone more than three hundred miles, and on the seventh day they came to a place where the Bashkírs had pitched their tents. It was all just as the tradesman had said. The people lived on the steppe, by a river, in felt-covered tents. They neither tilled the ground, nor ate bread. Their cattle and horses grazed in herds on the steppe. The colts were tethered behind the tents, and the mares were driven to them twice a day. The mares were milked, and from the milk kumiss was made. It was the women who prepared kumiss, and they also made cheese. As far as the men were concerned, drinking kumiss and tea, eating mutton, and playing on their pipes, was all they cared about. They were all stout and merry, and all the summer long they never thought of doing any work. They were quite ignorant, and knew no Russian, but were good-natured enough.

As soon as they saw Pahóm, they came out of their tents and gathered round their visitor. An interpreter was found, and Pahóm told them he had come about some land. The Bashkírs seemed very glad; they took Pahóm and led him into one of the best tents, where they made him sit on some down cushions placed on a carpet, while they sat round him. They gave him some tea and kumiss, and had a sheep killed, and gave him mutton to eat. Pahóm took presents out of his cart and distributed them among the Bashkírs, and divided the tea amongst them. The Bashkírs were delighted. They talked a great deal among themselves, and then told the interpreter to translate.

'They wish to tell you,' said the interpreter, 'that they like you, and that it is our custom to do all we can to please a guest and to repay him for his gifts. You have given us presents, now tell us which of the things we possess please you best, that we may present them to you.'

'What pleases me best here,' answered Pahóm, 'is your land. Our land is crowded and the soil is exhausted; but you have plenty of land and it is good land. I never saw the like of it.'

The interpreter translated. The Bashkírs talked among themselves for a while. Pahóm could not understand what they were saying, but saw that they were much amused and that they shouted and laughed. Then they were silent and looked at Pahóm while the interpreter said:

'They wish me to tell you that in return for your presents they will gladly give you as much land as you want. You have only to point it out with your hand and it is yours.'

The Bashkírs talked again for a while and began to dispute. Pahóm asked what they were disputing about, and the interpreter told him that some of them thought they ought to ask their Chief about the land and not act in his absence, while others thought there was no need to wait for his return.

VI

While the Bashkírs were disputing, a man in a large fox-fur cap appeared on the scene. They all became silent and rose to their feet. The interpreter said, 'This is our Chief himself.'

Pahóm immediately fetched the best dressing-gown and five pounds of tea, and offered these to the Chief. The Chief accepted them, and seated himself in the place of honour. The Bashkírs at once began telling him something. The Chief listened for a while, then made a sign with his head for them to be silent, and addressing himself to Pahóm, said in Russian:

'Well, let it be so. Choose whatever piece of land you like; we have plenty of it.'

'How can I take as much as I like?' thought Pahóm. 'I must get a deed to make it secure, or else they may say, "It is yours," and afterwards may take it away again.'

'Thank you for your kind words,' he said aloud. 'You have much land, and I only want a little. But I should like to be sure which bit is mine. Could it not be measured and made over to me? Life and death are in God's hands. You good people give it to me, but your children might wish to take it away again.'

'You are quite right,' said the Chief. 'We will make it over to you.'

'I heard that a dealer had been here,' continued Pahóm, 'and that you gave him a little land, too, and signed title-deeds to that effect. I should like to have it done in the same way.'

The Chief understood.

'Yes,' replied he, 'that can be done quite easily. We have a scribe, and we will go to town with you and have the deed properly sealed.'

'And what will be the price?' asked Pahóm.

'Our price is always the same: one thousand rúbles a day.'

Pahóm did not understand.

'A day? What measure is that? How many acres would that be?'

'We do not know how to reckon it out,' said the Chief. 'We sell it by the day. As much as you can go round on your feet in a day is yours, and the price is one thousand rúbles a day.'

Pahóm was surprised.

'But in a day you can get round a large tract of land,' he said.

The Chief laughed.

'It will all be yours!' said he. 'But there is one condition: If you don't return on the same day to the spot whence you started, your money is lost.'

'But how am I to mark the way that I have gone?'

'Why, we shall go to any spot you like and stay there. You must start from that spot and make your round, taking a spade with you. Wherever you think necessary, make a mark. At every turning, dig a hole and pile up the turf; then afterwards we will go round with a plough from hole to hole. You may make as large a circuit as you please, but before the sun sets you must return to the place you started from. All the land you cover will be yours.'

Pahóm was delighted. It was decided to start early next morning. They talked a while, and after drinking some more kumiss and eating some more mutton, they had tea again, and then the night came on. They gave Pahóm a feather-bed to sleep on, and the Bashkírs dispersed for the night, promising to assemble the next morning at daybreak and ride out before sunrise to the appointed spot.

VII

Pahóm lay on the feather-bed, but could not sleep. He kept thinking about the land.

'What a large tract I will mark off!' thought he. 'I can easily do thirty-five miles in a day. The days are long now, and within a circuit of thirty-five miles what a lot of land there will be! I will sell the poorer land, or let it to peasants, but I'll pick out the best and farm it. I will buy two ox-teams, and hire two more labourers. About a hundred and fifty acres shall be plough-land, and I will pasture cattle on the rest.'

Pahóm lay awake all night, and dozed off only just before dawn. Hardly were his eyes closed when he had a dream. He thought he was lying in that same tent and heard somebody chuckling outside. He wondered who it could be, and rose and went out, and he saw the Bashkír Chief sitting in front of the tent holding his sides and rolling about with laughter. Going nearer to the Chief, Pahóm asked: 'What are you laughing at?' But he saw that it was no longer the Chief, but the dealer who had recently stopped at his house and had told him about the land. Just as Pahóm was going to ask, 'Have you been here long?' he saw that it was not the dealer, but the peasant who had come up from the Vólga, long ago, to Pahóm's old home. Then he saw that it was not the peasant either, but the Devil himself with hoofs and horns, sitting there and chuckling, and before him lay a man barefoot, prostrate on the ground, with only trousers and a shirt on. And Pahóm dreamt that he looked more attentively to see what sort of a man it was that was lying there, and he saw that the man was dead, and that it was himself! He awoke horror-struck.

'What things one does dream,' thought he.

Looking round he saw through the open door that the dawn was breaking.

'It's time to wake them up,' thought he. 'We ought to be starting.'

He got up, roused his man (who was sleeping in his cart), bade him harness; and went to call the Bashkírs.

'It's time to go to the steppe to measure the land,' he said.

The Bashkírs rose and assembled, and the Chief came too. Then they began drinking kumiss again, and offered Pahóm some tea, but he would not wait.

'If we are to go, let us go. It is high time,' said he.

VIII

The Bashkírs got ready and they all started: some mounted on horses, and some in carts. Pahóm drove in his own small cart with his servant and took a spade with him. When they reached the steppe, the morning red was beginning to kindle. They ascended a hillock (called by the Bashkírs a *shikhan*) and dismounting from their carts and their horses, gathered in one spot. The Chief came up to Pahóm and stretching out his arm towards the plain:

'See,' said he, 'all this, as far as your eye can reach, is ours. You may have any part of it you like.'

Pahóm's eyes glistened: it was all virgin soil, as flat as the palm of your hand, as black as the seed of a poppy, and in the hollows different kinds of grasses grew breast high.

The Chief took off his fox-fur cap, placed it on the ground and said:

'This will be the mark. Start from here, and return here again. All the land you go round shall be yours.'

Pahóm took out his money and put it on the cap. Then he took off his outer coat, remaining in his sleeveless under-coat. He unfastened his girdle and tied it tight below his stomach, put a little bag of bread into the breast of his coat, and tying a flask of water to his girdle, he drew up the tops of his boots, took the spade from his man, and stood readily to start. He considered for some moments which way he had better go—it was tempting everywhere.

'No matter,' he concluded, 'I will go towards the rising sun.'

He returned his face to the east, stretched himself, and waited for the sun to appear above the rim.

'I must lose no time,' he thought, 'and it is easier walking while it is still cool.'

The sun's rays had hardly flashed above the horizon, before Pahóm, carrying the spade over his shoulder, went down into the steppe.

Pahóm started walking neither slowly nor quickly. After having gone a thousand yards he stopped, dug a hole, and placed pieces of turf one on another to make it more visible. Then he went on; and now that he had walked off his stiffness he quickened his pace. After a while he dug another hole.

Pahóm looked back. The hillock could be distinctly seen in the sunlight, with the people on it, and the glittering tyres of the cart-wheels. At a rough guess Pahóm concluded that he had walked three miles. It was growing warmer; he took off his under-coat, flung it across his shoulder, and went on again. It had grown quite warm now; he looked at the sun, it was time to think of breakfast.

'The first shift is done, but there are four in a day, and it is too soon yet to turn. But I will just take off my boots,' said he to himself.

He sat down, took off his boots, stuck them into his girdle, and went on. It was easy walking now.

'I will go on for another three miles,' thought he, 'and then turn to the left. This spot is so fine, that it would be a pity to lose it. The further one goes, the better the land seems.'

He went straight on for a while, and when he looked round, the hillock was scarcely visible and the people on it looked like black ants, and he could just see something glistening there in the sun.

'Ah,' thought Pahóm, 'I have gone far enough in this direction, it is time to turn. Besides I am in a regular sweat, and very thirsty.'

He stopped, dug a large hole, and heaped up pieces of turf. Next he untied his flask, had a drink, and then turned sharply to the left. He went on and on; the grass was high, and it was very hot

Pahóm began to grow tired: he looked at the sun and saw that it was noon.

'Well,' he thought, ' I must have a rest.'

He sat down, and ate some bread and drank some water; but he did not lie down, thinking that if he did he might fall asleep. After sitting a little while, he went on again. At first he walked easily: the food had strengthened him; but it had become terribly hot and he felt sleepy, still he went on, thinking: 'An hour to suffer, a life-time to live.'

He went a long way in this direction also, and was about to turn to the left again, when he perceived a damp hollow: 'It would be a pity to leave that out,' he thought. 'Flax would do well there.' So he went on past the hollow, and dug a hole on the other side of it before he turned the corner. Pahóm looked towards the hillock. The heat made the air hazy: it seemed to be quivering, and through the haze the people on the hillock could scarcely be seen.

'Ah!' thought Pahóm, 'I have made the sides too long; I must make this one shorter.' And he went along the third side, stepping faster. He looked at the sun: it was nearly half-way to the horizon, and he had not yet done two miles of the third side of the square. He was still ten miles from the goal.

'No,' he thought, 'though it will make my land lop-sided, I must hurry back in a straight line now. I might go too far, and as it is I have a great deal of land.'

So Pahóm hurriedly dug a hole, and turned straight towards the hillock.

IX

Pahóm went straight towards the hillock, but he now walked with difficulty. He was done up with the heat, his bare feet were cut and bruised, and his legs began to fail. He longed to rest, but it was impossible if he meant to get back before sunset. The sun waits for no man, and it was sinking lower and lower.

'Oh dear,' he thought, 'if only I have not blundered trying for too much! What if I am too late?'

He looked towards the hillock and at the sun. He was still far from his goal, and the sun was already near the rim.

Pahóm walked on and on; it was very hard walking but he went quicker and quicker. He pressed on, but was still far from the place. He began running, threw away his coat, his boots, his flask, and his cap, and kept only the spade which he used as a support.

'What shall I do,' he thought again, 'I have grasped too much and ruined the whole affair. I can't get there before the sun sets.'

And this fear made him still more breathless. Pahóm went on running, his soaking shirt and trousers stuck to him and his mouth was parched. His breast was working like a blacksmith's bellows, his heart was beating like a hammer, and his legs were giving way as if they did not belong to him. Pahóm was seized with terror lest he should die of the strain.

Though afraid of death, he could not stop. 'After having run all that way they will call me a fool if I stop now,' thought he. And he ran on and on, and drew near and heard the Bashkírs yelling and shouting to him, and their cries inflamed his heart still more. He gathered his last strength and ran on.

The sun was close to the rim, and cloaked in mist looked large, and red as blood. Now, yes now, it was about to set! The sun was quite low, but he was also quite near his aim. Pahóm could already see the people on the hillock waving their arms to hurry him up. He could see the fox-fur cap on the ground and the money on it, and the Chief sitting on the ground holding his sides. And Pahóm remembered his dream.

'There is plenty of land,' thought he, 'but will God let me live on it? I have lost my life, I have lost my life! I shall never the reach the spot!'

Pahóm looked at the sun, which had reached the earth: one side of it had already disappeared. With all his remaining strength he rushed on, bending his body forward so that his legs could hardly follow fast enough to keep him from falling. Just as he reached the hillock it suddenly grew dark. He looked up—the sun had already set! He gave a cry: 'All my labour has been in vain,' thought he, and was about to stop, but he heard the Bashkírs still shouting, and remembered that though to him, from below, the sun seemed to have set, they on the hillock could still see it. He took a long breath and ran up the hillock. It was still light there. He reached the top and saw the cap. Before it sat the Chief laughing and holding his sides. Again Pahóm remembered his dream, and he uttered a cry: his legs gave way beneath him, he fell forward and reached the cap with his hands.

'Ah, that's a fine fellow!' exclaimed the Chief. 'He has gained much land!'

Pahóm's servant came running up and tried to raise him, but he saw that blood was flowing from his mouth. Pahóm was dead!

The Bashkírs clicked their tongues to show their pity.

His servant picked up the spade and dug a grave long enough for Pahóm to lie in, and buried him in it. Six feet from his head to his heels was all he needed.

Under the Lion's Paw
Hamlin Garland

It was the last of autumn and first day of winter coming together. All day long the ploughmen on their prairie farms had moved to and fro in their wide level fields through the falling snow, which melted as it fell, wetting them to the skin—all day, notwithstanding the frequent squalls of snow, the dripping, desolate clouds, and the muck of the furrows, black and tenacious as tar.

Under their dripping harness the horses swung to and fro silently, with that marvellous uncomplaining patience which marks the horse. All day the wild geese, honking wildly, as they sprawled sidewise down the wind, seemed to be fleeing from an enemy behind, and with neck outthrust and wings extended, sailed down the wind, soon lost to sight.

Yet the ploughman behind his plough, though the snow lay on his ragged great-coat, and the cold clinging mud rose on his heavy boots, fettering him like gyves, whistled in the very beard of the gale. As day passed, the snow, ceasing to melt, lay along the ploughed land, and lodged in the depth of the stubble, till on each slow round the last furrow stood out black and shining as jet between the ploughed land and the gray stubble.

When night began to fall, the geese, flying low, began to alight invisibly in the near corn-field, Stephen Council was still at work "finishing a land." He rode on his sulky plough when going with the wind, but walked when facing it. Sitting bent and cold but cheery under his slouch hat, he talked encouragingly to his four-in-hand.

"Come round there, boys!—Round again! We got t' finish this land. Come in there, Dan! *Stiddy*, Kate,—stiddy! None o' y'r tantrums, Kittie. It's purty tuff, but got a be did. *Tchk! tchk*! Step along, Pete! Don't let Kate git y'r single-tree on the wheel. *Once* more!"

They seemed to know what he meant, and that this was the last round, for they worked with greater vigor than before.

"Once more, boys, an' then, sez I, oats an' a nice warm stall, an' sleep f'r all."

By the time the last furrow was turned on the land it was too dark to see the house, and the snow was changing to rain again. The tired and hungry man could see the light from the kitchen shining through the leafless hedge, and he lifted a great shout, "Supper f'r a half a dozen!"

It was nearly eight o'clock by the time he had finished his chores and started for supper. He was picking his way carefully through the mud, when the tall form of a man loomed up before him with a premonitory cough.

"Waddy ye want?" was the rather startled question of the farmer.

"Well, ye see," began the stranger, in a deprecating tone, "we'd like t' git in f'r the night. We've tried every house f'r the last two miles, but they hadn't any room f'r us. My wife's jest about sick, 'n' the children are cold and hungry—"

"Oh, y' want 'o stay all night, eh?"

"Yes, sir; it 'ud be a great accom—"

"Waal, I don't make it a practice t' turn anybuddy way hungry, not on sech nights as this. Drive right in. We ain't got much, but sech as it is—"

But the stranger had disappeared. And soon his steaming, weary team, with drooping heads and swinging single-trees, moved past the well to the block beside the path. Council stood at the side of the "schooner" and helped the children out—two little half-sleeping children—and then a small woman with a baby in her arms.

"There ye go!" he shouted jovially, to the children. "*Now* we're all right! Run right along to the house there, an' tell Mam' Council you wants sumpthin' t' eat. Right this way, Mis'—keep right off t' the right there. I'll go an' git a lantern. Come," he said to the dazed and silent group at his side.

"Mother," he shouted, as he neared the fragrant and warmly lighted kitchen, "here are some wayfarers an' folks who needs sumpthin' to' eat an' a place t' snooze." He ended by pushing them all in.

Mrs. Council, a large, jolly, rather coarse-looking woman, took the children in her arms. "Come right in, you little rabbits. 'Most asleep, hey? Now here's a drink o' milk f'r each o' ye. "I'll have s'm tea in a minute. Take off y'r things and set up t' the fire."

While she set the children to drinkin milk, Council got out his lantern and went out to the barn to help the stranger about his team, where his loud, hearty voice could be heard as it came and went between the hay-mow and the stalls.

The woman came to light as a small, timid, and discouraged-looking woman, but still pretty, in a thin and sorrowful way.

"Land sakes! An' you've travelled all the way from Clear Lake t'-day in this mud! Waal! waal! No wonder you're all tired out. Don't wait f'r the men, Mis'—" She hesitated, waiting for the name.

"Haskins."

"Mis' Haskins, set right up to the table a' take a good swig o' tea whilst I make y' s'm toast. It's green tea, an' it's good. I tell Council as I git older I don't seem to enjoy Young Hyson n'r Gunpowder. I want the reel green tea, jest as it comes off' the vines. Seems t' have more heart in it, some way. Don't s'pose it has. Council says it's all in m' eye."

Going on in this easy way, she soon had the children filled with bread and milk and the woman thoroughly at home, eating some toast and sweet-melon pickles, and sipping the tea.

"See the little rats!" she laughed at the children. "They're full as they can stick now, and they want to go to bed. Now, don't git up, Mis' Haskins; set right where you are an' let me look after 'em. I know all about young ones, though I'm all alone now. Jane went an' married last fall. But, as I tell Council, it's lucky we keep our health. Set right there, Mis' Haskins; I won't have you stir a finger."

It was an unmeasured pleasure to sit there in the warm, homely kitchen, the jovial chatter of the housewife driving out and holding at bay the growl of the impotent, cheated wind.

The little woman's eyes filled with tears which fell down upon the sleeping baby in her arms. The world was not so desolate and cold and hopeless, after all.

"Now I hope Council won't stop out there and talk politics all night. He's the greatest man to talk politics an' read the *Tribune*—How old is it?"

She broke off and peered down at the face of the babe.

"Two months 'n' five days," said the mother, with a mother's exactness.

"Ye don't say! I want 'o know! The dear little pudzy-wudzy!" she went on, stirring it up in the neighborhood of the ribs with her fat fore-finger.

"Pooty rough on 'oo to go gallivant'n' 'cross lots this way—"

"Yes, that's so; a man can't lift a mountain," said Council, entering the door. "Mother, this is Mr. Haskins, from Kansas. He's been eat up 'n' drove out by grasshoppers."

"Glad t' see ye!—Pa, empty that wash-basin 'n' give him a chance t' wash."

Haskins was a tall man, with a thin, gloomy face. His hair was a reddish brown, like his coat, and seemed equally faded by the wind and sun, and his sallow face, though hard and set, was pathetic somehow. You would have felt that he had suffered much by the line of his mouth showing under his thin, yellow mustache.

"Hain't Ike got home yet, Sairy?"

"Hain't seen 'im."

"W-a-a-l, set right up, Mr. Haskins; wade right into what we've got; 'tain't much, but we manage to live on it—she gits fat on it," laughed Council, pointing his thumb at his wife.

After supper, while the women put the children to bed, Haskins and Council talked on, seated near the huge cooking-stove, the steam rising from their wet clothing. In the Western fashion Council told as much of his own life as he drew from his guest. He asked but few questions, but by and by the story of Haskins' struggles and defeat come out. The story was a terrible one, but he told it quietly, seated with his elbows on his knees, gazing most of the time at the hearth.

"I didn't like the looks of the country, anyhow," Haskins said, partly rising and glancing at his wife. "I was use t' northern Ingyannie, where we have lots o' timber 'n' lots o' rain, 'n' I didn't like the looks o' that dry prairie. What galled me the worst was goin' s' far away acrosst so much fine land layin' all through here vacant."

"And the 'hoppers eat ye four years, hand runnin', did they?"

"Eat! They wiped us out. They chawed everything that was green.

They jest set around waitin' f'r us to die t' eat us, too. My God! I ust t' dream of 'em stittin' 'round on the bedpost, six feet long, workin' their jaws. They eet the fork-handles. They got worse 'n' worse till they jest rolled on one another, piled up like snow in winter. Well, it ain't no use. If I was t' talk all winter I couldn't tell nawthing'. But all the while I couldn't help thinkin' of all that land back here that nobuddy was usin' that I ought 'o had 'stead o' bein' out there in that cussed country."

"Waal, why didn't ye stop an' settle here?" asked Ike, who had come in an was eating his supper.

"Fer the simple reason that you fellers wantid ten 'r fifteen dollars an acre fer the bare land, and I hadn't no money fer that kind o' thing."

"Yes, I do my own work," Mrs. Council was heard to say in the pause which followed. "I'm a gettin' purty heavy t' be on m' laigs all day, but we can't afford t' hire, so I keep rackin' around somehow, like a foundered horse. S' lame—I tell Council he can't tell how lame I am, f'r I'm jest a lame in one laig as t' other." And the good soul laughed at the joke on herself as she took a handful of flour and dusted the biscuit-board to keep the dough from sticking.

"Well, I hain't *never* been very strong," said Mrs. Haskins. "Our folks was Canadians an' small-boned, and then since my last child I hain't got up again fairly. I don't like t' complain. Tim has about all he can bear now—but they was days this week when I jest wanted to lay right down an' die."

"Waal, now, I'll tell ye," said Council, from his side of the stove, silencing everybody with his good-natured roar, "I'd go down and see Butler, *anyway*, if I was you. I guess he'd let you have his place purty cheap; the farm's all run down. He's ben anxious t' let t' somebuddy next year. It 'ud be a good chance fer you. Anyhow, you go to bed and sleep like a babe. I've got some ploughin' t' do, anyhow, an' we'll see if somethin' can't be done about your case. Ike, you go out an' see if the horses is all right, an' I'll show the folks t' bed."

When the tired husband and wife were lying under the generous quilts of the spare bed, Haskins listened a moment to the wind in the eaves, and then said, with a slow and solemn tone,

"There are people in this world who are good enough t' be angels, an' only haff t' die to *be* angels."

II

Jim Butler was one of those men called in the West "land poor." Early in the history of Rock River he had come into the town and started in the grocery business in a small way, occupying a small building in a mean part of the town. At this period of his life he earned all he got, and was up early and late sorting beans, working over butter and carting his goods to and from the station. But a chance came over him at the end of the second year, when he sold a lot of land for four times what he paid for it. From that time forward he believed in land speculation as the surest way of getting rich. Every cent he could save or spare from his trade he put into land at forced sale, or mortgages on land, which were "just as good as the wheat," he was accustomed to say.

Farm after farm fell into his hands, until he was recognized as one of the leading landowners of the country. His mortgages were scattered all over Cedar County, and as they slowly but surely fell in he sought usually to retain the former owner as tenant.

He was not ready to foreclose; indeed, he had the name of being one of the "easiest" men in the town. He let the debtor off again and again, extending the time whenever possible.

"I don't want y'r land," he said. "All I'm after is the in'rest on my money—that's all. Now, if y' want 'o stay on the farm, why, I'll give y' a good chance. I can't have the land layin' vacant." And in many cases the owner remained as tenant.

In the meantime he had sold his store; he couldn't spend time in it; he was mainly occupied now with sitting around town on rainy days smoking and "gassin' with the boys," or in riding to and from his farms. In fishing-time he fished a good deal. Doc Grimes, Ben Ashley, and Cal Cheatham were his cronies on these fishing excursions or hunting trips in the time of chickens or partridges. In winter they went to Northern Wisconsin to shoot deer.

In spite of all these signs of easy life Butler persisted in saying he "hadn't enough money to pay taxes on his land," and was careful to convey the impression that he was poor in spite of his twenty farms. At one time he was said to be worth fifty thousand dollars, but land had been a little slow of sale of late, so that he was not worth so much.

A fine farm, known as the Higley place, had fallen into his hands in the usual way the previous year, and he had not been able to find a tenant for it. Poor Higley, after working himself nearly to death on it in the attempt to lift the mortgage, had gone off to Dakota, leaving the farm and his curse to Butler.

This was the farm which Council advised Haskins to apply for; and the next day Council hitched up his team and drove down town to see Butler.

"You jest let *me* do the talkin'," he said. "We'll find him wearin' out his pants on some salt barrel somew'ers; and if he thought you *wanted* a place he'd sock it to you hot and heavy. You jest keep quiet; I'll fix 'im."

Butler was seated in Ben Ashley's store telling fish yarns when Council sauntered in casually.

"Hello, But; lyin' agin, hey?"

"Hello, Steve! how goes it?"

"Oh, so-so. Too dang much rain these days. I thought it was goin' to' freeze up f'r good last night. Tight squeak if I get m' ploughin' done. How's farmin' with *you* these days?"

"Bad. Ploughin' aint' half done."

"It 'ud be a religious idee f'r you t' go out an' take a hand y'rself."

"I don't haff to," said Butler, with a wink.

"Got anybody on the Higley place?"

"No. Know of anybody?"

"Waal, no; not eggsackly. I've got a relation back t' Michigan who's ben hot an' cold on the idee o' comin' West f'r some time. *Might* come if he could get a good lay-out. What do you talk on the farm?"

"Well, I d' know. I'll rent it on shares or I'll rent it money rent."

"Waal, how much money, say?"

"Well, say ten per cent, on the price—two-fifty."

"Waal, that ain't bad. Wait on 'im till 'e thrashes?"

Haskins listened eagerly to his important question, but Council was coolly eating a dried apple which he had speared out of a barrel with his knife. Butler studied him carefully.

"Well, knocks me out of twenty-five dollars interest."

"My relation'll need all he's got t' git his crops in," said Council, in the safe, indifferent way.

"Well, all right; *say* wait," concluded Butler.

"All right; this is the man. Haskins, this is Mr. Butler—no relation to Ben—the hardest-working man in Cedar County."

On the way home Haskins said: "I ain't much better off. I'd like that farm; its a good farm, but it's all run down, an' so 'm I. I could make a good farm of it if I had half a show. But I can't stock it n'r seed it."

"Waal, now, don't you worry," roared Council in his ear. "We'll pull y' through somehow till next harvest. He's agreed t' hire it ploughed, an' you can earn a hundred dollars ploughin' an' y' c'n git the seed o' me, an' pay me back when y' can."

Haskins was silent with emotion, but at last he said, "I ain't got nothin' to' live in."

"Now, don't you worry 'about that. You jest make your headquarters at ol' Steve Council's. Mother'll take a pile o' comfort in havin' y'r wife an' children 'round. Y' see, Jane's married off lately, an' Ike's away a good 'eal, so we'll be darn glad t' have y' stop with us this winter. Nex' spring we'll see if y' can't git a start agin." And he chirruped to the team, which sprang forward with the rumbling, clattering wagon.

"Say, looky here, Council, you can't do this. I never saw—" shouted Haskins in his neighbor's ear.

Council moved about uneasily in his seat and stopped his stammering gratitude by saying: "Hold on, now; don't make such a fuss over a little thing. When I see a man down, an' things all on top of 'm, I jest like to' kick 'em off an' help 'm up. That's the kind of religion I got, an' it's about the *only* kind."

They rode the rest of the way home in silence. And when the red light of the lamp shone out into the darkness of the cold and windy night, and he thought of this refuge for his children and wife, Haskins could have put his arm around the neck of his burly companion and squeezed him like a lover. But he contented himself with saying, "Steve Council, you'll git y'r pay f'r this some day."

"Don't want any pay. My religion ain't run on such business principles."

The wind was growing colder, and the ground was covered with a white frost, as they turned into the gate of the Council farm, and the children came rushing out, shouting, "Papa's come!" They hardly looked like the same children who had sat at the table the night before. Their torpidity, under the influence of sunshine and Mother Council, had given way to a sort of spasmodic cheerfulness, as insects in winter revive when laid on the hearth.

III

Haskins worked like a fiend, and his wife, like the heroic woman that she was, bore also uncomplainingly the most terrible burdens. They rose early and toiled without intermission till the darkness fell on the plain, then tumbled into bed, every bone and muscle aching with fatigue, to rise with the sun next morning to the same round of the same ferocity of labor.

The eldest boy drove a team all through the spring, ploughing and seeding, milked the cows, and did chores innumerable, in most ways taking the place of a man.

An infinitely pathetic but common figure—this boy on the American farm, where there is no law against child labor. To see him in his coarse clothing, his huge boots, and his ragged cap, as he staggered with a pail of water from the well, or trudged in the cold and cheerless dawn out into the frosty field behind his team, gave the city-bread visitor a sharp pang of sympathetic pain. Yet Haskins loved his boy, and would have saved him from this if he could, but he could not.

By June the first year the result of such Herculean toil began to show on the farm. The yard was cleaned up and sown to grass, the garden ploughed and planted, and the house mended.

Council had given them four of his cows.

"Take 'em an' run 'em on shares. I don't want 'o milk s' many. Ike's away s' much now, Sat'dys an' Sund'ys, I can't stand the bother anyhow."

Other men, seeing the confidence of Council in the newcomer, had sold him tools on time; and as he was really an able farmer, he soon had round him many evidences of his care and thrift. At the advice of Council he had taken the farm for three years, with the privilege of re-renting or buying at the end of the term.

"It's a good bargain, an' y' want 'o nail it," said Council. "If you have any kind ov a crop, you c'n pay y'r debts, an' keep seed an' bread."

The new hope which now sprang up in the heart of Haskins and his wife grew great almost as a pain by the time the wide field of wheat began to wave and rustle and whirl in the winds of July. Day after day he would snatch a few moments after supper to go and look at it.

"Have ye seen the wheat t'-day, Nettie?" he asked one night as he rose from supper.

"No, Tim, I ain't had time."

"Well, take time now. Le's go look at it."

She threw an old hat on her head—Tommy's hat—and looking almost pretty in her thin, sad way, went out with her husband to the hedge.

"Ain't it grand, Nettie? Just look at it."

It was grand. Level, russet here and there, heavy-headed, wide as a lake, and full of multitudinous whispers and gleams of wealth, it stretched away before the gazers like the fabled field of the cloth of gold.

"Oh, I think—I *hope* we'll have a good crop, Tim; and oh, how good the people have been to us!"

"Yes; I don't know where we'd be t'-day if it hadn't ben f'r Council and his wife."

"They're the best people in the world," said the little woman, with a great sob of gratitude.

"We'll be in the field on Monday, sure," said Haskins, gripping the rail of the fence as if already at the work of the harvest.

The harvest came, bounteous, glorious, but the winds came and blew it into tangles, and the rain matted it here and there close to the ground increasing the work of gathering it threefold.

Oh, how they toiled in those glorious days! Clothing dripping with sweat, arms aching, filled with briers, fingers raw and bleeding, backs broken with the weight of heavy bundles, Haskins and his man toiled on. Tommy drove the harvester, while his father and a hired man bound on the machine. In this way they cut ten acres every day, and almost every night after supper, when the hand went to bed, Haskins returned to the field shocking the bound grain in the light of the moon. Many a night he worked till his anxious wife came out at ten o'clock to call him in to rest and lunch.

At the same time she cooked for the men, took care of the children, washed and ironed, milked the cows at night, made the butter, and sometimes fed the horses and watered them while her husband kept at the shocking.

No slave in the Roman galleys could have toiled so frightfully and lived, for this man thought himself a free man, and that he was working for his wife and babes.

When he sank into his bed with a deep groan of relief, too tired to change his grimy, dripping clothing, he felt that he was getting nearer and nearer to a home of his own, and pushing the wolf of want a little farther from his door.

There is no despair so deep as the despair of a homeless man or woman. To roam the roads of the country or the streets of the city, to feel there is no rood of ground on which the feet can rest, to halt weary and hungry outside lighted windows and hear laughter and song within,—these are the hungers and rebellions that drive men to crime and women to shame.

It was the memory of this homelessness, and the fear of its coming again, that spurred Timothy Haskins and Nettie, his wife, to such ferocious labor during that first year.

IV

"'M, yes; 'm, yes; first rate," said Butler, as his eye took in the neat garden, the pig-pen, and the well-filled barnyard. "You're gitt'n' quite a stock around yeh. Done well, eh?"

Haskins was showing Butler around the place. He had not seen it for a year, having spent the year in Washington and Boston with Ashley, his brother-in-law, who had been elected to Congress.

"Yes, I've laid out a good deal of money durin' the last three years. I've paid out three hundred dollars f'r fencin'."

"Um—h'm! I see, I see," said Butler, while Haskins went on:

"The kitchen there cost two hundred; the barn ain't cost much in money, but I've put a lot o' time on it. Iv'e dug a new well, and I—"

"Yes, yes, I see. You've done well. Stock worth a thousand dollars," said Butler, picking his teeth with a straw.

"About that," said Haskins, modestly. "We begin to feel 's if we was gitt'n' a home f'r ourselves; but we've worked hard. I tell you we begin to feel it, Mr. Butler, and we're goin' t' begin to ease up purty soon. We've been kind o' plannin' a trip back t' *her* folks after the fall ploughin's done."

"*Eggs*-actly!" said Butler, who was evidently thinking of something else. "I suppose you've kind o' calc'lated on stayin' here three years more?"

"Well, yes. Fact is, I think I c'n buy the farm this fall, if you'll give me a reasonable show."

"Um—m! What do you call a reasonable show?"

"Well, say a quarter down and three years' time."

Butler looked at the huge stacks of wheat, which filled the yard, over which the chickens were fluttering and crawling, catching grasshoppers, and out of which the crickets were singing innumerably. He smiled in a peculiar way as he said, "Oh, I won't be hard on yeh. But what did you expect to pay f'r the place?"

"Why, about what you offered it for before, two thousand five hundred, or *possibly* three thousand dollars," he added quickly, as he saw the owner shake his head.

"This farm is worth five thousand and five hundred dollars," said Butler, in a careless and decided voice.

"*What!*" almost shrieked the astounded Haskins. "What's that? Five thousand? Why, that's double what you offered it for three years ago."

"Of course, and its worth it. It was all run down then; now it's in good shape. You've laid out fifteen hundred dollars in improvements, according to your own story."

"But *you* had nothin' t' do about that. It's my work an' my money."

"You bet it was; but it's my land."

"But what's to pay me for all my—"

"Ain't you had the use of 'em?" replied Butler, smiling calmly into his face.

Haskins was like a man struck on the head with a sandbag; he couldn't think; he stammered as he tried to say: "But—I never'd git the use—, You'd rob me! More 'n that: you agreed—you promised that I could buy or rent at the end of three years at—"

"That's all right. But I didn't say I'd let you carry off the improvements, nor that I'd go on renting the farm at two-fifty. The land is doubled in value, it don't mater how; it don't enter into the question; an' now you can pay me five hundred dollars a year rent, or take it on your own terms at fifty-five hundred, or—git out."

He was turning away when Haskins, the sweat pouring from his face, fronted him, saying again:

"But *you've* done nothing to make it so. You hain't added a cent. I put it all there myself, expectin' to buy. I worked an' sweat to improve it. I was workin' for myself an' babes—"

"Well, why didn't you buy when I offered to sell? What y' kickin' about?"

"I'm kickin' about payin' you twice f'r my own things,—my own fences, my own kitchen, my own garden."

Butler laughed. "You're too green t' eat, young feller. *Your* improvements! The law will sing another tune."

"But I trusted your word."

"Never trust anybody, my friend. Besides, I didn't promise not to do this thing. Why, man, don't look at me like that. Don't take me for a thief. It's the law. The reg'lar thing. Everybody does it."

"I don't care if they do. It's stealin' jest the same. You take three thousand dollars of my money—the work o' my hands and my wife's." He broke down at this point. He was not a strong man mentally. He could face hardship, ceaseless toil, but he could not face the cold and sneering face of Butler.

"But I don't take it," said Butler, coolly. "All you've got to do is to go on jest as you've been a-doin', or give me a thousand dollars down, and a mortgage at ten percent on the rest."

Haskins sat down blindly on a bundle of oats near by, and with staring eyes and drooping head went over the situation. He was under the lion's paw. He felt a horrible numbness in his heart and limbs. He was hid in a mist, and there was no path out.

Butler walked about, looking at the huge stacks of grain, and pulling now and again a few handfuls out, shelling the heads in his hands and blowing the chaff away. He hummed a little tune as he did so. He had an accommodating air of waiting.

Haskins was in the middle of the terrible toil of the last year. He was walking again in the rain and the mud behind his plough; he felt the dust and dirt of the threshing. The ferocious husking-time, with its cutting wind and biting, clinging snows, lay hard upon him. Then he thought of his wife, how she had cheerfully cooked and baked, without holiday and without rest.

"Well, what do you think of it?" inquired the cool, mocking insinuating voice or Butler.

"I think you're a thief and a liar!" shouted Haskins, leaping up. "A black-hearted houn'!" Butler's smile maddened him; with a sudden leap he caught a fork in his hands, and whirled it in the air. "You'll never rob another man, damn ye!" he grated through his teeth, a look of pitiless ferocity in his accusing eyes.

Butler shrank and quivered, expecting the blow; stood, held hypnotized by the eyes of the man he had a moment before despised—a man transformed in an avenging demon. But in the deadly hush between the lift of the weapon and its fall there came a gush of faint, childish laughter and then across the range of his vision far away and dim, he saw the sun-bright head of his baby girl, as with the pretty, tottering run of a two-year-old, she moved across the grass of the dooryard. His hands relaxed; the fork fell to the ground; his head lowered.

"Make out y'r deed an' mor'gage, an' git off'n my land, an' don't ye never cross my line agin; if y' do, I'll kill ye."

Butler backed away from the man in wild haste, and climbing into his buggy with trembling limbs drove off down the road, leaving Haskins seated dumbly on the sunny pile of sheaves, his head sunk into his hands.

18

Contracts and Negotiable Instruments

A deliberate promise in writing, made freely and without any mistake, one which may lead the party to whom it is made into contracts and expenses, cannot be broken without a violation of moral duty. But if there was nothing paid or promised for it, the law, perhaps wisely, leaves the execution of it to the conscience of him who makes it. It is only when the party making the promise gains something, or he to whom it is made loses something, that the law gives the promise validity.

Mills v. Wyman,
Supreme Judicial Court of Massachusetts,
1825, 3 Pick. 207

In the short story "Under the Lion's Paw," Butler offers to sell a farm to Haskins for $2,500. When Haskins cannot pay for the property, Butler withdraws his offer and makes a new offer to lease the farm to Haskins. Haskins naively believes that the original selling price of $2,500 continues for the period of the three-year lease, but once the lease is terminated, Butler renegotiates all of the terms. Although Haskins "was like a man struck on the head with a sand-bag" when he realized that the new offer of sale was nearly double the old price, most of us would realize that an offer to contract does not remain open indefinitely and that Haskins has given nothing in return for this expectation. It is fundamental to contract law that "consideration" is needed on both sides. According to the Restatement of Contracts, Second, the element of consideration is satisfied if there is a bargained for exchange of promises. What does Haskins give in exchange for his expectation that Butler will keep his offer open? He believes mistakenly that his work on the farm entitles him to buy the farm at or close to the original price; unfortunately, for him, he has no binding contract that can be enforced for he has given no consideration.

When we speak in formal terms of contract requirements, we are usually speaking of all of the elements required if the bargained for exchange of promises is to be interpreted as a contract which can be enforced in a court of law, but think about how many formal *and* informal contracts you might enter into during the period of one day, one week, one month, one year, or a lifetime. A day's activities might include some of the following:

- You promise your son a mountain bike in June if he gets straight A's for the semester.

- You promise your other son $2,000 if he gives up smoking for one year.

- You take items off the grocery shelves for which you pay the clerk $93 at the checkout counter.

- You receive a credit card in the mail and return the accompanying form with your signature as requested.

- You go to the hospital for a chest X-ray and the hospital sends you a bill.

- You sign a purchase contract for the building of a new home and apply to the bank for a mortgage.

If the person with whom you exchanged promises fails to uphold his or her end of the bargain, you may or may not be able to maintain a suit in a court of law. Some contracts have to be in writing whereas others can be enforced even if they are only oral, and every contract requires certain formalities upon which the contract may stand or fall. In each contract, however, the element of consideration must be present. Is consideration present in the promise to pay your son $2,000 if he refrains from smoking for one year? You might conclude that your offer is a gift—that your son is not giving you anything in the way of consideration. In 1891, in *Hamer v. Sidway*, the New York Court of Appeals found that an uncle's promise to pay his nephew $5,000 if he ceased drinking alcohol and using tobacco for a period of years was sufficient consideration on the part of the nephew for the contract to be binding on the uncle. The court found that the nephew *forbore* to do something which he had a legal right to do and that such forbearance was tantamount to consideration. The offer to pay your son money if he gives up smoking might in fact be a legally binding contract.

We don't usually concern ourselves with the legal ramifications of the informal contracts that we make with our families every day, but family law is an area in which new contract theory has caused controversy—particularly in the area of contracts relating to reproductive rights. The "Baby M" case—see the list of films which follows—illustrates some of the problems involved in surrogate motherhood. What happens if a woman contracts to accept money in consideration for carrying a baby for another couple after being artificially inseminated with the sperm of another woman's husband, but then later decides that she wants to keep the baby? Or if she contracts to be implanted with a fertilized egg taken from the other woman and previously fertilized by the other woman's husband's sperm?

Does she have a better defense to an apparent breach of contract in the former than in the latter situation? Should the Court be able to set aside provisions of such contracts as a matter of public policy?

In the short story "Hippolyte's Claim," by Guy de Maupassant, we see what might be called the precursor of contract law as it relates to reproduction. Hippolyte tells us very clearly the nature of consideration, which he states is "a promise given, a promise kept"—Madame Luneau promised to pay one hundred francs if he performed. Notice how Madame Luneau attempts to thwart Hippolyte's performance of his contract.

Madame Luneau and Hippolyte have an oral contract that the judge enforces, but negotiable instruments cannot be oral and always require a writing. The same kind of humor that Guy de Maupassant brings to contract theory, Sir Alan Herbert brings to negotiable instruments as he plays with the element of the requisite "writing" in "The Negotiable Cow." If the cow is determined to be a negotiable instrument, who ends up with the cow? The Internal Revenue agent would march the cow to the bank; the bank would issue the money; and the bank would get stuck with the cow. Or would the bank send it back to the farmer like a cancelled check with a rubber stamp on its rear, warning: "Do not bend or breed, fold or feed, mutilate or milk?"

Hippolyte's Claim
Guy de Maupassant

The fat Justice of the Peace, with one eye closed and the other half-open, is listening with evident displeasure to the plaintiffs. Once in a while he gives a sort of grunt that foretells his opinion, and in a thin voice resembling that of a child, he interrupts them to ask questions. He has just rendered judgment in the case of Monsieur Joly against Monsieur Petitpas, the contestants having come to court on account of the boundary of a field which had been accidentally over-stepped by Monsieur Petitpas's farmhand, while the latter was plowing.

Now he calls the case of Hippolyte Lacour, vestryman and ironmonger, against Madame Céleste Césarine Luneau, widow of Anthime Isidore Luneau.

Hippolyte Lacour is forty-five years old; he is tall and gaunt, with a clean-shaven face and long hair, and he speaks in a slow, singsong voice.

Madam Luneau appears to be about forty years of age. She is built like a prize-fighter, and her plain dress is stretched tightly over her portly form. Her enormous hips hold up her overflowing bosom in front, while in the back they support the great rolls of flesh that cover her shoulders. Her face, with strongly-cut features, rests on a short, fat neck, and her strong voice is pitched at a key that makes the windows and the eardrums of her auditors vibrate. She is about to become a mother and her huge form protrudes like a mountain.

The witnesses for the defense are waiting to be called.

His Honor begins: Hippolyte Lacour, state your complaint.

The plaintiff speaks: Your Honor, it will be nine months on Saint-Michael's day that the defendant came to me one evening, after I had rung the Angelus, and began an explanation relating to her barrenness.

The Justice of the Peace: Kindly be more explicit.

Hippolyte: Very well, your Honor. Well, she wanted to have a child and desired my participation. I didn't raise any objection, and she promised to give me one hundred francs. The thing was all cut and dried, and now she refuses to acknowledge my claim, which I renew before your Honor.

The Justice: I don't understand in the least. You say that she wanted a child! What kind of child? Did she wish to adopt one?

Hippolyte: No, your Honor, she wanted a new one.

The Justice: What do you mean by a new one?

Hippolyte: I mean a newborn child, one that we were to beget as if we were man and wife.

The Justice: You astonish me. To what end did she make this abnormal proposition?

Hippolyte: Your Honor, at first I could not make out her reasons, and was taken a little aback. But as I don't do anything without thoroughly investigating beforehand, I called on her to explain matters to me, which she did. You see, her husband, Anthime Isidore, whom you knew as you know me, had died the week before, and his money reverted to his family. This greatly displeased her on account of the loss it meant, so she went to a lawyer who told her all about what might happen if a child should be born to her after ten months. I mean by this that if she gave birth to a child inside of ten months following the death of Anthime Isidore, her offspring would be considered legitimate and would entitle her to the inheritance. She made up her mind at once to run the risk and came to me after church, as I have already had the honor of telling you, seeing that I am the father of eight living children, the eldest of whom is a grocer in Caen, department of Calvados, and legitimately married to Victoire-Elisabeth Rabou—

The Justice: These details are superfluous. Go back to the subject.

Hippolyte: I am getting there, your Honor. So she said to me: "If you succeed, I'll give you one hundred francs as soon as I get the doctor's report." Well, your Honor, I made ready to give entire satisfaction, and after eight weeks or so I learned with pleasure that I had succeeded. But when I asked her for the hundred francs she refused to pay me. I renewed my demands several times, never getting so much as a pin. She even called me a liar and a weakling, a libel which can be destroyed by glancing at her.

The Justice: Defendant, what have you to say?

Madame Luneau: Your Honor, I say that this man is a liar.

The Justice: How can you prove this assertion?

Madame Luneau: [red in the face, choking and stammering]: How can I prove it? What proofs have I? I haven't a single real proof that the child isn't his. But, your Honor, it isn't his, I swear it on the head of my dead husband.

The Justice: Well, whose is it, then?

Madame Luneau: [stammering with rage]: How do I know? How do—do I know? Everybody's, I suppose. Here are my witnesses, your honor, they're all here, the six of them. Now make them testify, make them testify. They'll tell—

The Justice: Collect yourself, Madame Luneau, collect yourself and reply calmly to my questions. What reasons have you to doubt that this man is the father of the child you are carrying?

Madame Luneau: What reasons? I have a hundred to one, a hundred? No, two hundred, five hundred, ten thousand, a million and more reasons to believe he isn't. After the proposal I made to him, with the promise of one hundred francs, didn't I learn that he wasn't the father of his own children, your Honor, not the father of one of 'em?

Hippolyte: [calmly]: That's a lie.

Madame Luneau: [exasperated]: A lie! A lie, is it? I guess his wife has been seen by everybody around here. Call my witnesses, your Honor, and make them testify?

Hippolyte: [calmly]: It's a lie.

Madame Luneau: It's a lie, is it? How about the red-haired ones, then? I suppose they're yours, too?

The Justice: Kindly refrain from personal attacks, or I shall be obliged to call you to order.

Madame Luneau: Well, your Honor, I had my doubts about him, and said I to myself, two precautions are better than one, so I explained my position to Césaire Lepic, the witness who is present. Says he to me, "At your disposal, Madame Luneau," and he lent me his assistance in case Hippolyte should turn out to be unreliable. But as soon as the other witnesses heard that I wanted to make sure against any disappointment, I could have had more than a hundred, your Honor, if I had wanted them. That tall one over there, Lucas Chandelier, swore at the time that I oughtn't to give Hippolyte Lacour a cent, for he hadn't done more than the rest of them who had obliged me for nothing.

Hippolyte: What did you promise for? I expected the money, your honor. No mistake with me,—a promise given, a promise kept.

Madame Luneau: [beside herself]: One hundred francs! One hundred francs! One hundred francs for that, you liar! The others there didn't ask a red cent! Look at 'em, all six of 'em! Make them testify, your Honor, they'll tell sure. [To Hippolyte.] Look at 'em, you liar! They're as good as you. They're only six, but I could have had one, two, three, five hundred of 'em for nothing, too, you robber!

Hippolyte: Well, even if you'd had a hundred thousand—

Madame Luneau: I could, if I'd wanted 'em.

Hippolyte: I did my duty, so it doesn't change matters.

Madame Luneau: [slapping her protuberant form with both hands]: Then prove that it's you that did it, prove it, you robber! I defy you to prove it!

Hippolyte: [calmly]: Maybe I didn't do any more than anybody else. But you promised me a hundred francs for it. What did you ask the others for, afterward? You had no right to. I guess I could have done it alone.

Madame Luneau: It is not true, robber! Call my witnesses, your Honor; they'll answer, sure.

The Justice called the witnesses in behalf of the defense. Six red, awkward individuals appeared.

The Justice: Lucas Chandelier, have you any reason to suppose that you are the father of the child Madame Luneau is carrying.

Lucas Chandelier: Yes, sir.

The Justice: Célestin-Pierre Sidoine, have you any reason to suppose that you are the father of the child Madam Luneau is carrying?

Célestin-Pierre Sidoine: Yes, sir.

The four other witnesses testified to the same effect.

The Justice, after a pause, pronounced judgment: Whereas the plaintiff has reasons to believe himself the father of the child which Madame Luneau desired, Lucas Chandelier, Célestin-Pierre Sidoine, and others, have similar, if not conclusive reasons to lay claim to the child.

But whereas Mme. Luneau had previously asked the assistance of Hippolyte Lacour for a duly stated consideration:

And whereas one may not question the absolute good faith of Hippolyte Lacour, though it is questionable whether he had a perfect right to enter into such an agreement, seeing that the plaintiff is married, and compelled by the law to remain faithful to his lawful spouse:

Therefore the Court condemns Madame Luneau to pay an indemnity of twenty-five francs to Hippolyte Lacour for loss of time and unjustifiable abduction.

The Negotiable Cow
Sir Alan Herbert

'Was the cow crossed?'

'No, your worship, it was an open cow.'

These and similar passages provoked laugher at Bow Street today when the Negotiable Cow case was concluded.

Sir Joshua Hoot, K. C. (appearing for the Public Prosecutor): Sir Basil, these summonses, by leave of the Court, are being heard together, an unusual but convenient arrangement.

The defendant, Mr. Albert Haddock, has for many months, in spite of earnest endeavors on both sides, been unable to establish harmonious relations between himself and the Collector of Taxes. The Collector maintains that Mr. Haddock should make over a large part of his earnings to the Government. Mr. Haddock replies that the proportion demanded is excessive, in view of the inadequate service or consideration which he himself has received from that government. After an exchange of endearing letters, telephone calls, and even cheques, the sum demanded was reduced to fifty-seven pounds; and about this sum the exchange of opinions continued.

On the 31st of May the collector was diverted from his respectable labours by the apparition of a noisy crowd outside his windows. The crowd, Sir Basil, had been attracted by Mr. Haddock, who was leading a large white cow of malevolent aspect. On the back and sides of the cow were clearly stencilled in red ink the following words:

> *To the London and Literary Bank, Ltd.*
> 'Pay the Collector of Taxes, who is no gentleman, or
> Order, the sum of fifty-seven pounds (and may he rot!).
> '£57/o/o
>
> 'ALBERT HADDOCK'

Mr. Haddock conducted the cow into the Collector's office, tendered it to the Collector in payment of income-tax and demanded a receipt.

Sir Basil String: Did the cow bear the statutory stamp?

Sir Joshua: Yes, a two-penny stamp was affixed to the dexter horn. The Collector declined to accept the cow, objecting that it would be difficult or even impossible to pay the cow into the bank. Mr. Haddock, throughout the interview, maintained the friendliest demeanour; and he now remarked that the Collector could endorse the cow to any third party to whom he owed money, adding that there must be many persons in that position. The Collector then endeavoured to endorse the cheque—

Sir Basil String: Where?

Sir Joshua: On the back of the cheque, Sir Basil, that is to say, on the abdomen of the cow. The cow, however, appeared to resent endorsement and adopted a menacing posture. The Collector, abandoning the attempt, declined finally to take the cheque. Mr. Haddock led the cow away and was arrested in Trafalgar Square for causing an obstruction. He has also been summoned by the Board of Inland Revenue for nonpayment of income-tax.

Mr. Haddock, in the witness-box, said that he had tendered a cheque in payment of income-tax, and if the Commissioners did not like his cheque they could do the other thing. A cheque was only an order to a bank to pay money to the person in possession of the cheque or a person named on the cheque. There was nothing in statute or customary law to say that that order must be written on a piece of paper of specified dimension. A cheque, it was well known, could be written on a piece of notepaper. He himself had drawn cheques on the backs of menus, on napkins, on handkerchiefs, on the labels of wine-bottles; all these cheques had been duly honoured by his bank and passed through the Bankers' Clearing House. He could see no distinction in law between a cheque written on a napkin and a cheque written on a cow. The essence of each document was a written order to pay money, made in the customary form and in accordance with statutory requirements as to stamps, etc. A cheque was admittedly not legal tender in the sense that it could not lawfully be refused; but it was accepted by custom as a legitimate form of payment. There were funds in his bank sufficient to meet the cow; the Commissioners might not like the cow, but, the cow having been tendered, they were estopped from charging him with failure to pay. (Mr. Haddock here cited *Spowers v. The Strand Magazine, Lucas v. Finck,* and *Wadsworth v. The Metropolitan Water Board.*)

As to the action of the police, Mr. Haddock said it was a nice thing if in the heart of the commercial capital of the world a man could not convey a negotiable instrument down the street without being arrested. He had instituted proceedings against Constable Boot for false imprisonment.

Cross-examined as to motive, witness said that he had no cheque-forms available and, being anxious to meet his obligations promptly, had made use of the only material to hand. Later he admitted that there might have been present in his mind a desire to make the Collector of Taxes ridiculous. But why not? There was no law against deriding the income-tax.

Sir Basil String (after the hearing of further evidence): This case has at least brought to the notice of the Court a citizen who is unusual both in his clarity of mind and integrity of behaviour. No thinking man can regard those parts of the Finance Acts which govern the income-tax with anything but contempt. There may be something to be said—not much—for taking from those who have inherited wealth a certain proportion of that wealth for the service of the State and the benefit of the poor and needy; and those who by their own ability, brains, industry, and exertion have earned money may reasonably be invited to surrender a small portion of it towards the maintenance of those public services by which they benefit, to wit, the Police, the Navy, the Army, the public sewers, and so forth. But to compel such individuals to bestow a large part of their earnings upon other individuals, whether by way of pensions, unemployment grants, or education allowances, is manifestly barbarous and indefensible. Yet this is the law. The original and only official basis of taxation was that individual citizens, in return for their money, received collectively some services from the State, the defence of their property and persons, the care of their health or the education of their children. All that has now gone. Citizen A, who has earned money is commanded simply to give it to Citizens B, C, and D, who have not, and by force of habit this has come to be regarded as a normal and proper proceeding, whatever the comparative industry or merits of citizens A, B, C, and D. To be alive has become a virtue, and the mere capacity to inflate the lungs entitled Citizen B to a substantial share in the laborious earnings of Citizen A. The defendant, Mr. Haddock, repels and resents this doctrine, but, since it has received the sanction of Parliament, he dutifully complies with it. Hampered by practical difficulties, he took the first steps he could to discharge his legal obligations to the State. Paper was not available, so he employed instead a favourite cow. Now, there can be nothing obscene, offensive, or derogatory in the presentation of a cow by one man to another. Indeed, in certain parts of our Empire the cow is venerated as a sacred animal. Payment in kind is the oldest form of payment, and payment in kind more often than not meant payment in cattle. Indeed, during the Saxon period, Mr. Haddock tells us, cattle were described as *viva pecunia*, or 'living money,' from their being received as payment on most occasions, at certain regulated prices. So that, whether the cheque was valid or not, it was impossible to doubt that validity of the cow; and whatever the Collector's distrust of the former it was at least his duty to accept the latter and credit Mr. Haddock's account with its value. But, as Mr. Haddock protested in his able argument, an order to pay is an order to pay, whether it is made on the back of an envelope or on the back of a cow. The evidence of the bank is that Mr. Haddock's account was in funds. From every point of view, therefore, the Collector of Taxes did wrong, by custom if not by law, in refusing to take the proffered animal, and the summons issued at his instance will be discharged.

As for the second charge, I hold again that Constable Boot did wrong. It cannot be unlawful to conduct a cow through the London streets. The horse, at the present time a much less useful animal, constantly appears in those streets without protest, and the motorcar, more unnatural and unattractive still, is more numerous than either animal. Much less can the cow be regarded as an improper or unlawful companion when it is invested (as I have shown) with all the dignity of a bill of exchange.

If people choose to congregate in one place upon the apparition of Mr. Haddock with a promissory cow, then Constable Boot should arrest the people, not Mr. Haddock. Possibly, if Mr. Haddock had paraded Cockspur Street with a paper cheque for one million pounds made payable to bearer, the crowd would have been as great, but that is not to say that Mr. Haddock would have broken the law. In my judgment Mr. Haddock has behaved throughout in the manner of a perfect knight, citizen, and taxpayer. The charge brought by the Crown is dismissed; and I hope with all my heart that in his action against Constable Boot Mr. Haddock will be successful. What is the next case, please?

19

Torts

Instead, therefore, of saying that the liability for negligence should be co-extensive with the judgment of each individual, which would be as variable as the length of the foot of each individual, we ought rather to adhere to the rule, which requires in all cases a regard to caution such as a man of ordinary prudence would observe.

Vaughan v. Menlove,
Common Pleas,
1837, 3 Bing., N.C., 468

Proof of negligence in the air, so to speak, will not do.
Pollock, Torts, 11th Ed. p. 455.
Cited in *Palsgraf v. Long Island R.R. Co.*
248 N.Y. 339 (1928)

Was the behavior of Hippolyte or the behavior of Madame Luneau unreasonable? Would a reasonable man in Haskins's position expect Butler's offer to remain open for three years? Certianly the notion of what is reasonable plays a role in contract theory, but the "reasonable man standard" is utilized mostly in the area of torts, an injury caused by means other than by a breach of contract.

Torts fall into two basic categories—the intentional torts of battery, assault, infliction of mental disorders, false imprisonment, conversion, trespass, and nuisance; and the unintentional torts that cause injury to persons or property as a result of the negligence of another. It is the latter system—the negligence system—which gives us the concept of the reasonable man.

In *United States v. Carroll Towing Co.*, 159 F.2d 169 (2d Cir. 1947) Judge Learned Hand attempted a formula to accommodate the standard of reasonable care expected of the reasonable man. This formula came to be known as the "BPL" test. In the equation, $C = P \times D$, C is the care needed to avoid the risk; D represents the possible injuries; and P is the probability of the injuries occurring if the necessary care is not taken. Without belaboring the obvious difficulties inherent in attempting to apply this formula, let it just be said that this utilitarian approach to negligence uses an economic base to weigh benefits and choices.

In taking into account the need for evaluating the probability of the injuries occurring, Judge Learned Hand was dealing with the notion of foreseeability. A reasonable person cannot be expected to protect against injuries that cannot be foreseen, and such foreseeability is the subject of the famous *Palsgraf v. Long Island Railroad* case decided in 1928 by the New York Court of Appeals. In that case, a man carrying a small package containing fireworks jumped aboard a slow moving train with the help of two station guards. The fireworks fell; the explosion tipped over some scales at the other end of the platform; the scale struck the plaintiff causing injuries. Although the Court concluded that such injury was unforeseeable, Justice Andrews dissenting stated the foreseeability formula thus: "Every one owes to the world at large the duty of refraining from those acts that may unreasonably threaten the safety of others . . . [but] the damages must be so connected with the negligence that the latter may be said to be the proximate cause of the former." Justice Andrews concluded that it needed "no great foresight to predict that the natural result [in this case] would be to injure one on the platform at no greater distance from its scene than was the plaintiff." Thus, to him it was foreseeable that the plaintiff would be injured by the railroad worker's action of helping the passenger board the train.

After having just seen Sir Alan Herbert's humor in action in his short story "The Negotiable Cow," we turn now to his equally delightful story "Fardell & Potts: The Reasonable Man." The notion of irony was discussed earlier, and the reader was cautioned to be careful in making assumptions about what it is the author is satirizing. Lest any female readers take exception to Sir Alan Herbert's suggestion that there is no such thing as a reasonable woman, it should be noted that the respondent brought a suit for damages caused by a cold which he caught from his fall into the River Thames. Is this the aciton of a reasonable man? If Sir Alan Herbert attempts to teach anything, it is not that women are unreasonable but that there are, in fact, some delightful biological differences between men and women which make total equality between the sexes an impossibility.

"The Most Outrageous Consequences," by James Reid Parker, shows how contract and tort theory intermingle in the area of products liability. *MacPherson v. Buick Motor Company*, referred to in this story, is the 1916 New York Court of Appeals case that gave us the rules set forth in "The Most Outrageous Consequences." Notice in Parker's story how skillfully the lawyer persuades his client that precedent is alive and well.

Fardell & Potts:
The Reasonable Man
Sir Alan Herbert

The Court of Appeal to-day delivered judgment in this important case.

The Master of the Rolls: In this case the appellant was a Mrs. Fardell, a woman, who, while navigating a motor-launch on the River Thames, collided with the respondent, who was navigating a punt, as a result of which the respondent was immersed and caught cold. The respondent brought an action for damages, in which it was alleged that the collision and subsequent immersion were caused by the negligent navigation of the appellant. In the Court below the learned judge decided that there was evidence on which the jury might find that the defendant had not taken reasonable care, and, being of that opinion, very properly left to the jury the question whether in fact she had failed to use reasonable care or not. The jury found for the plaintiff and awarded him two hundred and fifty pounds damages. This verdict we are asked to set aside on the ground of misdirection by the learned judge, the contention being that the case should never have been allowed to go to the jury; and this contention is supported by a somewhat novel proposition, which has been ably, though tediously, argued by Sir Ethelred Rutt.

The Common Law of England has been laboriously built about a mythical figure—the figure of 'The Reasonable Man.' In the field of jurisprudence this legendary individual occupies the place which in another science is held by the Economic Man, and in social and political discussions by the Average or Plain Man. He is an ideal, a standard, the embodiment of all those qualities which we demand of the good citizen. No matter what may be the particular department of human life which falls to be considered in these Courts, sooner or later we have to face the question: Was this or was it not the conduct of a reasonable man? Did the defendant take such care to avoid shooting the plaintiff in the stomach as might reasonably be expected of a reasonable man? (*Moocat v. Radley* (1883) 2 Q.B.) Did the plaintiff take such precautions to inform himself of the circumstances as any reasonable man would expect of an ordinary person having the ordinary knowledge of an ordinary person of the habits of wild bulls when goaded with garden-forks and the persistent agitation of red flags? (*Williams v. Dogbody* (1841) 2 A.C.)

I need not multiply examples. It is impossible to travel anywhere or to travel for long in that confusing forest of learned judgments which constitutes the common Law of England without encountering the Reasonable Man. He is at every turn, an ever-present help in time of trouble, and his apparitions mark the road to equality and right. There has never been a problem, however difficult, which His Majesty's judges have not in the end been able to resolve by asking themselves the simple question, 'Was this or was it not the conduct of a reasonable man?' and leaving that question to be answered by the jury.

This noble creature stands in singular contrast to his kinsman the Economic Man, whose every action is prompted by the single spur of selfish advantage and directed to the single end of monetary gain. The Reasonable Man is always thinking of others; prudence is his guide, and 'Safety First,' if I may borrow a contemporary catchword, is his rule of life. All solid virtues are his, save only that peculiar quality by which the affection of other men is won. For it will not be pretended that socially he is much less objectionable than the Economic Man. Though any given example of his behaviour must command our admiration, when taken in the mass his acts create a very different set of impressions. He is one who invariably looks where he is going, and is careful to examine the immediate foreground before he executes a leap or bound; who neither star-gazes nor is lost in meditation when approaching trap-doors or the margin of a dock; who records in every case upon the counterfoils of cheques such ample details as are desirable, scrupulously substitutes the word 'Order' for the word 'Bearer,' crosses the instrument 'a/c Payee only,' and registers the package in which it is despatched; who never mounts a moving omnibus, and does not alight from any car while the train is in motion; who investigates exhaustively the *bona fides* of every mendicant before distributing alms, and will inform himself of the history and habits of a dog before administering a caress; who believes no gossip, nor repeats it, without firm basis for believing it to be true; who never drives his ball till those in front of him have definitely vacated the putting-green which is his own objective; who never from one year's end to another makes an excessive demand upon his wife, his neighbours, his servants, his ox, or his ass; who in the way of business looks only for that narrow margin of profit which twelve men such as himself would reckon to be 'fair,' and contemplates his fellow-merchants, their agents, and their goods, with that degree of suspicion and distrust which the law deems admirable; who never swears, gambles, or loses his temper; who uses nothing except in moderation, and even while he flogs his child is meditating only on the golden mean. Devoid, in short, of any human weakness, with not one single saving vice, *sans* prejudice, procrastination, ill-nature, avarice, and absence of mind, as careful for his own safety as he is for that of others, this excellent but odious character stands like a monument in our Courts of Justice, vainly appealing to his fellow-citizens to order their lives after his own example.

I have called him a myth; and, in so far as there are few, if any, of his mind and temperament to be found in the ranks of living men, the title is well chosen. But it is a myth which rests upon solid and even, it may be, upon permanent foundations. The Reasonable Man is fed and kept alive by the most valued and enduring of our juridical institutions—the common jury. Hateful as he must necessarily be to any ordinary citizen who privately considers him, it is a curious paradox that where two or three are gathered together in one place they will with one accord pretend an admiration for him; and, when they are gathered together in the formidable surroundings of a British jury, they are easily persuaded that they themselves are, each and generally, reasonable men. Without stopping to consider how strange a chance it must have been that has picked fortuitously from a whole people to fewer than twelve examples of a species so rare, they immediately invest themselves with the attributes of the Reasonable Man, and are therefore at one with the Courts in their anxiety to support the tradition that such a being in fact exists. Thus it is that while the Economic Man has under the stress of modern conditions almost wholly disappeared from view his Reasonable cousin has gained in power with every case in which he has figured.

To return, however, as every judge must ultimately return, to the case which is before us—it has been urged for the appellant, and my own researches incline me to agree, that in all that mass of authorities which bears upon this branch of the law *there is no single mention of a reasonable woman.* It was ably insisted before us that such an omission, extending over a century and more of judicial pronouncements, must be something more than a coincidence; that among the innumerable tributes to the reasonable man there might be expected at least some passing reference to a reasonable person of the opposite sex; that no such reference is found, for the simple reason that no such being is contemplated by the law; that legally at least there *is* no reasonable woman, and that therefore in this case the learned judge should have directed the jury that, while there was evidence on which they might find that the defendant had not come up to the standard required of a reasonable man, her conduct was only what was to be expected of a woman, as such.

It must be conceded at once that there is merit in this contention, however unpalatable it may at first appear. The appellant relies largely on *Baxter's Case,* 1639 (2 Bole, at page 100), in which it was held that for the purposes of *estover* the wife of a tenant by the mesne was at law in the same position as an ox or other *cattle demenant* (to which a modern parallel may perhaps be found in the statutory regulations of many railway companies, whereby, for the purposes of freight, a typewriter is counted as a musical instrument). It is probably no mere chance that in our legal text-books the problems relating to married women are usually considered immediately after the pages devoted to idiots and lunatics. Indeed, there is respectable authority for saying that at Common Law this was the status of a woman. Recent legislation has whittled away a great part of this venerable conception, but so far as concerns the law of negligence, which is our present consideration, I am persuaded that it remains intact. It is no bad thing that the law of the land should here and there conform with the known facts of everyday experience. The view that there exist a class of beings, illogical, impulsive, careless, irresponsible, extravagant, prejudiced, and vain, free for the most part from those worthy and repellent excellences which distinguish the Reasonable Man, and devoted to the irrational arts of pleasure and attraction, is one which should be as welcome and as well accepted in our Courts as it is in our drawing-rooms—and even in Parliament. The odd stipulation is often heard there that some new committee or Council shall consist of so many persons 'one of which must be a woman': the assumption being that upon scientific principles of selection no woman would be added to a body having serious deliberative functions. That assumption, which is at once accepted and resented by those who maintain the complete equality of the sexes, is not founded, as they suppose, in some prejudice of man but in the considered judgments of Nature. I find that at Common Law a reasonable woman does not exist. The contention of the respondent fails and the appeal must be allowed. Costs to be costs in the action, above and below, but not costs in the case.

Bungay, L.J., and *Blow*, L.J., concurred.

The Most Outrageous Consequences
James Reid Parker

Mr. Devore almost never lost a client except through the regrettable but inescapable eventuality—in his own restful phrase—of death. It was unthinkable that he should lose the Wolverine Commercial Car Corporation, which presumably wasn't susceptible to death and whose affairs at the New York end were as profitable to the law firm of Forbes, Hathaway, Bryan & Devore as those of any business they looked after. And yet this very catastrophe, Mr. Devore told himself, might occur if he continued to suffer reversals in court, as he had been doing lately. Suppose this latest difficulty, *Drucker v. Wolverine Comm. Car Corp.*, a rather minor case in its own way, proved to be the breaking point? Mr. Devore, who was about to go over, and have a scheduled talk with Mr. Hibben, Wolverine's vice-president in charge of the New York office, was thoroughly downcast. There could be no doubt that Drucker, a taxi-driver who had been driving a Wolverine-built cab for the Sun-Lite system at the time of his accident, had a legal precedent for action. In the Sate of New York, at least. It was really a horrible precedent, handed down by a judge for whom Mr. Devore entertained bitter loathing, but in Mr. Hibben's eyes this would not excuse defeat, as Mr. Devore knew very well.

Perhaps what grieved the old lawyer most was that his sympathies were with Wolverine, for basically there was something about a Comm. Car Corp. that appealed to him. He loved Wolverine. Nor was his devotion altogether that of a pensioner; he felt toward Wolverine much as a dog might feel toward a life-long, if at times unreasonable, master. Mr. Devore put on his derby, selected Ames and Smith's "Law of Torts" from his bookcase, and gloomily started for the Wolverine offices. His first job, clearly, was to mollify Mr. Hibben, if such a thing could be accomplished.

Mr. Hibben greeted him with the barest civility and at once asked the question that Mr. Devore least wanted to hear.

"Well, what chance have we got?"

Before replying, Mr. Devore seated himself very solemnly, although the vice-president had not suggested that he do so, placed the tort collection on the desk in an impressively deliberate manner, and tried to look as much as possible like Mr. Chief Justice Stone on a Monday afternoon.

"The first thing we must consider," he said slowly, caressing the torts as if to put himself under the protection of all the great adjudicators of the past, "is the historic attitude of the courts toward liability."

Mr. Hibben failed to assume the attentive expression of one about to enjoy a scholarly excursion into legal history. "That's not answering my question," he said.

Recklessly, Mr. Devore evaded the issue. "When a somewhat similar case was decided in the Court of the Exchequer in 1842, our American courts lost no time in adopting the decision as a precedent for this country. I'm happy to say that it was a complete and triumphant vindication of the defendant."

"And you say America adopted the same law intact?" Mr. Hibben asked eagerly.

"America accepted the precedent," Mr. Devore acknowledged, wondering how on earth to proceed from this point. It had perhaps been bad strategy to appease Mr. Hibben at the very beginning. The vice-president was nodding with satisfaction and saying, "Fine! Good thing Americans knew enough to tell right from wrong in those days. They don't seem to any more." If Mr. Hibben would only refrain from asking whether the precedent had ever been set aside!

"Is this law still O.K.?" Mr. Hibben asked. "You're sure the judges all know about it?"

"Oh, yes, they all know about it," said Mr. Devore soothingly and with perfect truth. "The case that set the precedent was really very much like the Drucker affair. I'd like to tell you about it."

Mr. Hibben now seemed more disposed toward a little excursion into the annals of the Court of the Exchequer. He offered his counsellor a cigar.

"It involved a chattel-maker's liability, or to be more exact, a chattel *vendor's* liability, to a third person," said Mr. Devore, making a heroic effort to be elementary. "The defendant Wright had contracted to supply mailcoaches to the Postmaster General, who had in turn contracted with a man named Atkinson, and his business associates, for a regular supply of horses and coachmen. Atkinson engaged the plaintiff Winterbottom to drive a coach between Hartford and Holyhead. In other words, A contracted with B, who contracted with C, who contracted with D. One day, most unfortunately, Winterbottom's mailcoach broke down because of a latent defect in its manufacture and he became lamed for life. Seeking damages, D sued not C, his employer, not B, the Postmaster General, but the original A, with whom D had entered into no contract of any sort whatever."

After digesting these complications, Mr. Hibben said, "If D was hired by C, I think C was the one D should have picked to sue."

Mr. Devore agreed that this would have been a more usual procedure, but added that A was probably a wealthier firm and therefore a more tempting victim against whom to secure a judgment. The analogy was at once apparent to Mr. Hibben, who grunted in a shocked manner. Matters were progressing smoothly at the moment, but it meant only temporary relief for Mr. Devore. Nevertheless, he opened his Ames and Smith with convincing equanimity and turned to *Winterbottom v. Wright.*

"I'm sure you'll agree with me that Lord Abinger, the Chief Baron, expressed the whole issue very satisfactorily when he said, 'If the plaintiff can sue, every passenger, or even every person passing along the road, who was injured by the upsetting of the coach, might bring similar action. Unless we confine the operations of such contracts as this to the parties who entered into them, the most absurd and outrageous consequences, to which I can see no limit, would ensure.'"

"Exactly!" said Mr. Hibben. "That's almost word for word what I told our legal adviser in Flint when I talked to him on the phone several days ago. It looks as if you've found a loophole all right, Devore." Mr. Hibben beamed at him. "I've always *said* it wouldn't pay Wolverine to maintain a full-sized legal department when we've got Forbes, Hathaway to take care of us. Frankly, Devore, the fellows out in Flint have been a little disappointed with your work lately, but they'll be tickled to death about *this*."

Mr. Devore tried to smile but wasn't quite able to manage it. Something told him that the fellows in Flint weren't going to do any elaborate rejoicing. And if Wolverine were suddenly to install a full-sized legal department, what would happen to Forbes, Hathaway, Bryan & Devore? What, especially, would happen to Devore?

"I certainly like what he says about confining the operations of such contracts," said Mr. Hibben. "Let's hear that part again."

"Unless we confine the operations of such contracts to the parties who entered into them?"

"That's it!" Mr. Hibben said. "That's telling 'em! Why, we never had any dealings at all with Drucker. What we did was sell a cab to the Sun-Lite people, and Drucker was hired by Sun-Lite. Furthermore, it was a defective steering column that broke, and we don't even make steering columns. We buy them from Collins & Kemper!"

His exuberance was a terrible spectacle to Mr. Devore, who didn't quite know how to cut it short.

"Every passer-by," Mr. Hibben said, "every Tom, Dick, and Harry under the sun would start suing. They'd say they were suffering from mental shock or something as a result of being on the scene when the accident happened. Who is this man Abinger, anyway? I'd like to meet him."

"You're forgetting when the case was decided," Mr. Devore reminded him gently. "It was decided back in 1842."

He turned to another section of his Ames and Smith and, marshalling such courage as he had left, prepared to explain why Wolverine, and not Sun-Lite, would be required by law to yield to the plaintiff.

"In recent years," he began, "the most malign forces imaginable have been at work in this country. They have penetrated our government and—much as I dislike confessing the fact—our bar and our bench as well."

A look of surprise crossed Mr. Hibben's face. "You don't have to tell me that!" he snapped.

The unhappy counselor not only had to tell him but had to tell him without any further postponement.

"You'd be amazed at something that happened once in the Court of Appeals right here in New York," Mr. Devore said lightly. "It was the really unusual case of MacPherson against the Buick Motor Company—I mean the old Buick company, not the General Motors subsidiary. What happened was that the manufacturer sold one of its cars to a retail dealer, who in turn sold it to this man MacPherson. While MacPherson was driving the car, one of the wheels suddenly collapsed. He was thrown out and injured. The wheel had been made of faulty wood. The wheel wasn't made by Buick; it was bought from another manufacturer, just as you buy your steering columns from Collins & Kemper. The Court decided there was evidence, however, that the defects could have been discovered by reasonable inspection, and that inspection was omitted."

"Certainly inspection was omitted," said Mr. Hibben. "They probably bought their wheels from a reputable firm, and they certainly couldn't go around inspecting hundreds of thousands of wheels just on the chance that maybe they'd find one that wasn't exactly uniform. Why, in our case the steering column on Drucker's cab was the first defective column we'd ever heard about."

"I rather imagined that you'd see a similarity between the Drucker case and MacPherson against Buick."

"Of course I see a similarity," said Mr. Hibben.

Mr. Devore took a deep breath and jumped into the flames.

"I think you'll be interested in hearing what one of the judges said about it." The vice-president nodded, evidently retaining great faith in the book from which Mr. Devore had produced the fascinating mailcoach decision. "The judge held that 'if the nature of a thing is such that it is reasonably certain to place life and limb in peril when negligently made, it is then a thing of danger. Its nature gives warning of the consequences to be expected. If to the element of danger there is added knowledge that the thing will be used by persons other than the purchaser, and used without new tests, then, irrespective of contract, the manufacturer of this thing of danger is under a duty to make it carefully.'" He coughed nervously as he neared the most disagreeable part of the whole wretched decision. "'We are dealing now with the manufacturer of the finished product, who puts it on the market to be used without inspection by his customers. If he is negligent where danger is to be foreseen, a liability will follow.'"

"Wait a minute," said Mr. Hibben. "That line about 'the manufacturer of the finished product' would apply to Collins & Kemper. Drucker could sue *them* if he wanted to. Why don't you write him a letter and tell him about it?"

Mr. Devore shook his head and went on hastily.

"'We think the defendant was not absolved from a duty of inspection because it brought the wheels from a reputable manufacturer.'" Here Mr. Hibben opened his mouth in horrified astonishment but made no comment. "'It was not merely a dealer in automobiles. It was a manufacturer of automobiles. It was responsible for the finished product. It was not at liberty to put the finished product on the market without subjecting the component parts to ordinary and simple tests.'"

"You mean to say he's blaming the automobile manufacturers even though it was someone else who made the defective wheel?" asked Mr. Hibben. "You mean they'd be just as likely to blame *us*?"

But Mr. Devore, now that his great step had been taken, was unable to stop reading. "'The defendant knew the danger. It knew also that the car would be used by persons other than the buyer.'"

"Why, it might be a *child* talking," Mr. Hibben gasped.

"'Precedents drawn from the days of travel by stagecoach do not fit the conditions of travel today,'" Mr. Devore quoted, reading as quickly as possible. "'The principle that the danger must be imminent does not change, but the things subject to the principle do change. They are whatever the needs of life in a developing civilization require them to be.'" He closed the book with an abrupt gesture. His own patience had worn quite as thin as the vice-president's.

There was a long silence before Mr. Hibben said wearily, "Where did you say this terrible thing happened? Here in New York?"

"Yes. In 1916."

"Couldn't we take it to the Supreme Court? They may have *some* sense of honor and decency left."

Mr. Devore lighted one of his own cigars and closed his eyes. "That opinion was written by Benjamin Cardozo. No court in the United States would reverse a Cardozo ruling, even if it wanted to. Not in times like these."

"I see what you mean," murmured the vice-president. "Good God!" There was infinite worry in the way he spoke the words.

"Well, there you are, Hibben," said Mr. Devore presently. He waited for the storm to break. And then, even as he waited, the realization came to him that everything was going to be all right. It had been Cardozo, and not he, who had jumped into the flames. If Mr. Hibben entertained any feeling toward him, it was the sympathetic feeling that the same malign forces were in league against them both. Wolverine still loved him, and if he played his cards carefully, it would continue to do so. He leaned back and for the first time really tasted the flavor of his cigar.

20

Domestic Relations

One was never married, and that's his hell;
another is, and that's his plague.
Anatomy of Melancholy
Robert Burton

Evening star, you bring all things
which the bright dawn has scattered:
you bring the sheep, you bring the goat,
you bring the child back to its mother.
Sappho,
c. 612 B.C.

In his book *Uncommon Law*, Sir Alan Herbert tells us that "the critical period in matrimony is breakfast-time." Anyone practicing family law, particularly matrimonial law, knows that the critical period does not limit itself to breakfast-time! Because of the acrimony which often develops during the process of divorce, many people argue that it should be harder to get married than to obtain a divorce, but a few states still require some finding of fault on the part of the defendant if the plaintiff is to maintain a successful matrimonial action. In New York, an obviously concocted complaint alleging cruel and inhuman treatment will be dismissed by the judge at the end of the plaintiff's case upon the requisite motion by the defendant's attorney. What public policy dictates that married couples should stay together if one party wants to be released? Is it to ensure that husbands are not too free to establish a home with a wife and children and then leave the woman at his whim? Should this be a concern if the courts have the necessary power and discretion to ensure that the husband provides for his wife and children financially? However skilled the attorneys are in matrimonial practice, there are no real winners or losers and very few happy clients. There are impossible demands. Emotions run high making the proceeding difficult for the clients, their attorneys, and the judge; but occasionally humor finds its way into matrimonial cases. Consider the following "true" tales:

- An irate husband is told that his wife of thirty years is entitled to half of everything they own under New York's Equitable Distribution law. He proceeds to take an ax and chop all of their furniture and belongings in half—including the refrigerator.

• A woman filed for divorce alleging cruel and inhuman treatment. These are the facts that she related on the stand under oath. The wife put dinner on the table at six o'clock as per her usual habit. When the husband did not come in from the farm, she headed to the barn where she saw him engaged in deviant sexual behavior with a cow. The wife headed back to the kitchen. Half an hour later when the husband returned for dinner, the wife said: "I saw what you were doing with the cow in the barn. What do you have to say for yourself?"; and the husband replied: "Cow's bett'r'n you are." Without any further testimony the Judge responded, "Divorce granted."

• In a no-fault state, the lawyer asks his client the two critical questions: (1) Have you lived separate and apart from your wife for six months? To which the plaintiff responds "yes." (2) During that time did you have sexual relations with your wife? To which the plaintiff asks: "Does oral sex count?" From the bench the judge declares: "It counts—action dismissed."

Humor is reflected in Frank O'Connor's short story "Counsel for Oedipus," but consider the following serious questions that that story raises:

• Feminists argue that female judges are needed in the family law area. However, if judges have a "mother fixation" are wives actually better off with a male judge?

• To what extent should the attorney coach a client in the way of dress, mannerisms, and speech before the trial?

• In the case of the farmer's wife in the anecdote told previously, you might imagine that it would be difficult and embarrassing for the wife to describe exactly what took place. Notice here that the judge allows the wife to write down the delicate details on a piece of paper.

• Mickie Joe, the lawyer, has a tendency "to identify with his client." Is this a thing no real lawyer *would* do, or is it a thing no real lawyer *should* do?

• Notice how the husband's attorney manages to shape the truth to fit his purposes. It is said that for each lawsuit the lawyer should develop a theme and a theory. What is Mickie Joe's theme and theory in this case?

• Mrs. Lynam says she wanted her husband to be reasonable. Should the "reasonable man" find his way into matrimonial law?

The last piece in this anthology, Giovanni Boccaccio's "Madame

Filippa Is Accused of Wronging Her Husband," is another humorous account of a domestic matter. The clever orator here is not an attorney but rather the defendant. Once again, the judge exhibits his Oedipus complex with his observation of Madame Filippa's beauty, manners, and courage, and by his obvious compassion.

Finally, we conclude by putting family law back into perspective by ending on a note of pathos in presenting a letter written by an eight-year-old boy. His mother was constrained by a separation agreement to leave him with his father for the summer awaiting the judge's final determination concerning custody:

Dear Judge,

I'm writing you this letter because I want to move to California and not stay in NY State.

I think I have a better life at my Mom's house.

I have never been away from my Mom for over 6 weeks. Even if my friends are in NY I can make new ones.

At my Mom's we are running out of money to pay you people. I want to get this over with.

I have an Uncle that I have seen once in three years. He lives in San Francisco.

Counsel for Oedipus
Frank O'Connor

To sit in court and watch a case between wife and husband is like seeing a performance of Oedipus. You know that no matter what happens the man hasn't a chance. A colt will consider it a matter of conscience to pass a filly, and a court of law is the same. Even the man's own counsel will be ashamed of him and envy counsel for the wife, who, whatever she did or didn't do, has the ear of the court. As for judges—every single one that I've known had a mother fixation.

But the worst thing of all is that even the man is divided against himself. Now, take the day when Mickie Joe Dougherty was defending a big countryman called Lynam, whose wife was suing him for legal separation and accusing him of cruelty and adultery. The adultery was admitted, and all that was needed to prove the cruelty was to put Tom Lynam in the box. He was a big, good-looking man with a stiff, morose manner; one of those men who are deceptively quiet and good-humoured for months on end and then lay you out with a stick for a casual remark about politics.

His wife was a trim, mousy little female about half his height and a quarter his weight, with an anxious face and a gentle, bedraggled air. She cocked her little head while she listened to her counsel's questions, as though they were uttered in a foreign language, and replied to them in something of the same way, raising her colourless little voice and illustrating her answers with pathetic, half-completed gestures. It reminded you of fourth-form French. All the same, it gave impressiveness to the picture she drew of her husband, drunk and violent, smashing everything in the kitchen on her. You could see O'Meara, the judge, adored her. "Come over here where we can hear you, ma'am," he said, pointing to a seat on the bench beside him, and he leaned one elbow on the bench, crossed his legs, and studied her. Poor O'Meara was a bad case; he had blood pressure as well as a mother fixation. Once or twice, as she gave her evidence, she glanced sadly and pityingly at her husband, who stared back at her with a gloomy hatred that was awe-inspiring. Most men, hearing how they have beaten and strangled their wives, even if they never laid a finger on them, don't know where to look—the poor devils are wondering what everyone thinks of them—but here was a man who watched his wife as if he was wondering why the blazes he hadn't taken a hatchet and finished the job as he was at it.

"And what did he say then?" asked Kenefick, her counsel.

"He called me—do I have to say that?" she asked with a wistful girlish look at O'Meara.

"Oh, not at all, not at all, ma'am," he said hastily. "Write it down," and pushed pencil and paper towards her. She wrote as she talked, slowly and carefully, raising her eyes sightlessly as she thought of all the cruel things her husband had said to her. Then she passed the paper apologetically to the judge, who glanced at it and passed it down to counsel. Tom Lynam, his face black with fury, leaned forward and whispered something to his solicitor, Matt Quill, but Matt only shook his head. If Matt had had his way, he'd have settled the case out of court.

"Did he say anything else?" asked Kenefick.

"Only if I didn't get out of the house in five minutes, sir, that he'd do to me what the Jews did to Jesus."

"What the Jews did to who?" O'Meara asked incredulously.

"Jesus, my lord," she replied, bowing her head reverently at the Holy Name. "Our Blessed Lord, you know. Crucify me, he meant."

"Huh!" snorted O'Meara with his blood pressure going up several degrees.

"Tell my lord what happened then," prompted Kenefick.

"So then I told him I could not go out at that hour of night, and the state of feebleness I was in," Mrs. Lynam continued with growing animation, "and he dragged me off the sofa and twisted my wrist behind my back." She illustrated "wrist" and "back" with another feeble gesture which she didn't complete.

"And did he know the state you were in?"

"Sure, how could he not know it?" cried Mrs. Lynam with her little hands outspread. "I wasn't able to get up from the sofa the whole day. That was what he had against me, of course. He wouldn't believe I was sick. Shamming he said I was."

"And what did he do?"

"Oh, he kicked me."

"Where was this?"

Her hand went to her back again, and she blushed. "Oh, in the—"

"No, no, no. I don't mean that. Where did this occur? What direction did he kick you in?"

"Oh, out the front door, sir," she replied hastily. "I fell on the path. Tommy—that's our little boy—knelt alongside me and began to cry, and my husband told him if he didn't get to bed, he'd do the same to him."

"He'd do the same to Tommy. How old is the child?"

"Five, sir, the 14th of February."

"And your husband made no effort to see were you injured in the fall?"

"Oh, indeed he didn't, sir," she replied with a smile like a rainbow—an optical illusion between two downpours. "Only to give me another kick off the path and into the flower-bed."

"And didn't you, at any time, make some appeal to him to cease this cruel treatment?" demanded Kenefick, stepping up his voice to indignation.

"Oh, indeed, I did, sir," she replied, responding sadly with a shake of her head. Whatever brand of French she spoke, it was clearly going down well, and she was beginning to enjoy it herself. "I asked him did he think I was in a fit state to go crawling across the fields in the dark to a neighbour's house, but he only used a filthy expression and banged the door in my face."

"And those were the marks that you showed next day to Dr. O'Mahony?"

"They were, sir. The same. A week he made me stop in bed with them."

"Tell me, ma'am," the judge interrupted, "this second kick he gave you—the one that sent you off the path into the flower-bed—where were you when he did that?"

"Oh, on the ground, my lord. I was too bad to get up. Half the way across the fields, I was crawling like that, on my hands and knees."

After this it was scarcely necessary to prove her husband's behavior with Nora MacGee, a woman of notorious bad character, for in fact she had a child by him and his paternity was not denied. He had even visited her and nursed the child himself.

"And did you ask him to give up seeing this woman?"

"Why then, indeed, I did, sir. A dozen times if I did it once."

"And what did he say?"

"He said he wouldn't give up seeing a Lynam child for all the Hanafeys that were ever pupped, sir. The Hanafeys are my family," she added with her rainbow smile.

At this, Kenefick sat down as though he could not bear to prolong the poor woman's agony further, and Mickie Joe rose. Now, it cannot be pretended that, the best day he ever was, Mickie Joe was much of a lawyer or made a good appearance in court. Mickie Joe had begun life as a schoolmaster, but abandoned it, first for politics and then for the law. He really loved the art of oratory, and his soul filled with emotion whenever he spoke of the great orators of old who swayed vast audiences with the power of their voices, but Mickie Joe's own voice was like the whistle of a train, and the only effect he had ever had on an audience was to make them laugh. He had a long, thin, mournful face, and big, blackberry-coloured sunken eyes, and he looked at you over his pince-nez as though at any moment he might burst into tears. Everybody loved Mickie Joe, everybody tried to throw business in his way, but nobody ever took him seriously. He had a tendency which was very obvious in the Lynam case to identify himself with his client, a thing no real lawyer will do. A client is a fact, and a true lawyer hates facts. A lawyer is like an actor who can never bother about what sort of play he appears in, but tells himself some little story to cover as many of the incidents as he can be bothered to remember. The only thing he hates is to be reminded—for instance by the author—what the real story is about.

But Mickie Joe got up bursting with indignation, and even O'Meara smiled at the picture of Mickie Joe, who never said a cross word to anybody, identifying himself with this uproarious, drunken farmer. He felt Tom Lynam had been wronged and was bent on proving it. What made it funnier was that he began with a series of questions which nobody understood, which only reflected further Mrs. Lynam's virtue and his client's beastliness, but which he asked with a bitter reserve. Mrs. Lynam wasn't afraid of him. No woman was ever afraid of Mickie Joe. She answered steadily and quietly. Yes, she had been educated in a convent. Yes, she was a great friend of Sister Dominic. And of Father O'Regan, the parish priest. Yes, she had asked their advice before beginning proceedings against her husband. Yes, she was a member of the Women's Sodality and the Children of Mary.

Then Mickie Joe began to expand, and it became clear what his purpose had been. But it also looked as though Mickie Joe had lost his reason. It's bad enough to attack a woman, but to attack her because she's a pious woman is to go looking for trouble.

"And when you were at the Women's Sodality," he asked icily, looking at her between the wig and the pince-nez, "who got your husband's supper?"

"Sometimes he got it himself."

"And the children's supper?"

"Of an odd time."

"And when you were out at Mass, he got his breakfast, I suppose?"

"Unless he wanted to wait till I got it."

"But you always got it for him when you came in?"

"Always, except when I wasn't able."

"And I take it you weren't always able?"

"Well, no," she admitted candidly. "Not always." She still didn't take him seriously.

"You were able to go to Mass," he said, drawling every word, "but you were not able to get your husband's breakfast? Is that what you're telling my lord?"

"Sometimes I went to Mass when I wasn't able, either," she replied with a noble pathos which would have silenced another man but not Mickie Joe.

"You went to Mass when you weren't able," he repeated with a bitter smile, "but you didn't get your husband's breakfast when you weren't able. Is that what you mean?"

"I think I ought to explain that," she said, beginning to get flurried. "I'm not strong. I have a pain in my back. I hurted it years ago in a fall I got. Dr. O'Mahony treated me."

"Mrs. Lynam, do you also suffer from headaches?"

"I do. Bilious," she replied, pointing to her stomach.

"Really, Mr. Dougherty," said O'Meara wearily, "if a headache is an offence we're all bad characters."

Of course, by this time O'Meara was champing at the bit, waiting to get on with his judgment. For a judge with a mother fixation to listen to evidence at all when he wants to rush to the rescue of some poor afflicted female is an ordeal in itself, but it made it worse that all there was between himself and it was a poor fish like Mickie Joe. But for once Mickie Joe did not give way. He looked at the judge reprovingly over his pince-nez and replied in a wail:

"My lord, if the petitioner is presented to the court as something out of a medical museum, I have nothing more to say."

"Oh, go on, Mr. Dougherty, go on!" said O'Meara, but all the same he grew red. He was beginning to notice like the rest of us that Mickie Joe had ceased to be a figure of fun, but no more than ourselves did he realize what was happening. The truth was that there is only one person who can stand up to a man with a mother fixation, and that is a woman-hater. Exactly as O'Meara wanted to get at that big hulk of a man in the court, Mickie Joe wanted to get at that gentle, pious little woman sitting up beside the judge with her hands in her lap. And, in a queer way, his dislike was beginning to affect people's opinion. It wasn't only that you couldn't any longer patronize Mickie Joe. You couldn't any longer see her the way you had seen her first. Whether it was right or wrong, another picture was beginning to emerge of a woman who was both ruthless and designing and who ruled her great brute of a husband by her weakness. This was only one state of his ruin. In the next she would be living in comfort in a terrace house on his earnings, while he dragged out an impoverished and lonely existence.

Lynam himself began to perk up, and, instead of looking at his wife, looked at the people round him. The court had gradually begun to fill up, the way it does when a case gets interesting. He still scowled, but now he seemed to be challenging the people in court to say if he wasn't justified.

"Did you and your husband do much visiting together, Mrs. Lynam?" Mickie Joe asked gently.

"Well, you can't do much with two children, sir, can you?" she asked with soft reproach.

"That depends, ma'am," he said with a mournful smile. "A lot of people seem to be able to do it."

"I dare say they have servants," she said nervously.

"Strange to say, ma'am, friendships have been known to persist even in the humblest homes," sighed Mickie Joe with a smile like a glacier.

"I'm sure I don't know how they manage it, then."

"There are such things as neighbours, ma'am."

"Well, you can't be always asking the neighbours."

"No," he said bitterly. "You can ask them to put you up after a quarrel with your husband, but you can't ask them to mind your children. And how much attention do the children need? What age is your little girl, ma'am?"

"She's ten."

"And she couldn't look after the little fellow and herself?"

"Well, I can explain that," she said with a nervous glance at the judge. "You see, they don't get on, and you couldn't leave little Tommy with her, on account of that."

"You mean, she would beat him?" Mickie Joe asked sternly.

"Well, not beat him exactly," said Mrs. Lynam, getting more rattled than ever. "But she might be tormenting him."

"Mrs. Lynam," he asked gravely, "is that why you didn't like to ask the neighbours or the neighbours didn't like to be asked?"

"I don't know why you say that," she said, shaking her head. "The children don't like going to strange houses, and you wouldn't blame them."

"Do you mean that, ma'am, or do you mean they did not like going to houses where they would have to behave themselves? Mrs. Lynam, isn't it true that your children are too spoiled and vicious to be left in the home of any reasonable person?"

"No," she replied shrilly, starting in her seat. "Certainly not. I never heard such a thing."

But Tom Lynam himself looked at his counsel with such an expression of astonishment that it was clear to everyone that intuitively Mickie Joe had stumbled on the truth. He knew it himself too, and for the first time a smile of satisfaction played about his thin, mournful lips.

"Did many of your husband's friends visit you?"

"Some of them did, yes."

"He had a lot of friends at the time he married you, hadn't he?"

"He had. A few."

"And at the time of this break-up, how many of them were still coming to the house?"

The witness's eyes sought out one tall man sitting at the back of the court.

"I'm sure I couldn't say," she replied doubtfully. "There was one of them at any rate."

"The local St. Sebastian, I presume?"

"The local—I beg your pardon; I didn't catch."

"Mrs. Lynam, every married man has at least one friend who sticks to him, even in spite of his wife's attempts to separate them," Mickie Joe said savagely. "What happened [to] his other friends?"

"I'm sure I don't know."

"Mrs. Lynam, why did they stop coming to your house? Was it, for instance, that when they came for a meal, you sent your husband out to do the shopping?"

"Only a couple of times," she said excitedly. "And that is a thing that might happen to anybody. No matter how careful a housekeeper you were, you couldn't remember everything."

"And I dare say that while he was out, you left them there to entertain themselves?" he asked with a wicked smile.

"Only if I was putting the children to bed, sir," she said sanctimoniously.

"And I suppose, too, that when this last remaining friend of your husband—this Last Rose of Summer left blooming alone—came to bring him out, say, to the greyhounds, it sometimes happened that they couldn't go?"

"Well, I explained about my back," she said earnestly.

"You did, ma'am, fully," said Mickie Joe cruelly. "We are now better acquainted with your back than with any other portion of your anatomy. And we may take it that your husband and his friend had to stay at home and mind the children instead of enjoying themselves."

"I'm sure they enjoyed themselves more that I did," she said. "They played cards a lot. They're both very fond of cards."

But Tom Lynam was still staring incredulously at Mickie Joe. The tall man at the back of the court had grown red. He smiled and nodded amiably to the judge, to the counsel, and even to the pressmen. The Last Rose of Summer, a shy, neighbourly sort of man, was clearly enjoying the publicity. Lynam leaned forward and whispered something to his solicitor, but Quill only frowned and brushed him off. Quill was beginning to see the power and pathos of the play Mickie Joe was producing and no more than any other man of the theatre had he time to spare for the author's views.

"Tell me, ma'am," Mickie Joe asked, "how long is it since you had relations with your husband?"

"Since I what?" she asked in a baby voice, her head raised expectantly.

"Since you went to bed with him, if you like."

"Oh, I forgot to mention that," she said hastily. "He doesn't sleep with me, of course. He has a bedroom of his own."

"Oh, he has a bedroom of his own, has he?" Mickie Joe asked with a new light in his eye. "We'll come back to that. But that wasn't the question I asked just now. The question I asked was how long it was since you had relations with him."

"Well, with my back," she began, raising her hand illustratively to her hip.

"Never mind your back now, Ma'am. It's not your back we're talking about at the moment. How long is it?"

"Oh, I suppose about two years," she replied pertly.

"Or more?"

"It could be."

"No doubt it left no impression on your mind," said Mickie Joe. "But when you asked your husband not to have further relations with Mrs. MacGee, you weren't inviting him to have them with you?"

"He never asked me."

"And when he was at Mrs. MacGee's, nursing his child by her, he was in the only decent sort of home he had," said Mickie Joe with a throb of pathos in his voice that, for once, didn't make anybody laugh. "Would it be true to say that you don't think much of married life, ma'am?"

"Oh, I wouldn't say that," she replied vigorously. "The Church, of course, takes a very high view of it."

"I was referring to you, ma'am, not to the Church. Now, weren't you always baaing and bleating to Sister Dominic about the drawbacks of married life?"

"I went to her for advice," Mrs. Lynam replied anxiously. She was beginning to be doubtful of the impression she was creating, and small wonder.

"On your oath, ma'am," shouted Mickie Joe, "didn't you say to Sister Dominic that you never had a happy day after you left the convent?"

"Did I?" Mrs. Lynam asked nervously with a finger to her chin.

"Didn't you?"

"I don't remember. But I might, when I was upset."

"And to Father O'Regan, when you were trying to set him against your unfortunate, decent husband?"

"I never tried to set anyone against him" she retorted indignantly. "All I asked Father O'Regan was to ask him to be more natural."

"Natural?"

"Reasonable, I mean. Ah, 'tis all very well to be talking, Mr. Dougherty. That may be all right for young people, but 'tis no way for people like us to be behaving."

The tables were turned now with a vengeance. Tom Lynam had ceased to look at anyone now but his wife, and at her he looked with an expression of overpowering gravity. He seemed to be saying: "I told you what would happen and you wouldn't believe me. Now look at the result." He knew as everyone else did that she had failed to prove her case, and that even the policemen at the back of the court who had wives of cast iron were looking reproachfully at the gentle, insinuating little woman who was being revealed as a grey, grim, discontented monster with a mania for power.

When the court adjourned, Mickie Joe's cross-examination wasn't over, but he could easily have closed there, for even O'Meara's mother fixation could find nothing to fix on in the petitioner's case. She was probably the only person in court who didn't realize she had lost, but even she was badly shaken. She grabbed her handbag and waddled quickly down the court, looking neither to right nor to left. As she passed, her husband looked reproachfully at her, but she refused to catch his eye. Suddenly to everyone's astonishment he jumped up and followed her. The lawyers followed too without delay. They were afraid that in their moment of triumph he would snatch the victory from them by finishing the job in the hall. Instead, when they went out he was standing before her, talking in a low, pleading voice. She, with an actressy air, was listening, but half turned away from him as if caught in flight. Finally he approached Quill and Mickie Joe with a frown on his handsome face.

"Nellie and me are settling this between us," he muttered.

"You're what?" Quill asked in consternation. "But damn it, man, you have it won."

"I know that," Lynam replied in an apologetic mutter, "and I'm very grateful, but I wouldn't like her to have to answer any more questions. She thinks I told you all the things you mentioned. You know yourself I didn't."

Mickie Joe was fit to be tied. He stared at his client over his pincenez.

"You mean you're going back to live with that woman?" he asked coldly.

"I am."

"And you know that within forty-eight hours she'll be making your life a misery again?"

"If she does itself, we'll settle it between us," Tom Lynam retorted in a low voice, though his anger could be heard rumbling beneath, like a volcano.

"You certainly will," Mickie Joe said with icy fury. "You will not get me to assist you. A man tries to help you, but it is only talent thrown away. Go and commit suicide in your own way. I have nothing further to do with you."

"There's a pair of us there," Lynam exploded. "I don't know where you got your information, but you can go back to the people that told you and tell them to mind their own business. I won't let you or anyone talk to my wife that way."

Quill almost had to separate them. Two madder men he had rarely seen. But from the window of the barrister's room he and Mickie Joe saw the Lynams depart together, she small and sprightly, he tall and morose, and realized that never would they see justice done to a man in a court of law. It was like Oedipus. You couldn't say whether it was the Destiny that pursued the man or the man the Destiny; but you could be quite sure that nothing in the world would ever keep the two of them apart.

Madame Filippa Is Accused of Wronging Her Husband
Giovanni Boccaccio

Fiammetta had been silent some time, but Scalza's novel argument to prove the pre-eminent nobility of the Baronci kept all still laughing, when the queen called for a story from Filostrato, who thus began:—Noble ladies, an excellent thing is apt speech on all occasions, but to be proficient therein I deem then most excellent when the occasion does most imperatively demand it. As was the case with a gentlewoman, of whom I purpose to speak to you, who not only ministered gaiety and merriment to her hearers, but extricated herself, as you shall hear, from the toils of an ignominous death.

       There was aforetime in the city of Prato a statute no less censurable than harsh, which, making no distinction between the wife whom her husband took in adultery with her lover, and the woman found pleasuring a stranger for money, condemned both alike to be burned. While this statute was in force, it befell that a gentlewoman, fair and beyond measure enamoured, Madonna Filippa by name, was by her husband, Rinaldo de'Pugliesi, found in her own chamber one night in the arms of Lazzarino de'Guazzagliotri, a handsome young noble of the same city, whom she loved even as herself. Whereat Rinaldo, very wroth, scarce refrained from falling upon them and killing them on the spot; and indeed, but that he doubted how he should afterwards fare himself, he had given way to the vehemence of his anger, and so done. Nor, though he so far mastered himself, could he forebear recourse to the statute, thereby to compass that which he might not otherwise lawfully compass, to wit, the death of his lady. Wherefore, having all the evidence needful to prove her guilt, he took no further counsel; but, as soon as 'twas day, he charged the lady and had her summoned. Like most ladies that are veritably enamoured, the lady was of a high courage; and, though not a few of her friends and kinsfolk sought to dissuade her, she resolved to appear to the summons, having liefer die bravely confessing the truth than basely flee and for defiance of the law live in exile, and shew herself unworthy of such a lover as had had her in his arms that night. And so, attended by many ladies and gentlemen, who all exhorted her to deny the charge, she came before the Podestà, and with a composed air and unfaltering voice asked whereof he would interrogate her. The Podestà, surveying her, and taking note of her extraordinary beauty, and exquisite manners, and the high courage that her words evinced, was touched with compassion for her, fearing she might make some admission, by reason whereof, to save his honour, he must needs do her to death. But still, as he could not refrain from examining her of that which was laid to her charge, he said:—"Madam, here, as you see, is your husband, Rinaldo, who prefers to charge against you, alleging that he has taken you in adultery, and so he demands that, pursuant to a statute which is in force here I punish you with death: but this I may not do, except you confess; wherefore be very careful what you answer, and tell me if what your husband alleges against you be true." The lady, no wise dismayed, and in a tone not a little jocund, thus made answer:—"True it is, sir, that Rinaldo is my husband, and that last night he found me in the arms of Lazzarino, in whose arms for the whole-hearted love that I bear him I have ofttimes lain; nor shall I ever deny it; but, as well I wot you know, the law ought to be common and enacted with the common consent of all that they affect; which conditions are wanting to this law, inasmuch as it binds only us poor women, in whom to be liberal is much less reprehensible than it were in men; and furthermore the consent of no woman was—I say not had, but—so much as asked before 'twas made; for which reasons it justly deserves to be called a bad law. However, if in scathe of my body and your own soul, you are minded to put it in force, 'tis your affair; but, I pray you, go not on to try this matter in any wise, until you have granted me this trifling grace, to wit, to ask my husband if I ever gainsaid him, but did not rather accord him, when and so often as he craved it, complete enjoyment of myself." Whereto Rinaldo, without awaiting the Podestà's question, forthwith answered, that assuredly the lady had ever granted him all that he had asked of her for his gratification. "Then," promptly continued the lady, "if he has ever had of me as much as sufficed for his solace, what was I or am I to do with the surplus? Am I to cast it to the dogs? Is it not much better to bestow it on a gentleman that loves me more dearly than himself, than to suffer it to come to nought or worse?" Which jocund question being heard by well-nigh all the folk of Prato, who had flocked thither all agog to see a dame so fair and of such quality on her trail for such an offence, they laughed aloud and long, and then all with one accord, and as with one voice, exclaimed that the lady was in the right and said well; nor left they the court until in concert with the Podestà they had so altered the harsh statute as that thenceforth only such women as should wrong their husbands for money should be within its purview.

Wherefore Rinaldo left the court, discomfited of his foolish enterprise; and the lady blithe and free, as if rendered back to life from the burning, went home triumphant.

Appendix A

Wigmore's List of Legal Novels

Aldrich, Thomas Bailey:
    The Stillwater Tragedy

Allen, Grant:
    Miss Cayley's Adventures

Balzac, Honoré de:
    César Birotteau
    Cousin Pons
    Père Goriot
    Lucien de Rubempré
    The Lesser Bourgeoisie
    Gobseck
    Colonel Chabert
    A Commission in Lunacy
    The Last Incarnation of Vautrin
    A Start in Life
    The Marriage Contract

Baring-Gould, Sabine:
    Broom Squire

Becke, Louis, and Jeffrey Walter:
    First Fleet Family

Besant, Walter:
    St. Katherine's by the Tower
    For Faith and Freedom
    Orange Girl

Besant, Walter, and Rice, James:
    The Chaplain of the Fleet

Blackmore, R. D.:
    Lorna Doone

Burnett, Frances Hodgson:
    The DeWilloughby Claim

Caine, Hall:
    The Deemster

Collins, Wilkie:
    The Law and the Lady

Cooper, James Fenimore:
    The Ways of the Hour
    The Redskins
    Satanstoe
    The Chainbearer

Cox, E. M.:
    The Achievements of John
        Caruthers

Craddock, Chas. Egbert (pseud., i.e., Mary Murfree):
    The Prophet of the Great
        Smoky Mountains

Crawford, Francis Marion:
    Sant' Ilario

Crockett, Samuel R.:
    The Gray Man

Dickens, Charles:
    Barnaby Rudge
    Bleak House
    The Old Curiosity Shop
    Oliver Twist

The Pickwick Papers
A Tale of Two Cities

Doyle, Arthur Conan:
Micah Clarke

Dumas, Alexandre:
The Black Tulip
The Count of Monte Cristo
Marguerite de Valois
Twenty Years After, Part II

Eggleston, Edward:
The Mystery of Metropolisville
The Graysons

Eliot, George (pseud., i.e., Marian Evans):
Adam Bede
Felix Holt

Erckmann, Emile, and Chatrian, L.G.C.:
The Polish Jew

Fielding, Henry:
Jonathan Wild
Tom Jones

Fletcher, Joseph S.:
The Middle Temple Murder

Foote, Mary Hallcok:
John Bodewin's Testimony

Ford, Paul Leicester:
The Honorable Peter Stirling

Franzos, Karl Emil:
The Chief Justice

Frederic, Harold:
The Damnation of Theron Ware

Gaboriau, Emile:
File No. 113
Monsieur Lecoq

Goldsmith, Oliver:
The Vicar of Wakefield

Grant, Charles:
Stories of Naples and the Camorra

Grant, Robert:
"The Law-Breakers"
"An Eye for an Eye"

Grey (or Gray), Maxwell (pseud., i.e., Mary Gleed Tuttiett):
The Silence of Dean Maitland

Haggard, H. Rider:
Mr. Meeson's Will

Hale, Edward Everett:
Philip Nolan's Friends

Harte, Francis Bret:
Gabriel Conroy
"An Heiress of Red Dog"

Hawthorne, Nathaniel:
The Scarlet Letter

Herrick, Robert:
The Common Lot

Hill, Frederick Trevor:
Tales Out of Court

Holland, Josiah Gilbert:
Sevenoaks

Howells, William Dean:
A Modern Instance

Hugo, Victor:
Les Misérables
Ninety-three
The Man Who Laughed

James, George P. R.:
Moreley Ernstein

Kingsley, Henry:
  Austin Elliot

LeSage, Alain R.:
  The Adventures of Gil Blas

Lytton, Edward:
  Eugene Aram
  Paul Clifford

Mitchell, S. Weir:
  Constance Trescot

O'Reilly, John Boyle:
  Moondyne

Ouida (pseud., i.e., Louise de La Ramée):
  Under Two Flags

Page, Thomas Nelson:
  Red Rock

Parker, Gilbert:
  The Right of Way

Read, Opie:
  A Tennessee Judge
  The Jucklins

Reade, Charles:
  Griffith Gaunt
  It Is Never Too Late to Mend
  Hard Cash

Scott, Walter:
  Anne of Geierstein
  The Fortunes of Nigel
  Guy Mannering
  The Heart of Midlothian
  The Fair Maid of Perth
  The Antiquary
  Ivanhoe
  Peveril of the Peak
  Quentin Durward
  Redgauntlet
  Rob Roy

Sienkiewicz, Henryk:
  "A Comedy of Errors"

Stevenson, Robert Louis:
  Kidnapped: with its sequel
  David Balfour
  Weir of Hermiston

Stimson, Frederic J.:
  The Residuary Legatee

Stockton, Frank R.:
  The Late Mrs. Null

Thackeray, William Makepeace:
  Pendennis

Thanet, Octave (pseud., i.e., Alice French):
  The Missionary Sheriff
  We All

Tolstoi, Leo N.:
  Resurrection

Train, Arthur:
  Tutt and Mr. Tutt
  By Advice of Counsel
  As It Was in the Beginning

Trollope, Anthony:
  Orley Farm
  Mr. Maule's Attempt
  The Vicar of Bullhampton

Twain, Mark (pseud., i.e. Samuel L. Clemens):
  Pudd'nhead Wilson

Warren, Samuel:
  Ten Thousand a Year

Weyman, Stanley:
  The Story of Francis Cludde
  My Lady Rotha
  The Man in Black

Woolson, Constance Fenimore:
  Anne

Zangwill, Israel:
   The Big Bow Mystery

Appendix B

Weisberg and Kretschman's Expanded List of Law-Related Literary Works

Aeschylus:
  The Eumenides

Anonymous:
  The Song of Roland
  Nibelungenlied
  Njal's Saga
  The Old Testament
  Poem de mio Cid ("The Cid")
  Le Roman de Renart
  Le Roman de Thebes

Ashford, Jeffrey:
  Burden of Proof

Auchincloss, Louis:
  "Arnold and Degener, One
    Chase Manhattan Plaza"
    (in Tales of Manhattan)
  A Law for the Lion
  The Great World and Timothy
    Colt
  I Come as a Thief
  "The Legends of Henry
    Everett" (in The Romantic
    Egoists)
  The Partners
  Powers of Attorney

Balzac, Honoré de:
  An Historical Mystery
  The Gallery of Antiquities
  Lost Illusions
  Scenes from a Courtesan's Life
  Ursule Mirouët

Barth, John:
  The Floating Opera

Basso, Hamilton:
  The View from Pompey's
    Head

Becker, Stephen:
  A Covenant with Death

Béroul:
  Le Roman de Tristan

Betti, Ugo:
  Landslide (In Three Plays on
    Justice)

Bok, Curtis:
  Backbone of the Herring
  I, Too, Nicodemus
  Star Wormwood

Böll, Heinrich:
  End of a Mission

Borden, Mary:
  Action for Slaner
  You, the Jury

Botein, Bernard:
  The Prosecutor

Boulle, Pierre:
  The Executioner
  Face of a Hero

Burgess, Anthony:
    A Clockwork Orange

Busch, Niven:
    The San Franciscans

Camus, Albert:
    The Fall
    The Rebel
    The Stranger

Carlisle, Henry:
    Voyage to the First of
        December

Cecil, Henry:
    According to the Evidence
    Alibi for a Judge
    Brief to Counsel
    Brothers in Law
    Daughters in Law
    Friends at Court
    Full Circle
    Independent Witness
    Long Arm
    Natural Causes
    No Bail for the Judge
    Settled Out of Court
    Tipping the Scales
    Ways and Means

Chaucer, Geoffrey:
    "The Man of Law's Tale" (in
        The Canterbury Tales)

Chrétien de Troyes:
    Yvain
    Lancelot

Churchill, Winston:
    Mr. Crewe's Career

Clark, Walter Van Tilburg:
    The Ox-Bow Incident

Cozzens, James G.:
    By Love Possessed
    The Just and the Unjust

Deal, Borden:
    The Advocate

Dewlen, Al:
    Twilight of Honor

Doctorow, E. L.:
    The Book of Daniel

Dostoevski, Fyodor:
    The Brothers Karamazov
    Crime and Punishment
    The Idiot

Dreiser, Theodore:
    An American Tragedy

Drury, Allen:
    Advise and Consent
    Capable of Honor
    Preserve and Protect
    A Shade of Difference

Dürrenmatt, Friedrich:
    A Dangerous Game ("Die
        Panne")
    The Marriage of Mr.
        Mississippi

Eliot, George (pseud., i.e., Marian Evans):
    Middlemarch
    Mill on the Floss

Faulkner, William:
    Sanctuary

Gaither, Frances Ormond:
    Double Muscadine

Gardner, John:
    Dialogues
    The Sunlight

Garfield, Brian Wynne:
    Death Sentence

Gerber, Albert:
    The Lawyer

Ovid:
"The Argument Between Ajax
and Ulysses for the Armor
of Achilles" (Metamor-
phoses, Book XIII)

Pangborn, Edgar:
The Trial of Callista Blake

Pearson, William:
Trial of Honor

Porter, Katherine Anne:
"Noon Wine"

Porter, Monica E.:
The Mercy of the Court

Powell, Richard:
The Philadelphian

Prescott, Julian:
Case for the Accused

Reywall, John:
Trial of Alvin Boaker

Rosmond, Babette:
The Lawyers

Rylee, Robert:
Deep Dark River

Sartre, Jean-Paul:
No Exit

Schweitzer, Gertrude:
Born

Shakespeare, William:
Hamlet
King Lear
Measure for Measure
The Merchant of Venice
Othello
Richard II
A Winter's Tale

Smith, Edgar:
Reasonable Doubt

Snow, C. P.:
The Affair
Corridors of Power
In Their Wisdom
Strangers and Brothers

Solmssen, Arthur R. G.:
Alexander's Feat
The Comfort Letter
Rittenhouse Square

Solzhenitsyn, Aleksandr:
The First Circle
The Gulag Archipelago I, II

Sophocles:
Antigone
Oedipus Rex

Stein, Sol:
The Magician

Strindberg, August:
The Scapegoat

Tolstoi, Leo N.:
The Death of Ivan Ilych

Train, Arthur:
Ambition
McAllister and His Double
Mr. Tutt at His Best
Mr. Tutt Comes Home
Mr.Tutt Finds a Way
Page Mr. Tutt
Tut, Tut, Mr. Tutt

Trell, Max:
Lawyer Man

Uris, Leon:
QB VII

Vidal, Gore:
Burr

Villon, François:
    Le Testament

Voelker, John D.:
    Anatomy of a Murder

Warren, Robert Penn:
    All the King's Men
    Meet Me in the Green Glen

Warren, Samuel:
    Confessions of an Attorney
    Experiences of a Barrister

West, Jessamyn:
    The Masssacre at Fall Creek

West, Morris L.:
    Daughter of Silence

Williams, Ben Ames:
    Leave Her to Heaven

Woolfolk, William:
    Opinion of the Court

Wouk, Herman:
    The Caine Mutiny

Wright, Richard:
    Native Son

---

* Weisberg and Kretschman, *Wigmore's "Legal Novels" Expanded: A Collaborative Effort*, 50 N.Y.St. B.J. 123 (1978).

Appendix C
Fifty Law-Related Films

Adam's Rib (U.S. 1949)
   Writers: Ruth Gordon and Garson Kanin

Agnes of God (U.S. 1985)
   Play and Screenplay: John Pielmeier

All the King's Men (U.S. 1949)
   Novel: Robert Penn Warren

All the President's Men (U.S. 1976)
   Book: Carl Bernstein and Bob Woodward

Anatomy of a Murder (U.S. 1959)
   Novel: Robert Traver

Baby M (U.S. 1988)
   Fact-based account of the custody battle between William and
   Elizabeth Stern and Mary Beth Whitehead, the surrogate mother

Bartleby (G.B. 1970)
   Short Story: Herman Melville

Being There (U.S. 1979)
   Screenplay and Novel: Jerzy Kosinski

Beyond a Reasonable Doubt (U.S. 1956)
   Writer: Douglas Morrow

Billy Budd (G.B. 1962)
   Novel: Herman Melville

Boston Strangler, The (U.S. 1968)
   Book: Gerold Frank

Caine Mutiny, The (U.S. 1954)
 Novel: Herman Wouk

Candidate, The (U.S. 1972)
 Writer: Jeremy Larner

Clockwork Orange, A (G.B. 1971)
 Novel: Anthony Burgess

Crainquebille (France 1922; Remade 1933 and 1954)
 Story: Anatole France

Crime and Punishment (U.S. 1935; France 1935; U.S. 1958)
 Novel: Dostoyevsky

Defiant Ones, The (U.S. 1958)
 Writers: Nathan E. Douglas and Harold Jacob Smith

Devil and Daniel Webster, The (U.S. 1941)
 Screenplay: Dan Totheroh and Stephen Vincent Benét
 Story: Stephen Vincent Benét

Fortune Cookie, The (U.S. 1966)
 Writers: Billy Wilde and I. A. L. Diamond

Girl in the Red Velvet Swing, The (U.S. 1955)
 Writers: Walter Reisch and Charles Brackett

Godfather, The (U.S. 1972)
 Novel: Mario Puzo

Grapes of Wrath, The (U.S. 1940)
 Novel: John Steinbeck

Helter Skelter (U.S. 1975)
 Fact-based account of the Charles Manson murders

In Cold Blood (U.S. 1967)
 Book: Truman Capote

Inherit the Wind (U.S. 1960)
 Play: Jerome Lawrence and Robert E. Lee

Intruder in the Dust (U.S. 1949)
 Novel: William Faulkner

Kramer vs. Kramer (U.S. 1979)
 Novel: Avery Corman

Lord of the Flies (G.B. 1963; U.S. 1990)
   Novel: William Golding

Man for All Seasons, A (G.B. 1966)
   Book and Screenplay: Robert Bolt

Milagro Beanfield War, The (U.S. 1988)
   Novel: John Treadwell Nichols

Mr. Smith Goes to Washington (U.S. 1939)
   Story: Lewis R. Foster

Mutiny on the Bounty, The (U.S. 1935; U.S. 1962)
   Book: Charles Nordhoff and James Hall

Of Mice and Men (U.S. 1939)
   Novel: John Steinbeck

One Day in the Life of Ivan Denisovich (G.B. 1971)
   Novel: Alexander Solzhenitsyn

One Flew Over the Cuckoo's Nest (U.S. 1975)
   Novel: Ken Kesey

Onion Field, The (U.S. 1979)
   Screenplay and book: Joseph Wambaugh

Ox-Bow Incident, The (U.S. 1943)
   Novel: Walter Van Tilburg Clark

Paper Chase, The (U.S. 1973)
   Novel: John Jay Osborn, Jr.

Papillon (U.S. 1973)
   Book: Henry Charrière

Paths of Glory (U.S. 1957)
   Novel: Humphrey Cobb

Presumed Innocent (U.S. 1990)
   Novel: Scott Turow

Riot in Cell Block Eleven (U.S. 1954)
   Writer: Richard Collins

Scarlet Letter, The (U.S. 1910, 1911, 1913, 1917, 1920, 1926, 1934;
   G.B. 1922; Germany 1971)
   Novel: Nathaniel Hawthorne

Tale of Two Cities, A (U.S. 1935; G.B. 1958)
    Novel: Charles Dickens

To Kill a Mockingbird (U.S. 1962)
    Novel: Harper Lee

Trial, The (France, Italy, West Germany 1962)
    Novel: Franz Kafka

Trials of Oscar Wilde, The (Title in the U.S.: **The Man with the Green Carnation**; G.B. 1960)
    Writer: Ken Hughes

Twelve Angry Men (U.S. 1957)
    Play and Screenplay: Reginald Rose

Verdict, The (U.S. 1982)
    Novel: Barry Reed

Witness for the Prosecution (U.S. 1957)
    Play: Agatha Christie

9 780878 754724

Breinigsville, PA USA
08 January 2010

230412BV00002B/145/P